Merry Christmas (1957)
to
Daddy & Catherine
from
Jeanne & Dick

READING
FOR PLEASURE

BOOKS BY BENNETT CERF

LIFE OF THE PARTY
GOOD FOR A LAUGH
LAUGHTER, INC.
SHAKE WELL BEFORE USING
ANYTHING FOR A LAUGH
LAUGHING STOCK
TRY AND STOP ME
POCKETBOOK OF WAR HUMOR

BOOKS EDITED BY BENNETT CERF

AN ENCYCLOPEDIA OF AMERICAN HUMOR
BEDSIDE BOOK OF FAMOUS BRITISH STORIES
BEDSIDE BOOK OF FAMOUS AMERICAN STORIES

READING
FOR PLEASURE

Chosen, with Introduction and Comment by

Bennett Cerf

Harper & Brothers

PUBLISHERS • NEW YORK

Acknowledgments

As everyone knows, material which is in copyright cannot be reprinted without the permission of the author or publisher controlling the rights. Since nearly all of the material in this volume falls into that category, *Reading for Pleasure* could not have come into existence without such permissions, for which I am very grateful. Detailed acknowledgments will be found on the first page of each selection.

For invaluable assistance in selecting the contents of this volume and tracking down elusive copyrights and permissions, I am indebted to Joseph Gies, of *This Week* Magazine. Also essential were my old friends Saxe Commins and Leonora and Arthur Hornblow. Many authors and publishers granted permission for the use of prized material they never had allowed to be anthologized before. I appreciate the compliment and hope that an early opportunity will be provided to reciprocate in kind.

I also wish to acknowledge the constant and friendly interest of book-sellers and readers of the *Saturday Review* since the project, at its outset, was outlined in the pages of that magazine.

BENNETT CERF

Contents

CONTENTS

Introduction

In a thirty-year span a book publisher, contrary to the belief of numerous
disgruntled authors, does a powerful lot of reading. Most of it, mercifully,
he forgets immediately. Some bits and pieces make such an impression
that he never forgets them. He adds them to the favorites he has stored
up in his memory from his undergraduate or salad days of reading, and
subconsciously defies the new generation of writers knocking on his door
to "Surpass these—or tie them—*if you can!*"

This book is a guided tour of some of the high spots I've encountered
in a lifetime of reading. Not all of them, obviously, since many could not
possibly be condensed, or properly excerpted, for a collection like this.
Others that certainly would qualify are available in so many other editions
that it seemed pointless to trot them out once again. This may be the first
anthology of its kind in the past decade that includes neither "The Snows
of Kilimanjaro," "A Rose for Emily," "The Secret Life of Walter Mitty,"
or "The Girls in Their Summer Dresses." These are all wonderful stories,
but by this time a confirmed anthology buff should be able to recite them
by heart. The stories I *have* included in *Reading for Pleasure* are there for
one simple reason: they justify the title of the book. They impressed and
delighted me so much when I first discovered them that I have remembered them ever since.

One uncompromising old professor on the Columbia campus turned
pale from merely reading the table of contents. He was appalled that I
should jumble recognized classics with stories frankly culled from slick-
paper magazines, and excerpts from boisterous, slapstick best sellers of
1957 next to beloved period pieces that had brought tears to his eyes when
novels still retailed for $1.08 a copy. By his standard, my selections were
hopelessly haphazard; by my own they simply were honest.

This is not a collection of pieces you *ought* to enjoy (like those ques-
tionable lists of "The Books That Meant Most to Me" so shamelessly
fabricated each Christmastime by pompous pundits), but pieces you *will*
enjoy. I will stake my reputation as a publisher, a columnist, and an
editor on that!

What an engaging title *Reading for Pleasure* makes for an anthology,
and what a wide latitude it allows the editor! I can say this without
blushing, because the title is not my own. It was presented to me on a
platter by the editors of Harper's.

Statistics reveal that a million or so more Americans are "reading for pleasure" every year, although you never would believe this by listening to the moans of the publishing fraternity. Publishers cry more easily than anybody else on earth. A simple, routine inquiry like "How's business?" is enough to make their tears flow like water, diluting their vintage wines and drenching the decks of their private yachts.

To hear them tell it, there's always something threatening to bankrupt half the publishers in America. Seventy years ago, believe it or not, a spokesman for the industry predicted that interurban trolley cars would be the doom of the reading habit! So many people were swinging and swaying aboard these dangerous contraptions that there soon would be nobody left to appreciate Shakespeare and Aristotle!

Then came the menace of the bicycle, followed closely by cheap automobiles, magazines, giant economy-size Sunday newspapers, motion pictures, radio, and now, of course, television.

Anybody fortunate enough, however, to have learned the joys of reading in his formative years—usually through the inspired guidance of one wise, gratefully remembered, and disgracefully underpaid schoolteacher—knows that there never has been, and never will be a substitute for a really good book. All the wisdom of the ages, all the tales that have delighted mankind for generations, are there at your fingertips, at negligible cost, to be picked up, savored, digested, and laid down exactly as your fancy dictates. That's why more good books are sold in America every season, despite all other gimmicks and distractions. As a result the publishers survive, if not affluently.

Glancing over the table of contents of *Reading for Pleasure,* as a matter of fact, I was amused to note how many of the stories already have been adapted for television or the screen. I predict that those that have not will be!

I hope you will approve of the device of "companion pieces" in the first section of the book. The thinking behind most of the special groupings will be obvious, but one or two are more tenuous and call for special explanations. These you will find at the top of each section. At the back of the book there are short biographical notes about every author represented. The remainder of the contents has been divided so that you may find at a glance precisely the kind of story you feel like reading: tender, exciting, factual, nostalgic, or humorous. I loved them all. I hope you will, too!

BENNETT CERF

Mount Kisco, New York
June, 1957

I

Companion Pieces

The story of how an island came into being, the description of a grotesque but fascinating species of sea monster that thrives near an island's protective shores, and the enthralling account of how a famous expedition on a raft was dashed to destruction on a forbidding island reef struck me as logical "companion pieces." Furthermore, the three selections are by masters of their craft—two of them from books that, unexpectedly, dominated best-seller lists for months on end.

"The Birth of an Island" is a typical chapter from Rachel Carson's *The Sea Around Us,* a crystal-clear and authoritative summarization by a woman who, amazingly enough, was born inland and never even had a glimpse of the sea until she had been graduated from college. *The Sea Around Us* won the National Book Award for nonfiction in 1953.

Equally popular was Thor Heyerdahl's *Kon-Tiki,* an account of how, aboard a primitive balsa raft, he and his companions drifted successfully all the way across the Pacific, duplicating what may have been the route traversed by intrepid Incas to the South Seas centuries before. The chapter reprinted here is the climax of the story.

Gilbert Klingel's "In Defense of Octopuses" is an off-beat gem that certainly told me, in a few pages, just about all I care to know about octopuses. (In 1899 they became so abundant off the shores of Britain that they were described as a "veritable plague" in scareheads of London newspapers.) Klingel's piece was first called to my attention by Hollywood producer Arthur Hornblow, who never reads the books other people seem to be talking about.

The popularity of *The Sea Around Us* and *Kon-Tiki* coincided with the publication of *The Caine Mutiny* and *The Cruel Sea*—the only time in publishing history when the four top-selling books in America all were dedicated to the same general subject: the seas and the men who sailed them.

ED.

The Birth of an Island

By RACHEL L. CARSON

Many a green isle needs must be
In the deep, wide sea . . .
SHELLEY

MILLIONS of years ago, a volcano built a mountain on the floor of the Atlantic. In eruption after eruption, it pushed up a great pile of volcanic rock, until it had accumulated a mass a hundred miles across at its base, reaching upward toward the surface of the sea. Finally its cone emerged as an island with an area of about two hundred square miles. Thousands of years passed, and thousands of thousands. Eventually the waves of the Atlantic cut down the cone and reduced it to a shoal—all of it, that is, but a small fragment which remained above water. This fragment we know as Bermuda.

With variations, the life story of Bermuda has been repeated by almost every one of the islands that interrupt the watery expanses of the oceans far from land. For these isolated islands in the sea are fundamentally different from the continents. The major land masses and the ocean basins are today much as they have been throughout the greater part of geologic time. But islands are ephemeral, created today, destroyed tomorrow. With few exceptions, they are the result of the violent, explosive, earth-shaking eruptions of submarine volcanoes, working perhaps for millions of years to achieve their end. It is one of the paradoxes in the ways of earth and sea that a process seemingly so destructive, so catastrophic in nature, can result in an act of creation.

Islands have always fascinated the human mind. Perhaps it is the instinctive response of man, the land animal, welcoming a brief intrusion of earth in the vast, overwhelming expanse of sea. Here in a great ocean basin, a thousand miles from the nearest continent, with miles of water under our vessel, we come upon an island. Our imaginations can follow its slopes down through darkening waters to where it rests on the sea floor. We wonder why and how it arose here in the midst of the ocean.

The birth of a volcanic island is an event marked by prolonged and violent travail: the forces of the earth striving to create, and all the forces of the sea opposing. The sea floor, where an island begins, is probably nowhere more than about fifty miles thick—a thin covering over the vast bulk of the earth. In it are deep cracks and fissures, the results of unequal cooling and shrinkage in past ages. Along such lines of weakness the molten lava from the earth's interior presses up and finally bursts forth into the sea. But a submarine volcano is different from a terrestrial eruption, where the lava, molten rocks, gases, and other ejecta are hurled into the air through an open crater. Here on the bottom of the ocean the volcano has resisting it all the weight of the ocean water above it. Despite the immense pressure of, it may be, two or three miles of sea water, the new volcanic cone builds upward toward the surface, in flow after flow of lava. Once within reach of the waves, its soft ash and tuff are violently attacked, and for a long period the potential island may remain a shoal, unable to emerge. But, eventually, in new eruptions, the cone is pushed up into the air and a rampart against the attacks of the waves is built of hardened lava.

Navigators' charts are marked with numerous, recently discovered submarine mountains. Many of these are the submerged remnants of the islands of a geologic yesterday. The same charts show islands that emerged from the sea at least fifty millions years ago, and others that arose within our own memory. Among the undersea mountains marked on the charts may be the islands of tomorrow, which at this moment are forming, unseen, on the floor of the ocean and are growing upward toward its surface.

For the sea is by no means done with submarine eruptions; they occur fairly commonly, sometimes detected only by instruments, sometimes obvious to the most casual observer. Ships in volcanic zones may suddenly find themselves in violently disturbed water. There are heavy discharges of steam. The sea appears to bubble or boil in a furious turbulence. Fountains spring from its surface. Floating up from the deep, hidden places of the actual eruption come the bodies of fishes and other deep-sea creatures, and quantities of volcanic ash and pumice.

One of the youngest of the large volcanic islands of the world is Ascension in the South Atlantic. During the Second World War the American airmen sang

> If we don't find Ascension
> Our wives will get a pension

this island being the only piece of dry land between the hump of Brazil and the bulge of Africa. It is a forbidding mass of cinders, in which the vents of no less than forty extinct volcanoes can be counted. It has not always been so barren, for its slopes have yielded the fossil remains of trees. What happened to the forests no one knows; the first men to explore the island, about the year 1500, found it treeless, and today it has no natural greenness except on its highest peak, known as Green Mountain.

In modern times we have never seen the birth of an island as large as Ascension. But now and then there is a report of a small island appearing where none was before. Perhaps a month, a year, five years later, the island has disappeared into the sea again. These are the little, stillborn islands, doomed to only a brief emergence above the sea.

About 1830 such an island suddenly appeared in the Mediterranean between Sicily and the coast of Africa, rising from one-hundred-fathom depths after there had been signs of volcanic activity in the area. It was little more than a black cinder pile, perhaps two hundred feet high. Waves, wind, and rain attacked it. Its soft and porous materials were easily eroded; its substance was rapidly eaten away and it sank beneath the sea. Now it is a shoal, marked on the charts as Graham's Reef.

Falcon Island, the tip of a volcano projecting above the Pacific nearly two thousand miles east of Australia, suddenly disappeared in 1913. Thirteen years later, after violent eruptions in the vicinity, it as suddenly rose again above the surface and remained as a physical bit of the British Empire until 1949. Then it was reported by the Colonial Undersecretary to be missing again.

Almost from the moment of its creation, a volcanic island is fore-doomed to destruction. It has in itself the seeds of its own dissolution, for new explosions, or landslides of the soft soil, may violently accelerate its disintegration. Whether the destruction of an island comes quickly or only after long ages of geologic time may also depend on external forces: the rains that wear away the loftiest of land mountains, the sea, and even man himself.

South Trinidad, or in the Portuguese spelling, "Ilha Trinidade," is an example of an island that has been sculptured into bizarre forms through centuries of weathering—an island in which the signs of dissolution are clearly apparent. This group of volcanic peaks lies in the open Atlantic, about a thousand miles northeast of Rio de Janeiro. E. F. Knight wrote in 1907 that Trinidad "is rotten throughout, its substance has been dis-integrated by volcanic fires and by the action of water, so that it is every-where tumbling to pieces." During an interval of nine years between Knight's visits, a whole mountainside had collapsed in a great landslide of broken rocks and volcanic debris.

Sometimes the disintegration takes abrupt and violent form. The greatest explosion of historic time was the literal evisceration of the island of Krakatoa. In 1680 there had been a premonitory eruption on this small island in Sunda Strait, between Java and Sumatra in the Netherlands Indies. Two hundred years later there had been a series of earthquakes. In the spring of 1883, smoke and steam began to ascend from fissures in the volcanic cone. The ground became noticeably warm, and warning rumblings and hissings came from the volcano. Then, on 27 August, Krakatoa literally exploded. In an appalling series of eruptions, that lasted two days, the whole northern half of the cone was carried away. The sudden inrush of ocean water added the fury of superheated steam to the cauldron. When the inferno of white-hot lava, molten rock, steam, and smoke had finally subsided, the island that had stood fourteen hundred feet above the sea had become a cavity a thousand feet below sea level. Only along one edge of the former crater did a remnant of the island remain.

Krakatoa, in its destruction, became known to the entire world. The eruption gave rise to a hundred-foot wave that wiped out villages along the Strait and killed people by tens of thousands. The wave was felt on the shores of the Indian Ocean at Cape Horn; rounding the Cape into the Atlantic, it sped northward and retained its identity even as far as the English Channel. The sound of the explosions was heard in the Philippine Islands, in Australia, and on the Island of Madagascar, nearly three thousand miles away. And clouds of volcanic dust, the pulverized rock that had been torn from the heart of Krakatoa, ascended into the strato-sphere and were carried around the globe to give rise to a series of spectacular sunsets in every country of the world for nearly a year.

Although Krakatoa's dramatic passing was the most violent eruption that modern man has witnessed, Krakatoa itself seems to have been the product of an even greater one. There is evidence that an immense volcano once stood where the waters of Sunda Strait now lie. In some remote period a titanic explosion blew it away, leaving only its base represented by a broken ring of islands. The largest of these was Krakatoa, which, in its own demise, carried away what was left of the original crater ring. But in 1929 a new volcanic island arose in this place—Anak Krakatoa, Child of Krakatoa.

Subterranean fires and deep unrest disturb the whole area occupied by the Aleutians. The islands themselves are the peaks of a thousand-mile chain of undersea mountains, of which volcanic action was the chief architect. The geologic structure of the ridge is little known, but it rises abruptly from oceanic depths of about a mile on one side and two miles on the other. Apparently this narrow ridge indicates a deep fracture of the earth's crust. On many of the islands volcanoes are now active, or only temporarily quiescent. In the short history of modern navigation in this region, it has often happened that a new island has been reported but perhaps only the following year could not be found.

The small island of Bogoslof, since it was first discovered in 1796, has altered its shape and position several times and has even disappeared completely, only to emerge again. The original island was a mass of black rock, sculptured into fantastic, towering shapes. Explorers and sealers coming upon it in the fog were reminded of a castle and named it Castle Rock. At the present time there remain only one or two pinnacles of the castle, a long spit of black rocks where sea lions haul out, and a cluster of higher rocks resounding with the cries of thousands of sea birds. Each time the parent volcano erupts, as it has done at least half a dozen times since men have been observing it, new masses of steaming rocks emerge from the heated waters, some to reach heights of several hundred feet before they are destroyed in fresh explosions. Each new cone that appears is, as described by the volcanologist Jaggar, "the live crest, equivalent to a crater, of a great submarine heap of lava six thousand feet high, piled above the floor of the Bering Sea where the Aleutian mountains fall off to the deep sea."

One of the few exceptions to the almost universal rule that oceanic islands have a volcanic origin seems to be the remarkable and fascinating group of islets known as the Rocks of St. Paul. Lying in the open Atlantic between Brazil and Africa, St. Paul's Rocks are an obstruction thrust up from the floor of the ocean into the midst of the racing Equatorial Current, a mass against which the seas, which have rolled a thousand miles unhindered, break in sudden violence. The entire cluster of rocks covers not more than a quarter of a mile, running in a curved line like a horseshoe. The highest rock is not more than sixty feet above the sea; spray wets it to the summit. Abruptly the rocks dip under water and slope steeply down into great depths. Geologists since the time of Darwin have puzzled over the origin of these black, wave-washed islets. Most of them agree that they are composed of material like that of the sea floor itself. In some remote period, inconceivable stresses in the earth's crust must have pushed a solid rock mass upward more than two miles.

So bare and desolate that not even a lichen grows on them, St. Paul's Rocks would seem one of the most unpromising places in the world to look for a spider, spinning its web in arachnidan hope of snaring passing insects. Yet Darwin found spiders when he visited the Rocks in 1833, and forty years later the naturalists of H.M.S. *Challenger* also reported them, busy at their web-spinning. A few insects are there, too, some as parasites on the sea birds, three species of which nest on the Rocks. One of the insects is a small brown moth that lives on feathers. This very nearly completes the inventory of the inhabitants of St. Paul's Rocks, except for the grotesque crabs that swarm over the islets, living chiefly on the flying fish brought by the birds to their young.

St. Paul's Rocks are not alone in having an extraordinary assortment of inhabitants, for the faunas and floras of oceanic islands are amazingly different from those of the continents. The pattern of island life is peculiar and significant. Aside from forms recently introduced by man, islands remote from the continents are never inhabited by any land mammals, except sometimes the one mammal that has learned to fly—the bat. There are never any frogs, salamanders, or other amphibians. Of reptiles, there may be a few snakes, lizards, and turtles, but the more remote the island from a major land mass, the fewer reptiles there are, and the really isolated islands have none. There are usually a few species of land birds, some insects, and some spiders. So remote an island as Tristan da Cunha in the South Atlantic, fifteen hundred miles from the nearest continent, has no land animals but these: three species of land birds, a few insects, and several small snails.

With so selective a list, it is hard to see how, as some biologists believe, the islands could have been colonized by migration across land bridges, even if there were good evidence for the existence of the bridges. The very animals missing from the islands are the ones that would have had to come dry-shod, over the hypothetical bridges. The plants and animals that we find on oceanic islands, on the other hand, are the ones that could have come by wind or water. As an alternative, then, we must suppose that the stocking of the islands has been accomplished by the strangest migration in earth's history—a migration that began long before man appeared on the earth and is still continuing, a migration that seems more like a series of cosmic accidents than an orderly process of nature.

We can only guess how long after its emergence from the sea an oceanic island may lie uninhabited. Certainly in its original state it is a land bare, harsh, and repelling beyond human experience. No living thing moves over the slopes of its volcanic hills; no plants cover its naked lava fields. But little by little, riding on the winds, drifting on the currents, or rafting in on logs, floating brush, or trees, the plants and animals that are to colonize it arrive from the distant continents.

So deliberate, so unhurried, so inexorable are the ways of nature that the stocking of an island may require thousands or millions of years. It may be that no more than half a dozen times in all these eons does a particular form, such as a tortoise, make a successful landing upon its shores. To wonder impatiently why man is not a constant witness of such arrivals is to fail to understand the majestic pace of the process.

Yet we have occasional glimpses of the method. Natural rafts of up-rooted trees and matted vegetation have frequently been seen adrift at sea, more than a thousand miles off the mouths of such great tropical rivers as the Congo, the Ganges, the Amazon, and the Orinoco. Such rafts could easily carry an assortment of insect, reptile, or mollusk passengers. Some of the involuntary passengers might be able to withstand long weeks at sea; others would die during the first stages of the journey. Probably the ones best adapted for travel by raft are the wood-boring insects, which, of all the insect tribe, are most commonly found on oceanic islands. The poorest raft travelers must be the mammals. But even a mammal might cover short interisland distances. A few days after the explosion of Kraka-toa, a small monkey was rescued from some drifting timber in Sunda Strait. She had been terribly burned, but survived the experience.

No less than the water, the winds and the air currents play their part in bringing inhabitants to the islands. The upper atmosphere, even during the ages before man entered it in his machines, was a place of congested traffic. Thousands of feet above the earth, the air is crowded with living creatures, drifting, flying, gliding, ballooning, or involuntarily swirling along on the high winds. Discovery of this rich aerial plankton had to wait until man himself had found means to make physical invasion of these regions. With special nets and traps, scientists have now collected from the upper atmosphere many of the forms that inhabit oceanic islands. Spiders, whose almost invariable presence on these islands is a fascinating problem, have been captured nearly three miles above the earth's surface. Airmen have passed through great numbers of the white, silken filaments of spiders' "parachutes" at heights of two or three miles. At altitudes of six thousand to sixteen thousand feet, and with wind velocities reaching forty-five miles an hour, many living insects have been taken. At such heights and on such strong winds, they might well have been carried hundreds of miles. Seeds have been collected at altitudes up to five thousand feet. Among those commonly taken are members of the Composite family, especially the so-called "thistledown" typical of oceanic islands.

An interesting point about transport of living plants and animals by wind is the fact that in the upper layers of the earth's atmosphere the winds do not necessarily blow in the same direction as at the earth's surface. The trade winds are notably shallow, so that a man standing on the cliffs of St. Helena, a thousand feet above the sea, is above the wind, which blows with great force below him. Once drawn into the upper air, insects, seeds, and the like can easily be carried in a direction contrary to that of the winds prevailing at island level.

The wide-ranging birds that visit islands of the ocean in migration may also have a good deal to do with the distribution of plants, and perhaps even of some insects and minute land shells. From a ball of mud taken from a bird's plumage, Charles Darwin raised eighty-two separate plants, belonging to five distinct species! Many plant seeds have hooks or prickles, ideal for attachment to feathers. Such birds as the Pacific golden plover, which annually flies from the mainland of Alaska to the Hawaiian Islands and even beyond, probably figure in many riddles of plant distribution.

The catastrophe of Krakatoa gave naturalists a perfect opportunity to observe the colonization of an island. With most of the island itself destroyed, and the remnant covered with a deep layer of lava and ash that remained hot for weeks, Krakatoa after the explosive eruptions of 1883 was, from a biological standpoint, a new volcanic island. As soon as it was possible to visit it, scientists searched for signs of life, although it was hard to imagine how any living thing could have survived. Not a single plant or animal could be found. It was not until nine months after the eruption that the naturalist Cotteau was able to report: "I only discovered one microscopic spider—only one. This strange pioneer of the renovation was busy spinning its web." Since there were no insects on the island, the web-spinning of the bold little spider was presumably in vain, and, except for a few blades of grass, practically nothing lived on Krakatoa for a quarter of a century. Then the colonists began to arrive—a few mammals in 1908; a number of birds, lizards, and snakes; various mollusks, insects, and earthworms. Ninety per cent of Krakatoa's new inhabitants, Dutch scientists found, were forms that could have arrived by air.

Isolated from the great mass of life on the continents, with no opportunity for the crossbreeding that tends to preserve the average and to eliminate the new and unusual, island life has developed in a remarkable manner. On these remote bits of earth, nature has excelled in the creation of strange and wonderful forms. As though to prove her incredible versatility, almost every island has developed species that are endemic—that is, they are peculiar to it alone and are duplicated nowhere else on earth.

It was from the pages of earth's history written on the lava fields of the Galapagos that young Charles Darwin got his first inkling of the great truths of the origin of species. Observing the strange plants and animals—giant tortoises, black, amazing lizards that hunted their food in the surf, sea lions, birds in extraordinary variety—Darwin was struck by their vague similarity to mainland species of South and Central America, yet was haunted by the differences, differences that distinguish them not only from the mainland species but from those on other islands of the archipelago. Years later he was to write in reminiscence: "Both in space and time, we seem to be brought somewhat near to that great fact—that mystery of mysteries—the first appearance of new beings on earth."

Of the "new beings" evolved on islands, some of the most striking examples have been birds. In some remote age before there were men, a small, pigeonlike bird found its way to the island of Mauritius, in the Indian Ocean. By processes of change at which we can only guess, this bird lost the power of flight, developed short, stout legs, and grew larger until it reached the size of a modern turkey. Such was the origin of the fabulous dodo, which did not long survive the advent of man on Mauritius. New Zealand was the sole home of the moas. One species of these ostrichlike birds stood twelve feet high. Moas had roamed New Zealand from the early part of the Tertiary; those that remained when the Maoris arrived soon died out.

Other island forms besides the dodo and the moas have tended to become large. Perhaps the Galapagos tortoise became a giant after its arrival on the islands, although fossil remains on the continents cast doubt on this. The loss of wing use and even of the wings themselves (the moas had none) are common results of insular life. Insects on small, wind-swept islands tend to lose the power of flight—those that retain it are in danger of being blown out to sea. The Galapagos Islands have a flightless cormorant. There have been at least fourteen species of flightless rails on the islands of the Pacific alone.

One of the most interesting and engaging characteristics of island species is their extraordinary tameness—a lack of sophistication in dealings with the human race, which even the bitter teachings of experience do not quickly alter. When Robert Cushman Murphy visited the island of South Trinidad in 1913 with a party from the brig *Daisy,* terns alighted on the heads of the men in the whaleboat and peered inquiringly into their faces. Albatrosses on Laysan, whose habits include wonderful ceremonial dances, allowed naturalists to walk among their colonies and responded with a grave bow to similar polite greetings from the visitors. When the British ornithologist David Lack visited the Galapagos Islands, a century after Darwin, he found that the hawks allowed themselves to be touched, and the flycatchers tried to remove hair from the heads of the men for nesting material. "It is a curious pleasure," he wrote, "to have the birds of the wilderness settling upon one's shoulders, and the pleasure could be much less rare were man less destructive."

But man, unhappily, has written one of his blackest records as a destroyer on the oceanic islands. He has seldom set foot on an island that he has not brought about disastrous changes. He has destroyed environments by cutting, clearing, and burning; he has brought with him as a chance associate the nefarious rat; and almost invariably he has turned loose upon the islands a whole Noah's Ark of goats, hogs, cattle, dogs, cats, and other non-native animals as well as plants. Upon species after species of island life, the black night of extinction has fallen.

In all the world of living things, it is doubtful whether there is a more delicately balanced relationship than that of island life to its environment. This environment is a remarkably uniform one. In the midst of a great ocean, ruled by currents and winds that rarely shift their course, climate changes little. There are few natural enemies, perhaps none at all. The harsh struggle for existence that is the normal lot of continental life is softened on the islands. When this gentle pattern of life is abruptly changed, the island creatures have little ability to make the adjustments necessary for survival.

Ernst Mayr tells of a steamer wrecked off Lord Howe Island east of Australia in 1918. Its rats swam ashore. In two years they had so nearly exterminated the native birds that an islander wrote, "This paradise of birds has become a wilderness, and the quietness of death reigns where all was melody."

On Tristan da Cunha almost all of the unique land birds that had evolved there in the course of the ages were exterminated by hogs and rats. The native fauna of the island of Tahiti is losing ground against the horde of alien species that man has introduced. The Hawaiian Islands, which have lost their native plants and animals faster than almost any other area in the world, are a classic example of the results of interfering with natural balances. Certain relations of animal to plant, and of plant to soil, had grown up through the centuries. When man came in and rudely disturbed the balance, he set off a whole series of chain reactions.

Vancouver brought cattle and goats to the Hawaiian Islands, and the resulting damage to forests and other vegetation was enormous. Many plant introductions were as bad. A plant known as the pamakani was brought in many years ago, according to report, by a Captain Makee for his beautiful gardens on the island of Maui. The pamakani, which has light, windborne seeds, quickly escaped from the captain's gardens, ruined the pasture lands on Maui, and proceeded to hop from island to island. The CCC boys were at one time put to work to clear it out of the Honouliuli Forest Reserve, but as fast as they destroyed it, the seeds of new plants arrived on the wind. Lantana was another plant brought in as an ornamental species. Now it covers thousands of acres with a thorny, scrambling growth—despite large sums of money spent to import parasitic insects to control it.

There was once a society in Hawaii for the special purpose of introducing exotic birds. Today when you go to the islands, you see, instead of the exquisite native birds that greeted Captain Cook, mynas from India, cardinals from the United States or Brazil, doves from Asia, weavers from Australia, skylarks from Europe, and titmice from Japan. Most of the original bird life has been wiped out, and to find its fugitive remnants you would have to search assiduously in the most remote hills.

Some of the island species have, at best, the most tenuous hold on life. The Laysan teal is found nowhere in the world but on the one small island of Laysan. Even on this island it occurs only on one end, where there is a seepage of fresh water. Probably the total population of this species does not exceed fifty individuals. Destruction of the small swampy bit of land that is its home, or the introduction of a hostile or competing species, could easily snap the slender thread of life.

Most of man's habitual tampering with nature's balance by introducing exotic species has been done in ignorance of the fatal chain of events that would follow. But in modern times, at least, we might profit by history. About the year 1513, the Portuguese introduced goats onto the recently discovered island of St. Helena, which had developed a magnificent forest of gumwood, ebony, and brazilwood. By 1560 or thereabouts, the goats had so multiplied that they wandered over the island by the thousand, in flocks a mile long. They trampled the young trees and ate the seedlings. By this time the colonists had begun to cut and burn the forests, so that it is hard to say whether men or goats were the more responsible for the destruction. But of the result there was no doubt. By the early 1800's the forests were gone, and the naturalist Alfred Wallace later described this once beautiful, forest-clad volcanic island as a "rocky desert," in which the remnants of the original flora persisted only in the most inaccessible peaks and crater ridges.

When the astronomer Halley visited the islands of the Atlantic about 1700, he put a few goats ashore on South Trinidad. This time, without the further aid of man, the work of deforestation proceeded so rapidly that it was nearly completed within the century. Today Trinidad's slopes are the place of a ghost forest, strewn with the fallen and decaying trunks of long-dead trees; its soft volcanic soils, no longer held by the interlacing roots, are sliding away into the sea.

One of the most interesting of the Pacific islands was Laysan, a tiny scrap of soil which is a far outrider of the Hawaiian chain. It once supported a forest of sandalwood and fanleaf palms and had five land birds, all peculiar to Laysan alone. One of them was the Laysan rail, a charming, gnomelike creature no more than six inches high, with wings that seemed too small (and were never used as wings), and feet that seemed too large, and a voice like distant, tinkling bells. About 1887, the captain of a visiting ship moved some of the rails to Midway, about three hundred miles to the west, establishing a second colony. It seemed a fortunate move, for soon thereafter rabbits were introduced on Laysan. Within a quarter of a century, the rabbits had killed off the vegetation of the tiny island, reduced it to a sandy desert, and all but exterminated themselves. As for the rails, the devastation of their island was fatal, and the last rail died about 1924.

Perhaps the Laysan colony could later have been restored from the Midway group had not tragedy struck there also. During the war in the Pacific, rats went ashore to island after island from ships and landing crafts. They invaded Midway in 1943. The adult rails were slaughtered. The eggs were eaten, and the young birds killed. The world's last Laysan rail was seen in 1944.

The tragedy of the oceanic islands lies in the uniqueness, the irreplaceability of the species they have developed by the slow processes of the ages. In a reasonable world men would have treated these islands as precious possessions, as natural museums filled with beautiful and curious works of creation, valuable beyond price because nowhere in the world are they duplicated. W. H. Hudson's lament for the birds of the Argentine pampas might even more truly have been spoken of the islands: "The beautiful has vanished and returns not."

In Defense of Octopuses

By GILBERT C. KLINGEL

I FEEL about octopuses—as Mark Twain did about the devil—that someone should undertake their rehabilitation. All writers about the sea, from
Victor Hugo down to the present, have published volumes against them;
they have been the unknowing and unwitting victims of a large and
very unfair amount of propaganda, and have long suffered under the
stigma of being considered horrible and exceedingly repulsive. No one
has ever told the octopuses' side of the story; nor has anyone ever defended them against the mass of calumnies which have been heaped on
their peculiar and marvelously shaped heads. We have convicted them
without benefit of a hearing, which is a most partial and unjust proceeding. I propose that the octopuses, and their near relatives the squids, are
among the most wonderful of all earth's creatures, and as such are deserving of our respect, if not our admiration.

My personal interest in octopi dates back to the moment when I turned
to climb out of the drowned ravine at the base of the Inaguan barrier reef.
I had reached the lower portion of the final slope and was about to seize
on a piece of yellow rock to steady myself when I noticed that from the
top of the boulder was peering a cold dark eye that neither blinked nor
stirred. In vain I looked for eyelids; the orb apparently belonged to the
rock itself.

Then suddenly, I felt a chill wave creep up my spine. Before my gaze
the rock started to melt, began to ooze at the sides like a candle that had
become too hot. There is no other way to describe the action. I was so
startled at the phenomenon that it was a full second or two before I was
conscious of what I was watching.

It was my first acquaintance with a live, full-grown octopus. The beast
flowed down the remainder of the boulder, so closely did its flesh adhere
to the stone, and then slowly, with tentacles spread slightly apart, slithered
into a crevasse nearby. The head of the octopus was about as big as a
football, but as it reached the fissure, which was not more than four
inches in width, it flattened out and wedged itself into the opening. It

seemed somewhat irritated at my disturbing it, for it rapidly flushed from pebbled yellow to mottled brown and then back to a livid white. It remained white for about twenty seconds and then altered slowly to a dark gray edged with maroon. I stood stock-still, but it made no overt motions and I slowly edged away. Quite possibly it might have been a nasty customer, for the tentacles were about five feet from tip to tip.

This last statement may seem a contradiction to my opening paragraph; and, I must admit, that is the way I felt about the octopus at the time. However, since that hour I have collected and observed a number of these creatures, including the squids. I have found them animals of unusual attainments and they should be ranked among the most remarkable denizens of the sea. They are endowed with considerable intelligence and they have reached a system of living all their own which they have maintained for approximately 500,000,000 years. As far back as the Ordovician period of geology we find their ancestors, and there is good evidence that at one time the forefathers of the present octopi very nearly ruled the world. Had they been able to pass the barrier of the edge of the ocean as the early fish-derived amphibians did there might have been no limit to the amazing forms which would have peopled the earth.

Within the bounds of pure speculation, however, the fact remains that the cephalopods, as the entire octopi-like group of animals is termed, have missed the status of brainy intelligence, of which man is the highest criterion, only by a very narrow margin. There is reason to believe that they are the most keen-witted creatures in the ocean and had they developed an opposable thumb and fingers instead of suckers with which to manipulate various objects the entire course of the earth's existence might have been altered.

There are some very curious similarities between the development of intelligence in man and in the modern cephalopod. Both acquired brains after their individual fashions because the course of organic evolution left them without adequate physical protection against the vicissitudes of nature. Man, the weak and the puny, without claws and rending fangs to battle the beasts and without long legs with which to flee, had to acquire cunning or perish. That marvelous addition, the opposable thumb, made possible holding and using tools and gave a stimulus to cunning that nothing else in the mechanics of evolution could have provided. The thumb is by far the most remarkable portion of man's anatomy. Literature, music, art, philosophy, religion, civilization itself are directly the result of man's possession of this digit.

Like man, the modern cephalopods have been thrown upon the world naked and without the armor protection of their ancestors. For cephalopods are shellfish, blood brothers to the oyster, the clam and the conch; they are mollusks which have been deprived of their shells. The only present-day cephalopods which still retain their shells are the Nautiloids which are direct descendants of the ancient types whose fossils are found in the tightly compressed rocks of the Upper Cambrian. Over three thousand fossil Nautiloids have been named, an imposing group ranging in size from a tiny seven-millimeter creature called *Cyrtoceras* to the immense fourteen-foot cone of *Endoceras!* Only four closely related species of this mighty shelled host remain, all occurring in the South Pacific.

To compensate for the loss of their shells, which were their bulwarks against fate, these unclothed cephalopods have developed, like man, cunning and intelligence. Alone among the mollusks they have acquired by concentration of their chief nerve ganglia what may be truly considered a brain. With the casting aside of the shell they have also gained their freedom, speed and mobility.

Safety often goes hand in hand with degeneration. It is a curious circumstance that those creatures which live completely guarded lives also have a very dull existence. What, for example, could be safer and more stupid and sedentary than an oyster, clad in its house of lime? The loss of a shell not only rescued the cephalopods from dullness but it probably also saved them from extinction. The most highly ornate shelled cephalopods of all time, the gracefully coiled Ammonoids, which are so named because of their resemblance to the ramlike horns of the deity Jupiter Ammon, and which developed during the Upper Silurian and lasted until the close of the Age of Reptiles, went out of existence because the extent of their external sculpture and complexity of septation rendered them so specialized that they failed to respond to change. Some of these fantastic Ammonoids, of which six thousand species are known, possessed coiled shells more than six feet in diameter!

"Cephalopods," the scientific name of the octopi and squids, immediately characterizes them as something unusual, for it signifies that they walk on their heads. This is precisely what they do, for their tentacles or "feet" are located between their eyes and mouths. No other animals on earth utilize this position or method of progression.

However, it is in their mode of swimming that the motion of these weird beings is most amazing. They are beautifully streamlined when in action, and can dart about at remarkable speed. I recall once being out to sea in a fishing trawler off the Virginia Capes. I was sitting in the dark on deck watching the stars and swaying to the slight roll of the boat when suddenly I heard a rapidly reiterated splashing in the sea. The sound was slightly reminiscent of the pattering noise of flying fish. I knew that I was too far north for any quantity of these volant creatures. I went below and returned on deck with a flashlight. Its beam pierced the dark and glowed on the wave tops. The ship was passing through a school of small surface fish. They were being preyed upon by hundreds of *Loligo* squid. The squid were shuttling back and forth through the water at incredible speed. Most wonderful was the organization with which they seemed to operate. Entire masses of these cephalopods, all swimming in the same direction, would dart at the mass of fish, quickly seize and bite at them, then abruptly wheel as a unit and sweep through the panic-stricken victims which scurried everywhere. Some of these squid were traveling so rapidly that when they approached the top of the water they burst through and went skimming through the air for several yards, falling back with light splashes. In the morning I found several on the deck of the trawler where they had jumped, a vertical distance of at least six feet! There is another record made near the coast of Brazil of a swarm of squids flying out of the water on the deck of a ship which was twelve feet above the surface and which was further protected by a high bulwark, making a minimum jump of fifteen feet! Several score were shoveled off the ship when daylight came.

The cephalopods and particularly the squids might be compared to living fountain pens or animated syringes, for they accomplish their flight-like swimming by pulling liquid into their body cavities and squirting it out again. Their likeness to a living fountain pen is even further heightened when one considers that some of the cephalopods contain ink and a quill. Nor is this all, for nature, not content to offer all these wonders in one creature, has ordained that they may swim, not only forward like all other creatures of the sea, but backward! They can swim forward and sideways, too, but the normal mode is stern foremost.

The quill of these mobile fountain pens is the remnant of the shells of their prehistoric ancestors, and it persists, like our vermiform appendix, as a useless but telltale evidence of former usage. The quill, reduced in the octopi to two chitinous rods, and in the squid to a long narrow fluted pen, remarkably resembling an old-fashioned quill, is buried deep within the tissue. In a sense, the octopi and squids are shellfish which have surrounded their shells.

It is in the ink of these cephalopods that we are confronted with a true paradox. This ink, basis of the familiar India ink, is utilized for two diametrically opposite purposes. It is intended to provide concealment and, diversely, to enable the animal to keep in touch with its fellows. When there is fear of an attack by enemies, the ink is expelled into the water to form a "smoke screen" behind which the cephalopod flees to shelter. Thus the modern military technique of employing the smoke screen to conceal retreating movements was conceived by the cephalopods as early as the Jurassic, as is proved by a beautifully preserved fossil of that period which shows the ink bag prominently limned in the highly compressed tissue impression of a squid. However, when night closes down on the water shrouding the blue vastness of the deeps in impenetrable gloom it is by means of this same ink that the members of a school of squids are able to keep in contact with one another. It is believed that the ink is extruded in very small quantities and is picked up by unusually sensitive olfactory organs. The more solitary octopi use it in much the same manner to locate their mates.

I had no idea of the efficiency of this inky fluid until my third or fourth meeting with the octopus of the valley. I had been going down for a half hour or so each day near the same spot in the reef and almost always finished the day's dive with a final excursion to the limit of the hose on the base of the ravine. In these trips I saw a number of octopuses, mostly much smaller than the first. These seemed to live in the crevasses near the base of the reef, and often all that I saw of them was a tentacle or two twitching or writhing languidly from a fissure. Some I discovered by the neat piles of mussel shells and other mollusks near the entrances to their hiding places. Some of these shells were, surprisingly, unopened and, it can be assumed, were being stored against an hour of larger appetite. Also, most interesting, the only locality on Inagua where the mussels were to be found in any abundance was in the area of the surf, a living habit that might be attributed to the ceaseless raids of octopi on colonies in more peaceful localities. The mussels, in self-defense as it were, had established themselves in the only place where they might live undisturbed, which was, in contradiction, the most violent area of all the world of underwater. They were, so to speak, between the devil and the deep blue sea, or, to be more exact, between the devil and the hot dry air.

Most of these octopi were exceedingly shy, fleeing into their shelters at my approach, and drawing far back out of reach, a reaction quite at variance with the accepted theories of ferocity and malignancy. I tried to capture some of the smaller ones, but they were too fast for me. The big fellow on the slope of the ravine, however, while it did not seem quite so timid always gave me a wide berth and invariably, the few times I encountered it, withdrew to its fissure where it was never quite hidden, but was revealed by a portion of the body and the restless arms. At first I left it strictly alone, but curiosity about its peculiar color changes prompted me to come closer.

It always seemed irritated at my presence. Its nervousness may have been caused by fear, for it certainly made no pretense of belligerency, and it constantly underwent a series of pigment alterations that were little short of marvelous. Blushing was its specialty. No schoolgirl with her first love was ever subjected to a more rapid or recurring course of excited flushes than this particular octopus. The most common colors were creamy white, mottled Vandyke brown, maroon, bluish gray, and finally light ultramarine nearly the color of the water. When most agitated it turned livid white, which is I believe the reaction of fear. During some of the changes it became streaked, at times in wide bands of maroon and cream, and once or twice in wavy lines of lavender and deep rose. Even red spots and irregular purplish polka dots were included in its repertoire, though these gaudy variations seldom lasted for long.

I had heard that a light touch on the skin would leave a vivid impression of color and I was anxious to see if this were the case. From the boatman I borrowed a long stick and dropped down to the sea floor again. The octopus was still in place and I walked over to it with the pole in my hand. At first I was hesitant about the experiment. The creature had behaved so nicely that I almost decided to give it up. But the old curiosity prevailed and with my pole I slowly reached out and stroked it along the side of its body.

Then things began to happen. The stick was snatched from my fingers and went floating to the surface. The octopus flashed out of the fissure and ejected an immense cloud of purplish ink. For a brief moment I saw it swimming away, long and sleek in shape, and then I was surrounded by the haze. The fog was not opaque but imparted much the same quality of non-vision as thick smoke in dry air, except that I did not notice much in the way of wreaths. In fact, I was so confused and startled that my only thought was to get away. From underneath the helmet there arose a faint odor quite unlike anything else. Fishy musk is the nearest description I can think of. The color was most interesting, as I had always been under the impression that cephalopod ink was black. Rather, it appeared dark purple which later faded to a somber shade of azure. I can also remember, when it thinned considerably, seeing vague shafts of reddish when the rays of sunlight far above caught the substance at oblique angles. The ink spread out in a cloud extending over several yards and in the still depths of the ravine took quite a time to dissipate. Actually it floated away as a hazy smudge before it evaporated.

I was not able to continue my observations on color changes until several days later when I netted a baby octopus from some turtle weed growing a few yards from shore near the place where the reef reached its final termination in a mass of sandy shoals. I transferred the mite, a youngster of seven or eight inches' spread, to the tidepool near my old house where I kept it for several days. It took to its new surroundings very gracefully and made no attempt to escape but made life miserable for the numerous small crabs and fishes that shared the pond. The crabs were its principal prey which it captured by stealth and by lying patiently in wait. Patience was its most evident virtue, and much to my disgust it would sit for hours in one spot without moving, staring endlessly at the moving forms in the water. It used a great deal of intelligence in securing the crabs and selected a spot to lurk where it had ready command of an entire corner of the pond.

The rocks of its dwelling were creamy brown, and this was the exact hue it assumed while waiting to make a capture. It had perfect control of its pigmentation. In comparison the renowned chameleons are but rank amateurs. The mechanics of this alteration of hue are very complex but are controlled by the expansion and contraction of a group of cells attached to pigmented sacks, known as chromatophores, residing in the outer layers of skin over the entire surface of the body. In addition there is scattered over the body another great series of cells capable of reflecting light. These are yellow and impart a strange iridescent shimmer, slightly suggestive of the glow of pearls. The chromatophores, which are of a variety of colors, are opened and shut at will producing any or all colors of the rainbow.

These color cells are manipulated by highly sensitive nerves communicating with the brain and with the eye. The eye principally dictates the choice of color although emotion also seems to have a definite influence. When frightened the octopi usually blanch to a whitish or light tone; irritation will cause them to break out in dark pigments. No other creatures in the world can alter their color as quickly and completely. Emotion will cause a human being to flush with anger or become pale with pain or anxiety; but no one can hold his hand and will it to be green with yellow stripes, or even yellow or plain brown, let alone lavender or ultramarine. An artist may paint a picture; only an octopus can color its skin with the portrait of its emotions, or duplicate exactly the pattern of the soil on which it rests. Only a very highly organized creature, one with a brain and an unusually well co-ordinated nervous system, could accomplish the mechanical marvel of operating several thousands of cells at once, rapidly opening and closing them in proper order.

The cephalopods are not limited to color change but are also credited with being able to produce the most brilliant light known in the realm of animals. While this luminescence is limited to a very few deep-sea species of decapods, which are the ten-armed squids, their light is so vivid that they outshine the fireflies. These light organs may be found on any portion of the body, including the eyeball itself, and, oddly enough, even in the interior of the animal! In these last forms the body tissues are quite transparent, so the light is not necessarily concealed. These light organs are quite varied, some being but mounds of glowing fluid, others complex and carefully constructed lenses with mirrors of reflecting tissue. As yet very little is known of these abyssal octopi and squid, though a few captured specimens have been observed burning with a strong light for several hours. Some day when the means of exploring the vast deeps of the ocean comfortably and safely has been devised we will learn more of these unbelievable cephalopods.

Quite unseen, my octopus would wait until a crab ventured near. Then it would either swoop quickly over the victim smothering it in its diminutive tentacles or suddenly dart out an arm and seize its meal before it had time to flee. It seldom missed but when it did it usually retrieved its dinner by a quick pursuit before it had gone far. Before twenty-four hours were up the entire bottom of the pool was littered with the hollow carapaces of crabs. Peculiarly, the animal almost always devoured its victim bottom side up, biting through the softer lower shell with its small parrot-like beak and rasping out the contents with its filed tongue before casting the empty shell away. The legs and feet were seldom eaten and were usually torn off and discarded. Little of this feeding was done during the day. At high noon I even saw a crab crawl over the relaxed tentacles without being molested or becoming aware of the danger it was courting. In the evening, however, particularly just before sunset, the octopus seized everything within reach.

The capture of fish was not nearly so easy, and although I saw it make a number of attempts its only successful capture was a small goby that very injudiciously decided to rest a few inches below the octopus's chosen corner. As in the case of several of the crabs it was blanketed by a mass of writhing tentacles. Once the fish was grasped by the vacuum cups of these tentacles it was finished, for in their method of attacking, the octopi utilize one of the most efficient systems devised, a principle more certain than curving claws or the sharpness of teeth. Only the hand of man with its opposable thumb is superior.

The feel of these vacuum cups on the bare flesh is most unusual. It is not unpleasant, and in a small specimen gives the sensation of hundreds of tiny wet clammy hands pulling at the skin. The strength of the suckers is amazing. When I tried to lift the youngster off my wrist it clung tenaciously, and even when I had dislodged all the tentacles except one I still had to give a strong pull in proportion to its size to release the suckers. There have been cases in which the tentacles have been torn apart before the suckers released their grip. These suckers, which operate on much the same principle as the little rubber cups with which we attach objects to automobile windshields, are actuated by a muscular piston. The rim of the cup is fastened to an object, then the floor of the center is raised and retracted to form a vacuum. The cups, I found, would slip easily from side to side but when pulled directly exercised considerable power. In the octopods the suckers are sessile, or are mounted on low mounds; the squids carry the mechanism a bit further and produce them on stalks. In the giant squid the rims of the suckers are even equipped with fine teeth to render them more efficient. Whalers have recorded capturing whales with dozens of circular scars on their heads, inflicted in gargantuan battles with these monsters of the open ocean. Some of these scars have measured over two inches in diameter so that the creatures that possessed them must have been huge.

How large do the squid and octopi grow? There is an authentic record of a North Atlantic squid which measured fifty-two feet over all! Its tentacles had an abnormal reach of thirty-five feet and the remaining seventeen feet was taken up by the cylindrical body which had a circumference of twelve feet. The eye of this fabulous animal was seven by nine inches, the largest visual organ in the world. The suckers had a diameter of two and a quarter inches, and as some of the scars on captured whales have exceeded this measurement it is not unreasonable to assume that there may exist somewhere in the abyssal depths of the North Atlantic still larger squid of perhaps sixty or seventy feet. Even these amazing squid, however, are preyed upon by the great sperm whales which tear them apart with their long shearing teeth. In that old classic and favorite *The Cruise of the Cachalot,* the author, Mr. Frank Bullen, gives a vivid description of a battle between a large sperm whale and one of these squid.

"At about eleven A.M.," he writes, "I was leaning over the rail, gazing steadily at the bright surface of the sea, when there was a violent commotion in the sea right where the moon's rays were concentrated, so great that, remembering our position, I was at first inclined to alarm all hands, for I had often heard of volcanic islands suddenly lifting their heads from the depths below, or disappearing in a moment, and . . . I felt doubtful indeed of what was now happening. Getting the night glasses out of the cabin scuttle where they were always hung in readiness, I focused them on the troubled spot, perfectly satisfied by a short examination that neither volcano nor earthquake had anything to do with what was going on; yet so vast were the forces engaged that I might well have been excused for my first supposition. A very large whale was locked in deadly conflict with a cuttlefish or squid almost as large as himself, whose interminable tentacles seemed to enclose the whole of his great body. The head of the whale especially seemed a perfect network of writhing arms. Naturally, I suppose, for it appeared as if the whale had the tail part of the mollusk in his jaws, and, in a business-like methodical way was sawing through it. By the side of the black columnar head of the whale appeared the head of a great squid, as awful an object as one could well imagine, even in a fevered dream. Judging as carefully as possible, I estimated it to be at least as large as one of our pipes, which contained three hundrd and fifty gallons; but it may have been, and probably was, a good deal larger. The eyes were very remarkable for their size and blackness, which, contrasted with the livid whiteness of the head, made their appearance all the more striking. They were at least a foot in diameter, and seen under such conditions looked decidedly eerie and hobgoblin-like. All around the combatants were numerous sharks, like jackals around a lion, ready to share the feast, and apparently assisting in the destruction of the large Cephalopod."

Unfortunately Bullen does not tell the result of the combat, but one might assume that the whale was the victor, for the food of sperm whales consists almost exclusively of squid.

If the squid and octopi are accused of being fearsome and savage, it might be argued that they live in an underwater world in which savagery and primitive instincts are the most common passions, and the only way to exist is to conform to the mode. There is no doubt that an enraged large cephalopod could be a formidable antagonist. The authentic instances of octopi or squid attacking human beings or divers, however, are so rare as to be considered non-existent in spite of a large literature to the contrary. Most of their savagery is confined to securing their food, which is a normal and reasonable function.

The tentacles serve still another and more wonderful purpose, for it is by means of their arms that these unorthodox creatures are able to perpetuate their race. The arms that serve in this function are known as hectocotylized arms and this name was derived from an honest and understandable mistake by Cuvier. The name also signifies the arm of a hundred cells, and the mistake was made when the detached portion of one of these many-celled arms was found clinging in the mantle cavity of a female paper nautilus where it was erroneously thought to be some new sort of parasitic worm. The strange worm was named hectocotylus and the error was not discovered until further researches had been undertaken in regard to the animal's breeding habits. It appears that the arm of the male paper nautilus is extended during breeding time until it looks like a long wormlike lash. This lash is charged with the fertilizing spermatophores. When the male and female meet they intertwine their tentacles in a Medusalike embrace, and when they disengage from their fantastic love-making, the end of the lash is deposited under the mantle of the female, where it is held for a time, for the female is not yet ready to spawn. When her eggs are eventually extruded, they are fertilized by the waiting sperm. The broken arm is not completely lost, for the male can grow another and still another.

The cephalopods are so delightfully versatile that they have still other systems of reproducing. In some forms the hectocotylized arm is not detached but is specially modified so that it can develop and transfer spermatophores to the females' mantle cavity near the oviduct. The spermatophore is itself the most remarkable creation of all this complex mating. It is a long tubular structure loaded with sperm, an apparatus for extruding it, and most wonderful a cement gland for attaching it to the female. It can be utilized at will; a thoughtful provision considering that the female may then take her good time in depositing her eggs under favorable circumstances. In other species the spermatophore is grasped by the male as it passes from his mantle and is placed in her mantle cavity or attached to the membrane around her mouth where the eggs are sometimes fertilized.

Some of the cephalopods show an amazing amount of mother love and parental care. The common octopus *vulgaris* has been observed in aquaria guarding its eggs which were attached to the stone walls. It fiercely resented any interference and kept a constant circulation of water flowing over them to insure that no parasites would take hold and that proper oxygenation would occur. The eggs were not even left long enough for the mother to secure food, even though the period of incubation lasted for a considerable time. So intense was this guardianship that another octopus in the same tank which ventured close too frequently was set upon and slain. Mother love in an octopus seems a strange and out-landish emotion, but no doubt it is actuated by the same flame that causes human parents to sacrifice their pleasures and desires that Junior, or his sister, for example, might go to college.

Cephalopodian care of the egg is responsible for another of the truly paradoxical things about these creatures. In the genus *Argonauta* the female carries about with her a beautifully coiled and graceful shell. This seems a contradiction to an earlier statement that the modern cephalopods are creatures which have cast aside their shells. Actually the shell of the Argonauts is not a true shell but is an egg case formed on the spiral shell pattern, which is mechanically a very strong and structurally efficient shape. The Argonaut is not bound to the shell in any way, for it may leave it whenever it desires, which it has been reported to do under cer-tain conditions. No other mollusk is so equipped. Imagine an oyster, for example, opening its valves and stepping out for an airing! The shell is held in position by two arms which are specially formed for the purpose. Only the female possesses this protection, and she forms the shell, not with the mantle as do all other mollusks, but with her two modified arms with their expanded membranous disks. When the Argonauts are first born they have no shells and they do not begin their construction until they are a week or two old. Unfortunately for the natural history of Aristotle, they do not sail over the surface of the sea like miniature ships with the arms held as sails as that ancient and inquiring naturalist so quaintly believed, but creep and crawl along the bottom or swim by means of their siphons like any other cephalopod. While the eggs of the Argonauts are well protected and carefully mothered, the adult has paid a reverse penalty for its acquisition of a shell, even though that shell is not a true one. The Argonauts have lost some of the intelligence and freedom of other octopods, for they appear to be the most sluggish and stupid of their class.

Inagua from above the sea gives no hint of the host of octopods that must harbor in its reefs, or of the tiny frond-colored squids that shelter in the growth of sargassum weed that float ceaselessly by on the currents, or of the larger and more appalling-looking decapods that move about in small groups in the open water. Nor is there much indication even to the diver of their presence. Unlike the reef fishes they are mostly nocturnal. During the bright hours they lie quiescent, curled up in the crevasses of their coral homes or float suspended and still, in the magic manner of underwater between top and bottom, waiting patiently with staring round eyes for the sun to drop and extend vague shadows over the blue depths.

Then they creep from their dens and go slithering over the coral boulders or swim like living arrows through the green waters, pouncing on their prey and doing whatever amazing things fall to the lot of cephalopods.

Whenever I think of the great barrier reef of Inagua I think always of two things: first, of the fairyland of the coral itself and the pastel colors, and second, of the octopus of the drowned ravine with its weird eye and rubbery body. More than any other creature, the octopus is the spirit of the reef; unreal themselves, completely fantastic, unbelievable, weird, they are fitting residents of a world in which all the accepted routines are nullified, in which animals play at being vegetables, where worms are beautiful, where the trees are made of brittle stone, where crabs pretend to be things they are not, where flowers devour fishes, where fishes imitate sand and rocks and where danger lurks in innocent color or harmless shape. That they should, also, be inhabitants of the shadowy night places is the final touch on their characters. The octopi fill a niche of creation claimed by no others and a niche which they occupy to perfection.

To the South Sea Islands

By THOR HEYERDAHL

ON THE night before July 30 there was a new and strange atmosphere about the *Kon-Tiki*. Perhaps it was the deafening clamor from all the sea birds over us which showed that something fresh was brewing. The screaming of birds with many voices sounded hectic and earthly after the dead creaking of lifeless ropes, which was all we had heard above the noise of the sea in the three months we had behind us. And the moon seemed larger and rounder than ever as it sailed over the lookout at the masthead.

At six o'clock Bengt came down from the masthead, woke Herman, and turned in. When Herman clambered up the creaking, swaying mast, the day had begun to break. Ten minutes later he was down the rope ladder again and was shaking me by the leg.

"Come out and have a look at your island!"

His face was radiant and I jumped up, followed by Bengt who had not quite gone to sleep yet. Hard on one another's heels, we huddled together as high as we could climb, at the point where the masts crossed. There were many birds around us, and a faint violet-blue veil over the sky was reflected in the sea as a last relic of the departing night. But over the whole horizon away to the east a ruddy glow had begun to spread, and far down to the southeast it gradually formed a blood-red background for a faint shadow, like a blue pencil line, drawn for a short way along the edge of the sea.

Land! An island! We devoured it greedily with our eyes and woke the others, who tumbled out drowsily and stared in all directions. Screaming sea birds formed a bridge across the sky in the direction of the distant island, which stood out sharper against the horizon as the red background widened and turned gold with the approach of the sun and the full daylight.

Our first thought was that the island did not lie where it should. As the island could not have drifted, the raft must have been caught up in a northward current in the course of the night. We had only to cast one glance over the sea to perceive at once, from the direction of the waves, that we had lost our chance in the darkness. Where we now lay, the wind no longer allowed us to press the raft on a course toward the island. The region round the Tuamotu Archipelago was full of strong, local ocean currents which twisted in all directions as they ran up against land; many of them varied in direction as they met powerful tidal currents flowing in and out over reefs and lagoons.

We laid the steering oar over, but we knew quite well that it was useless. At half-past six the sun rose out of the sea and climbed straight up as it does in the tropics. The island lay some few sea miles away and had the appearance of a quite low strip of forest creeping along the horizon. The trees were crowded close together behind a narrow light-colored beach, which lay so low that it was hidden behind the seas at regular intervals.

No extravagant outbursts were to be heard on board. After the sail had been trimmed and the oar laid over, we all formed a silent group at the masthead or stood on deck staring toward the land which had suddenly cropped up out in the middle of the endless, all-dominating sea. At last we had a visible proof that we had really been moving in all these months; we had not just been lying tumbling about in the center of the same eternal circular horizon. To us it seemed as if the island were mobile and had suddenly entered the circle of blue and empty sea in the center of which we had our permanent abode; as if the island were drifting slowly across our own domain. We were all filled with a warm, quiet satisfaction at having actually reached Polynesia, mingled with a faint momentary disappointment at having to submit helplessly to seeing the island lie there like a mirage while we continued our eternal drift across the sea westward.

At half-past eight Puka Puka sank into the sea astern of us, but right on till eleven o'clock we could see, on climbing to the masthead, that there was a faint blue streak above the horizon in the east. Then that too was gone, and a high cumulo-nimbus cloud, rising motionless skyward, was all that showed where Puka Puka lay. The birds disappeared. They kept by preference to windward of the islands so that they had the wind with them when they returned home in the evening with full bellies. The dolphins also had become noticeably scarcer, and there were again only a few pilot fish under the raft.

The very next morning we detected two new clouds rising up like the steam from two locomotives below the horizon. The map was able to tell us that the names of the coral islands they came from were Fangahina and Angatau. The cloud over Angatau lay the most favorably for us as the wind was blowing, so we set our course for that, lashed the oar fast, and enjoyed the wonderful peace and freedom of the Pacific. So lovely was life on this fine day on the bamboo deck of the *Kon-Tiki* that we drank in all the impressions in the certainty that the journey would soon be over now, whatever might await us.

For three days and nights we steered on the cloud over Angatau; the weather was brilliant, the oar alone held us on our course, and the current played us no tricks. On the fourth morning Torstein relieved Herman after the 4–6 watch and was told that Herman thought he had seen the outlines of a low island in the moonlight. When the sun rose just afterward Torstein stuck his head in at the cabin door and shouted:

"Land ahead!"

We all plunged out on deck, and what we saw made us hoist all our flags. First the Norwegian aft, then the French at the masthead because we were heading for a French colony. Soon the raft's entire collection of flags was fluttering in the fresh trade wind—the American, British, Peruvian, and Swedish flags besides the flag of the Explorers Club—so there was no doubt on board that now the *Kon-Tiki* was dressed. The island was ideally placed this time, right in our own course and a little farther away from us than Puka Puka had been when it cropped up at sunrise four days before. As the sun rose straight up over the sky astern of us, we could see a clear green glimmer high up toward the misty sky over the island. It was the reflection of the still, green lagoon on the inside of the surrounding reef. Some of the low atolls throw up mirages of this kind for many thousand feet into the air, so that they show their position to primitive seafarers many days before the island itself is visible above the horizon.

We knew that somewhere between us and the island there was a dangerous submerged shoal, lying in ambush for anything that approached the innocent island. This reef lay right under the deep, free roll of the swell from the east, and, as the huge masses of water lost their balance above the shoal, they wavered skyward and plunged down, thundering and foaming, over the sharp coral reef. Many vessels have been caught in the terrible suction against the submerged reefs in the Tuamotu group and have been smashed to pieces against the coral.

From the sea we saw nothing of this insidious trap. We sailed in, following the direction of the waves, and saw only the curved shining back of sea after sea disappearing toward the island. Both the reef and the whole frothing witches' dance over it were hidden behind rising rows of broad wave backs ahead of us. But along both ends of the island where we saw the beach in profile, both north and south, we saw that a few hundred yards from land the sea was one white boiling mass flinging itself high into the air.

We laid our course so as to graze the outside of the witches' kitchen off the southern point of the island, hoping, when we got there, to be able to steer along the atoll till we came round the point on the lee side or till we touched, before we drifted past, a place where it was so shallow that we could stop our drift with a makeshift anchor and wait till the wind changed and placed us under the lee of the island.

About noon we could see through the glass that the vegetation on shore consisted of young green coconut palms, which stood with their tops close together over a waving hedge of luxuriant undergrowth in the foreground.

At two o'clock we had come so close that we began to sail along the island, just outside the baffling reef. As we gradually approached, we heard the roar of the breakers like a steady waterfall against the reef, and soon they sounded like an endless express train running parallel with us a few hundred yards from our starboard side.

Two men at the same time stood turning the steering oar; they were behind the bamboo cabin and so had no view ahead whatever. Erik, as navigator, stood on the top of the kitchen box and gave directions to the two men at the heavy oar. Our plan was to keep as close in to the dangerous reef as was safe. We kept a continuous lookout from the masthead for a gap or opening in the reef where we could try to slip the raft through. The current was now driving us along the whole length of the reef and played us no tricks. The loose centerboards allowed us to steer at an angle of about 20 degrees to the wind on both sides, and the wind was blowing along the reef.

While Erik directed our zigzag course and took his loops as near the reef as was advisable in view of the suction, Herman and I went out in the rubber dinghy at the end of a rope. When the raft was on the inward tack, we swung after her on the rope and came so close to the thundering reef that we caught a glimpse of the glass-green wall of water that was rolling away from us and saw how, when the seas sucked themselves back, the naked reef exposed itself, resembling a torn-up barricade of rusty iron ore. As far as we could see along the coast there was no gap or passage. So Erik trimmed the sail by tightening the port and loosening the starboard sheets, and the helmsman followed with the steering oar, so that the *Kon-Tiki* turned her nose out again and tumbled away from the danger zone till her next drive inward.

Each time the *Kon-Tiki* stood in toward the reef and swung out again, we two who were in tow in the dinghy sat with our hearts in our mouths, for each time we came so close in that we felt the beat of the seas becoming nervous as it rose higher and fiercer. And each time we were convinced that this time Erik had gone too far, that this time there was no hope of getting the *Kon-Tiki* out again clear of the breakers which drew us in toward the devilish red reef. But each time Erik got clear with a smart maneuver, and the *Kon-Tiki* ran safely out into the open sea again, well out of the clutch of the suction. All the time we were gliding along the island, so close that we saw every detail on shore; yet the heavenly beauty there was inaccessible to us because of the frothing moat that lay between.

About three o'clock the forest of palms ashore opened, and through a wide gap we saw right into a blue glassy lagoon. But the surrounding reef lay as compact as ever, gnashing its blood-red teeth ominously in the foam. There was no passage, and the palm forest closed again as we plodded on along the island with the wind at our backs. Later the palm forest became thinner and thinner and gave us a view into the interior of the coral island. This consisted of the fairest, brightest salt-water lagoon, like a great silent tarn, surrounded by swaying coconut palms and shining bathing beaches. The seductive, green palm island itself formed a broad, soft ring of sand round the hospitable lagoon, and a second ring ran round the whole island—the rust-red sword which defended the gates of heaven.

All day we zigzagged along Angatau and had its beauty at close quarters, just outside the cabin door. The sun beat down on all the palms, and all was Paradise and joy on the island within. As our maneuvers gradually became a matter of routine, Erik got out his guitar and stood on deck in a huge Peruvian sun hat playing and singing sentimental South Sea songs, while Bengt served an excellent dinner on the edge of the raft. We opened an old coconut from Peru and drank to the young fresh nuts which hung on the trees inside.

It happened that this festal day off Angatau was the ninety-seventh day on board. Strangely enough, it was ninety-seven days that we had estimated in New York as the absolute minimum time in which, in theoretically ideal conditions, we could reach the nearest islands of Polynesia.

About five o'clock we passed two palm-roofed huts which lay among the trees on shore. There was no smoke and no sign of life.

At half-past five we stood in toward the reef again; we had sailed along the whole south coast and were getting near the west end of the island, and must have a last look round in the hope of finding a passage before we passed. The sun now stood so low that it blinded us when we looked ahead, but we saw a little rainbow in the air where the sea broke against the reef a few hundred yards beyond the last point of the island. This now lay as a silhouette ahead of us. On the beach inside we detected a cluster of motionless black spots. Suddenly one of them moved slowly down toward the water, while several of the others made off at full speed up to the edge of the woods. They were people! We steered along the reef as close in as we dared; the wind had died down so that we felt we were within an inch of getting under the lee of the island. Now we saw a canoe being launched, and two individuals jumped on board and paddled off on the other side of the reef. Farther down they turned the boat's head out, and we saw the canoe lifted high in the air by the seas as it shot through a passage in the reef and came straight out toward us.

The opening in the reef, then, was down there; there was our only hope. Now, too, we could see the whole village lying in among the palm trunks. But the shadows were already growing long.

The two men in the canoe waved. We waved back eagerly, and they increased their speed. It was a Polynesian outrigger canoe; two brown figures in singlets sat paddling, facing ahead. Now there would be fresh language difficulties. I alone of those on board remembered a few words of Marquesan from my stay on Fatu Hiva, but Polynesian is a difficult language to keep up, for lack of practice in our northern countries.

We felt some relief, therefore, when the canoe bumped against the raft's side and the two men leaped on board, for one of them grinned all over his face and held out a brown hand, exclaiming in English:

"Good night!"

"Good night," I replied in astonishment. "Do you speak English?"

The man grinned again and nodded.

"Good night," he said. "Good night."

This was his entire vocabulary in foreign languages, and thereby he scored heavily over his more modest friend, who just stood in the background and grinned, much impressed, at his experienced comrade.

"Angatau?" I asked, pointing toward the island.

"H'angatau," the man nodded affirmatively.

Erik nodded proudly. He had been right; we were where the sun had told him that we were.

"Maimaihee iuta," I tried.

According to my knowledge acquired on Fatu Hiva this should mean approximately, "Want to go to land."

They both pointed toward the invisible passage in the reef, and we laid the oar over and decided to take our chance.

At that moment fresher gusts of wind came from the interior of the island. A small rain cloud lay over the lagoon. The wind threatened to force us away from the reef, and we saw that the *Kon-Tiki* was not answering the steering oar at a wide enough angle to be able to reach the mouth of the opening in the reef. We tried to find bottom, but the anchor rope was not long enough. Now we had to have resort to the paddles, and pretty quickly, too, before the wind got a fair hold of us. We hauled down the sail at top speed and each of us got out his big paddle.

I wanted to give an extra paddle to each of the two natives, who stood enjoying the cigarettes they had been given on board. They only shook their heads vigorously, pointed out the course, and looked confused. I made signs that we must all paddle and repeated the words, "Want to go to land!" Then the most advanced of the two bent down, made a cranking motion in the air with his right hand, and said:

"Brrrrrrrr—!"

There was no doubt whatever that he wanted us to start the engine. They thought they were standing on the deck of a curiously deep loaded boat. We took them aft and made them feel under the logs to show them that we had no propeller or screw. They were dumbfounded and, putting out their cigarettes, flung themselves down on the side of the raft where we sat—four men on each outside log, dipping our paddles into the water. At the same time the sun sank straight into the sea behind the point, and the gusts of wind from the interior of the island freshened. It did not look as if we were moving an inch. The natives looked frightened, jumped back into the canoe, and disappeared. It grew dark, and we were alone once more, paddling desperately so as not to drift out to sea again. . . .

As darkness fell over the island, four canoes came dancing out from behind the reef, and soon there was a crowd of Polynesians on board, all wanting to shake hands and get cigarettes. With these fellows on board, who had local knowledge, there was no danger. They would not let us go out to sea again and out of sight, so we should be ashore that evening!

We quickly had ropes made fast from the sterns of all the canoes to the bow of the *Kon-Tiki,* and the four sturdy outrigger canoes spread out in fan formation, like a dog team, ahead of the wooden raft. Knut jumped into the dinghy and found a place as draft dog in among the canoes, and we others, with paddles, posted ourselves on the two outside logs of the *Kon-Tiki.* And so began, for the first time, a struggle against the east wind which had been at our back for so long.

It was now pitch dark until the moon rose, and there was a fresh wind. On land the inhabitants of the village had collected brushwood and lighted a big fire to show us the direction of the passage through the reef. The thundering from the reef surrounded us in the darkness like a ceaselessly roaring waterfall, and at first the noise grew louder and louder.

We could not see the team that was pulling us in the canoes ahead, but we heard them singing exhilarating war songs in Polynesian at the top of their lungs. We could hear that Knut was with them, for every time the Polynesian music died away we heard Knut's solitary voice singing Norwegian folk songs in the midst of the Polynesians' chorus.

We were overflowing with high spirits. Ninety-seven days. Arrived in Polynesia. There would be a feast in the village that evening. The natives cheered and bellowed and shouted. There was a landing on Angatau only once a year, when the copra schooner came from Tahiti to fetch coconut kernels. So there would indeed be a feast round the fire on land that evening.

But the angry wind blew stubbornly. We toiled till every limb ached. We held our ground, but the fire did not come any nearer and the thunder from the reef was just the same as before. Gradually the singing died away. All grew still. It was all and more the men could do to row. The fire did not move; it only danced up and down as we fell and rose with the seas. Three hours passed, and it was now nine o'clock. Gradually we began to lose ground. We were tired.

We made the natives understand that we needed more help from land. They explained to us that there were plenty of people ashore, but they had only these four seagoing canoes in the whole island.

Then Knut appeared out of the darkness with the dinghy. He had an idea; he could row in in the rubber dinghy and fetch more natives. Five or six men could sit crowded together in the dinghy at a pinch.

This was too risky. Knut had no local knowledge; he would never be able to feel his way forward to the opening in the coral reef in that pitch-black darkness. He then proposed to take with him the leader of the natives, who could show him the way. I did not think this plan a safe one, either, for the native had no experience in maneuvering a clumsy rubber dinghy through the narrow and dangerous passage. But I asked Knut to fetch the leader, who was sitting paddling in the darkness ahead of us, so that we might hear what he thought of the situation. It was clear enough that we were no longer able to prevent ourselves from drifting astern.

Knut disappeared into the darkness to find the leader. When some time had passed and Knut had not returned with the leader, we shouted for them but received no answer except from a cackling chorus of Polynesians ahead. Knut had vanished into the darkness. At that moment we undertood what had happened. In all the bustle, noise, and turmoil Knut had misunderstood his instructions and rowed shoreward with the leader. All our shouting was useless, for where Knut now was all other sounds were drowned by the thunder all along the barrier.

We quickly got hold of a Morse lamp, and a man climbed up to the masthead and signaled, "Come back. Come back."

But no one came back.

With two men away and one continuously signaling at the masthead our drift astern increased, and the rest of us had begun to grow really tired. We threw marks overboard and saw that we were moving slowly but surely the wrong way. The fire grew smaller and the noise from the breakers less. And the farther we emerged from under the lee of the palm forest, the firmer hold of us the eternal east wind took. We felt it again now; it was almost as it had been out at sea. We gradually realized that all hope had gone—we were drifting out to sea. But we must not slacken our paddling. We must put the brake on the drift astern with all our might till Knut was safe on board again.

Five minutes went. Ten minutes. Half an hour. The fire grew smaller; now and then it disappeared altogether when we ourselves slid down into the trough of the sea. The breakers became a distant murmur. Now the moon rose; we could just see the glimmer of its disk behind the palm tops on land, but the sky seemed misty and half clouded over. We heard the natives beginning to murmur and exchange words. Suddenly we noticed that one of the canoes had cast off its rope into the sea and disappeared. The men in the other three canoes were tired and frightened and were no longer pulling their full weight. The *Kon-Tiki* went on drifting out over the open sea.

Soon the three remaining ropes slackened and the three canoes bumped against the side of the raft. One of the natives came on board and said quietly with a jerk of his head:

"*Iuta* (To land)."

He looked anxiously at the fire, which now disappeared for long periods at a time and only flashed out now and again like a spark. We were drifting fast. The breakers were silent; only the sea roared as it used to, and all the ropes on board the *Kon-Tiki* creaked and groaned.

We plied the natives with cigarettes, and I hurriedly scrawled a note which they were to take with them and give to Knut if they found him. It ran:

"Take two natives with you in a canoe with the dinghy in tow. Do NOT come back in the dinghy alone."

We counted on the helpful islanders being willing to take Knut with them in a canoe, assuming they thought it advisable to put to sea at all; if they did not think it advisable, it would be madness for Knut to venture out on to the ocean in the dinghy in the hope of overtaking the runaway raft.

The natives took the scrap of paper, jumped into the canoes, and disappeared into the night. The last we heard was the shrill voice of our first friend out in the darkness calling politely:

"Good night!"

There was a murmur of appreciation from the less accomplished linguists, and then all was as silent, as free from sounds from without, as when we were two thousand sea miles from the nearest land.

At ten o'clock we gave up the last faint hope of seeing Knut again. We sat down in silence on the edge of the raft and munched a few biscuits, while we took turns flashing signals from the masthead, which seemed just a naked projection without the broad *Kon-Tiki* sail.

We decided to keep the lamp-signaling going all night, so long as we did not know where Knut was. We refused to believe that he had been caught by the breakers. Not one of us showed a sign of wanting to sleep.

It was half-past ten. Bengt was coming down to be relieved at the swaying masthead. Then we all started. We had heard voices clearly, out on the sea in the darkness. There it was again. It was Polynesians talking. We shouted into the black night with all the strength of our lungs. They shouted back, and—there was Knut's voice among the rest! We were mad with excitement. Our tiredness had gone; the whole thundercloud had lifted. What did it matter if we drifted away from Angatau? There were other islands in the sea. Now the nine balsa logs, so fond of travel, could drift where they like, so long as all six of us were assembled on board again.

Three outrigger canoes emerged from the darkness, riding over the swell, and Knut was the first man to jump across to the dear old *Kon-Tiki,* followed by six brown men. There was little time for explanations; the natives must have presents and be off on their adventurous journey back to the island. Without seeing light or land, and with hardly any stars, they had to find their course by paddling against wind and sea till they saw the light from the fire. We rewarded them amply with provisions, cigarettes, and other gifts, and each of them shook us heartily by the hand in a last farewell.

They were clearly anxious on our account; they pointed westward, indicating that we were heading toward dangerous reefs. The leader had tears in his eyes and kissed me tenderly on the chin, which made me thank Providence for my beard. Then they crept into the canoes, and we six comrades were left on the raft, together and alone.

We left the raft to her own devices and listened to Knut's story.

Knut had in good faith made for land in the dinghy with the native leader on board. The native himself was sitting at the little oars and rowing toward the opening in the reef, when Knut to his surprise saw the light signals from the *Kon-Tiki* asking him to come back. He made signs to the rowers to turn, but the native refused to obey. Then Knut took hold of the oars himself, but the native tore his hands away, and with the reef thundering round them it was no use starting a fight. They had bounded right in through the opening in the reef and gone on inside it, until they were lifted right up onto a solid coral block on the island itself. A crowd of natives caught hold of the dinghy and dragged it high up on the shore, and Knut stood alone under the palm trees surrounded by a huge crowd of natives chattering away in an unknown lingo. Brown, bare-legged men, women, and children of all ages flocked round him and felt the material of his shirt and trousers. They themselves wore ragged old European clothes, but there were no white men on the island.

Knut got hold of some of the smartest fellows and made signs to them that they should go out in the dinghy with him. Then a big fat man came waddling up who Knut presumed must be the chief, for he had an old uniform cap on his head and talked in a loud, authoritative voice. All made way for him. Knut explained both in Norwegian and in English that he needed men and must get back to the raft before we others drifted away. The chief beamed and understood nothing, and Knut, despite his most vehement protests, was pushed over to the village by the whole shouting crowd. There he was received by dogs and pigs and pretty South Sea girls who came along carrying fresh fruit. The natives' intention was obvious. They badly wanted our company, and they knew that there were a lot of good things on board white men's ships. If they could keep Knut ashore, the rest of us and the queer boat would certainly come in also.

Then the natives tried a trick; they indicated by signs that the rest of us were coming ashore on the other side of the point. Knut was puzzled for a few minutes, but then loud voices were heard down on the beach, where women and children were tending the flickering fire. The three canoes had come back, and the men brought Knut the note.

There followed a high-pitched, noisy argument among all the natives. Those who had been out and seen the raft understood perfectly well that it was of little use to keep Knut back in the hope of getting the rest of us ashore. The end of it was that Knut's promises and threats in international accents induced the crews of three canoes to accompany him out to sea in pursuit of the *Kon-Tiki*. They put out to sea in the tropical night with the dinghy dancing along in tow, while the natives stood motionless by the dying fire and watched their new blond friend disappear as quickly as he had come.

Knut and his companions could see the faint light signals from the raft far out to sea when the swell lifted the canoes. The long, slim Polynesian canoes, stiffened by pointed side floats, cut through the water like knives, but it seemed an eternity to Knut before he felt the thick round logs of the *Kon-Tiki* under his feet again.

"Have a good time ashore?" Torstein asked enviously.

"Oho, you just should have seen the hula girls," Knut teased him.

We left the sail down and the oar inboard, and all six of us crept into the bamboo cabin and slept like boulders on the beach at Angatau.

For three days we drifted across the sea without a sight of land.

We were drifting straight toward the ominous Takume and Raroia reefs, which together blocked up forty to fifty miles of the sea ahead of us. We made desperate efforts to steer clear, to the north of these dangerous reefs, and things seemed to be going well till one night the watch came hurrying in and called us all out.

The wind had changed. We were heading straight for the Takume reef. It had begun to rain, and there was no visibility at all. The reef could not be far off.

In the middle of night we held a council of war. It was a question of saving our lives now. To get past on the north side was now hopeless; we must try to get through on the south side instead. We trimmed the sail, laid the oar over, and began a dangerous piece of sailing with the uncertain north wind behind us. If the east wind came back before we had passed the whole façade of the fifty-mile-long reefs, we should be hurled in among the breakers, at their mercy.

We agreed on all that should be done if shipwreck was imminent. We laid the rubber raft loose on the deck and made fast to it a small watertight radio transmitter, a small quantity of provisions, water bottles, and medical stores. This would be washed ashore independently of us if we ourselves should get over the reef safe but empty-handed. In the stern of the *Kon-Tiki* we made fast a long rope with a float which also would be washed ashore, so that we could try to pull in the raft if she were stranded out on the reef. And so we crept into bed and left the watch to the helmsman out in the rain.

As long as the north wind held, we glided slowly but surely down along the façade of the coral reefs which lay in ambush below the horizon. But then one afternoon the wind died away, and when it returned it had gone round into the east. According to Erik's position we were already so far down that we now had some hope of steering clear of the southernmost point of the Raroia reef. We would try to get round it and into shelter before going on to other reefs beyond it.

When night came, we had been a hundred days at sea.

Late in the night I woke, feeling restless and uneasy. There was something unusual in the movement of the waves. The *Kon-Tiki's* motion was a little different from what it usually was in such conditions. We had become sensitive to changes in the rhythm of the logs. I thought at once of suction from a coast, which was drawing near, and was continually out on deck and up the mast. Nothing but sea was visible. But I could get no quiet sleep. Time passed.

At dawn, just before six, Torstein came hurrying down from the masthead. He could see a whole line of small palm-clad islands far ahead. Before doing anything else we laid the oar over to southward as far as we could. What Torstein had seen must be the small coral islands which lay strewn like pearls on a string behind the Raroia reef. A northward current must have caught us.

A survey from the masthead showed that, even if our bow pointed toward the bottom island in the chain, our drift sideways was so great that we were not advancing in the direction in which our bow pointed. We were drifting diagonally right in toward the reef. With fixed centerboards we should still have had some hope of steering clear. But sharks were following close astern, so that it was impossible to dive under the raft and tighten up the loose centerboards with fresh guy ropes.

We saw that we had now only a few hours more on board the *Kon-Tiki*. They must be used in preparation for our inevitable wreck on the coral reef. Every man learned what he had to do when the moment came; each one of us knew where his own limited sphere of responsibility lay, so that we should not fly round treading on one another's toes when the time came and seconds counted. The *Kon-Tiki* pitched up and down, up and down, as the wind forced us in. There was no doubt that here was the turmoil of the waves created by the reef—some waves advancing while others were hurled back after beating vainly against the surrounding wall.

We were still under full sail in the hope of even now being able to steer clear. As we gradually drifted nearer, half sideways, we saw from the mast how the whole string of palm-clad isles was connected with a coral reef, part above and part under water, which lay like a mole where the sea was white with foam and leaped high into the air. The Raroia atoll is oval in shape and has a diameter of twenty-five miles, not counting the adjoining reefs of Takume. The whole of its longer side faces the sea to eastward, where we came pitching in. The reef itself, which runs in one line from horizon to horizon, is only a few hundred yards clear, and behind it idyllic islets lie in a string round the still lagoon inside.

It was with mixed feelings that we saw the blue Pacific being ruthlessly torn up and hurled into the air all along the horizon ahead of us. I knew what awaited us; I had visited the Taumotu group before and had stood safe on land looking out over the immense spectacle in the east, where the surf from the open Pacific broke in over the reef. New reefs and islands kept on gradually appearing to southward. We must be lying off the middle of the façade of the coral wall.

On board the *Kon-Tiki* all preparations for the end of the voyage were being made. Everything of value was carried into the cabin and lashed fast. Documents and papers were packed into watertight bags, along with films and other things which would not stand a dip in the sea. The whole bamboo cabin was covered with canvas, and especially strong ropes were lashed across it. When we saw that all hope was gone, we opened up the bamboo deck and cut off with machete knives all the ropes which held the centerboards down. It was a hard job to get the centerboards drawn up, because they were all thickly covered with stout barnacles. With the centerboards up the draught of our vessel was no deeper than to the bottom of the timber logs, and we would therefore be more easily washed in over the reef. With no centerboards and with the sail down, the raft lay completely sideways on and was entirely at the mercy of wind and sea.

We tied the longest rope we had to the homemade anchor and made it fast to the step of the port mast, so that the *Kon-Tiki* would go into the surf stern first when the anchor was thrown overboard. The anchor itself consisted of empty water cans filled with used radio batteries and heavy scrap, and solid mangrove-wood sticks projected from it, set crosswise.

Order number one, which came first and last, was: Hold on to the raft! Whatever happened, we must hang on tight on board and let the nine great logs take the pressure from the reef. We ourselves had more than enough to do to withstand the weight of the water. If we jumped overboard, we should become helpless victims of the suction which would fling us in and out over the sharp corals. The rubber raft would capsize in the steep seas or, heavily loaded with us in it, it would be torn to ribbons against the reef. But the wooden logs would sooner or later be cast ashore, and we with them, if we only managed to hold fast.

Next, all hands were told to put on their shoes for the first time in a hundred days and to have their life belts ready. The last precaution, however, was not of much value, for if a man fell overboard he would be battered to death, not drowned. We had time, too, to put our passports and such few dollars as we had left into our pockets. But it was not lack of time that was troubling us.

Those were anxious hours in which we lay drifting helplessly sideways, step after step, in toward the reef. It was noticeably quiet on board; we all crept in and out from cabin to bamboo deck, silent or laconic, and carried on with our jobs. Our serious faces showed that no one was in doubt as to what awaited us, and the absence of nervousness showed that we had all gradually acquired an unshakable confidence in the raft. If it had brought us across the sea, it would also manage to bring us ashore alive.

Inside the cabin there was a complete chaos of provision cartons and cargo, lashed fast. Torstein had barely found room for himself in the radio corner, where he had got the shortwave transmitter working. We were now over four thousand sea miles from our old base at Callao, where the Peruvian Naval War School had maintained regular contact with us, and still farther from Hal and Frank and the other radio amateurs in the United States. But, as chance willed, we had on the previous day got in touch with a capable radio "ham" who had a set on Rarotonga in the Cook Islands, and the operators, quite contrary to all our usual practice, had arranged for an extra contact with him early in the morning. All the time we were drifting closer and closer in to the reef, Torstein was sitting tapping his key and calling Rarotonga.

Entries in the *Kon-Tiki's* log ran:

—8:15: *We are slowly approaching land. We can now make out with the naked eye the separate palm trees inside on the starboard side.*

—8:45: *The wind has veered into a still more unfavorable quarter for us, so we have no hope of getting clear. No nervousness on board, but hectic preparations on deck. There is something lying on the reef ahead of us which looks like the wreck of a sailing vessel, but it may be only a heap of driftwood.*

—9:45: *The wind is taking us straight toward the last island but one we see behind the reef. We can now see the whole coral reef clearly; here it is built up like a white and red speckled wall which barely sticks up out of the water as a belt in front of all the islands. All along the reef white foaming surf is flung up toward the sky. Bengt is just serving up a good hot meal, the last before the great action!*

It is a wreck lying in there on the reef. We are so close now that we

*can see right across the shining lagoon behind the reef and see the outlines
of other islands on the other side of the lagoon.*

As this was written, the dull drone of the surf came near again; it came
from the whole reef and filled the air like thrilling rolls of the drum,
heralding the exciting last act of the *Kon-Tiki.*

—9:50: *Very close now. Drifting along the reef. Only a hundred yards
or so away. Torstein is talking to the man on Rarotonga. All clear. Must
pack up log now. All in good spirits; it looks bad,* but we shall make it!

A few minutes later the anchor rushed overboard and caught hold of
the bottom, so that the *Kon-Tiki* swung around and turned her stern
inward toward the breakers. It held us for a few valuable minutes, while
Torstein sat hammering like mad on the key. He had got Rarotonga
now. The breakers thundered in the air and the sea rose and fell furiously.
All hands were at work on deck, and now Torstein got his message
through. He said we were drifting toward the Raroia reef. He asked
Rarotonga to listen in on the same wave length every hour. If we were
silent for more than thirty-six hours Rarotonga must let the Norwegian
Embassy in Washington know. Torstein's last words were:

"O.K. Fifty yards left. Here we go. Good-by."

Then he closed down the station, Knut sealed up the papers, and both
crawled out on deck as fast as they could to join the rest of us, for it was
clear now that the anchor was giving way.

The swell grew heavier and heavier, with deep troughs between the
waves, and we felt the raft being swung up and down, up and down,
higher and higher.

Again the order was shouted: "Hold on, never mind about the cargo,
hold on!"

We were now so near the waterfall inside that we no longer heard the
steady continuous roar from all along the reef. We now heard only a
separate boom each time the nearest breaker crashed down on the rocks.

All hands stood in readiness, each clinging fast to the rope he thought
the most secure. Only Erik crept into the cabin at the last moment; there
was one part of the program he had not yet carried out—he had not
found his shoes!

No one stood aft, for it was there the shock from the reef would come.
Nor were the two firm stays which ran from the masthead down to the
stern safe. For if the mast fell they would be left hanging overboard, over
the reef. Herman, Bengt, and Torstein had climbed up on some boxes
which were lashed fast forward of the cabin wall, and, while Herman
clung on to the guy ropes from the ridge of the roof, the other two held
on to the ropes from the masthead by which the sail at other times was
hauled up. Knut and I chose the stay running from the bow up to the
masthead, for, if mast and cabin and everything else went overboard, we

thought the rope from the bow would nevertheless remain lying inboard, as we were now head on to the seas.

When we realized that the seas had got hold of us, the anchor rope was cut and we were off. A sea rose straight up under us, and we felt the *Kon-Tiki* being lifted up in the air. The great moment had come; we were riding on the wave back at breathless speed, our ramshackle craft creaking and groaning as she quivered under us. The excitement made one's blood boil. I remember that, having no other inspiration, I waved my arm and bellowed "Hurrah!" at the top of my lungs; it afforded a certain relief and could do no harm anyway. The others certainly thought I had gone mad, but they all beamed and grinned enthusiastically. On we ran with the seas rushing in behind us; this was the *Kon-Tiki's* baptism of fire. All must and would go well.

But our elation was soon dampened. A new sea rose high up astern of us like a glittering, green glass wall. As we sank down it came rolling after us, and, in the same second in which I saw it high above me, I felt a violent blow and was submerged under floods of water. I felt the suction through my whole body, with such great power that I had to strain every single muscle in my frame and think of one thing only—hold on, hold on! I think that in such a desperate situation the arms will be torn off before the brain consents to let go, evident as the outcome is. Then I felt that the mountain of water was passing on and relaxing its devilish grip of my body. When the whole mountain had rushed on, with an earsplitting roaring and crashing, I saw Knut again hanging on beside me, doubled up into a ball. Seen from behind, the great sea was almost flat and gray. As it rushed on, it swept over the ridge of the cabin roof which projected from the water, and there hung the three others, pressed against the cabin roof as the water passed over them.

We were still afloat.

In an instant I renewed my hold, with arms and legs bent round the strong rope. Knut let himself down and with a tiger's leap joined the others on the boxes, where the cabin took the strain. I heard reassuring exclamations from them, but at the same time I saw a new green wall rise up and come towering toward us. I shouted a warning and made myself as small and hard as I could where I hung. In an instant hell was over us again, and the *Kon-Tiki* disappeared completely under the masses of water. The sea tugged and pulled with all the force it could bring to bear at the poor little bundles of human bodies. The second sea rushed over us, to be followed by a third like it.

Then I heard a triumphant shout from Knut, who was now hanging on to the rope ladder:

"Look at the raft—she's holding!"

After three seas only the double mast and the cabin had been knocked a bit crooked. Again we had a feeling of triumph over the elements, and the elation of victory gave us new strength.

Then I saw the next sea come towering up, higher than all the rest, and again I bellowed a warning aft to the others as I climbed up the stay, as high as I could get in a hurry, and hung on fast. Then I myself disappeared sideways into the midst of the green wall which towered high over us. The others, who were farther aft and saw me disappear first, estimated the height of the wall of water at twenty-five feet, while the foaming crest passed up fifteen feet above the part of the glassy wall into which I had vanished. Then the great wave reached them, and we had all one single thought—hold on, hold on, hold, hold, hold!

We must have hit the reef that time. I myself felt only the strain on the stay, which seemed to bend and slacken jerkily. But whether the bumps came from above or below I could not tell, hanging there. The whole submersion lasted only seconds, but it demanded more endurance than we usually have in our bodies. There is greater strength in the human mechanism than that of the muscles alone. I determined that, if I was to die, I would die in this position, like a knot on the stay. The sea thundered on, over and past, and as it roared by it revealed a hideous sight. The *Kon-Tiki* was wholly changed, as by the stroke of a magic wand. The vessel we knew from weeks and months at sea was no more; in a few seconds our pleasant world had become a shattered wreck.

I saw only one man on board besides myself. He lay pressed flat across the ridge of the cabin roof, face downward with his arms stretched out on both sides, while the cabin itself was crushed in, like a house of cards, toward the stern and toward the starboard side. The motionless figure was Herman. There was no other sign of life, while the hill of water thundered by, in across the reef. The hardwood mast on the starboard side was broken like a match, and the upper stump, in its fall, had smashed right through the cabin roof, so that the mast and all its gear slanted at a low angle over the reef on the starboard side. Astern, the steering block was twisted round lengthways and the crossbeam broken, while the steering oar was smashed to splinters. The splashboards at the bow were broken like cigar boxes, and the whole deck was torn up and pasted like wet paper against the forward wall of the cabin, along with boxes, cans, canvas, and other cargo. Bamboo sticks and rope ends stuck up everywhere, and the general effect was of complete chaos.

I felt cold fear run through my whole body. What was the good of my holding on? If I lost one single man here, in the run in, the whole thing would be ruined, and for the moment there was only one human figure to be seen after the last buffet. In that second Torstein's hunched-up form appeared outside the raft. He was hanging like a monkey in the ropes from the masthead and managed to get on to the logs again, where he crawled up on to the debris forward of the cabin. Herman, too, now turned his head and gave me a forced grin of encouragement, but did not move. I bellowed in the faint hope of locating the others and heard Bengt's calm voice call out that all hands were aboard. They were lying holding on to the ropes behind the tangled barricade which the tough plaiting from the bamboo deck had built up.

All this happened in the course of a few seconds, while the *Kon-Tiki* was being drawn out of the witches' caldron by the backwash, and a fresh sea came rolling over her. For the last time I bellowed "Hang on!" at the top of my lungs amid the uproar, and that was all I myself did; I hung on and disappeared in the masses of water which rushed over and past in those endless two or three seconds. That was enough for me. I saw the ends of the logs knocking and bumping against a sharp step in the coral reef without going over it. Then we were sucked out again. I also saw the two men who lay stretched out across the ridge of the cabin roof, but none of us smiled any longer. Behind the chaos of bamboo I heard a calm voice call out:

"This won't do."

I myself felt equally discouraged. As the masthead sank farther and farther out over the starboard side, I found myself hanging on to a slack line outside the raft. The next sea came. When it had gone by I was dead tired, and my only thought was to get up onto the logs and lie behind the barricade. When the backwash retreated, I saw for the first time the rugged red reef naked beneath us and perceived Torstein standing, bent double, on gleaming red corals, holding on to a bunch of rope ends from the mast. Knut, standing aft, was about to jump. I shouted that we must all keep on the logs, and Torstein, who had been washed overboard by the pressure of the water, sprang up again like a cat.

Two or three more seas rolled over us with diminishing force, and what happened then I do not remember, except that water foamed in and out and I myself sank lower and lower toward the red reef over which we were being lifted in. Then only crests of foam full of salt spray came whirling in, and I was able to work my way in onto the raft, where we all made for the after end of the logs which was highest up on the reef.

At the same moment Knut crouched down and sprang up on to the reef with the line which lay clear astern. While the backwash was running out, he waded through the whirling water some thirty yards in and stood safely at the end of the line when the next sea foamed in toward him, died down, and ran back from the flat reef like a broad stream.

Then Erik came crawling out of the collapsed cabin, with his shoes on. If we had all done as he did, we should have got off cheaply. As the cabin had not been washed overboard but had been pressed down pretty flat under the canvas, Erik lay quietly stretched out among the cargo and heard the peals of thunder crashing above him while the collapsed bamboo walls curved downward. Bengt had had a slight concussion when the mast fell but had managed to crawl under the wrecked cabin alongside Erik. We should all of us have been lying there if we had realized in advance how firmly the countless lashings and plaited bamboo sheets would hang on to the main logs under the pressure of the water.

Erik was now standing ready on the logs aft, and when the sea retired he, too, jumped up onto the reef. It was Herman's turn next, and then Bengt's. Each time the raft was pushed a bit farther in, and, when Torstein's turn and my own came, the raft already lay so far in on the reef that there was no longer any ground for abandoning her. All hands began the work of salvage.

We were now twenty yards away from that devilish step up on the reef, and it was there and beyond it that the breakers came rolling after one another in long lines. The coral polyps had taken care to build the atoll so high that only the very tops of the breakers were able to send a fresh stream of sea water past us and into the lagoon, which abounded in fish. Here inside was the corals' own world, and they disported themselves in the strangest shapes and colors.

A long way in on the reef the others found the rubber raft, lying drifting and quite waterlogged. They emptied it and dragged it back to the wreck, and we loaded it to the full with the most important equipment, like the radio set, provisions, and water bottles. We dragged all this in across the reef and piled it up on the top of a huge block of coral, which lay alone on the inside of the reef like a large meteorite. Then we went back to the wreck for fresh loads. We could never know what the sea would be up to when the tidal currents got to work around us.

In the shallow water inside the reef we saw something bright shining in the sun. When we waded over to pick it up, to our astonishment we saw two empty tins. This was not exactly what we had expected to find there, and we were still more surprised when we saw that the little boxes were quite bright and newly opened and stamped "Pineapple," with the same inscription as that on the new field rations we ourselves were testing for the quartermaster. They were indeed two of our own pineapple tins, which we had thrown overboard after our last meal on board the Kon-Tiki. We had followed close behind them up on the reef.

We were standing on sharp, rugged coral blocks, and on the uneven bottom we waded now ankle-deep, now chest-deep, according to the channels and stream beds in the reef. Anemones and corals gave the whole reef the appearance of a rock garden covered with mosses and cactus and fossilized plants, red and green and yellow and white. There was no color that was not represented, either in corals or algae or in shells and sea slugs and fantastic fish, which were wriggling about everywhere. In the deeper channels small sharks about four feet long came sneaking up to us in the crystal-clear water. But we had only to smack the water with the palms of our hands for them to turn about and keep at a distance.

Where we had stranded, we had only pools of water and wet patches of coral about us; farther in lay the calm blue lagoon. The tide was going out, and we continually saw more corals sticking up out of the water round us, while the surf which thundered without interruption along the reef sank down, as it were, a floor lower. What would happen there on the narrow reef when the tide began to flow again was uncertain. We must get away.

The reef stretched like a half-submerged fortress wall up to the north and down to the south. In the extreme south was a long island densely covered with tall palm forest. And just above us to the north, only six hundred or seven hundreds yards away, lay another but considerably smaller palm island. It lay inside the reef, with palm tops rising into the sky and snow-white sandy beaches running out into the still lagoon. The whole island looked like a bulging green basket of flowers, or a little bit of concentrated paradise.

This island we chose.

Herman stood beside me beaming all over his bearded face. He did not say a word, only stretched out his hand and laughed quietly. The *Kon-Tiki* still lay far out on the reef with the spray flying over her. She was a wreck, but an honorable wreck. Everything above deck was smashed up, but the nine balsa logs from the Quevedo forest in Ecuador were as intact as ever. They had saved our lives. The sea had claimed but little of the cargo, and none of what we had stowed inside the cabin. We ourselves had stripped the raft of everything of real value, which now lay in safety on the top of the great sun-smitten rock inside the reef.

Since I had jumped off the raft, I had genuinely missed the sight of all the pilot fish wriggling in front of our bow. Now the great balsa logs lay up on the reef in six inches of water, and brown sea slugs lay writhing under the bows. The pilot fish were gone. The dolphins were gone. Only unknown flat fish with peacock patterns and blunt tails wriggled inquisitively in and out between the logs. We had arrived in a new world. Johannes had left his hole. He had doubtless found another lurking place here.

I took a last look round on board the wreck and caught sight of a little baby palm in a flattened basket. It projected from an eye in a coconut to a length of eighteen inches, and two roots stuck out below. I waded in toward the island with the nut in my hand. A little way ahead I saw Knut wading happily landward with a model of the raft, which he had made with much labor on the voyage, under his arm. We soon passed Bengt. He was a splendid steward. With a lump on his forehead and sea water dripping from his beard, he was walking bent double pushing a box, which danced along before him every time the breakers outside sent a stream over into the lagoon. He lifted the lid proudly. It was the kitchen box, and in it were the primus and cooking utensils in good order.

I shall never forget that wade across the reef toward the heavenly palm island that grew larger as it came to meet us. When I reached the sunny sand beach, I slipped off my shoes and thrust my bare toes down into the warm, bone-dry sand. It was as though I enjoyed the sight of every footprint which dug itself into the virgin sand beach that led up to the palm trunks. Soon the palm tops closed over my head, and I went on, right in toward the center of the tiny island. Green coconuts hung under the palm tufts, and some luxuriant bushes were thickly covered with snow-white blossoms, which smelled so sweet and seductive that I felt quite faint. In the interior of the island two quite tame terns flew about my shoulders. They were as white and light as wisps of cloud. Small lizards shot away from my feet, and the most important inhabitants of the island were large blood-red hermit crabs which lumbered along in every direction with stolen snail shells as large as eggs adhering to their soft hinder parts.

I was completely overwhelmed. I sank down on my knees and thrust my fingers deep down into the dry warm sand.

The voyage was over. We were all alive. We had run ashore on a small uninhabited South Sea island. And what an island! Torstein came in, flung away a sack, threw himself flat on his back, and looked up at the palm tops and the white birds, light as down, which circled noiselessly just above us. Soon we were all six lying there. Herman, always energetic, climbed up a small palm and pulled down a cluster of large green coconuts. We cut off their soft tops with our machete knives, as if they were eggs, and poured down our throats the most delicious refreshing drink in the world—sweet, cold milk from young and seedless palm fruit. On the reef outside resounded the monotonous drum beats from the guard at the gates of paradise.

"Purgatory was a bit damp," said Bengt, "but heaven is more or less as I'd imagined it."

We stretched ourselves luxuriously on the ground and smiled up at the white trade-wind clouds drifting by westward up above the palm tops. Now we were no longer following them helplessly; now we lay on a fixed, motionless island, in Polynesia.

And as we lay and stretched ourselves, the breakers outside us rumbled like a train, to and fro, to and fro, all along the horizon.

Bengt was right; this was heaven.

Max Beerbohm's cynical tale of a dragon who descended upon the pre-historic settlement that later grew into the city of London (I do not believe it ever has appeared in an anthology before) is an obvious antithesis to Stephen Vincent Benét's more familiar fantasy of a day in the far future when the proud towers of Manhattan will lie crumbling in the dust.

Why have I interposed a chapter from Anne Lindbergh's *Gift from the Sea* between them? It struck me as a warning—and I felt it was addressed to me personally—that unless we simplify our lives, and reduce the clutter of useless things, outmoded prejudices, and worthless acquaintances in which we wallow, the grim collapse of our civilization depicted by Benét may come a lot sooner than we think!

ED.

The Dreadful Dragon of Hay Hill

By MAX BEERBOHM

I

IN THE faint early dawn of a day in the midst of a golden summer, a column of smoke was seen rising from Hay Hill, rising thickly, not without sparks in it. Danger to the lives of the dressmakers in Dover Street was not apprehended. The fire brigade was not called out. The fire brigade had not been called into existence. Dover Street had not yet been built. I tell of a time that was thirty-nine thousand years before the birth of Christ.

To imagine Hay Hill as it then was, you must forget much of what, as you approach it from Berkeley Square or from Piccadilly, it is now. You knew it in better days, as I did?—days when its seemly old Georgian charm had not vanished under the superimposition of two vast high barracks for the wealthier sort of bachelors to live in? You remember how, in frosty weather, the horse of your hansom used to skate hopelessly down the slope of it and collapse, pitching you out, at the foot of it? Such memories will not serve. They are far too recent. You must imagine just a green hill, with some trees and bushes on it. You must imagine it far higher than it is nowadays, tapering to a summit not yet planed off for the

From *A Variety of Things* by Max Beerbohm. Published in 1928 by William Heinemann, Ltd. Reprinted by permission of Lady Beerbohm.

purpose of Dover Street; and steeper; and with two caves aloft in it; and bright, bright green.

And conceive that its smiling wildness made no contrast with aught that was around. Berkeley Square smiled wildly too. Berkeley Square had no squareness. It was but a green valley that went, uninterrupted by any Piccadilly, into the Green Park. And through the midst of it a clear stream went babbling and meandering, making all manner of queer twists and turns on its offhand way to the marshlands of Pimlico down yonder. Modern engineers have driven this stream ignominiously underground; but at that time there it still was, visible, playful, fringed by reeds, darted about in by small fishes, licensed to reflect sky. And it had tributaries! The landscape that I speak of, the great rolling landscape that comprised all Mayfair, was everywhere intersected by tiny brooks, whose waters, for what they were worth, sooner or later trickled brightly into that main stream. Here and there, quite fortuitously, in groups or singly, stood willows and silver birches, full of that wistful grace which we regard as peculiarly modern. But not till the landscape reached Hyde Park did trees exert a strong influence over it. Then they exerted a very strong influence indeed. They hemmed the whole thing in. Hyde Park, which was a dense and immemorial forest, did not pause where the Marble Arch is, but swept on to envelop all Paddington and Marylebone and most of Bloomsbury, and then, skirting Soho, overran everything from Covent Garden to Fetter Lane, and in a rush southward was brought up sharp only by the edge of the sheer cliffs that banked this part of the Thames.

The Thames, wherever it was not thus sharply opposed, was as tyrannous as the very forest. It knew no mercy for the lowly. Westminster, like Pimlico, was a mere swamp, miasmal, malarial, frequented by frogs only, whose croaks, no other sound intervening, made hideous to the ear a district now nobly and forever resonant with the silver voices of choristers and the golden voices of senators. Westminster is firm underfoot nowadays; yet, even so, as you come away from it up the Duke of York's steps, you feel that you are mounting into a drier, brisker air; and this sensation is powerfully repeated when anon you climb St. James's Street. Not lower, you feel, not lower than Piccadilly would you have your home. And this, it would seem, was just what the average man felt forty-one thousand years ago. Nature had placed in the steep chalky slopes from the marshes a fair number of commodious caves; but these were almost always vacant. Only on the higher levels did human creatures abound.

And scant enough, by our present standards, that abundance was. In all the space which the forest had left free—not merely all Mayfair, remember: all Soho, too, and all that lies between them—the population was hardly more than three hundred souls. So low a figure is hard to grasp. So few people, in a place so teeming now, are almost beneath our notice. Almost, but not quite. What there was of them was not bad.

Nature, as a Roman truly said, does not work by leaps. What we call
Evolution is a quite exasperatingly slow process. We should like to compare favorably with even the latest of our predecessors. We wince whenever we read a declaration by some eminent biologist that the skull of the
prehistoric man whose bones have just been unearthed in this or that
district differs but slightly from the skull of the average man in the
twentieth century. I hate having to tell you that the persons in this narrative had well-shaped heads, and that if their jaws were more prominent,
their teeth sharper, their backs less upright, their arms longer and hairier,
and their feet suppler than our own, the difference in each case was so
faint as to be almost negligible.

Of course they were a simpler folk than we are. They knew far less
than we know. They did not, for example, know they were living thirty-
nine thousand years before Christ; and "protopalaeolithic" was a term
they *never* used. They regarded themselves as very modern and very
greatly enlightened. They marveled at their ingenuities in the use of flint
and stone. They held that their ancestors had been crude in thought and
in mode of life, but not unblest with a certain vigor and nobility of character which they themselves lacked. They thought that their descendants
would be a rather feeble, peevish race, yet that somehow in the far future,
a state of general goodness and felicity would set in, to abide forever.
But I seem to be failing in my effort to stress the difference between these
people and ourselves. Let us hold fast to the pleasing fact that they really
were less well educated.

They could neither read nor write, and were so weak in their arithmetic
that not a shepherd among them could count his sheep correctly, nor a
goatherd his goats. And their pitiful geography! Glancing northward
above their forest, they saw the mountainous gaunt region that is Hamp-
stead, that is Highgate; southward, across the river and its wide fens, the
ridges of a nameless Surrey; but as to how the land lay beyond those
barriers they had only the haziest notion. That there was land they knew.
For, though they themselves never ventured further than the edge of the
marshes, or than the fringe of the tangled forest that bounded the rest of
their domain, certain other people were more venturesome: often enough
it would happen that some stranger, some dark-haired and dark-eyed
nomad, passed this way, blinking from the forest or soaked from the
river; and glad always was such an one to rest awhile here, and tell to his
good hosts tales of the outlying world. Tales very marvelous to the
dwellers in this sleek safe homeland!—tales of rugged places where no
men are, or few, and these in peril by night and by day; tales of the lion,
a creature with yellow eyes and a great mop of yellow hair to his head,
a swift and strong creature, without pity; and of the tusked mastodon,
taller than the oldest oak, and shaking the ground he walks on; and of

the winged dragon, that huge beast, poising so high in the air that he looks no bigger than a hawk, yet reaching his prey on earth as instantly as a hawk his; and of the huge crawling dragon, that breathes fire through his nostrils and scorches black the grass as he goes hunting, hunting; of the elephant, who fears nothing but mastodons and dragons; of the hyena and the tiger, and of beasts beside whom these seem not dreadful.

Wide-eyed, open-mouthed, the homelanders would sit listening. "O wanderer," would say one, "tell us more of the mastodon, that is taller than the oldest oak." And another would say, "Make again for us, O wanderer, the noise that a lion makes." And another, "Tell us more of the dragon that scorches black the grass as he goes hunting, hunting." And another, "O you that have so much wandered, surely you will abide here always? Here is not hardship nor danger. We go not in fear of the beasts whose roast flesh you have tasted and have praised. Rather go they in great fear of us. The savory deer flees from us, and has swifter feet than we have, yet escapes not the point of the thrown spear, and falls, and is ours. The hare is not often luckier, such is our skill. Our goats and our sheep would flee from us, but dare not, fearing the teeth of certain dogs who love us. We slay what we will for food. For us all there is plenty in all seasons. You have drunk of the water of our stream. Is it not fresh and cold? Have you cracked in your wanderings better nuts than ours? or bitten juicier apples? Surely you will abide here always."

And to the wanderer it would seem no bad thing that he should do so. Yet he did not so. When the sun had sunk and risen a few times he would stretch his arms, maybe gazing round at the landscape with a rather sardonic smile, and be gone through the forest or across the water. And the homelanders, nettled, would shrug their shoulders, and thank their gods for having rid them of a fool.

Their gods were many, including the sun and moon, their clear stream, apple trees and cherry trees and fig trees and trees that gave nuts, rose-bushes in summer, rain, and also fire—fire, the god that themselves had learnt to make from flint, fire that made meat itself godlike. But they prayed to no god, not being aware that they needed anything. And they had no priesthood. When a youth lost his heart to a maid he approached her, and laid his hands gently upon her shoulders, and then, if she did not turn away from him, he put his hands about her waist and lifted her three times from the ground. This sufficed: they were now man and wife, and lived happily, or not so, ever after. Nor was it needful that the rite should be only thus. If a maid lost her heart to a youth, the laid hands could be hers, and the shoulders his, and if he turned not away from her, if thrice he lifted her from the ground, this too was wedlock.

If there were no good cave for them to take as their own, bride and bridegroom built them a hut of clay and wattles. Such huts were already numerous, dotted about in all directions. Elder folk thought them very ugly, and said that they spoilt the landscape. Yet what was to be done? It is well that a people should multiply. Though these homelanders now deemed themselves very many indeed (their number, you see, being so much higher than they ever could count up to, even incorrectly), yet not even the eldest of them denied that there was plenty of room and plenty of food for more. And plenty of employment, you ask? They did not worry about that. The more babies there were, the more children and grown folk would there be anon to take turns in minding the ample flocks and herds, and the more leisure for all to walk or sit around, talking about the weather or about one another. They made no fetish of employment.

I have said that they were not bad. Had you heard them talked about by one another, you might rather doubt this estimate. You would have heard little good of anyone. No family seemed to approve of its neighbors. Even between brothers and sisters mutual trust was rare. Even husbands and wives bickered. To strangers, as you have seen, these people could be charming, I do not say they were ever violent among themselves. That was not their way. But they lacked kindness.

Happiness is said to beget kindness. Were these people not happy? They deemed themselves so. Nay, there was to come a time when, looking back, they felt that they had been marvelously happy. This time began on the day in whose dawn smoke was seen rising from Hay Hill.

II

The title of my tale has enabled you to guess the source of that smoke: the nostrils of some dreadful dragon. But had you been the little girl named Thia, by whom first that smoke was seen, you would not have come upon the truth so quickly.

Thia had slept out under the stars, and, waking as they faded, had risen, brushed the dew from her arms and legs, shaken it off her little goatskin tunic, and gone with no glance around or upward to look for mushrooms. Presently, as there seemed to be no mushrooms this morning anywhere, she let her eyes rove from the ground (ground that is now Lord Lansdowne's courtyard) and, looking up, saw the thick smoke above the hill. She saw that it came from the cave where dwelt the widow Gra with her four children. How could Gra, how could anyone, want a fire just now? Thia's dark eyes filled with wonder. On wintry nights it was proper that there should be a fire at the mouth of every cave, proper that in wintry dawns these should still be smoldering. But—such smoke as this on such a morning! Heavier, thicker smoke than Thia had ever seen in all the ten years of her existence! Of course fire was a god. But surely he would not have us worship him today? Why then had Gra lit him? Thia gave it up, and moved away with eyes downcast in renewed hope of mushrooms.

She had not gone far before she stared back again, hearing a piteous shrill scream from the hill. She saw a little boy flying headlong down the slope—Thol, the little red-haired boy who lived in the other cave up there. Thol slipped, tumbled head over heels, rolled, picked himself up, saw Thia, and rushed weeping towards her.

"What ails you, O child?" asked Thia, than whom Thol was indeed a year younger and much smaller.

"Oh!" was all that the child vouchsafed between his sobs. "Oh!"

Thia thought ill of tears. Scorn for Thol fought the maternal instinct in her. But scorn had the worst of it. She put her arms about Thol. Quaveringly he told her what he had just seen, and what he believed it to be, and how it lay there asleep, with just its head and tail outside Gra's cave, snoring. Then he broke down utterly. Thia looked at the hill. Maternal instinct was now worsted by wonder and curiosity and the desire to be very brave—to show how much braver than boys girls are. Thia went to the hill, shaking off Thol's wild clutches and leaving him behind. Thia went up the hill, quickly but warily, on tiptoe, wide-eyed, with her tongue out upon her underlip. She took a sidelong course, and she noticed a sort of black path through the grass, winding from the mouth of Gra's cave, down one side of the hill, and away, away till it was lost in the white mists over the marshes. She climbed nearly level with the cave's mouth, and then, peering through a bush which hid her, saw what lay behind the veil of smoke.

Much worse the sleeping thing was than she had feared it would be, much huger and more hideous. Its face was as long as a man's body, and lay flat out along the ground. Had Thia ever seen a crocodile's face, that is of what she would have been reminded—a crocodile, but with great pricked-up ears, and snuffling forth fiery murk in deep, rhythmic, luxurious exhalations. The tip of the creature's tail, sticking out from the further side of the cave's mouth, looked to her very like an arrowhead of flint— green flint! She could awfully imagine the rest of the beast, curled around in the wide deep cave. And she shuddered with a great hatred, and tears started to her eyes, as she thought of Gra and of those others.

When she reached the valley, it was clear to Thol that she had been crying. And she, resenting his scrutiny, made haste to say, "I wept for Gra and for her children; but you, O child, because you are a coward."

At these words the boy made within him a great resolve. This was, that he would slay the dragon.

III

How? He had not thought of that. When? Not today, he felt, nor tomorrow. But some day, somehow. He knew himself to be small, even for his age, and the dragon big for whatever its age might be. He knew he was not very clever; he was sure the dragon was very clever indeed. So he said nothing to Thia of his great resolve that she should be sorry.

Meanwhile, the sun had risen over the hills beyond the water, and the birds been interrupted in their songs by the bleating of penned sheep. This sound recalled Thol from his dreams of future glory.

For he was a shepherd's lad. It was the custom that children, as they ceased to toddle, should begin to join in whatever work their parents were by way of doing for the common good. Indeed it was felt that work was especially a thing for the young. Thol had no parents to help; for his mother had died in giving him birth; and one day, when he was but seven years old, his father, who was a shepherd, had been attacked and killed by an angry ram. In the sleek safe homeland this death by violence had made a very painful impression. There was a general desire to hush it up, to forget it. Thol was a reminder of it. Thol was ignored, as much as possible. He was allowed to have the cave that had been his father's, but even the widow Gra, in the cave so near to his, disregarded him, and forbade her children to play with him. However, there dwelt hard by in the valley a certain shepherd, named Brud, and he, being childless, saw use for Thol as helping boy, and to that use put him. Every morning, it was Thol's first duty to wake his master. It was easy for Thol himself to wake early, for his cave faced eastwards. Today in his great excitement about the dragon he had forgotten his duty to Brud. He went running now to perform it.

Brud and his dog, awakened, came out and listened to Thol's tale. Truthfulness was regarded by all the homelanders as a very important thing, especially for the young. Brud took his staff, and "Now, O Thol," he said, "will I beat you for saying the thing that is not." But the boy protested that there was indeed a dragon in Gra's cave; so Brud said sagely, "Choose then one of two things: either to run hence into Gra's cave, or to be beaten." Thol so unhesitatingly chose to be beaten that it was clear he did believe his own story. Thia, moreover, came running up to say that there truly was a dragon. So Brud did not beat Thol very much, and went away with his dog towards the hill, curious to know what really was amiss up there.

Perhaps Thia was already sorry she had called Thol a coward, for, though he was now crying again loudly, she did but try to comfort him. His response to her effort was not worthy of a future hero: he complained through his tears that she had not been beaten, too, for saying there was a dragon. Thia's eyes flashed fiercely. She told Thol he was ugly and puny and freckle-faced, and that nobody loved him. All this was true, and it came with the more crushing force from pretty Thia, whom everyone petted.

No one ever made Thia work, though she was strong and agile, and did wondrously well whatever task she might do for the fun of it. She could milk a goat, or light a fire, or drive a flock of geese, or find mushrooms if there were any, as quickly and surely as though she had practised hard for years. But the homelanders preferred to see her go flitting freely all the day long, dancing and caroling, with flowers in her hair.

Thia's hair was as dark as her eyes. Thia was no daughter of the homeland. She was the daughter of two wanderers who, seven years ago, had sojourned here for a few days. Their child had then attained just that age which was always a crisis in the lives of wanderers' children: she had grown enough to be heavy in her parents' arms, and not enough to foot it beside them. So they had left her here, promising the homelanders that in time they would come back for her; and she, who had had no home, had one now. Although (a relic, this, of primitive days) no homelander ever on any account went near to the mouth of another's dwelling, Thia would go near and go in, and be always welcome. The homelanders seldom praised one another's children; but about Thia there was no cause for jealousy: they all praised her strange beauty, her fearless and bright ways. And withal she was very good. You must not blame her for lack of filial sense. How should she love parents whom she did not remember? She was full of love for the homelanders; and naturally she hated the thought they hated: that some day two wanderers might come and whisk her away.* She loved this people and this place the more deeply perhaps because she was not of them. Forget the harsh things she has just said to Thol. He surely was to blame. And belike she would even have begged his pardon had she not been preoccupied with thoughts for the whole homeland, with great fears of what the dreadful dragon might be going to do when he woke up.

IV

And a wonder it was that he did not wake forthwith, so loud a bellow of terror did Brud and his dog utter at the glimpse they had of him. The glimpse sufficed them: both bounded to the foot of the hill with incredible speed, still howling. From the mouths of caves and huts people darted and stood agape. Responsive sheep, goats, geese, what not, made great noises of their own. Brud stood waving his arms wildly towards the hill. People stared from him to the column of smoke, and from it to him. They were still heavy with sleep. Unusual behavior at any time annoyed them; they deeply resented behavior so unusual as this so early in the morning. Little by little, disapproval merged into anxiety. Brud became the center of a circle. But he did not radiate conviction. A dragon? A dragon in the homeland? Brud must be mad!

---

* Lest the reader assume that in the course of this narrative one or both of Thia's parents will return to claim her, let me at once state that within a few months of her being left in the homeland her father was killed by a lion, and her mother by a lioness, in what has since become Shropshire.

Brud called Thol to witness. Thol, afraid that if he told the truth he would be beaten by everybody but Brud, said nothing. Favorite Thia was not so reticent. She described clearly the dragon's head and tail and the black path through the grass. Something like panic passed around the circle; not actual panic, for—surely Thia's bright dark eyes had deceived her. A dragon was one thing, the homeland another: there couldn't be a dragon in the homeland. Mainly that they might set Thia's mind at rest, a few people went to reconnoiter. Presently, with palsied lips, they were admitting that there could be, and was, a dragon in the homeland.

They ran stuttering the news in all directions, ran knowing it to be true, yet themselves hardly believing it, ran hoping others would investigate it and prove it a baseless rumor, ran gibbering it to the very confines of the homeland. Slowly, incredulously, people from all quarters made their way to the place where so many were already gathered. The whole population was at length concentrated in what is Berkeley Square. Up the sky the sun climbed steadily. Surely, thought the homelanders, a good sign? This god of theirs could not look so calm and bright if there were really a dragon among his chosen people? Bold adventurers went scouting hopefully up the hill, only to return with horror in their eyes, and with the same old awful report upon their lips. Before noon the whole throng was convinced. Eld is notoriously irreceptive of new ideas; but even the oldest inhabitant stood convinced now.

Silence reigned, broken only by the bleatings, cacklings, quackings, of animals unreleased from their pens or coops, far and near. Up, straight up through the windless air went the column of smoke steadfastly, horribly, up higher than the eyes of the homelanders could follow it.

What was to be done? Could nothing be done? Could not someone, at any rate, say something? People who did not know each other, or had for years not been on speaking terms, found themselves eagerly conversing, in face of the common peril. Solemn parties were formed to go and view the dragon's track, its odious scorched track from the marshes. People remembered having been told by wanderers that when a dragon swam a river he held high his head, lest his flames should be quenched. The river that had been crossed last night by this monster was a great god. Why had he not drowned the monster? Well, fire was a great god also, and he deigned to dwell in dragons. One god would not destroy another. But again, would even a small god deign to dwell in a dragon? The homelanders revised their theology. Fire was not a god at all.

Then, why, asked some, had the river not done his duty? The more rigid logicians answered that neither was the river a god. But this doctrine was not well received. People felt they had gone quite far enough as it was. Besides, now was a time rather for action than for thought. Some of those who were skilled in hunting went to fetch their arrows and spears, formed a sort of army, and marched round and round the lower slopes of the hill in readiness to withstand and slay the dragon so soon as he should come down into the open. At first this had a cheering and heartening effect (on all but Thol, whose personal aspiration you remember). But soon there recurred to the minds of many, and were repeated broadcast, other words that had been spoken by wanderers. "So hard," had said one, "are the scales of a crawling dragon that no spear can prick him, howsoever sharp and heavy and strongly hurled." And another had grimly said, "Young is that dragon who is not older than the oldest man." And another, "A crawling dragon is not balked but by the swiftness of men's heels."

All this was most depressing. Confidence in the spearmen was badly shaken. The applause for them whenever they passed by was quieter, betokening rather pity than hope. Nay, there were people who now deprecated any attempt to kill the dragon. The dragon, they argued, must not be angered. If he were not mistreated he might do no harm. He had a right to exist. He had visited Gra's cave in a friendly spirit, but Gra had tried to mistreat him, and the result should be a lesson to them all.

Others said, more acceptably, "Let us think not of the dragon. What the spearmen can do, that will they do. Let this day be as other days, and each man to the task that is his." Brud was one of those who hurried away gladly. Nor was Thol loth to follow. The chance that the dragon might come out in his absence did not worry a boy so unprepared today for single combat; and if other hands than his were to succeed in slaying the dragon, he would liefer not have the bitterness of looking on.

Thia also detached herself from the throng. Many voices of men and women and children called after her, bidding her stay. "I would find me some task," she answered.

"O Thia," said one, "find only flowers for your hair. And sing to us, dance for us. Let this day be as other days." And so pleaded many voices.

But Thia answered them, "My heart is too sad. We are all in peril. For myself I am not afraid. But how should I dance, who love you? Not again, O dear ones, shall I dance, until the dragon be slain or gone back across the water. Neither shall I put flowers in my hair nor sing."

She went her way, and was presently guiding a flock of geese to a pond that does not exist now.

V

She sat watching the geese gravely, fondly, as they swam and dived and cackled. She was filled with a sense of duty to them. They too were homelanders and dear ones. She wished that all the others could be so unknowing and so happy.

A breeze sprang up, swaying the column of smoke and driving it across the valley, on which it cast a long, wide, dark shadow.

Thia felt very old. She remembered a happy and careless child who woke—how long ago!—and went looking for mushrooms. And this memory gave her another feeling. You see, she had eaten nothing all day.

Near the pond was a cherry tree. She looked at it. She tried not to. This was no day for eating. The sight of the red cherries jarred on her. They were so very red. She went to the tree unwillingly. She hoped no one would see her. In your impatience at the general slowness of man's evolution, you will be glad to learn that Thia, climbing that tree and swinging among the branches, had notably more of assurance and nimble ease than any modern child would have in like case. It was only her mind that misgave her.

Ashamed of herself, ashamed of feeling so much younger and stronger now, she dropped to the ground and wondered how she was to atone. She chose the obvious course. She ran around the homeland urging everyone to eat something. All were grateful for the suggestion. The length of their fast is the measure of the shock they had received that day, and of the strain imposed on them. Eating had ever been a thing they excelled in. Most of them were far too fat. Thia's suggestion was acted on with all speed. Great quantities of cold meat were consumed. And this was well. The night in store was to make special demands on the nerves of the homelanders.

As the sun drew near down to the west, the breeze dropped with it, and the smoke was again an upright column, reddened now by the sun. Later, while afterglow faded into twilight, to some of the homelanders it seemed that the base of the column was less steady, was moving. They were right. The time of their testing was at hand. The dragon was coming down the hill.

VI

The spearmen opened out their ranks quickly and hovered in skirmishing order. The dragon's pace was no quicker than that of a man strolling. His gait was at once ponderous and sinuous. The great body rocked on the four thick leglets that moved in a somehow light and stealthy fashion. They ended, these leglets, in webbed feet with talons. The long neck was craned straight forward, flush with the ground, but the tail, which was longer still, swung its barbed tip slowly from side to side, and sometimes rose, threshing the air. Neck, body and tail were surmounted by a ridge of upstanding spurs. In fact, the dragon was just what I have called him: dreadful.

Spears flew in the twilight. Ringing noises testified that many of them hit the mark. They rang as they glanced off the scales that completely sheathed the brute, who, now and again, coiled his neck round to have a look at them, as though they rather interested and amused him. One of them struck him full on the brow (if brow it can be called) without giving him an instant's pause.

Anon, however, he halted, rearing his neck straight up, turning his head slowly this way and that, and seemed to take, between his great puffs of fiery smoke, a general survey of the valley. Twilight was not fading into darkness, for a young moon rode the sky, preserving a good view for, and of, the dragon. Most of the homelanders had with one accord retired to the further side of the valley, across the dividing stream. Only the spearmen remained on the dragon's side, and some sheep that were in a fold there. One of the spearmen, taking aim, ventured rather near to the dragon—so near that the dragon's neck, shooting down, all but covered the distance. The clash of the dragon's jaws resounded. The spearman had escaped only by a hair's breadth. The homelanders made a faint noise, something between a sigh and a groan.

The dragon looked at them for a long time. He seemed to be in no hurry. He glanced at the moon, as though saying, "The night is young." He glanced at the sheepfold and slowly went to it. Wanderers had often said of dragons that they devoured no kind of beast in any land that had human creatures in it. What would this dragon do? The huddled sheep bleated piteously at him. He reared his neck high and examined them from that altitude. Suddenly a swoop and a clash. The neck was instantly erect again, with a ripple down it. The head turned slowly towards the homelanders, then slowly away again. The mind was seemingly divided. There was a pause. This ended in another swoop, clash, recoil and ripple. Another dubious pause; and now, neck to ground, the dragon headed amain for the homelanders.

They drew back, they scattered. Some rushed they knew not whither for refuge, wailing wildly; others swarmed up the trunks of high trees (swiftlier, yes, than we could). Across the stream stepped the dragon with a sort of cumbrous daintiness, and straightway, at his full speed, which was that of a man walking quickly, gave chase. If you care for the topographical side of history, you should walk out of Berkeley Square by way of Charles Street, into Curzon Street, past Chesterfield House, up Park Lane, along Oxford Street, down South Molton Street and back into Berkeley Square by way of Bruton Street. This, roughly, was the dragon's line of route. He did not go exactly straight along it. He often swerved and zigzagged; and he made in the course of the night many long pauses. He would thrust his head into the mouth of some cave or hut, on the chance that someone had been so foolish as to hide there; or he would crane his neck up among the lower branches of a tall tree, scorching these with his breath, and peering up into the higher branches, where refugees might or might not be; or he would just stay prone somewhere, doing nothing. For the rest, he pursued whom he saw. High speed he never achieved; but he had cunning, and had power to bewilder with fear. Before the night was out he was back again in his cave upon the hill. And the sleepless homelanders, forgathering in the dawn to hear and tell what things had befallen, gradually knew themselves to be the fewer by five souls.

VII

It is often said that no ills are so hard to suffer as to anticipate. I do not know that this is true. But it does seem to be a fact that people comport themselves better under the incidence of an ill than under the menace of it; better also in their fear of an ill's recurrence than when the ill is first feared. Some of the homelanders, you will have felt, had been rather ridiculous on the first day of the dragon's presence among them. They had not been so in the watches of the night. Even Brud and his dog had shown signs of courage and endurance. Even Thol had not cried much. Thia had behaved perfectly. But this is no more than you would expect of Thia. The point is that after their panic at the dragon's first quick onset, the generality of the homelanders had behaved well. And now, haggard though they were in the dawn, wan, disheveled, they were not without a certain collective dignity.

When everything had been told and heard, they stood for a while in silent mourning. The sun rose from the hills over the water, and with a common impulse they knelt to this great god, beseeching him that he would straightway call the dragon back beyond those hills, never to return. Then they looked up at the cave. Today the dragon was wholly inside, his smoke rolling up from within the cave's mouth. Long looked the homelanders for that glimmer of nether fire which would show that he was indeed moving forth. There was nothing for them to see but the black smoke. "Peradventure," said one, "the sun is not a god." "Nay," said another, "rather may it be that he is so great a god that we cannot know his purposes, nor he be turned aside from them by our small woes." This was accounted a strange but a wise saying. "Nevertheless," said the sayer, "it is well that we should ask help of him in woes that to us are not small." So again the homelanders prayed, and though their prayer was still unanswered they felt themselves somehow strengthened.

It was agreed that they should disperse to their dwellings, eat, and presently reassemble in formal council.

And here I should mention Shib; for he was destined to be important in this council, though he was but a youth, and on his cheeks and chin the down had but begun to lengthen. I may as well also mention Veo, his brother, elder than him by one year. They were the sons of Oc and Loga, with whom they lived in a cave near the valley. Veo had large eyes which seemed to see nothing, but saw much. Shib had small eyes which seemed to see much, and saw it. Shib's parents thought him very clever, as indeed he was. They thought Veo a fool; but Mr. Roger Fry, had he seen the mural drawings in their cave, would have assured them that he was a master.

Said Veo to Shib, as they followed their parents to the cave, "Though I prayed that he might not, I am glad that the dragon abides with us. His smoke is as the trunk of a great tree whose branches are the sky. When he comes crawling down the hill he is more beautiful than Thia dancing."

Shib's ideas about beauty were academic. Thia dancing, with a rosebush on one side of her and a sunset on the other, was beautiful. The dragon was ugly. But Shib was not going to waste breath in argument with his absurd brother. What mattered was not that the dragon was ugly, but that the dragon was a public nuisance, to be abated if it could not be suppressed. The spearmen had failed to suppress it, and would continue to fail. But Shib thought he saw a way to abatement. He had carefully watched throughout the night the dragon's demeanor. He had noted how, despite so many wanderers' clear testimony as to the taste of all dragons, this creature had seemed to palter in choice between the penned sheep near to him and the mobile people across the stream; noted that despite the great talons on his feet he did not attempt to climb any of the trees; noted the long rests he took here and there. On these observations Shib had formed a theory, and on this theory a scheme. And during the family meal in the cave he recited the speech he was going to make at the council. His parents were filled with admiration. Veo, however, did not listen to a word. Nor did he even attend the council. He stayed in the cave, making with a charred stick, on all vacant spaces, stark but spirited pictures of the dragon.

VIII

I will not report in even an abridged form the early proceedings of the council. For they were tedious. The speakers were many, halting, and not to the point. Shib, when his chance at length came, shone. He had a dry, unattractive manner; but he had something to say, he said it clearly and tersely, and so he held his audience.

Having stated the facts he had noted, he claimed no certainty for the deduction he had made from them. He did not say, "Know then surely, O homelanders, that this is a slothful dragon." Nor, for the matter of that, did he say he had furnished a working hypothesis, or a hypothesis that squared with the known facts, or a hypothesis that held the field. Such phrases, alas, were impossible in the simple and barbarous tongue of the homelanders. But "May it not be," Shib did say, "that this is a slothful dragon?" There was a murmur of meditative assent. "Hearken then," said Shib, "to my counsel. Let the spearmen go slay two deer. Let the shepherds go slay two sheep, and the goatherds two goats. Also let there be slain three geese and as many ducks. Or ever the sun leave us, and the dragon wake from his sleep, let us take all these up and lay them at the mouth of the cave that was Gra's cave. Thus it may be that this night shall not be as the last was, but we all asleep and safe. And if so it betide us, let us make to the dragon other such offerings tomorrow, and on all days that are to come."

There was prompt and unanimous agreement that this plan should be tried. The spearmen went hunting. Presently they returned with a buck and a roe. By this time the other animals prescribed had been slain in due number. It remained that the feast should be borne noiselessly up the hill and spread before the slumbering dragon. The homelanders surprised one another, surprised even themselves, by their zeal for a share of this task. Why should any one of them be wanting to do work that others could do? and willing to take a risk that others would take? Really they did not know. It was a strange foible. But there it was. A child can carry the largest of ducks; but as many as four men were lending a hand in porterage of a duck today. Not one of the porters enjoyed this work. But somehow they all wanted to do it, and did it with energy and good humor.

Very soon, up yonder on the flat shelf of ground in front of the cave's mouth, lay temptingly ranged in a semicircular pattern two goats, three ducks, two deer, three geese and two sheep. All had been done that was to be done. The homelanders suddenly began to feel the effects of their sleepless night. They would have denied that they were sleepy, but they felt a desire to lie down and think. The valley soon had a coverlet of sleeping figures, prone and supine. But, as you know, the mind has a way of waking us when it should; and the homelanders were all wide awake when the shadows began to lengthen.

Very still the air was; and very still stood those men and women and children, on the other side of the dividing stream. The sun, setting red behind them, sent their shadows across the stream, on and on slowly, to the very foot of the hill up to which they were so intently looking. The column of smoke, little by little, lost its flush. But anon it showed fitful glimpses of a brighter red at the base of it, making known that the dragon's head was not inside the cave. And now it seemed to the homelanders, in these long moments, that their hearts ceased beating, and all hope died in them. Suddenly—clash! the dragon's jaws echoed all over the valley; and then what silence!

Through the veil of smoke, dimly, it was seen that the red glow rose, paused, fell—clash! again.

Twelve was a number that the homelanders could count up to quite correctly. Yet even after the twelfth clash they stood silent and still. Not till the red glow faded away into the cave did they feel sure that tonight all was well with them.

Then indeed a great deep sigh went up from the throng. There were people who laughed for joy; others who wept for the same reason. None was happier than Thia. She was on the very point of singing and dancing, but remembered her promise, and the exact wording of it, just in time. In all the valley there was but one person whose heart did not rejoice.

This was Veo. He had come out late in the afternoon, to await, impatiently, the dragon's reappearance. He had particularly wanted to study the action of the hind legs, which he felt he had not caught rightly. Besides, he had wanted to see the whole magnificent creature again, just for the sight of it. Veo was very angry. Nobody, however, heeded him. Everybody heeded the more practical brother. It was a great evening for Oc and Loga. They were sorry there was a dragon in the homeland, but even more (for parents will be parents) were they proud of their boy's success. The feelings of Thol, too, were not unmixed. Though none of the homelanders, except Thia, had ever shown him any kindness, he regretted the dragon, and was very glad that the dragon was not coming out tonight; but he was even gladder that the dragon had not been slain by the spearmen nor called back across the water by the sun. It was true that if either of these things had happened he could have gone to sleep comfortably in his own cave, and that he dared not sleep there now, and saw no prospect of sleeping there at all until he had slain the dragon. But he bethought him of the many empty caves on the way down to the marshes. And he moved into that less fashionable quarter—sulkily indeed, but without tears, and sustained by a great faith in the future.

IX

On the morning of next day the homelanders prayed again to the sun that he would call the dragon away from them. He did not so. Therefore they besought him that he would forbid the dragon to come further than the cave's mouth, and would cause him to be well pleased with a feast like yesterday's.

Such a feast, in the afternoon, was duly laid at the cave's mouth; and again, when the sun was setting, the dragon did not come down the hill, but ate aloft there, and at the twelfth clash drew back his glowing jaws into the cave.

Day followed day, each with the same ritual and result.

Shib did not join in the prayers. He regarded them as inefficacious, and also as rather a slight to himself. The homelanders, be it said, intended no slight. They thought Shib wonderfully clever, and were most grateful to him; but it never occurred to them to rank him among gods.

Veo always prayed heartily that the dragon should be called away forthwith. He wanted to see the dragon by daylight. But he did not pray that the dragon should not come forth in the evening. Better a twilit dragon than none at all.

Little Thol, though he prayed earnestly enough that the dragon should stay at home by night, never prayed for him to leave the homeland. He prayed that he himself might grow up very quickly, and be very big and very strong and very clever and very brave.

For the rest, the homelanders were all orthodox in their devotions.

X

The young moon had grown old, had dwindled, and disappeared. The sound of the clashed jaws ceased to be a novelty. The vesperal gatherings in the valley became smaller. The great column of smoke, by day and by night, was for the homelanders a grim reminder of what had happened, and of what would happen again if once they failed to fulfil the needs of their uninvited guest. They were resolved that they would not fail. In this resolution they had a somber sense of security. But there came, before the leaves of the trees were yellow, an evening when the dragon left untasted the feast spread for him, and crawled down the hill. He was halfway down before any one noticed his coming. And on that night, a longer night than the other, he made a wider journey around the homeland, and took a heavier toll of lives.

Thenceforth always, at sunset, guards were posted to watch the hill and to give, if need were, the alarm. Nor did even this measure suffice. In the dawn of a day in winter, when snow was lying thick on the homeland, a goatherd observed with wonder a wide pathway through the snow from the dragon's cave; and presently he saw afar on the level ground the dragon himself, with his head inside the mouth of a lonely hut that was the home of a young man recently wedded. From the hut's mouth crept forth clouds of smoke, and, as the dragon withdrew his head, the goatherd, finding voice, raised such a cry as instantly woke many sleepers. That day lived long in the memory of the homelanders. The dragon was very active. He did not plod through the snow. He walked at his full speed upon the ground, the snow melting before him at the approach of his fiery breath. It was the homelanders that plodded. Some of them stumbled head foremost into snowdrifts and did not escape their pursuer. There was nothing slothful in the dragon's conduct that day. Hour after hour in the keen frosty air he went his way, and not before nightfall did he go home.

Thus was inaugurated what we may call the Time of Greater Stress. No one could know at what hour of night or day the dragon might again raid the homeland. Relays of guards had to watch the hill always. No one, lying down to sleep, knew that the dragon might not forthcome before sunrise; no one, throughout the day, knew that the brute might not be forthcoming at any moment. True, he forthcame seldom. The daily offerings of slain beasts and birds sufficed him, mostly. But he was never to be depended on—never.

Shib's name somewhat fell in the general esteem. Nor was it raised again by the execution of a scheme that he conceived. The roe and buck stuffed with poisonous herbs were swallowed by the dragon duly, but the column of smoke from the cave's mouth did not cease that evening, as had been hoped. And on the following afternoon—a sign that the stratagem had not been unnoticed—one of the men who were placing the food in front of the cave perished miserably in the dragon's jaws.

Other devices of Shib's failed likewise. The homelanders had to accept the dragon as a permanent factor in their lives. Year by year, night and day, rose the sinister column of smoke, dense, incessant. Happy those tiny children who knew not what a homeland without a dragon was like! So, at least, thought the elders.

And yet, were these elders so much less happy than they had erst been? Were they not—could they but have known it—happier? Did not the danger in which they lived make them more appreciative of life? Surely they had a zest that in the halcyon days was not theirs? Certainly they were quicker-witted. They spoke less slowly, their eyes were brighter, all their limbs nimbler. Perhaps this was partly because they ate less meat. The dragon's diet made it necessary that they should somewhat restrict their own, all the year round. The dragon, without knowing it, was a good physician to them.

Without being a moralist or a preacher, he had also improved their characters. Quarrels had become rare. Ill-natured gossip was frowned on. Suspicions throve not. Manners had unstiffened. The homelanders now liked one another. They had been drawn charmingly together in brotherhood and sisterhood. You would have been surprised at the change in them.

XI

But for his bright red hair, perhaps you would not have recognized Thol at all. He was a great gawky youth now. Spiritually, however, he had changed little. He was still intent on slaying the dragon.

In the preceding years he had thought of little else than this, and as he never had said a word about it he was not accounted good company. Nor had he any desire to shine—in any light but that of a hero. The homelanders would have been cordial enough to him, throughout those years, if he had wished them to be so. But he never was able to forget how cold and unkind they had been to him in his early childhood. It was not for their sake that he had so constantly nursed and brooded over his great wish. It was for his own sake only.

An unsympathetic character? Stay!—let me tell you that since the dawn of his adolescence another sake had come in to join his own: Thia's sake.

From the moment when she, in childhood, had called him a coward, it always had been Thia especially that he wished to impress. But in recent times his feeling had changed. How should such a lout as he ever hope to impress Thia, who was a goddess? Thol hoped only to make Thia happy, to see her go dancing and singing once more, with flowers in her hair. Thol did not even dare hope that Thia would thank him. Thol was not an unsympathetic character at all.

As for Thia, she was more fascinating than ever. Do not be misled by her seeming to Thol a goddess. Remember that the homelanders worshiped cherry trees and rain and fire and running water and all such things. There was nothing of the statuesque Hellenic ideal about Thia. She had not grown tall, she was as lissom and almost as slight as ever; and her alien dark hair had not lost its wildness: on windy days it flew out far behind her, like a thunder cloud, and on calm days hid her as in a bush. She had never changed the task that she chose on the day of the dragon's advent. She was still a goosegirl. But perhaps she was conscious now that the waddling gait of her geese made the grace of her own gait the lovelier by its contrast. Certainly she was familiar with her face. She had often leaned over clear pools to study it—to see what the homelanders saw in it. She was very glad of her own charms because they were so dear to all those beloved people. But sometimes her charms also saddened her. She had had many suitors—youths of her own age, and elder men too. Even Veo, thinking her almost as beautiful as the dragon, had laid his hands upon her shoulders, in the ritual mode. Even the intellectual Shib had done so. And even from such elders as these it was dreadful to turn away. Nor was Thia a girl of merely benevolent nature; she had warm desires, and among the younger suitors more than one had much pleased her fancy. But stronger than any other sentiment in her was her love for the homeland. Not until the dragon were slain or were gone away across the waters would Thia be wife of any man.

So far as she knew, she had sentenced herself to perpetual maidenhood. Even had she been aware of Thol's inflexible determination, she would hardly have become hopeful. Determination is one thing, doing is another.

The truth of that old adage sometimes forced itself on poor Thol himself, as he sat watching the sheep that he herded near his cave on the way to the marshes; and at such time his sadness was so great that it affected even his sheep, causing them to look askance at him and bleat piteously, and making drearier a neighborhood that was in itself dreary.

But, one day in the eighteenth summer of his years, Thol ceased to despond. There came, wet from the river and mossy from the marshes, an aged wanderer. He turned his dark eyes on Thol and said with a smile, pointing towards the thick smoke on the hill, "A dragon is here now?"

"Yea, O wanderer," Thol answered.

"There was none aforetime," said the old man. "A dragon was what your folk needed."

"They need him not. But tell me, O you that have so much wandered, and have seen many dragons, tell me how a dragon may be slain!"

"Mind your sheep, young shepherd. Let the dragon be. Let not your sheep mourn you."

"They shall not. I shall slay the dragon. Only tell me how! Surely there is a way?"

"It is a way that would lead you into his jaws, O fool, and not hurt him. Only through the roof of his mouth can a dragon be pierced and wounded. He opens not his jaws save when they are falling upon his prey. Do they not fall swiftly, O fool?"

"O wanderer, yea. But—"

"Could you deftly spear the roof of that great mouth, O prey, in that little time?"

"Yea, surely, if so the dragon would perish."

The old man laughed. "So would the dragon perish, truly; but so only. So would be heard what few ears have heard—the cry that a dragon utters as he is slain. But so only." And the old man went his way northward.

From that day on, Thol did not watch his sheep very much. They, on the other hand, spent most of their time in watching him. They rather thought he was mad, standing in that odd attitude and ever lunging his crook up at one of the nodding boughs of that ash tree.

Twice in the course of the autumn the dragon came down the hill; but when the watchmen sounded the alarm Thol did not go forth to meet him. He was not what his flock thought him.

He had now exchanged his crook for a spear—a straight well-seasoned sapling of oak, with a long sharp head of flint. With this, day by day, hour after hour, he lunged up at the boughs of fruit trees. His flock, deploring what seemed to them mania, could not but admire his progressive skill. Rarely did he fail now in piercing whatever plum or apple he aimed at.

When winter made bare the branches, it was at the branches that Thol aimed his thrusts. His accuracy was unerring now. But he had yet to acquire the trick of combining the act of transfixion with the act of leaping aside. Else would he perish even in victory.

Spring came. As usual, her first care was to put blossoms along the branches of such almond trees as were nearest to the marshes.

The ever side-leaping Thol pricked off any little single blossom that he chose.

XII

Spring was still active in the homeland when, one day, a little while before sunset, the watchers of the hill blew their horns. There came from all quarters the usual concourse of young and old, to watch the direction of the dragon and to keep out of it. Down came the familiar great beast, the never-aging dragon, picking his way into the green valley. And he saw an unwonted sight there. He saw somebody standing quite still on the nearer bank of the stream; a red-haired young person, holding a spear. About this young person he formed a theory which had long been held by certain sheep.

Little wonder that the homelanders also formed that theory! Little wonder that they needed no further proof of it when, deaf to the cries of entreaty that they uttered through the evening air, Thol stood his ground!

Slowly, as though to give the wretched young lunatic a chance, the dragon advanced.

But quickly, very terribly and quickly, when he was within striking distance, he reared his neck up. An instant later there rang through the valley—there seemed to rend the valley—a single screech, unlike anything that its hearers had ever heard.

Those who dared to look saw the vast length of the dragon, neck on grass, coiling slowly round. The tip of the tail met the head and parted from it. Presently the vast length was straight, motionless.

Yet even of those who had dared look none dared believe that the dragon was indeed dead.

But for its death cry, Thol himself would hardly have believed.

The second firm believer was Thia. Thia, with swift conviction, plucked some flowers and put them loosely into her hair. Thia, singing as well as though she had never ceased to sing, and dancing as prettily as though she had for years been practicing her steps, went singing and dancing towards the stream. Lightly she leapt the stream, and then very seriously and quietly walked to the spot where Thol stood. She looked up at him, and then, without a word, raised her arms and put her hands upon his shoulders. He, who had slain the dragon, trembled.

"O Thol," she said gently, "you turn not away from me, but neither do you raise me from the ground."

Then Thol raised Thia thrice from the ground.

And he said, "Let our home be the cave that was my father's."

Hand in hand, man and wife, they went up the hill, and round to the eastern side of its summit. But when they came to the mouth of the old cave there, he paused and let go her hand.

"O Thia," he said wonderingly, "is it indeed true that you love me?"

"O Thol," she answered, "it is most true."

"O Thia," he said, "love me always!"

"I have long ceased to love you, O Thol," she said, five years later, in a low voice. But I see that I have outstripped my narrative. I must hark back.

XIII

The sun had already risen far when Thol and Thia were wakened by a continuous great hum as of many voices. When they looked forth and down from the mouth of their high home, it seemed to them that all the homelanders were there beneath them, gazing up.

And this was indeed so. Earlier in the morning, by force of habit, all the homelanders had gone to what we call Berkeley Square, the place where for so many years they had daily besought the sun to call the dragon away

across the water. There, where lay the great smokeless and harmless carcass, was no need for prayers now; and with one accord the throng had
moved from the western to the eastern foot of the hill, and stayed there
gazing in reverence up to the home of a god greater than the sun.

When at length the god showed himself, there arose from the throng a
great roar of adoration. The throng went down on its knees to him,
flung up its arms to him, half-closed its eyes so as not to be blinded by the
sight of him. His little mortal mate, knowing not that he was a god,
thinking only that he was a brave man and her own, was astonished at
the doings of her dear ones. The god himself, sharing her ignorance, was
deeply embarrassed, and he blushed to the roots of his hair.

"Laugh, O Thol," she whispered to him. "It were well for them that
you should laugh." But he never had laughed in all his life, and was
much too uncomfortable to begin doing so just now. He backed into the
cave. The religious throng heaved a deep moan of disappointment as he
did so. Thia urged him to come forth and laugh as she herself was doing.
"Nay," he said, "but do you, whom they love, dance a little for them and
sing. Then will they go away happy."

It seemed to Thia that really this was the next best plan, and so, still
laughing, she turned round and danced and sang with great animation
and goodwill. The audience, however, was cold. It gave her its attention,
but even this, she began to feel, was not its kind attention. Indeed, the
audience was jarred. After a while—for Thia's pride forbade her to stop
her performance—the audience began to drift away.

There were tears in her eyes when she danced back into the cave. But
these she brushed away, these she forgot instantly in her lover's presence.

XIV

Love is not all. "I must go drive my geese," said the bride.

"And I my sheep," said the bridegroom.

"There is good grass, O Thol, round my geese's pond. Let your sheep
graze there always. Thus shall not our work sever us."

As they went forth, some children were coming up the hill, carrying
burdens. The burdens were cold roast flesh, dried figs, and a gourd of
water, sent by some elders as a votive offering to the god. The children
knelt at sight of the god and then ran shyly away, leaving their gifts on
the ground. The god and his mate feasted gladly. Then they embraced
and parted, making tryst at the pond.

When Thia approached the pond, she did not wonder that Thol was
already there, for sheep go quicker than geese. But—where were his
sheep? "Have they all strayed?" she cried out to him.

He came to meet her, looking rather foolish.

"O Thia," he explained, "as I went to the fold, many men and women
were around it. I asked them what they did there. They knelt and made

answer, 'We were gazing at the sheep that had been the god's.' When I made to unpen the flock, there was a great moaning. There was gnashing of teeth, O Thia, and tearing of hair. It was said by all that the god must herd sheep nevermore."

"And you, beloved, what said you?"

"I said nothing, O Thia, amid all that wailing. I knew not what to say."

Thia laughed long but tenderly. "And your sheep, beloved, what said they?"

"How should I know?" asked Thol.

"And you left them there? Do you not love them?"

"I have never loved them."

"But they were your task?"

"O Thia, the dragon was my task."

She stroked his arm. "The dragon is dead, O Thol. You have slain the dragon, O my brave dear one. That task is done. You must find some other. All men must work. Since you loved not your sheep, you shall love my geese, and I will teach you to drive them with me."

"That," said Thol, "would not be a man's work, O Thia."

"But they say you are a god! And I think a god may do as he will."

Her flock had swum out into the pond. She called it back to her, and headed it away towards some willows. From one of these she plucked for Thol a long twig such as she herself carried, and, having stripped it of its leaves, gave it to him and began to teach him her art.

XV

There was, as Thia had known there must be, a great concourse of people around and about the dragon.

There was a long line of children riding on its back; there were infants in arms being urged by their mothers never to forget that they had seen it; there were many young men and women trying to rip off some of its scales, as reminders; and there were elders exchanging reminiscences of its earliest raids and correcting one another on various points. And the whole crowd of holiday-makers was so intent that the gradual approach of that earnest worker, Thol, was not noticed until he came quite near.

Very gradual, very tortuous and irregular, his approach was. Thia, just now, was letting him shift for himself, offering no hints at all. For the homelanders' sake, she wished him to be seen at his worst. It was ill that they should worship a false god. To her, he was something better than a real god. But this was another matter. To the homelanders, he ought to seem no more than a man who had done a great deed and set a high example. And for his own sake, and so for hers—for how could his not be hers?—she wished him to have no more honor than was his due. Splendid man though he was, and only a year younger than herself, he was yet a child; and children, thought Thia—though she was conscious that she herself, for all the petting she had received, was rather perfect—are easily spoilt. Altogether, the goosegirl's motives were as pure as her perception was keen. Admirable, too, were her tactics; and they should have succeeded. Yet they failed. In the eyes of the homelanders the goose god lost not a jot of his divinity.

No hint of disillusion was in the moans evoked by the sight of him. Grief, shame, horror at his condescension, and a deep wrath against the whilom darling Thia, were all that was felt by the kneeling and swaying crowd.

Thia knew it. She was greatly disappointed. Indeed, she was near to shedding tears again. Pride saved her from that. Besides, she was angry, and not only angry but amused. And in a clear voice that was audible above the collective moaning, "Have patience, O homelanders," she cried. "He is new to his work. He will grow in skill. These geese will find that he is no fool. And it may be that hereafter, if you are all very good, I will teach him to sing and dance for you, with flowers in his bright red hair."

Having thus spoken, she ran to overtake her husband, and soon, guiding the flock in good order, went her way with him back to the pond.

XVI

There was a general desire that the dragon should not be buried anywhere within the confines of the homeland. Shib conceived that if the trunks of felled trees were used as rollers the carcass might be transported to the swamps and be sunk there. By its vast weight the carcass frustrated this scheme. A long deep trench must be dug beside it. All the able-bodied men of the homeland offered their services, and of course Shib was a most efficient director of the work.

You will be glad to hear that Shib was a more sympathetic character than he once was. The public spirit that had always been his was unmarred now by vanity and personal ambition. He was a quiet, disinterested, indefatigable worker for the common weal, burning always with that hard, gemlike flame which Mr. Pater discerned in the breasts of our own Civil Servants. He had forgotten, or he remembered without bitterness, the time when he was a popular hero. Thol's great deed was a source of genuine pleasure to him. Nay (for he had long ago outgrown his callow atheism), he accepted Thol as a god, though he was too cautious to rate him higher than the sun.

Thus he was much shocked when Thol came wishing to help in the labor. Rising, at Thol's earnest entreaty, from his knees, he ventured to speak firmly to the god—reverently but very firmly pointing out to him that the laborers, if their religious feelings were flouted, would probably cease work; and he hinted that he himself would have to consider whether he could retain his post. So Thol went back to the goose pond and was so much chidden by Thia for his weakness that he almost wished she believed him to be a god. Of course he was not a god. Of course Thia was right. Still, Shib was known to be a very wise man. It was strange that Shib should be mistaken. Inwardly, he could not agree with Thia that Shib was a fool. And I think she must have suspected him of this reservation, for she looked at him with much trouble in her eyes and was for a while silent, and then, fondlingly, made him promise that he never would trust anyone's thoughts but hers.

Three days later the great trench was finished; and down into it, by leverage of many stakes heftily wielded in unison, was heaved the dragon (and there, to this day, deep down under the eastern side of the garden and roadway of Berkeley Square, is the dragon's skeleton—an occult memorial of Thol's deed). Down into the trench, with a great thud that for a moment shook the ground, fell Thol's victim. Presently the trench brimmed with earth, and this earth was stamped firm by exultant feet, and more earth was added to it and stamped on till only a long brown path, that would soon be green and unnoticeable, marked the place of sepulture.

The great occasion lacked only the god's presence. Of course the god had been invited. Shib, heading a deputation on the banks of the goose pond, had besought him that he would deign to throw the first clod of earth upon the dragon; and he had diplomatically added that all the homelanders were hoping that Thia might be induced to sing and dance on the grave as soon as it had been filled. But Thia had answered that she could not give her husband leave, inasmuch as he had been idle at his work that day; he would like very much to come; but it was for that very reason that she would not let him: he must be punished. As for herself, she too would very much like to come, but she must stay and keep him to his work. Thol saying nothing, the deputation had then withdrawn, not without many obeisances, which Thia, with as many curtseys, roguishly took to herself.

However, even without the light of the god's countenance on it, the festival was a great and glorious one. Perhaps indeed the revelers enjoyed themselves more than would have been possible in the glare of that awful luminary. The revels lasted throughout the night, and throughout the next day, and did not cease even then. Dazed with sleepiness and heavy with surfeits of meat, the homelanders continued to caper around bonfires and to clap one another on the back; and only because they had not the secret of fermented liquor were there no regrettable scenes of intoxication. The revels had become a habit. It seemed as though they would never cease. But human strength is finite.

Thia would have liked to be in the midst of the great to-do. It was well that the homelanders should rejoice. And the homelanders were as dear to her as ever, though she had so much offended them for Thol's sake and theirs. Thol's nature was not social, as hers was; but she knew that even he would have liked to have glimpses of the fun. It grieved her to keep him aloof with her among the geese. She sang and danced round him and petted him and made much of him, all day long.

XVII

The autumn was rainy; and the winter was rainy too; and thus the brown path over the dragon's grave vanished even before spring came. Green also was the grass that had for so many years been black above and around the mouth of the dragon's cave. Valley and hill smiled as blandly at each other as though they had never seen a dragon.

Little by little, likewise, the souls of the homelanders had reverted, as we should say, to type. There were no signs now of that mutual good will which had been implanted in them by the common peril and had overflowed so wildly at the time when the peril ended. Mistrustfulness had revived, and surliness with it, and quickness to take offense, and a dull eagerness to retaliate on the offender. The shortcomings of others were once more the main preoccupation of the average homelander. Next to these, the weather was once more the favorite topic of conversation, especially if the weather were bad; but even if it were good, the prospect of bad weather was dwelt on with a more than sufficient emphasis. Work, of course, had to be done; but as little of it was done as might be, and that glumly, and not well. Meals were habitually larger than appetites. Eyes were duller, complexions less clear, chests narrower, stomachs more obtrusive, arms and legs less well developed, than they had been under the dragon's auspices. And prayers, of course, were not said now.

Thia in her childhood had thought the homelanders perfect; and thus after the coming of the dragon she had observed no improvement in them. But now, with maturer vision, she did see that they were growing less worthy of high esteem. This grieved her. She believed that she loved the homelanders as much as ever, she told herself truly enough that it was much her own fault that they had ceased to love her. In point of fact, their coldness to her, in course of time, cooled her feeling for them: she was human. What she did love as much as ever was the homeland. What grieved her was that the homeland should have an imperfect population.

She talked constantly to Thol about her sorrow. He was not a very apt auditor. Being a native of the homeland, he could not see it, as she could, from without. It was not to him an idea, as it was to Thia's deep alien eyes. It was just the homeland. As for the homelanders themselves, he had never, as you may remember, loved them; but he liked them quite well now. He supposed he really was not a god; but it no longer embarrassed him to be thought so; indeed it pleased him to be thought so. The homelanders no longer knelt when he passed by. He had asked them not to, and they reverently obeyed his wish. He supposed Thia was right in saying that they were less good than in the days of the dragon; but in those days he had hardly known them. He was glad to know them better now. His nature had, in fact, become more expansive. He wished Thia were not so troubled about the homeland. He wished she would think more gently of the homelanders, and think less about them, and talk less to him about them.

Sometimes she even tried to enlist his help. "To me," she would say, "they would not hearken. But you, O Thol, whom in their folly they still believe to be a god, could give light to them and shame them back to goodness and strength, and so to happiness. I would teach you what words to say." But Thol, even though he was to be spared the throes of composition, would look so blankly wretched that Thia's evangelical ardor was quenched in laughter. He did not know why she was laughing, and he hoped it was not at him that she was laughing: after all, he had slain the dragon. Nevertheless, her gaiety was a relief to him.

But her ardor was always flaming up again.

XVIII

She had very soon exempted him from that task which failed to cure the homelanders of their delusion about him. She agreed that goose-driving was not a man's work. As he did not wish to be a shepherd again, and as it was needful for his own good that he should be set to some sort of work, she urged him to be a goatherd. Goats, she said, were less dull than sheep; fiercer; more like dragons. So, beside the goose pond, he herded goats; but without the enthusiasm that she had hoped for.

One day, about a year after their marriage, he even suggested that he should have a lad to help him. She said, with a curl of the lip, that she had not known he was old and feeble. He replied, seriously, that he was younger than she; and, as for feebleness, he asked her to remember that he, not she, had slain the dragon. He then walked away, leaving his goats to their own devices, and his wife to hers, and spent the rest of the day in company that was more appreciative of him. He returned of course before sundown, fearful of a lecture. Thia, who had already driven his goats into their pen, did but smile demurely, saying that she would always be glad to do his work for him, and that she was trustier than any lad.

But, as time went on, her temper was not always so sweet. Indeed, it ceased to be sweet. In his steady, rather bovine way, he loved her as much as ever; but his love of being with her was less great, and his pleasure in the society of others was greater, than of yore. Perhaps if Thia had borne a child, she might have been less troubled about the welfare of the home-landers. But this diversion and solace was not granted. Thia's maternal instinct had to spend itself on a community which she could not help and did not now genuinely love, and on a husband who did not understand her simplest thoughts and was moreover growing fat. Her disposition

suffered under the strain. One day, when she was talking to him about
the homeland, she paused with sudden suspicion and asked him what she
had said last; and he could make no answer; and she asked him to tell her
what he had been thinking about; and he said that he had been thinking
about his having slain the dragon; and she, instead of chiding him tenderly, as she would have done in the old days, screamed. She screamed
that she would go mad if ever again he spoke to her of that old dragon.
She flung her arms out towards the hills across the waters and said, with
no lowering of her voice, that every day, out yonder, men were slaying
dragons and thinking nothing of it, and doing their work, and not growing fat. He asked her whether she meant that he himself was growing
fat. "Yea," she answered. He said that then indeed she was mad. Away
he strode, nor did he return at sundown; and it was late in the night before the god retired from a cheery party of worshipers and went up to the
cave, where Thia, faintly visible in the moonlight, lay sleeping, with a
look of deep disdain on her face.

XIX

Sometimes Thia wondered whether in her childhood the characters and
ways of the homelanders had been as they were now. She hated to think
that they had not been perfect in those days; but she reasoned that they
could not have been: before the coming of the dragon they must have
been as they were now, and the only difference was that they had then
loved her. Thus even the memory of her bright careless early years was
embittered to her.

In point of fact, the homelanders had not been exactly as they now
were. The sudden cessation of the strain imposed on them by the dragon's
presence, and of the comparative hardships also imposed by it, had caused
a reaction so strong as to restore to them in a rather accentuated form
what faults had originally been theirs. Human nature had grown rather
more human than ever. Labor was a less than ever alluring thing. Responsibilities had a greater irksomeness. Freedom was all. And, as having
special measure of vital force, especially were youths and maidens intent
on making the most of their freedom. Their freedom was their religion;
and, as every religion needs rites, they ritualistically danced. They danced
much during the day, and then much by moonlight or starlight or firelight, in a grim and purposeful, an angular and indeflexible manner, making it very clear that they were not to be trifled with.

Thia, when first she saw them engaged thus, had been very glad; she
imagined that they must be doing something useful. When she realized
that they were dancing, she drew a deep breath. She remembered how she
herself had danced—danced thoughtlessly and anyhow, from her heart,
with every scrap of her body. She blushed at the recollection. She did not
wonder that the homelanders had resented her dance on the morning

after her marriage. She wondered that they had so encouraged her to dance when she was a child. And she felt that there must, after all, be in these young people a deep fund of earnestness, auguring well for their future.

Time had not confirmed this notion. The young people danced through the passing seasons and the passing years with ever greater assiduity and solemnity; but other forms of seriousness were not manifested by them. Few of them seemed to find time even for falling in love and marrying. They all, however, called one another "beloved," and had a kind of mutual good will which their elders, among themselves, would have done well to emulate. And for those elders they had a tolerant feeling which ought to have been, yet was not, fully reciprocated.

Thol within five years of the dragon's death, Thol with his immense red beard and his stately deportment, was of course very definitely an elder; and still more so was that wife of his, that rather beautiful dark woman, Thia, whose face was so set and stern that she looked almost as though she—she!—were dancing. Thol was liked by the young people. They made much of him. They did not at all object to his being rather pompous: after all, he had slain that dragon, and they thought it quite natural that their parents should imagine he was a god. They liked him to be pompous. They humored him. They enjoyed drawing him out. Among the youths there were several who, in the hours not devoted to earnest dancing and cursory guardianship of flocks, made pictures upon white stones or upon slabs of chalk. They liked especially to make pictures of Thol, because he was so ready to pose for them, and because he stood so still for them. They drew in a manner of their own, a manner which made the veins of poor old Veo stand out upon his forehead, and moved him to declare that they would die young and would die in shame and in agony. Thol, however, was no critic. He was glad to be portrayed in any manner. And it much pleased him to have the color of his mane and beard praised constantly by the young artists. He had supposed the color was wrong. Thia had been wont to laugh at it, in her laughing days. Thia had never called him beautiful, in her praising days. It gladdened him that there were now many young women—Afa, for instance, and Ola, and Ispa, and Moa—who called him, to his face, "terribly" beautiful.

Thol's face, which Thia had admired for its steadfast look, and later had begun to like less for its heavy look, had now a look that was rather fatuous. Afa and the others did not at all object to this. They liked it; they encouraged it by asking him to dance with them. He did not, as they supposed, think that he was too old to dance: he only thought that he might not dance well and might lose his power over them. He believed that they loved him. How should they not? Thia, though she never told him so now, loved him with her whole heart, of course, and, for all the harsh words she spoke at times, thought that no man was his equal. How should these much gentler young women not have given their hearts to him? He felt that he himself could love one of them, if he were not Thia's husband. They were not beautiful, as Thia was; and they were not wise, as she was; but he felt that if he had never seen Thia he might love one of them, or even all of them.

XX

For lack of a calendar, the homelanders had not the habit of keeping anniversaries. They never knew on what day of the year a thing had happened—did not even know that there was a year. But they knew the four seasons. They remembered that the apple trees had been in blossom when Thol slew the dragon, and that since then the apple trees had blossomed four times. And it seemed good to them that at the close of a day when those blossoms were again on those branches, a feast should be held in that part of the valley where the great deed had been done. Shib, who organized the feast, was anxious that it should be preceded by a hymn in praise of the slayer god. He thought this would have a good effect on the rising generation. But Thol opposed the idea, and it was dropped. Shib had also been anxious that Thia should attend the feast, sitting at Thol's right hand and signifying to the young the blessedness of the married state. Thol promised that he would beg her to come; and he did so, as a matter of form, frequently. But Thia of course did not grace the convivial scene.

It was at a late hour of the moonlit night that Thol, flushed with adulation, withdrew from the revels, amidst entreaties that he should remain. He was still wearing the chaplet of flowers that Afa had woven for him. Afa herself was clinging to one of his arms, Moa to the other, as he went round to the eastern spur of the hill; and Ola and Ispa and many others were footing around lightly and lingeringly, appealingly. It was rather the thought of Thia's love for him than of his for her that withheld him from kissing these attendants before he bade them good night. For his own sake he wished, as he climbed the hill, that they would not stand cooing so many farewells up to him so loudly. Thia might not understand how true he was to her. He hoped she was sleeping. But she was awake. Nor was he reassured by the laughter with which, after a moment, she greeted him. She was looking at his head. He became suddenly aware that he had not shed that chaplet. He snatched it off. She laughed the more, but with no kindness in the sound of her laughter.

"O Thia," he said, after a search for words, "be not wroth against those maidens! I love none of them."

"Is that not cruel of you, O Thol? Do they not love you?"

"Though they love me, O Thia, I swear to you that I love not them."

"Why should you not?" she laughed. "Are you so foolish that you think I should be sorry?"

"O Thia," he rebuked her, "you speak empty words. You speak as though you did not love me."

"I have long ceased to love you, O Thol," she said in a low voice.

He stared at her blankly in the moonlight. His slow mind strove hard. "But you are my wife," he said at last. "I am your husband. O Thia, is it indeed true that you have ceased to love me?"

"O Thol, it is most true."

Then, by stress of the great anger that rose in him, his mind worked more quickly—or rather his tongue was loosened. He told Thia that she had never loved him. She denied this coldly. He said that she had never understood him. She denied this warmly. He reminded her that even when she was a little girl she had once called him a coward; and this too she denied; but he maintained that it was so; and she reminded him that after he had been beaten by his master for seeing the dragon he said that she too ought to have been beaten for seeing the dragon; and he denied this; but she persisted that it was so; and he then said that she ought to have been beaten; and she replied that she could be now, and she challenged him to beat her; but he did not accept her challenge; and this, she said, proved that he was a coward; and he asked her to repeat this, and she repeated it, and he then reminded her that he had slain the dragon; and she, stamping her foot, said she only wished the dragon had slain him; and she made a face at him, and rushed out of the cave, and if there had been a door she would have slammed it; and really he was quite glad that she had gone; and after she had run far she lay down upon the grass and slept till dawn, and then, rising and brushing the dew off her arms and legs, went in search of some lonely spot where she should built her a hut of clay and wattles.

And perhaps it was a sign of her alien blood that the spot chosen by her was in what we call Soho. It was the spot on which, many years later, many of my coævals were to dine in the little Restaurant du Bon-Accueil, halfway along Gerrard Street. Gone, as utterly as Thia's hut, is the dear little Restaurant du Bon-Accueil. But again I must hark back.

XXI

"Very surely," thought Thol, some moments after the sun had waked him and shown him the empty cave and brought back last night to his memory, "I shall find her by the pond."

Thither, with much dignity of gait, but with the promise of forgiveness on his brow, he presently went. She was not there. There only her geese were.

These he unpenned and let go into the pond, and then, having freed his goats also, sat down and waited. He waited all day long. She did not come. Nor was she there for him in the cave when he went back to it at sunset. Neither was she at the pond next morning. Not even her geese were there now.

That she had wanted them, and not him, was a bitter thought to Thol. He had not, till now, known how much he loved her. That she had been here this morning, or in the night, made the ground somehow wonderful to him. But he frowned away from his brow the promise of forgiveness. He would not forgive Thia now. Still less would he go in quest of her. He freed his goats, guided them to some long grass and, sitting down, tried to take an intelligent interest in their doings and a lively interest in their welfare, and not wonder where Thia was.

For three whole days he tried hard—tried with all that fixity of purpose which had enabled him at last to slay the dragon. It was Afa's visit that unmanned him.

Not she nor any other of those maidens had ever come to him at the pond in Thia's time. If they happened to pass that way, they would gaze straight before them, or up at the sky, greeting neither the husband nor the wife, and simpering elaborately, as much as to say, "We are unworthy." But now it was straight at Thol that the approaching Afa simpered. And she said, "I am come to be the goatherd's help!"

He marveled that there was a time when he had thought he might have loved one of these maidens. He was not even sure that he knew which of them this one was. He was sure only that he despised them all. And this sentiment so contorted his mild face that there was nothing for Afa to do but toss her head and laugh and leave him.

Presently the look of great scorn in his face was succeeded by a look of even greater love. He arose and went in search of Thia. But he did not in his quest of her throw dignity to the winds. He did not ask anybody where he should find her. He walked slowly, as though bent on no errand. It was near sunset when at length he espied his lost one near to a lonely pool at the edge of the forest.

She did not see him. She sat busily plaiting wattles. There was a great pile of these beside her. And in and around the pool were her geese.

It was they that saw him first, and at sight of him they began to quack, as though in warning. Thia looked up quickly and saw Thol. He held out his arms to her, he strode towards her, calling her name; but she was up, she was gone into the darkness of the forest.

Long he peered into that darkness, and called into it, and even groped through it, but vainly.

XXII

For people who are not accustomed to think, thought is a fatiguing affair. Thol, despite his robust body, was tired when he awoke next morning, for he had spent a great part of the night in wondering how to win back his wife to him. In the days before he slew the dragon he had been a constant thinker. Little by little he was now to regain the habit.

Step by step he reached the premise that in order to find a means of winning Thia back he must first make clear to himself why she had ceased to love him. He put together what he could recall of the many things that in the course of time she had said in anger against him. And he came to the conclusion that he had displeased her most by dwelling so much upon his great deed. He would dwell less upon it, try even to forget it. But this would not suffice. How was she to know that he was no longer dwelling as of yore? Perhaps he could do a second great deed? There seemed to be none to do. He must nevertheless try to think of one—some second great deed that would much please her. It was for the home-landers' sake that the first one had found favor in her sight. And then somehow the homelanders had become less good because of it. Thia had often said so. Of course she had never blamed him for that. Still, perhaps she would not have ceased to love him if his deed had not done harm. Was there no deed by which the harm could be undone? Day by day, night by night, Thol went on thinking.

After the lapse of what we should call a week or so, he began to act also.

He knew that there could be no great thickness of barrier between the back of his cave and the back of the cave that had been the dragon's; for in his childhood he had often heard through it quite clearly the sound of the voices of Gra and her children. To make in it now a breach big enough to crawl through on hands and knees was the first step in the plan that he had formed. With a great sharp stone, hour after hour, daily, he knelt at work. Fortunately—for else must the whole plan have come to naught—the barrier was but of earth, with quite small stones in it. Nevertheless, much of strength and patience had been exerted before the first little chink of daylight met Thol's eyes.

It was a glad moment for him when, that same evening, at sunset, at last he was able to crawl through into the western cave; but as he rose and gazed around the soot-blackened lair he did not exult. His work had but begun. And his work would never end while he lived. He prayed earnestly to the sun that he might live long and always do his work rightly. Also he prayed that Thia might soon again love him.

That night, in his own cave, just as he was falling asleep, he had a doubt which greatly troubled him. He arose and went forth to a place where some ducks were. One of these he took and slew and strode away with it to the marshes. There he heaved it into the ooze. It was quickly sucked down. This was well.

On the next night he became a woodman; and many were the nights he spent in going to and fro in the dark between his cave and the nearest margin of the forest, lopping off great branches and bearing them away for storage, and even uprooting saplings and bearing away these also, and, with a flint ax, felling young trees, and chopping them into lengths that were portable. He continued this night work until both caves were neatly stacked with wood enough to serve his purpose for a longish while.

And then—for he had thought out everything, with that thoroughness which is the virtue of slow minds—he wove two thick screens of osiers and withes, each screen rather bigger than either end of the tunnel. On the evening when the second of these was finished, he made in the dragon's cave, not far from the left-hand side of the cave's mouth, a thick knee-high heap of branches and logs, some of them dry, others green. He placed at the other side of the mouth two thick flat stones, one upon the other.

Back in his own cave, he smeared with sheep's fat a certain great stick of very dry pine wood.

XXIII

And on the following morning history began to repeat itself. With some variations, however. For example, it was not a puny little boy but a great strong man who, as the sun rose, came rushing with every symptom of terror down the western side of the hill. And the man was not really frightened. He only seemed so.

He careered around the valley, howling now like one distraught. Responsive sheep, goats, geese, what not, made great noises of their own. From the mouths of caves and huts people darted and stood agape. Thol waved his arms wildly towards the cave upon the hill. People saw a great column of smoke climbing up from it into the sky.

"A dragon! Another dragon!" was Thol's burthen.

People gathered round him in deep wonder and agitation. He told them, in gasps, that he had come down early—very early—to look for mushrooms—and had looked back and—seen a dragon crawling up the hill. He said that he had seen it only for a moment or two: it crawled very quickly—far more quickly than the old one. He added that it was rather smaller than the old one—smaller and yet far more terrible, though its smoke was less black. Also, that it held high its head, not scorching the grass on its way.

There was no panic.

"O Thol," said one, "we need not fear the dragon, for here are you, to come between us and him."

"Here by this stream," said another, "we shall presently bury him with great rejoicings, O high god."

The crowd went down on its knees, thanking Thol in anticipation. But he, provident plodder, had foreseen what would happen, and had his words ready. "Nay, O homelanders," he said, plucking at his great beard, "I am less young than I was. I am heavier, and not so brave. Peradventure some younger man will dare meet this dragon for us, some day. Meanwhile, let us tempt him with the flesh of beasts, as of yore, hoping that so he will come but seldom into our midst."

In consternation the crowd rose from its knees, and Thol walked quickly away, with a rather shambling gait.

The awful news spread apace. The valley was soon full. Long and earnestly the great throng prayed to the sun that he would call the dragon away from them. He did not so. Up, up went the steadfast smoke from within the cave. Less black it certainly was than that of the other dragon, but not less dreadful. Almost as great as the terror that it inspired was the general contempt for Thol. Many quite old men vowed to practice the needful stroke of the spear. All the youths vowed likewise—yea, and many of the maidens too. It was well known, of course, that Thol had practiced for a long while, and that any haste would be folly; but such knowledge rather heartened than dejected the vowers. Meanwhile, the thing to do was what the craven Thol had suggested before he slunk away: to offer food as of yore. Shib, bristling with precedents, organized the labor. Thol had said that the dragon was a smaller one than the other. Perhaps therefore not so much food would be needed. But it was better to be on the safe side and offer the same ration. Up to the little shelf of ground in front of the cave's mouth were borne two goats, three ducks, two deer, three geese and two sheep.

All day long the valley was crowded with gazers, hopers, comforters of one another, offerers up of prayers.

As day drew to its close, the tensity increased. Would this dragon wake and eat at sunset, as that other had been wont to do? How soon would appear through the smoke that glimpse of nether fire which proclaimed that his head was out of the cave, alert and active? And would that glow rise and fall, in the old way, twelve times, with the sound of the clashed jaws? What was in store for the homeland tonight?

None but Thol knew.

XXIV

He, very wisely, had rested all day in preparation for the tasks of evening and night. Two or three times, moving aside the screen that kept the smoke out of his cave, he had crawled through the opening and, drawing the other screen across the other side of it, had tended the fire. For the rest, he had been all inactive.

As twilight crept into the cave, he knelt in solemn supplication to the departing sun. Presently, when darkness had descended, he struck two flints, lit one end of his pinewood staff, moved the screen aside, drew a long deep breath, and crawled swiftly into the other cave. Slowly he moved his torch from side to side of the cave's mouth, along the ground. He was holding it in his left hand, and in his right hand was holding one of the two flat stones. After a pause, still kneeling, he raised high the torch for a moment or two and then sharply lowered it in the direction of one of the smoke-clouded animals. At the same time he powerfully clashed the one stone down upon the other. Another pause, and he repeated these actions exactly, directing the torch towards the next animal. He performed them ten times in all. Then he extinguished his torch and crept quickly home, puffing and spluttering and snorting, glad to escape into clear air.

When he had regained his breath, he crawled back to drag the carcasses in. The roe and the buck he left where they were. He had calculated that three nightly journeys to the marshes and back would be all that he could achieve. First he would take the two sheep, one on each shoulder; next, the goats; lastly the birds, three necks in either hand. The buck and the roe would be too heavy to be carried together, and for five journeys there would certainly not be time. It was for this reason that he had described the dragon as smaller than the old one, and had clashed the stones ten times only.

From the valley rose sounds of rejoicing that all was well for the homeland tonight. One by one, Thol transferred the carcasses to his own cave. He waited there among them till the dead of night, when all folk would be sleeping. Then, shouldering the two sheep, he sallied forth down the hill and away to the marshes.

He accomplished the whole of his night work before the stars had begun to fade. Then, having replenished and banked the fire, he lay down to sleep. Some four hours later he woke to go and tend the fire again, and then again slept.

XXV

It was a toilsome, lonesome, monotonous and fuliginous life that Thol had chosen; but he never faltered in it. Always at nightfall he impersonated the dragon, and in the small hours went his journeys to the marshes; and never once did he let the fire die.

The afternoons passed very slowly. He wished he could sally forth into the sunshine, like other men. He paced round and round his cave, hour after hour, a strange figure, dark-handed, dark-visaged, dark-bearded.

In so far as they deigned to remember him at all, the homelanders supposed he had gone away, that first morning, across the waters or through the forests, to some land where he could look men in the face.

Here he was, however, in their midst, a strenuous and faithful servant. He had a stern grim joy in the hardness of his life—save that he could never ask Thia to share it with him. He had not foreseen—it was the one thing he had not thought out well—how hard the life would be. The great deed by which he had thought to bring Thia back to him must forever keep them asunder. Thus he had done an even greater deed than he intended. And his stern grim joy in it was thereby the greater.

XXVI

Had she so wished, Thia might have become very popular and have regained something of her past glory. After Thol's confession of cowardice she had instantly risen in the homelanders' esteem. How very right she had been to leave him! Friendly eyes and friendly words greeted her. But when they all knelt praying the sun to call the dragon away, she remained upright and mute. And afterwards, when she was asked why, she said that it was well that the dragon should abide among them, for thus would they all be the better, in heart and deed, and therefore truly the happier, could they but know it. She said that whether or not they could know it, so it was.

These sayings of hers were taken in bad part, and she was shunned because of them. This did not mar the joy she had in knowing that all was well once more in the homeland.

She felt herself not at all unblest in the quiet spinsterly life she was leading, in and out of her trim new hut, with her dear flock of geese about her.

Of Thol, nowadays, she thought more gently. She felt that if he had stayed in the homeland she would have gone back to him. It would have been her bounden duty to be with him and to comfort him in his shame. Indeed his shame made him dear to her once more. As the days passed she thought more and more about him. It was strange that he had gone from the homeland. No homelander ever had gone forth into the perils of the lands beyond. If she herself, daughter of wanderers, had roved away instead of building this hut to dwell in, she might not have much marveled at herself, less brave though she was than Thol. And Thol was no longer brave. How had he, fearing a dragon smaller than that other, conquered his fear of known and unknown things that were worse yet, far worse yet?

And one evening a strange doubt came to her. Might it not be that Thol was still in the homeland? In one of all these dark forests he might be living, with nuts and berries to support life. Or, she further guessed, he might even be in his own cave, stealing out at night when all but the watchmen on the other side of the hill were sleeping. This notion, foolish though it seemed to her, possessed her mind.

So soon as silence and sleep had descended on the homeland, Thia herself stole out into the clear starlit night. Not far from the eastern spur of the hill she lay down in a clump of long grass, and thence, gazing up, watched the cave's mouth steadily.

XXVII

Someone presently came forth: and yes, it was Thol. Slowly he came down the hill, with his head bent forward, with his hands up to his bowed shoulders, and two burdens at his back—two goats, as Thia saw when presently Thol turned aside southward. He looked very strange. His hair and face seemed to have grown quite dark. And what was he doing with those two goats? Thia lay still, with a fast-beating heart. She felt that her voice would not have come, even had she tried to call to him.

She watched him out of sight, then rose to her feet and, hesitatingly, went to the foot of the hill, and then, quickly and resolutely, went up it and into the cave.

Quick-witted though she was, the sight of three geese and three ducks and of two sheep puzzled her deeply; and not less did she wonder at the quantity of stacked wood. And what was that fence of osiers against the wall? She moved it slightly and saw a great breach in the wall; and through this some smoke came drifting in. And now her quick wits began to work—but in such wise as to make her bewilderment the deeper.

Suddenly, drawing a deep breath, she went down on her hands and knees, and crawled, quick as a serpent, through the smoke.

She was soon back again. Blinking hard and shaking the smoke from her nostrils, she went to breathe the clear air at the cave's mouth. But, good though this air was, she hardly tasted it. She had burst out sobbing. She, who never in all her life had shed tears, sobbed much now. But she remembered that tears make people's eyes ugly. So she controlled herself and dried her eyes vigorously. She had not remembered that the palms of her hands must be all black from her crawl. When she saw them, and knew what her face must be now, she burst out laughing. And the sound made her feel very young, for it was long since she had laughed. But, as she wished to please Thol's eyes, she retired to the back of the cave and crouched where she would scarcely be seen by him when he came.

He came at last, and then, very softly, she cried out to him, "Thol!"

He, brave though he was, started violently.

"Do not look at me, O Thol! Not yet! For my face is black and would displease you. Look at me only after you have heard me. O Thol, if they said now that you were a god, almost would I believe them. But if you were a god your deed would be less great. The wonder is that you are a man, and were once mine. O Thol, forgive me, keep me here with you, need me!"

But he slowly answered, "Nay, O Thia, this cave is not now for a woman."

"Not for a woman that is your wife and lover? Think! Was it not for my sake and for love of me that you thought to do what you are doing?"

"Yea, O Thia. Yet, now that I am doing it, itself suffices me. I am strong, and suffer not under the burden of it. The very heaviness of it makes me glad. And now your knowledge of it gladdens me, too. But I would not have you bear the least part of it with me. Go to your own home!"

"You speak firmly, O great dragon! Yet will not I obey you. Tell me of your work. Is it to the marshes that you take the beasts and the birds?"

"Yea. Begone, small dear one!" And he stooped down to take the two sheep.

"Once, long ago, you wished that a lad might help you in your hard work. O Thol, I am as I was, trustier than any lad. It were better that you should go twice, not thrice, every night, to the marshes. I will always take the birds." And she rose to take them.

But a thought came to her, giving her pause. And she said, "The fire must first be tended."

"It has no need yet," he answered. "I tend it when I come back from the last journey."

"Tonight it shall be tended earlier. And I will so tend it that it shall last long." She was down on her knees and off into the smoke before he could stop her. He followed her, protesting that such work was not for her. She did it, nevertheless, very well. And presently, side by side, he with two sheep, she with three birds' necks in either fist, they went forth into the starlight, and down away to the marshes.

There, having duly sunk their burdens, they took each other by the hand, and turned homeward. At one of the running brooks on their way home, Thia halted. "Here," she said, "will I wash myself well. And do you too, O Thol, so that when we wake in the morning my face shall not displease you."

XXVIII

Every night Thia accompanied Thol on one of the two journeys; and during the other she would go to the forest and gather wood, so that there should always be plenty of fuel in hand. She was sorry to have had to abandon her geese, for she felt they would not be as happy with anyone as they had been with her. Nothing else whatever was there to mar her joy in the life that she and Thol were leading together, and in the good that they were doing. It amused her to know that the homelanders would think she had wandered away—she who was serving them so well. Its very secrecy made her life the more joyous.

Daily she prayed to the sun and other gods that she and Thol might live to be very old and might never fail in their work.

But the sun and those others were not good listeners.

As the nights lengthened and the leaves began to fall, the mists over the marshes and around them grew ever thicker. It was not easy to find the way through them; and they were very cold, and had a savor that was bitter to the tongue and to the nostrils. And one morning Thia, when she woke, was shivering from head to foot, though she was in Thol's arms. She slipped away from him without waking him, and went not merely to tend the fire but also to warm herself at it. All through the morning she was shivering; and in the evening her hands became hot, as did her face and all her body. She felt very weak. She could laugh no more now at Thol's disquietude. She lay down, but could not lie very still. At about the time when they were wont to sally forth, she rose up, feeling that even though she might not be able to carry the birds tonight the journey would freshen her. She soon found that she was too weak even to stand. Thol was very loth to leave her; but she insisted that the work must be done. Again and again, next day and during the next night, she implored him that if she died he would not mourn her very much and would not once falter in the work. He promised that he would not falter. Other days and nights passed. It seemed to Thol that Thia had ceased to know him. She did not even follow him with her eyes now. One morning, at day-break, soon after his return from the third journey, she seemed, by her gaze, to know him. But presently she died in his arms.

On that night he went to the forest and dug a grave for his wife. Then, returning to the cave, he took her in his arms for the last time, and carried her away, and buried her.

In the time that followed, he was not altogether lonely. He felt by day that somehow she was in the cave with him still, and by night he felt that she walked with him. He never faltered in the work.

He faltered not much even when the marshes did to him as they had done to Thia. Shivering in every limb, or hot and aching, and very weak, he yet forced himself to tend the fire and at nightfall to brandish the torch and clash the stones and drag in the beasts and birds. It irked him that he was not strong enough to carry even one sheep away. Surely he would be strong again soon? For Thia's sake, and for the homeland's, he wished ardently to live. But there came an evening when the watchers in the valley saw no rising and falling, heard no clashing, of the dragon's jaws.

XXIX

Would the dragon come forth tonight? The valley on the further side of the stream was now thickly crowded. On the nearer side were many single adventurers, with spears. Their prowess and skill were not tested. The dragon came not forth.

In the dawn it was noted that his smoke was far less thick than it was wont to be. Soon it ceased altogether. What had happened? Perchance the dragon was ailing? But even an ailing dragon would breathe. A great glad surmise tremulously formed itself. Was the dragon dead?

The surmise quickly became a firm belief—so firm that, in spite of protests from the precise Shib, songs of thanksgiving were heartily sung before the cave was approached and examined.

People were much puzzled. The dead man lying at the cave's mouth, grasping in one hand a flat stone and in the other a charred staff, was not instantly recognized as Thol, so black were his hair and skin; nor was he instantly recognized as the dragon. The quantities of stacked wood, the tunnel into the cave where Thol had lived, did not quickly divulge their meaning. Only after long arguments and many conjectures did the home-landers understand the trick that had been played on them. Why, with what evil intent, it had been played, they were almost too angry to discuss at present. But certain words of Thia's were remembered; and it was felt that she herself perhaps had put the trick into Thol's mind and that this was why she had fled the homeland. She had better not set foot in it again.

Before the sun sank, Thol was buried without honor, and far from Thia.

And before the sun sank many other times the homelanders were as they had been before the coming of the true dragon, and as they had been again before the false one was among them.

FINIS

And thus—does our tale end unhappily? I think not. After all, the home-landers at large are rather shadowy to us. Oc and Loga, Shib and Veo, Afa and her like, and all those others, all those nameless others, do not mean much to us. It is Thol and Thia that we care about. For their sake we wish that the good they did could have been lasting. But it is not in the nature of things that anything—except the nature of things—should last. Saints and wise statesmen can do much. Their reward is in the doing of it. They are lucky if they do not live long enough to see the undoing. It should suffice us that Thol and Thia together in their last days knew a happiness greater than they had ever known—Thol a greater happiness than in the days of his glory, and Thia than in the days of hers.

Channeled Whelk

By ANNE MORROW LINDBERGH

THE SHELL in my hand is deserted. It once housed a whelk, a snail-like creature, and then temporarily, after the death of the first occupant, a little hermit crab, who has run away, leaving his tracks behind him like a delicate vine on the sand. He ran away, and left me his shell. It was once a protection to him. I turn the shell in my hand, gazing into the wide-open door from which he made his exit. Had it become an encumbrance? Why did he run away? Did he hope to find a better home, a better mode of living? I too have run away, I realize, I have shed the shell of my life, for these few weeks of vacation.

But his shell—it is simple; it is bare, it is beautiful. Small, only the size of my thumb, its architecture is perfect, down to the finest detail. Its shape, swelling like a pear in the center, winds in a gentle spiral to the pointed apex. Its color, dull gold, is whitened by a wash of salt from the sea. Each whorl, each faint knob, each crisscross vein in its egg-shell texture, is as clearly defined as on the day of creation. My eye follows with delight the outer circumference of that diminutive winding staircase up which this tenant used to travel.

My shell is not like this, I think. How untidy it has become! Blurred with moss, knobby with barnacles, its shape is hardly recognizable any more. Surely, it had a shape once. It has a shape still in my mind. What is the shape of my life?

The shape of my life today starts with a family. I have a husband, five children and a home just beyond the suburbs of New York. I have also a craft, writing, and therefore work I want to pursue. The shape of my life is, of course, determined by many other things; my background and childhood, my mind and its education, my conscience and its pressures, my heart and its desires. I want to give and take from my children and husband, to share with friends and community, to carry out my obligations to man and to the world, as a woman, as an artist, as a citizen.

But I want first of all—in fact, as an end to these other desires—to be at peace with myself. I want a singleness of eye, a purity of intention, a central core to my life that will enable me to carry out these obligations and activities as well as I can. I want, in fact—to borrow from the language of the saints—to live "in grace" as much of the time as possible. I am not using this term in a strictly theological sense. By grace I mean an inner harmony, essentially spiritual, which can be translated into outward harmony. I am seeking perhaps what Socrates asked for in the prayer from the *Phaedrus* when he said, "May the outward and inward man be at one." I would like to achieve a state of inner spiritual grace from which I could function and give as I was meant to in the eye of God.

Vague as this definition may be, I believe most people are aware of periods in their lives when they seem to be "in grace" and other periods when they feel "out of grace," even though they may use different words to describe these states. In the first happy condition, one seems to carry all one's tasks before one lightly, as if borne along on a great tide; and in the opposite state one can hardly tie a shoestring. It is true that a large part of life consists in learning a technique of tying the shoestring, whether one is in grace or not. But there are techniques of living too; there are even techniques in the search for grace. And techniques can be cultivated. I have learned by some experience, by many examples, and by the writings of countless others before me, also occupied in the search, that certain environments, certain modes of life, certain rules of conduct are more conductive to inner and outer harmony than others. There are, in fact, certain roads that one may follow. Simplification of life is one of them.

I mean to lead a simple life, to choose a simple shell I can carry easily—like a hermit crab. But I do not. I find that my frame of life does not foster simplicity. My husband and five children must make their way in the world. The life I have chosen as wife and mother entrains a whole caravan of complications. It involves a house in the suburbs and either household drudgery or household help which wavers between scarcity and non-existence for most of us. It involves food and shelter; meals, planning, marketing, bills, and making the ends meet in a thousand ways. It involves not only the butcher, the baker, the candlestickmaker but countless other experts to keep my modern house with its modern "simplifications" (electricity, plumbing, refrigerator, gas-stove, oil burner, dishwasher, radios, car, and numerous other labor-saving devices) functioning properly. It involves health; doctors, dentists, appointments, medicine, cod-liver oil, vitamins, trips to the drugstore. It involves education, spiritual, intellectual, physical; schools, school conferences, car pools, extra trips for basketball or orchestra practice; tutoring; camps, camp equipment and transportation. It involves clothes, shopping, laundry, cleaning, mending, letting skirts down and sewing buttons on, or finding someone else to do it. It involves friends, my husband's, my children's, my own, and endless arrangements to get together; letters, invitations, telephone calls and transportation hither and yon.

For life today in America is based on the premise of ever-widening circles of contact and communication. It involves not only family demands, but community demands, national demands, international demands on the good citizen, through social and cultural pressures, through newspapers, magazines, radio programs, political drives, charitable appeals, and so on. My mind reels with it. What a circus act we women perform every day of our lives. It puts the trapeze artist to shame. Look at us. We run a tight rope daily, balancing a pile of books on the head. Baby carriage, parasol, kitchen chair, still under control. Steady now!

This is not the life of simplicity but the life of multiplicity that the wise men warn us of. It leads not to unification but to fragmentation. It does not bring grace; it destroys the soul. And this is not only true of my life, I am forced to conclude; it is the life of millions of women in America. I stress America, because today, the American woman more than any other has the privilege of choosing such a life. Woman in large parts of the civilized world has been forced back by war, by poverty, by collapse, by the sheer struggle to survive, into a smaller circle of immediate time and space, immediate family life, immediate problems of existence. The American woman is still relatively free to choose the wider life. How long she will hold this enviable and precarious position no one knows. But her particular situation has a significance far above its apparent economic, national or even sex limitations.

For the problem of the multiplicity of life not only confronts the American woman, but also the American man. And it is not merely the concern of the American as such, but of our whole modern civilization, since life in America today is held up as the ideal of a large part of the rest of the world. And finally, it is not limited to our present civilization, though we are faced with it now in an exaggerated form. It has always been one of the pitfalls of mankind. Plotinus was preaching the dangers of multiplicity of the world back in the third century. Yet, the problem is particularly and essentially woman's. Distraction is, always has been, and probably always will be, inherent in woman's life.

For to be a woman is to have interests and duties, raying out in all directions from the central mother-core, like spokes from the hub of a wheel. The pattern of our lives is essentially circular. We must be open to all points of the compass; husband, children, friends, home, community; stretched out, exposed, sensitive like a spider's web to each breeze that blows, to each call that comes. How difficult for us, then, to achieve a balance in the midst of these contradictory tensions, and yet how necessary for the proper functioning of our lives. How much we need, and how arduous of attainment is that steadiness preached in all rules for holy living. How desirable and how distant is the ideal of the contemplative, artist, or saint—the inner inviolable core, the single eye.

With a new awareness, both painful and humorous, I begin to understand why the saints were rarely married women. I am convinced it has nothing inherently to do, as I once supposed, with chastity or children. It has to do primarily with distractions. The bearing, rearing, feeding and educating of children; the running of a house with its thousand details; human relationships with their myriad pulls—woman's normal occupations in general run counter to creative life, or contemplative life, or saintly life. The problem is not merely one of *Woman and Career, Woman and the Home, Woman and Independence*. It is more basically: how to remain whole in the midst of the distractions of life; how to remain balanced, no matter what centrifugal forces tend to pull one off center; how to remain strong, no matter what shocks come in at the periphery and tend to crack the hub of the wheel.

What is the answer? There is no easy answer, no complete answer. I have only clues, shells from the sea. The bare beauty of the channeled whelk tells me that one answer, and perhaps a first step, is in simplification of life, in cutting out some of the distractions. But how? Total retirement is not possible. I cannot shed my responsibilities. I cannot permanently inhabit a desert island. I cannot be a nun in the midst of family life. I would not want to be. The solution for me, surely, is neither in total renunciation of the world, nor in total acceptance of it. I must find a balance somewhere, or an alternating rhythm between these two extremes; a swinging of the pendulum between solitude and communion, between retreat and return. In my periods of retreat, perhaps I can learn something to carry back into my worldly life. I can at least practice for these two weeks the simplification of outward life, as a beginning. I can follow this superficial clue, and see where it leads. Here, in beach living, I can try.

One learns first of all in beach living the art of shedding; how little one can get along with, not how much. Physical shedding to begin with, which then mysteriously spreads into other fields. Clothes, first. Of course, one needs less in the sun. But one needs less anyway, one finds suddenly. One does not need a closet-full, only a small suitcase-full. And what a relief it is! Less taking up and down of hems, less mending, and—best of all—less worry about what to wear. One finds one is shedding not only clothes—but vanity.

Next, shelter. One does not need the airtight shelter one has in winter in the North. Here I live in a bare seashell of a cottage. No heat, no telephone, no plumbing to speak of, no hot water, a two-burner oil stove, no gadgets to go wrong. No rugs. There were some, but I rolled them up the first day; it is easier to sweep the sand off a bare floor. But I find I don't bustle about with unnecessary sweeping and cleaning here. I am no longer aware of the dust. I have shed my Puritan conscience about absolute tidiness and cleanliness. Is it possible that, too, is a material burden? No curtains. I do not need them for privacy; the pines around my house are enough protection. I want the windows open all the time, and I don't want to worry about rain. I begin to shed my Martha-like anxiety about many things. Washable slipcovers, faded and old—I hardly see them; I don't worry about the impression they make on other people. I am shedding pride. As little furniture as possible; I shall not need much. I shall ask into my shell only those friends with whom I can be completely honest. I find I am shedding hypocrisy in human relationships. What a rest that will be! The most exhausting thing in life, I have discovered, is being insincere. That is why so much of social life is exhausting; one is wearing a mask. I have shed my mask.

I find I live quite happily without those things I think necessary in winter in the North. And as I write these words, I remember, with some shock at the disparity in our lives, a similar statement made by a friend of mine in France who spent three years in a German prison camp. Of course, he said, qualifying his remark, they did not get enough to eat, they were sometimes atrociously treated, they had little physical freedom. And yet, prison life taught him how little one can get along with, and what extraordinary spiritual freedom and peace such simplification can bring. I remember again, ironically, that today more of us in America than anywhere else in the world have the luxury of choice between simplicity and complication of life. And for the most part, we, who could choose simplicity, choose complication. War, prison, survival periods, enforce a form of simplicity on man. The monk and the nun choose it of their own free will. But if one accidentally finds it, as I have for a few days, one finds also the serenity it brings.

Is it not rather ugly, one may ask? One collects material possessions not only for security, comfort or vanity, but for beauty as well. Is your sea-shell house not ugly and bare? No, it is beautiful, my house. It is bare, of course, but the wind, the sun, the smell of the pines blow through its bareness. The unfinished beams in the roof are veiled by cobwebs. They are lovely, I think, gazing up at them with new eyes; they soften the hard lines of the rafters as gray hairs soften the lines on a middle-aged face. I no longer pull out gray hairs or sweep down cobwebs. As for the walls, it is true they looked forbidding at first. I felt cramped and enclosed by their blank faces. I wanted to knock holes in them, to give them another dimension with pictures or windows. So I dragged home from the beach gray arms of driftwood, worn satin-smooth by wind and sand. I gathered trailing green vines with floppy red-tipped leaves. I picked up the whitened skeletons of conchshells, their curious hollowed-out shapes faintly reminiscent of abstract sculpture. With these tacked to walls and propped up in corners, I am satisfied. I have a periscope out to the world. I have a window, a view, a point of flight from my sedentary base

I am content. I sit down at my desk, a bare kitchen table with a blotter, a bottle of ink, a sand dollar to weight down one corner, a clam shell for a pen tray, the broken tip of a conch, pink-tinged, to finger, and a row of shells to set my thoughts spinning.

I love my sea shell of a house. I wish I could live in it always. I wish I could transport it home. But I cannot. It will not hold a husband, five children and the necessities and trappings of daily life. I can only carry back my little channeled whelk. It will sit on my desk in Connecticut, to remind me of the ideal of a simplified life, to encourage me in the game I played on the beach. To ask how little, not how much, can I get along with. To say—is it necessary?—when I am tempted to add one more accumulation to my life, when I am pulled toward one more centrifugal activity.

Simplification of outward life is not enough. It is merely the outside. But I am starting with the outside. I am looking at the outside of a shell, the outside of my life—the shell. The complete answer is not to be found on the outside, in an outward mode of living. This is only a technique, a road to grace. The final answer, I know, is always inside. But the outside can give a clue, can help one to find the inside answer. One is free, like the hermit crab, to change one's shell.

Channeled whelk, I put you down again, but you have set my mind on a journey, up an inwardly winding spiral staircase of thought.

By the Waters of Babylon

By STEPHEN VINCENT BENÉT

THE NORTH and the west and the south are good hunting ground, but it is forbidden to go east. It is forbidden to go to any of the Dead Places except to search for metal and then he who touches the metal must be a priest or the son of a priest. Afterward, both the man and the metal must be purified. These are the rules and the laws; they are well made. It is forbidden, to cross the great rivers and look upon the place that was the Place of the Gods—this is most strictly forbidden. We do not even say its name though we know its name. It is there that spirits live, and demons—it is there that there are the ashes of the Great Burning. These things are forbidden—they have been forbidden since the beginning of time.

My father is a priest; I am the son of a priest. I have been in the Dead Places near us, with my father—at first, I was afraid. When my father went into the house to search for the metal, I stood by the door and my heart felt small and weak. It was a dead man's house, a spirit house. It did not have the smell of man, though there were old bones in a corner. But it is not fitting that a priest's son should show fear. I looked at the bones in the shadow and kept my voice still.

Then my father came out with the metal—a good, strong piece. He looked at me with both eyes but I had not run away. He gave me the metal to hold—I took it and did not die. So he knew that I was truly his son and would be a priest in my time.That was when I was very young— nevertheless, my brothers would not have done it, though they are good hunters. After that, they gave me the good piece of meat and the warm corner by the fire. My father watched over me—he was glad that I should be a priest. But when I boasted or wept without a reason, he punished me more strictly than my brothers. That was right.

After a time, I myself was allowed to go into the dead houses and search for metal. So I learned the ways of those houses—and if I saw bones, I was no longer afraid. The bones are light and old—sometimes they will fall into dust if you touch them. But that is a great sin.

I was taught the chants and the spells—I was taught how to stop the

From *Selected Works of Stephen Vincent Benét* published by Rinehart & Co. Copyright 1937 by Stephen Vincent Benét.

running of blood from a wound and many secrets. A priest must know many secrets—that was what my father said. If the hunters think we do all things by chants and spells, they may believe so—it does not hurt them. I was taught how to read in the old books and how to make the old writings—that was hard and took a long time. My knowledge made me happy—it was like a fire in my heart. Most of all, I liked to hear of the Old Days and the stories of the gods. I asked myself many questions that I could not answer, but it was good to ask them. At night, I would lie awake and listen to the wind—it seemed to me that it was the voice of the gods as they flew through the air.

We are not ignorant like the Forest People—our women spin wool on the wheel, our priests wear a white robe. We do not eat grubs from the tree, we have not forgotten the old writings, although they are hard to understand. Nevertheless, my knowledge and my lack of knowledge burned in me—I wished to know more. When I was a man at last, I came to my father and said, "It is time for me to go on my journey. Give me your leave."

He looked at me for a long time, stroking his beard, then he said at last, "Yes. It is time." That night, in the house of the priesthood, I asked for and received purification. My body hurt but my spirit was a cool stone. It was my father himself who questioned me about my dreams.

He bade me look into the smoke of the fire and see—I saw and told what I saw. It was what I have always seen—a river, and, beyond it, a great Dead Place and in it the gods walking. I have always thought about that. His eyes were stern when I told him—he was no longer my father but a priest. He said, "This is a strong dream."

"It is mine," I said, while the smoke waved and my head felt light. They were singing the Star song in the outer chamber and it was like the buzzing of bees in my head.

He asked me how the gods were dressed and I told him how they were dressed. We know how they were dressed from the book, but I saw them as if they were before me. When I had finished, he threw the sticks three times and studied them as they fell.

"This is a very strong dream," he said. "It may eat you up."

"I am not afraid," I said and looked at him with both eyes. My voice sounded thin in my ears but that was because of the smoke.

He touched me on the breast and the forehead. He gave me the bow and the three arrows.

"Take them," he said. "It is forbidden to travel east. It is forbidden to cross the river. It is forbidden to go to the Place of the Gods. All these things are forbidden."

"All these things are forbidden," I said, but it was my voice that spoke and not my spirit. He looked at me again.

"My son," he said. "Once I had young dreams. If your dreams do not eat you up, you may be a great priest. If they eat you, you are still my son. Now go on your journey."

I went fasting, as is the law. My body hurt but not my heart. When the dawn came, I was out of sight of the village. I prayed and purified myself, waiting for a sign. The sign was an eagle. It flew east.

Sometimes signs are sent by bad spirits. I waited again on the flat rock, fasting, taking no food. I was very still—I could feel the sky above me and the earth beneath. I waited till the sun was beginning to sink. Then three deer passed in the valley, going east—they did not wind me or see me. There was a white fawn with them—a very great sign.

I followed them, at a distance, waiting for what would happen. My heart was troubled about going east, yet I knew that I must go. My head hummed with my fasting—I did not even see the panther spring upon the white fawn. But, before I knew it, the bow was in my hand. I shouted and the panther lifted his head from the fawn. It is not easy to kill a panther with one arrow but the arrow went through his eye and into his brain. He died as he tried to spring—he rolled over, tearing at the ground. Then I knew I was meant to go east—I knew that was my journey. When the night came, I made my fire and roasted meat.

It is eight suns' journey to the east and a man passes by many Dead Places. The Forest People are afraid of them but I am not. Once I made my fire on the edge of a Dead Place at night and, next morning, in the dead house, I found a good knife, little rusted. That was small to what came afterward but it made my heart feel big. Always when I looked for game, it was in front of my arrow, and twice I passed hunting parties of the Forest People without their knowing. So I knew my magic was strong and my journey clean, in spite of the law.

Toward the setting of the eighth sun, I came to the banks of the great river. It was half a day's journey after I had left the god-road—we do not use the god-roads now for they are falling apart into great blocks of stone, and the forest is safer going. A long way off, I had seen the water through trees but the trees were thick. At last, I came out upon an open place at the top of a cliff. There was the great river below, like a giant in the sun. It is very long, very wide. It could eat all the streams we know and still be thirsty. Its name is Ou-dis-sun, the Sacred, the Long. No man of my tribe had seen it, not even my father, the priest. It was magic and I prayed.

Then I raised my eyes and looked south. It was there, the Place of the Gods.

How can I tell what it was like—you do not know. It was there, in the red light, and they were too big to be houses. It was there with the red light upon it, mighty and ruined. I knew that in another moment the gods would see me. I covered my eyes with my hands and crept back into the forest.

Surely, that was enough to do, and live. Surely it was enough to spend the night upon the cliff. The Forest People themselves do not come near. Yet, all through the night, I knew that I should have to cross the river and walk in the Places of the Gods, although the gods ate me up. My magic did not help me at all and yet there was a fire in my bowels, a fire in my mind. When the sun rose, I thought, "My journey has been clean. Now I will go home from my journey." But, even as I thought so, I knew I could not. If I went to the Place of the Gods, I would surely die, but, if I did not go, I could never be at peace with my spirit again. It is better to lose one's life than one's spirit, if one is a priest and the son of a priest.

Nevertheless, as I made the raft, the tears ran out of my eyes. The Forest People could have killed me without fight, if they had come upon me then, but they did not come. When the raft was made, I said the sayings for the dead and painted myself for death. My heart was cold as a frog and my knees like water, but the burning in my mind would not let me have peace. As I pushed the raft from the shore, I began my death song—I had the right. It was a fine song.

"I am John, son of John," I sang. "My people are the Hill People. They are the men.
I go into the Dead Places but I am not slain.
I take the metal from the Dead Places but I am not blasted.
I travel upon the god-roads and am not afraid. E-yah! I have killed the panther, I have killed the fawn!
E-yah! I have come to the great river. No man has come there before.
It is forbidden to go east, but I have gone, forbidden to go on the great river, but I am there.
Open your hearts, you spirits, and hear my song.
Now I go to the Place of the Gods, I shall not return.
My body is painted for death and my limbs weak, but my heart is big as I go to the Place of the Gods!"

All the same, when I came to the Place of the Gods, I was afraid, afraid. The current of the great river is very strong—it gripped my raft with its hands. That was magic, for the river itself is wide and calm. I could feel evil spirits about me, in the bright morning; I could feel their breath on my neck as I was swept down the stream. Never have I been so much alone—I tried to think of my knowledge, but it was a squirrel's heap of winter nuts. There was no strength in my knowledge any more and I felt small and naked as a new-hatched bird—alone upon the great river, the servant of the gods.

Yet, after a while, my eyes were opened and I saw. I saw both banks of the river—I saw that once there had been god-roads across it, though now they were broken and fallen like broken vines. Very great they were, and wonderful and broken—broken in the time of the Great Burning when the fire fell out of the sky. And always the current took me nearer to the Place of the Gods, and the huge ruins rose before my eyes.

I do not know the customs of rivers—we are the People of the Hills. I tried to guide my raft with the pole but it spun around. I thought the river meant to take me past the Place of the Gods and out into the Bitter Water of the legends. I grew angry then—my heart felt strong. I said aloud, "I am a priest and the son of a priest!" The gods heard me—they showed me how to paddle with the pole on one side of the raft. The current changed itself—I drew near to the Place of the Gods.

When I was very near, my raft struck and turned over. I can swim in our lakes—I swam to the shore. There was a great spike of rusted metal sticking out into the river—I hauled myself up upon it and sat there, panting. I had saved my bow and two arrows and the knife I found in the Dead Place but that was all. My raft went whirling downstream toward the Bitter Water. I looked after it, and thought if it had trod me under, at least I would be safely dead. Nevertheless, when I had dried my bowstring and restrung it, I walked forward to the Place of the Gods.

It felt like ground underfoot; it did not burn me. It is not true what some of the tales say, that the ground there burns forever, for I have been there. Here and there were the marks and stains of the Great Burning, on the ruins, that is true. But they were old marks and old stains. It is not true either, what some of our priests say, that it is an island covered with fogs and enchantments. It is not. It is a great Dead Place—greater than any Dead Place we know. Everywhere in it there are god-roads, though most are cracked and broken. Everywhere there are the ruins of the high towers of the gods.

How shall I tell what I saw? I went carefully, my strung bow in my hand, my skin ready for danger. There should have been the wailings of spirits and the shrieks of demons, but there were not. It was very silent and sunny where I had landed—the wind and the rain and the birds that drop seeds had done their work—the grass grew in the cracks of the broken stone. It is a fair island—no wonder the gods built there. If I had come there, a god, I also would have built.

How shall I tell what I saw? The towers are not all broken—here and there one still stands, like a great tree in a forest, and the birds nest high. But the towers themselves look blind, for the gods are gone. I saw a fish-hawk, catching fish in the river. I saw a little dance of white butterflies over a great heap of broken stones and columns. I went there and looked about me—there was a carved stone with cut letters, broken in half. I can read letters but I could not understand these. They said UBTREAS. There was also the shattered image of a man or a god. It had been made of white stone and he wore his hair tied back like a woman's. His name was ASHING, as I read on the cracked half of a stone. I thought it wise to pray to ASHING, though I do not know that god.

How shall I tell what I saw? There was no smell of man left, on stone or metal. Nor were there many trees in that wilderness of stone. There are many pigeons, nesting and dropping in the towers—the gods must have loved them, or, perhaps, they used them for sacrifices. There are wild cats that roam the god-roads, green-eyed, unafraid of man. At night they wail like demons but they are not demons. The wild dogs are more dangerous, for they hunt in a pack, but them I did not meet till later. Everywhere there are the carved stones, carved with magical numbers or words.

I went north—I did not try to hide myself. When a god or a demon saw me, then I would die, but meanwhile I was no longer afraid. My hunger for knowledge burned in me—there was so much that I could not understand. After a while, I knew that my belly was hungry. I could have hunted for my meat, but I did not hunt. It is known that the gods did not hunt as we do—they got their food from enchanted boxes and jars. Sometimes these are still found in the Dead Places—once, when I was a child and foolish, I opened such a jar and tasted it and found the food sweet. But my father found out and punished me for it strictly, for, often, that food is death. Now, though, I had long gone past what was forbidden, and I entered the likeliest towers, looking for the food of the gods.

I found it at last in the ruins of a great temple in the mid-city. A mighty temple it must have been, for the roof was painted like the sky at night with its stars—that much I could see, though the colors were faint and dim. It went down into great caves and tunnels—perhaps they kept their slaves there. But when I started to climb down, I heard the squeaking of rats, so I did not go—rats are unclean, and there must have been many tribes of them, from the squeaking. But near there, I found food, in the heart of a ruin, behind a door that still opened. I ate only the fruits from the jars—they had a very sweet taste. There was drink, too, in bottles of glass—the drink of the gods was strong and made my head swim. After I had eaten and drunk, I slept on the top of a stone, my bow at my side.

When I woke, the sun was low. Looking down from where I lay, I saw a dog sitting on his haunches. His tongue was hanging out of his mouth; he looked as if he were laughing. He was a big dog, with a gray-brown coat, as big as a wolf. I sprang up and shouted at him but he did not move—he just sat there as if he were laughing. I did not like that. When I reached for a stone to throw, he moved swiftly out of the way of the stone. He was not afraid of me; he looked at me as if I were meat. No doubt I could have killed him with an arrow, but I did not know if there were others. Moreover, night was falling.

I looked about me—not far away there was a great, broken god-road, leading north. The towers were high enough, but not so high, and while

many of the dead-houses were wrecked, there were some that stood. I
went toward this god-road, keeping to the heights of the ruins, while the
dog followed. When I had reached the god-road, I saw that there were
others behind him. If I had slept later, they would have come upon me
asleep and torn out my throat. As it was, they were sure enough of me;
they did not hurry. When I went into the dead-house, they kept watch
at the entrance—doubtless they thought they would have a fine hunt.
But a dog cannot open a door and I knew, from the books, that the gods
did not like to live on the ground but on high.

I had just found a door I could open when the dogs decided to rush.
Ha! They were surprised when I shut the door in their faces—it was a
good door, of strong metal. I could hear their foolish baying beyond it
but I did not stop to answer them. I was in darkness—I found stairs and
climbed. There were many stairs, turning around till my head was dizzy.
At the top was another door—I found the knob and opened it. I was in
a long small chamber—on one side of it was a bronze door that could not
be opened, for it had no handle. Perhaps there was a magic word to open
it but I did not have the word. I turned to the door in the opposite side
of the wall. The lock of it was broken and I opened it and went in.

Within, there was a place of great riches. The god who lived there
must have been a powerful god. The first room was a small anteroom—I
waited there for some time, telling the spirits of the place that I came in
peace and not as a robber. When it seemed to me that they had had time
to hear me, I went on. Ah, what riches! Few, even, of the windows had
been broken—it was all as it had been. The great windows that looked
over the city had not been broken at all though they were dusty and
streaked with many years. There were coverings on the floors, the colors
not greatly faded, and the chairs were soft and deep. There were pictures
upon the walls, very strange, very wonderful—I remember one of a
bunch of flowers in a jar—if you came close to it, you could see nothing
but bits of color, but if you stood away from it, the flowers might have
been picked yesterday. It made my heart feel strange to look at this
picture—and to look at the figure of a bird, in some hard clay, on a table
and see it so like our birds. Everywhere there were books and writings,
many in tongues that I could not read. The god who lived there must
have been a wise god and full of knowledge. I felt I had right there, as I
sought knowledge also.

Nevertheless, it was strange. There was a washing place but no water—
perhaps the gods washed in air. There was a cooking place but no wood,
and though there was a machine to cook food, there was no place to put
fire in it. Nor were there candles or lamps—there were things that looked
like lamps but they had neither oil nor wick. All these things were magic,
but I touched them and lived—the magic had gone out of them. Let me
tell one thing to show. In the washing place, a thing said "Hot" but it was

not hot to the touch—another thing said "Cold" but it was not cold. This must have been a strong magic but the magic was gone. I do not understand—they had ways—I wish that I knew.

It was close and dry and dusty in their house of the gods. I have said the magic was gone but that is not true—it had gone from the magic things but it had not gone from the place. I felt the spirits about me, weighing upon me. Nor had I ever slept in a Dead Place before—and yet, tonight, I must sleep there. When I thought of it, my tongue felt dry in my throat, in spite of my wish for knowledge. Almost I would have gone down again and faced the dogs, but I did not.

I had not gone through all the rooms when the darkness fell. When it fell, I went back to the big room looking over the city and made fire. There was a place to make fire and a box with wood in it, though I do not think they cooked there. I wrapped myself in a floor covering and slept in front of the fire—I was very tired.

Now I tell what is very strong magic. I woke in the midst of the night. When I woke, the fire had gone out and I was cold. It seemed to me that all around me there were whisperings and voices. I closed my eyes to shut them out. Some will say that I slept again, but I do not think that I slept. I could feel the spirits drawing my spirit out of my body as a fish is drawn on a line.

Why should I lie about it? I am a priest and the son of a priest. If there are spirits, as they say, in the small Dead Places near us, what spirits must there not be in that great Place of the Gods? And would not they wish to speak? After such long years? I know that I felt myself drawn as a fish is drawn on a line. I had stepped out of my body—I could see my body asleep in front of the cold fire, but it was not I. I was drawn to look out upon the city of the gods.

It should have been dark, for it was night, but it was not dark. Everywhere there were lights—lines of light—circles and blurs of light—ten thousand torches would not have been the same. The sky itself was alight —you could barely see the stars for the glow in the sky. I thought to myself, "This is strong magic," and trembled. There was a roaring in my ears like the rushing of rivers. Then my eyes grew used to the light and my ears to the sound. I knew that I was seeing the city as it had been when the gods were alive.

That was a sight indeed—yes, that was a sight: I could not have seen it in the body—my body would have died. Everywhere went the gods, on foot and in chariots—there were gods beyond number and counting and their chariots blocked the streets. They had turned night to day for their pleasure—they did not sleep with the sun. The noise of their coming and going was the noise of many waters. It was magic what they could do—it was magic what they did.

I looked out of another window—the great vines of their bridges were mended and the god-roads went east and west. Restless, restless, were the gods and always in motion! They burrowed tunnels under rivers—they flew in the air. With unbelievable tools they did giant works—no part of the earth was safe from them, for if they wished for a thing, they summoned it from the other side of the world. And always, as they labored and rested, as they feasted and made love, there was a drum in their ears—the pulse of the giant city, beating and beating like a man's heart.

Were they happy? What is happiness to the gods? They were great, they were mighty, they were wonderful and terrible. As I looked upon them and their magic, I felt like a child—but a little more, it seemed to me, and they would pull down the moon from the sky. I saw them with wisdom beyond wisdom and knowledge beyond knowledge. And yet not all they did was well done—even I could see that—and yet their wisdom could not but grow until all was peace.

Then I saw their fate come upon them and that was terrible past speech. It came upon them as they walked the streets of their city. I have been in the fights with the Forest People—I have seen men die. But this was not like that. When gods war with gods, they use weapons we do not know. It was fire falling out of the sky and a mist that poisoned. It was the time of the Great Burning and the Destruction. They ran about like ants in the streets of their city—poor gods, poor gods! Then the towers began to fall. A few escaped—yes, a few. The legends tell it. But, even after the city had become a Dead Place, for many years the poison was still in the ground. I saw it happen, I saw the last of them die. It was darkness over the broken city and I wept.

All this, I saw. I saw it as I have told it, though not in the body. When I woke in the morning, I was hungry, but I did not think first of my hunger for my heart was perplexed and confused. I knew the reason for the Dead Places but I did not see why it had happened. It seemed to me it should not have happened, with all the magic they had. I went through the house looking for an answer. There was so much in the house I could not understand—and yet I am a priest and the son of a priest. It was like being on one side of the great river, at night, with no light to show the way.

Then I saw the dead god. He was sitting in his chair, by the window, in a room I had not entered before and, for the first moment, I thought that he was alive. Then I saw the skin on the back of his hand—it was like dry leather. The room was shut, hot and dry—no doubt that had kept him as he was. At first I was afraid to approach him—then the fear left me. He was sitting looking out over the city—he was dressed in the clothes of the gods. His age was neither young nor old—I could not tell his age. But there was wisdom in his face and great sadness. You could see that he would have not run away. He had sat at his window, watching his city die—then he himself had died. But it is better to lose one's life than one's spirit—and you could see from the face that his spirit had not been lost. I knew that, if I touched him, he would fall into dust—and yet, there was something unconquered in the face.

That is all of my story, for then I knew he was a man—I knew then that they had been men, neither gods nor demons. It is a great knowledge, hard to tell and believe. They were men—they went a dark road, but they were men. I had no fear after that—I had no fear going home, though twice I fought off the dogs and once I was hunted for two days by the Forest People. When I saw my father again, I prayed and was purified. He touched my lips and my breast, he said, "You went away a boy. You come back a man and a priest." I said, "Father, they were men! I have been in the Place of the Gods and seen it! Now slay me, if it is the law— but still I know they were men."

He looked at me out of both eyes. He said, "The law is not always the same shape—you have done what you have done. I could not have done it in my time, but you come after me. Tell!"

I told and he listened. After that, I wished to tell all the people but he showed me otherwise. He said, "Truth is a hard deer to hunt. If you eat too much truth at once, you may die of the truth. It was not idly that our fathers forbade the Dead Places." He was right—it is better the truth should come little by little. I have learned that, being a priest. Perhaps, in the old days, they ate knowledge too fast.

Nevertheless, we make a beginning. It is not for the metal alone we go to the Dead Places now—there are the books and the writings. They are hard to learn. And the magic tools are broken—but we can look at them and wonder. At least, we make a beginning. And, when I am chief priest we shall go beyond the great river. We shall go to the Place of the Gods— the place newyork—not one man but a company. We shall look for the images of the gods and find the god ASHING and the others—the gods Lincoln and Biltmore and Moses. But they were men who built the city, not gods or demons. They were men. I remember the dead man's face. They were men who were here before us. We must build again.

George Meredith's *The Ordeal of Richard Feverel* was published in 1859; Irwin Shaw's *The Young Lions* in 1948. The memorable chapters from these books reprinted here both treat of love in bloom, but what a startling contrast there is between the leisurely tempo and muted grace of romance in the peaceful England of Victorian days and the compulsive, feverish haste necessarily displayed by young lovers caught in the meshes of World War Two!

Do you, like myself, remember exactly where and when you first read the books you cherish most? *The Ordeal of Richard Feverel* was required reading in a freshman English course I took under Professor Harrison Steeves. This was the man who persuaded me that Meredith, Hardy, Wells, and Galsworthy had infinitely more to offer me than the sports stories in *Popular* and *Top Notch* Magazines, and I shall never stop blessing him. I loved the chapter, "A Diversion Played on a Penny Whistle" so much that I read it aloud to a Columbia football squad—which was shellacked by Williams the next afternoon, something like 20 to o.

I tore through the galleys of Irwin Shaw's *The Young Lions,* rooted beside the swimming pool at Moss Hart's Bucks County estate in 1948, oblivious to the party going on inside, although the guest list was the stuff dreams—and Hollywood super-epics—are made of.

Rereading these chapters in the cold light of the present day, I feel that my first enthusiasm, in both instances, was amply justified.

ED.

A Diversion Played on a
Penny Whistle

By GEORGE MEREDITH

AWAY with Systems! Away with a corrupt World! Let us breathe the air of the Enchanted Island!

Golden lie the meadows: golden run the streams: red gold is on the pine stems. The Sun is coming down to Earth, and walks the fields and the waters.

The sun is coming down to Earth, and the fields and the waters shout to him golden shouts. He comes, and his heralds run before him, and

From *The Ordeal of Richard Feverel* by George Meredith.

touch the leaves of oaks, and planes, and beeches, lucid green, and the pine stems redder gold; leaving brightest footprints upon thickly weeded banks, where the foxglove's last upper bells incline, and bramble shoots wander amid moist rich herbage. The plumes of the woodland are alight; and beyond them, over the open, 'tis a race with the long-thrown shadows; a race across the heaths and up the hills, till, at the farthest bourne of mounted eastern cloud, the heralds of the sun lay rosy fingers, and rest.

Sweet are the shy recesses of the woodland. The ray treads softly there. A film athwart the pathway quivers many-hued against purple shade fragrant with warm pines, deep moss beds, feathery ferns. The little brown squirrel drops tail, and leaps: the inmost bird is startled to a chance tuneless note. From silence into silence things move.

Peeps of the reveling splendor above, and around, enliven the conscious full heart within. The flaming West, the crimson heights, shower their glories through voluminous leafage. But these are bowers where deep bliss dwells, imperial joy, that owes no fealty to yonder glories in which the young lamb gambols, and the spirits of men are glad. Descend, Great Radiance! embrace Creation with beneficent fire, and pass from us! You, and the vice-regal Light that succeeds to you, and all heavenly pageants, are the ministers and the slaves of the throbbing Content within.

For this is the home of the Enchantment. Here, secluded from vexed shores, the Prince and Princess of the Island meet; here like darkling nightingales they sit, and into eyes, and ears, and hands, pour endless ever-fresh treasures of their souls.

Roll on, grinding wheels of the world: cries of ships going down in a calm; groans of a System which will not know its rightful hour of exultation; complain to the Universe. You are not heard here.

He calls her by her name, Lucy: and she, blushing at her great boldness, has called him by his, Richard. Those two names are the keynotes of the wonderful harmonies the Angels sing aloft.

"Lucy! my beloved!"

"O Richard!"

Keynotes of the harmonies Earth even now revolves to, shadowing slowly to its bright-eyed kindred.

Out in the world there, on the skirts of the woodland, a sheep-boy pipes to meditative Eve on a penny whistle.

Love's musical Instrument is as old, and as poor; it has but two stops; and yet, you see, the Cunning Musician does thus much with it!

Other speech they have little; light foam playing upon waves of feeling, and of feeling compact, that bursts only when the sweeping volume is too wild, and is no more than their sigh of tenderness spoken.

Perhaps Love played his tune so well, because their natures had unblunted edges, and were keen for bliss, confiding in it as natural food.

To gentlemen and ladies he fine-draws upon the viol, ravishingly; or blows into the mellow bassoon; or rouses the heroic ardors of the trumpet; or, it may be, commands the whole Orchestra for them. And they are pleased. He is still the Cunning Musician. They languish, and taste ecstasy: but it is, however sonorous, an earthly concert. For them the spheres move not to Two Notes. They have lost, or forfeited and never known, the first supersensual spring of the ripe senses into passion; when they carry the soul with them, and have the privileges of spirits to walk disembodied, boundlessly to feel. Or one has it, and the other is a dead body! Ambrosia let them eat, and drink the Nectar: here sit a couple to whom Love's simple Bread and Water is a finer feast.

Pipe, happy sheep-boy, Love! Irradiated Angels, unfold your wings and lift your voices!

They have outflown Philosophy. Their Instinct has shot beyond the ken of Science. Imperiously they know we were made for this Eden: and would you gainsay them who are outside the Gates, and argue from the Fall?

"And this divine Gift was in store for me!"

So runs the internal outcry of each, clasping each: their recurring refrain to the harmonies. How it illumined the years gone by, and suffused the living Future!

"You for me: I for you!"

"We are born for each other!"

They believe that the Angels have been busy about them from their cradles. The celestial hosts have worthily striven to bring them together. And, O Victory! O Wonder! after toil, and pain, and difficulties exceeding, the celestial hosts have succeeded!

"Here we two sit who are written above as one!"

Pipe, happy Love! pipe on to these dear Innocents!

The tide of color has ebbed from the upper sky. In the West the sea of sunken fire draws back; and the stars leap forth, and tremble, and retire before the advancing moon, who slips the silver train of cloud from her shoulders, and, with her foot upon the pine tops, surveys Heaven.

"Lucy, did you never dream of meeting me?"

"O Richard! yes; for I remembered you."

"Lucy! and did you pray that we might meet?"

"I did!"

Young as when she looked upon the Lovers in Paradise the Fair Immortal journeys onward. Fronting her, it is not Night but veiled Day. Full half the sky is flushed. Not Darkness; not Day; the Nuptials of the twain.

"My own! my own forever! You are pledged to me? Whisper!"

He hears the delicious music.

"And you are mine?"

A soft beam travels to the fern covert under the pinewood where they sit, and for answer he has her eyes: turned to him an instant, timidly fluttering over the depths of his, and then downcast; for through her eyes her soul is naked to him.

"Lucy! my bride! my life!"

The nightjar spins his dark monotony on the branch of the pine. The soft beam travels round them, and listens to their hearts. Their lips are locked.

Pipe no more, Love, for a time! Pipe as you will you cannot express their first kiss; nothing of its sweetness, and of its sacredness nothing. St. Cecilia up aloft, before the silver organ pipes of Paradise, pressing fingers upon all the notes of which Love is but one, from her you may hear it.

So Love is silent. Out in the world there, on the skirts of the woodland, the self-satisfied sheep-boy delivers a last complacent squint down the length of his penny whistle, and, with a flourish correspondingly wry-faced, he also marches into silence, hailed by supper. The woods are still. There is heard but the nightjar spinning on the pine branch, circled by moonlight.

Love in Wartime

By IRWIN SHAW

NOAH was nervous. This was the first party he had ever given, and he tried to remember what parties looked like in the movies and parties he had read about in books and magazines. Twice he went into the kitchen-ette to inspect the three dozen ice cubes he and Roger had bought at the drugstore. He looked at his watch again and again, hoping that Roger would get back from Brooklyn with his girl before the guests started to come, because Noah was sure that he would do some awful, gauche thing, just at the moment it was necessary to be relaxed and dignified.

He and Roger Cannon shared a room near Riverside Drive, not far from Columbia University in New York City. It was a large room, and it had a fireplace, although you couldn't light a fire there, and from the bathroom window, by leaning out only a little, you could see the Hudson River.

After his father's death, Noah had drifted back across the country. He had always wanted to see New York. There was nothing to moor him in any other place on the face of the earth, and he had been able to find a job in the city two days after he landed there. Then he had met Roger in the Public Library on Fifth Avenue.

It was hard to believe now that there had been a time when he didn't know Roger, a time when he had wandered the city streets for days without saying a word to anyone, a time when no man was his friend, no woman had looked at him, no street was home, no hour more attractive than any other hour.

He had been standing dreamily in front of the library shelves, staring at the dull-colored rows of books. He had reached up for a volume, he remembered it even now, a book by Yeats, and he had jostled the man next to him, and said "Excuse me." They had started to talk and had gone out into the rainy streets together, and had continued talking. Roger had invited him into a bar on Sixth Avenue and they had had two beers and had agreed before they parted to have dinner together the next night.

Noah had never had any real friends. His shifting, erratic boyhood, spent a few months at a time among abrupt and disinterested strangers, had made it impossible to form any but the most superficial connections.

And his stony shyness, reinforced by the conviction that he was a drab, unappealing child, had put him beyond all overtures. Roger was four or five years older than Noah, tall and thin, with a lean, dark, close-cropped head, and he moved with a certain casual air that Noah had always envied in the young men who had gone to the better colleges. Roger hadn't gone to college, but he was one of those people who seem to be born with confidence in themselves, secure and unshakable. He regarded the world with a kind of sour, dry amusement that Noah was trying now desperately to emulate.

Noah could not understand why, but Roger had seemed to like him. Perhaps, Noah thought, the truth was that Roger had pitied him, alone in the city, in his shabby suit, gawky, uncertain, fiercely shy. At any rate, after they had seen each other two or three times, for drinks in the horrible bars that Roger seemed to like, or for dinner in cheap Italian restaurants, Roger, in his quiet, rather offhand way, had said, "Do you like the place you're living in?"

"Not much," Noah had said, honestly. It was a dreary cell in a rooming house on Twenty-eighth Street, with damp walls and bugs and the toilet pipes roaring above his head.

"I've got a big room," Roger had said. "Two couches. If you don't mind my playing the piano every once in a while in the middle of the night."

Gratefully, still astonished that there was anyone in this crowded, busy city who could find profit, of any kind whatsoever, in his friendship, Noah had moved into the large, rundown room near the river. Roger was almost like the phantom friend lonely children invent for themselves in the long, unpeopled stretches of the night. He was easy, gentle, accomplished. He made no demands on anyone and he seemed to take pleasure, in his rambling, unostentatious way, in putting the younger man through a rough kind of education. He talked in a random, probing way, about books, music, paintings, politics, women. He had been to France and Italy, and the great names of ancient cities and charming towns sounded intimate and accessible in his slow, rather harsh New England accent. He had dry, sardonic theories about the British Empire and the workings of democracy in the United States, and about modern poetry, and the ballet and the movies and the war. He didn't seem to have any ambition of his own. He worked, sporadically and not very hard, for a company that took polls for commercial products. He didn't pay much attention to money, and he wandered from girl to girl with slightly bored, good-humored lust. All in all, with his careless, somehow elegant clothes, and his crooked, reserved smile, he was that rare product of modern America, his own man.

He and Noah took rambling walks together along the river, and on the University campus. Roger had found Noah a good job through some friends as a playground director at a settlement house down on the East Side. Noah was making thirty-six dollars a week, more money than he ever had made before, and as they trudged along the quiet pavements late at night, side by side, with the cliffs of Jersey rearing up across the river, and the lights of the boats winking below them, Noah listened, thirsty and delighted, like an eavesdropper on an unsuspected, glowing world, as Roger said, "Then there was this defrocked priest near Antibes who drank a quart of Scotch every afternoon, sitting in the café on the hill, translating Baudelaire . . ." or "The trouble with American women is they all want to be captain of the team or they won't play. It comes from putting an inflated value on chastity. If an American woman pretends to be faithful to you, she thinks she has earned the right to chain you to the kitchen stove. It's better in Europe. Everyone knows everyone else is unchaste, and there is a more normal system of values. Infidelity is a kind of gold stand-ard between the sexes. There is a fixed rate of exchange and you know what things cost you when you go shopping. Personally, I like a submis-sive woman. All the girls I know say I have a feudal attitude toward women, and maybe they're right. But I'd rather they submitted to me than have me submit to them. One or the other is bound to happen, and I'm in no rush, I'll find a proper type eventually. . . ."

Walking beside him, it seemed to Noah that life could not improve on his condition now . . . being young, at home on the streets of New York, with a pleasant job and thirty-six dollars a week, and a book-crowded room nearly overlooking the river, and a friend like Roger, urbane, thoughtful, full of strange information. The only thing lacking was a girl, and Roger had decided to fix even that. That was why they had planned the party.

Roger had had a good time all one evening casting about among his old address books for likely candidates for Noah. And now, tonight, they were coming, six of them, besides the girl that Roger was bringing him-self. There were going to be some other men, of course, but Roger had slyly selected funny-looking ones or slow-witted ones among his friends, so that the competition would not be too severe. As Noah looked around the warm, lamp-lit room, with cut flowers in vases and a print by Braque on the wall, and the bottles and the glasses shining like a vision from a better world on the desk, he knew, with delicious, fearful certainty, that tonight he would finally find himself a girl.

Noah smiled as he heard the key in the door because now he would not have to face the ordeal of greeting the first guests by himself. The door opened and Roger came in. Roger had his girl with him, and Noah took her coat and hung it up without accident, not tripping over anything or wrenching the girl's arm. He smiled to himself inside the closet as he heard the girl saying to Roger, "What a nice room. It looks as though there hasn't been a woman in here since 1750."

Noah came back into the room. Roger was in the kitchenette getting some ice and the girl was standing in front of the picture on the wall, with her back to Noah. Roger was singing softly over the ice behind the screen, his nasal voice bumbling along on a song he sang over and over again, whose words went, "You make time and you make love dandy, You make swell molasses candy. But, honey, are you makin' any money, That's all I want to know."

The girl had on a plum-colored dress with a full skirt that caught the lamplight. She was standing, very serious and at home, with her back to the room, in front of the fireplace. She had pretty, rather heavy legs, and a narrow, graceful waist. Her hair was pulled to the back in a severe, feminine knot, like a pretty schoolteacher in the movies. The sight of her, the sound of ice, his friend's silly, good-humored song from behind the screen, made the room, the evening, the world, seem wonderfully domestic and dear and melancholy to Noah. Then the girl turned around. Noah had been too busy and excited really to look at her when she first came in and he didn't even remember what her name was. Seeing her now was like looking through a glass that is suddenly brought to focus.

She had a dark, pointed face and grave eyes. Somehow, as he looked at her, Noah felt that he had been hit, physically, by something solid and numbing. He had never felt anything like this before. He felt guilty and feverish and absurd.

Her name, Noah discovered later, was Hope Plowman, and she had come down from a small town in Vermont two years before. She lived in Brooklyn now with an aunt. She had a direct, serious way of talking, and she didn't wear any perfume and she worked as a secretary to a man who made printing machinery in a small factory near Canal Street. Noah felt a little irritated and foolish through the night, as he found out all these things, because it was somehow simple-minded and unworldly to be so riotously overcome by a rather ordinary small-town Yankee girl who worked prosaically as a stenographer in a dull office, and who lived in Brooklyn. Like other shy, bookish young men, with their hearts formed in the library, and romance blooming only out of the volumes of poetry stuck in their overcoat pockets, it was impossible to conceive of Isolde taking the Brighton Express, Beatrice at the Automat. No, he thought, as he greeted the new guests and helped with the drinks, no, I am not going to let this happen. Most of all, she was Roger's girl, and even if any girl would desert that handsome, superior man, for an awkward craggy boy like himself, it was inconceivable that he, Noah, could repay the generous acts of friendships even by the hidden duplicity of unspoken desire.

But the other guests, men and women alike, were merely blurs, and he moved dreamlike and tortured among them, staring hungrily at the girl, the memory of her every calm, controlled movement burned on his brain, the crisp music of her every inflection singing with a terrible mixture of shame and jubilance in his ears. He felt like a soldier caught in his first battle, like an heir who has just been left a million dollars, like a believer who has just been excommunicated, like a tenor who has just sung Tristan for the first time at the Metropolitan Opera House. He felt like a man who has just been found in a hotel bedroom with the wife of his best friend, like a general leading his troops into a captured city, like Nobel prize winners, like condemned criminals being led to the gallows, like heavyweight champions who have just knocked out all contenders, like a swimmer drowning in the middle of the night, thirty miles from shore in a cold ocean, like a scientist who has just discovered the serum which will make the race immortal . . .

"Miss Plowman," he said, "would you like a drink?"

"No, thank you," she said. "I don't drink."

And he went off into a corner to ponder this and discover whether this was good or bad, hopeful or not.

"Miss Plowman," he said later, "have you known Roger long?"

"Oh, yes. Nearly a year."

Nearly a year! No hope, no hope.

"He's told me a lot about you." The direct, dark gaze, the soft, definite voice.

"What did he say?" How lame, how hungry, how hopeless.

"He likes you very much . . ."

Treachery, treachery . . . Friend who snatched the lost waif among the library shelves, who fed and sheltered and loved . . . Friend now, all thoughtless and laughing, at the center of the bright group, fingering the piano lightly, singing in the pleasant, intelligent voice, "Joshua fit the battle of Jericho, Jericho, Jericho . . ."

"He said," once more the troubling, dangerous voice . . . "He said, when you finally woke up you would be a wonderful man . . ."

Ah, worse and worse, the thief armed with his friend's guarantee, the adulterer given the key to the wife's apartment by the trusting husband.

Noah stared blankly and wearily at the girl. Unreasonably, he hated her. At eight that evening he had been a happy man, secure and hopeful, with friend and home and job, with the past clean behind him, the future shining ahead. At nine he was a bleeding fugitive in an endless swamp, with the dogs baying at him, and a roster of crimes dark against his name on the books of the county. And she was the cause of it, sitting there, demure, falsely candid, pretending she had done nothing, knew nothing, sensed nothing. A little, unpretentious, rock-farm hill girl, who probably sat on her boss's knee in the office of the printing-machinery factory near Canal Street, to take dictation.

". . . and the walls came tumbling down . . ." Roger's voice and the strong chords of the old piano against the wall filled the room.

Noah stared wildly away from the girl. There were six other girls in the room, young, with fair complexions and glowing hair, with soft bodies and sweet, attentive voices . . . They had been brought here for him to choose from and they had smiled at him, full of kindness and invitation. And now, for all of him, they might as well have been six tailor's dummies in a closed store, six numbers on a page, six doorknobs. It could only happen to him, he thought. It was the pattern of his life, grotesque, savagely humorous, essentially tragic.

No, he thought, I will put this away from me. If it shatters me, if I collapse from it, if I never touch a woman as long as I live. But he could not bear to be in the same room with her. He went over to the closet in which his clothes hung side by side with Roger's, and got his hat. He would go out and walk around until the party had broken up, the merry-makers dispersed, the piano silent, the girl safe with her aunt beyond the bridge in Brooklyn. His hat was next to Roger's on the shelf and he looked with guilt and tenderness at the rakishly creased old brown felt. Luckily, most of the guests were grouped around the piano and he got to the door unobserved; he would make up some excuse for Roger later. But the girl saw him. She was sitting talking to one of the other girls, facing the door, and an expression of quiet inquiry came into her face as she looked at Noah, standing at the door, taking one last, despairing look at her. She stood up and walked over to him. The rustle of her dress was like artillery in his ears.

"Where are you going?" she asked.

"We . . . we . . ." he stuttered, hating himself for the ineptness of his tongue. "We need some more soda, and I'm going out to get it."

"I'll go with you," she said.

"No!" he wanted to shout. "Stay where you are! Don't move!" But he remained silent and watched her get her coat and a plain, rather unbecoming hat, that made tidal waves of pity and tenderness for her youth and her poverty sweep him convulsively. She went to Roger, sitting at the piano, and leaned over, holding his shoulder, to whisper into his ear. Now, Noah thought, blackly, now it will all be known, now it is over, and he nearly plunged out into the night. But Roger turned and smiled at him, waving with one hand, while still playing the bass with the other. The girl came across the room with her unpretentious walk.

"I told Roger," she said.

Told Roger! Told him what? Told him to beware strangers? Told him to pity no one, told him to be generous never, to cut down love in his heart like weed in a garden?

"You'd better take your coat," the girl said. "It was raining when we came."

Stiffly, silently, Noah went over and got his coat. The girl waited at the door and they closed it behind them in the dark hall. The singing and the laughter within sounded far away and forbidden to them as they walked slowly, close together, down the steps to the wet street outside.

"Which way is it?" she asked, as they stood irresolutely with the front door of the house closed behind them.

"Which way is what?" Noah asked, dazedly.

"The soda. The place where you can buy the soda?"

"Oh . . ." Noah looked distractedly up and down the gleaming pavements. "Oh. That, I don't know. Anyway," he said, "we don't need soda."

"I thought you said . . ."

"It was an excuse. I was getting tired of the party. Very tired. Parties bore me." Even as he spoke, he listened to his voice and was elated at the real timbre of sophistication and weariness with frivolous social affairs that he heard there. That was the way to handle this matter, he decided. With urbanity. Be cool, polite, slightly amused with this little girl . . .

"I thought that was a very nice party," the girl said, seriously.

"Was it?" Noah asked offhandedly. "I hadn't noticed." That was it, he told himself, gloomily pleased, that was the attack. Remote, slightly vague, like an English baron after an evening's drinking, frigidly polite. It would serve a double purpose. It would keep him from betraying his friend, even by so much as a word. And also, and he felt a delicious thrill of guilty promise at the thought, it would impress this simple little Brooklyn secretary with his rare and superior qualities.

"Sorry," he said, "if I got you down here in the rain under false pretenses."

The girl looked around her. "It's not raining," she said, practically.

"Ah." Noah regarded the weather for the first time. "Ah, so it is." There was something baffling about the grammar here, but the tone still was right, he felt.

"What are you going to do?" she asked.

He shrugged. It was the first time he had ever shrugged in his whole life. "Don't know," he said. "Take a stroll." Even his vocabulary suddenly took on a Galsworthian cast. "Often do. In the middle of the night. Very peaceful, walking along through the deserted streets."

"It's only eleven o'clock now," the girl said.

"So it is," he said. He would have to be careful not to say that again. "If you want to go back to the party . . ."

The girl hesitated. A horn blew out on the misty river and the sound, low and trembling, went to the core of Noah's bones.

"No," she said, "I'll take a walk with you."

They walked side by side, without touching, down to the tree-bordered avenue that ran high above the river. The Hudson, smelling of spring and its burden of salt that had swept up from the ocean on the afternoon's tide, slipped darkly past the misty shores. Far north was the string of soaring lights that was the bridge to Jersey and across the river the Palisades loomed like a castle. There were no other strollers. Occasionally a car rushed by, its tires whining on the pavement, making the night and the river and themselves moving slowly along under the budding branches of the glistening trees, extraordinary and mysterious.

They walked in silence alongside the flowing river, their footsteps lonely and brave. Three minutes, Noah thought, looking at his shoes, four minutes, five minutes, without talking. He began to grow desperate. There was a sinful intimacy about their silence, an almost tangible longing and tenderness about the echoing sound of their footsteps and the quiet intake of their breath, and the elaborate precautions not to touch each other with shoulder or elbow or hand as they went downhill along the uneven pavement. Silence became the enemy, the betrayer. Another moment of it, he felt, and the quiet girl walking slyly and knowingly beside him, would understand everything, as though he had mounted the balustrade that divided street from river and there made an hour-long speech on the subject of love.

"New York City," he said hoarsely, "must be quite frightening to a girl from the country."

"No," she said, "it isn't."

"The truth is," he went on, desperately, "that it is highly overrated. It puts on a big act of being sophisticated and cosmopolitan, but at heart it's unalterably provincial." He smiled, delighted with the "unalterably."

"I don't think so," the girl said.

"What?"

"I don't think it's provincial. Anyway, not after Vermont."

"Oh . . ." He laughed patronizingly. "Vermont."

"Where have you been?" she asked.

"Chicago," he said, "Los Angeles, San Francisco . . . All over." He waved vaguely, with a debonair intimation that these were merely the first names that came to mind and that if he had gone through the whole list, Paris, Budapest and Vienna would certainly have been on it.

"I must say, though," he went on, "that New York has beautiful women. A little flashy, but very attractive." Here he thought with satisfaction, looking at her anxiously, here we have struck the right note. "American women, of course," he said, "are best when they're young. After that . . ." Once more he tried to shrug and once more he achieved it. "For myself," he said, "I prefer the slightly older Continental type. They are at their best when American women are bridge-playing harpies with spread behinds." He glanced at her a little nervously. But the girl's expression hadn't changed. She had broken off a twig from a bush and was absently running it along the stone fence, as though she were pondering what he had just said. "And by that time, too, a Continental woman has learned how to handle men . . ." He thought back hurriedly about the foreign women he had known. There was that drunk in the bar the night his father died. It was quite possible that she was Polish. Poland was not a terribly romantic place, but it was on the Continent all right.

"How does a Continental woman learn how to handle men?" the girl asked.

"She learns how to submit," he said. "The women I know say I have a feudal attitude . . ." Oh, friend, friend at the piano, forgive me for this theft tonight, I will make it up some other time . . .

After that it flowed freely. "Art," he said. "Art? I can't stand the modern notion that art is mysterious and the artist an irresponsible child."

"Marriage?" he said. "Marriage? Marriage is a desperate admission on the part of the human race that men and women do not know how to live in the same world with each other."

"The theater," he said, "the American theater? It has a certain lively, childish quality, but as for taking it seriously as an art form in the twentieth century . . ." He laughed loftily. "Give me Disney."

After a while they looked around them and discovered that they had walked thirty-four blocks along the dark sliding river and that it had begun to rain again and that it was very late. Standing close to the girl, cupping a match to keep out the wind so that they could see what time it was on his wrist watch, with the small fragrance of the girl's hair mingling with smell of the river in his nostrils, Noah suddenly decided to be silent. This was too painful, this wild flood of nonsensical talk, this performance of the jaundiced young blood dilettante and connoisseur.

"It's late," he said abruptly, "we'd better go back to the party."

But he couldn't resist the gesture of hailing a taxi that was cruising slowly past them. It was the first time he had taken a taxi in New York and he stumbled over the little letdown chairs, but he felt elegant and master of himself and social life as he sat far away from the girl on the back seat. She sat quietly in the corner. Noah sensed that he had made a strong impression on her and he gave the driver a quarter tip although the entire fare had only been sixty cents.

Once more they stood at the closed door of the house in which he lived. They looked up. The lights were out and no sound of conversation, music or laughter came from behind the closed windows.

"It's over," he said, his heart sinking with the realization that Roger would now be certain he had stolen his girl. "Nobody's there."

"It looks that way, doesn't it?" the girl said placidly.

"What'll we do?" Noah felt trapped.

"I guess you'll have to take me home," the girl said.

Brooklyn, Noah thought, heavily. Hours there and hours back, and Roger waiting accusingly in the dawn light in the rumpled room where late the party had been so merry, waiting with the curt, betrayed, final dismissal on his lips. The night had started out so wonderfully, so hopefully. He remembered the moment when he had been alone in the apartment waiting for the guests, before Roger had arrived. He remembered the warm expectancy with which he had inspected the shabby, shelf-lined room that had seemed at that moment so friendly and promising.

"Can't you go home alone?" he asked bleakly. He hated her standing there, pretty, a little drab, with the rain wilting on her hair and her clothes.

"Don't you dare talk like that," she said. Her voice was sharp and commanding. "I'm not going home alone. Come on."

Noah sighed. Now, aside from everything else, the girl was angry at him.

"Don't sigh like that," she said crisply. "Like a henpecked husband."

What's happened, Noah thought dazedly, how did I get here, how did this girl get the right to talk to me this way? . . .

"I'm going," she said, and turned with definiteness and started off toward the subway. He watched her for a moment, baffled, then hurried after her.

The trains were dank and smelly with the ghost of the rain that the riders brought in with them from the streets above. There was a taste of iron in the unchanging air and the bosomy girls who advertised toothpaste and laxatives and brassieres on the garish cards seemed foolish and improbable in the light of the dusty lamps. The other passengers in the cars, returning from unknown labors and unimaginable assignations, swayed on the stained yellow seats.

The girl sat tight-lipped and silent. When they had to change trains at a station she merely stood with unbending disapproval and walked out onto the platform, leaving Noah to shuffle lamely after her.

They had to change again and again, and wait interminably for new connections on the almost deserted platforms, with the water from the rain and leaking mains dripping down the graying tiles and rusted iron of the tunnels. This girl, Noah thought with dull hostility, this girl must live at the end of the city, five hundred yards past the ultimate foot of track, out among the dump heaps and cemeteries. Brooklyn, Brooklyn, how long was Brooklyn, stretched in the sleeping night from the East River to Gravesend Bay, from the oily waters of Greenpoint to the garbage scows of Canarsie. Brooklyn, like Venice, was clasped in the waters of the sea, but its Grand Canal was the Fourth Avenue Local.

How demanding and certain of herself this girl was, thought Noah, glaring at her, to drag a man she had just met so far and so long through the clanging, sorrowful labyrinth of the Borough's mournful underground. His luck, he thought, with a prescient, murky vision of himself, night after night on these grim platforms, night after night among the late-riding charladies and burglars and drunken merchant seamen who made up the subway dawn passenger lists, his luck, with one million women living within a radius of fifty blocks of him, to be committed to a sharp-tempered, unrelenting girl, who made her home at the dreary other end of the largest city known to man.

Leander, he thought, swam the Hellespont for another girl; but he did not have to take her home later in the evening, nor did he have to wait twenty-five minutes among the trash baskets and the signs that warned against spitting and smoking on DeKalb Avenue.

Finally, they got off at a station and the girl led him up the steps to the streets above.

"At last," he said, the first words he had spoken in an hour. "I thought we were down there for the summer season."

The girl stopped at the corner. "Now," she said coldly, "we take the streetcar."

"Oh, God!" Noah said. Then he began to laugh. His laughter sounded mad and empty across the trolley tracks, among the shabby store fronts and dingy brownstone walls.

"If you're going to be so unpleasant," the girl said, "you can leave me here."

"I have come this far," Noah said, with literary gravity. "I will go the whole way."

He stopped laughing and stood beside her, silent under the lamppost, with the raw wind smashing against them in rough wet gusts, the wind that had come across the Atlantic beaches and the polluted harbors, across the million acres of semidetached houses across the brick and wood wastes of Flatbush and Bensonhurst, across the sleeping, tortured souls of millions of their fellowmen, who in their uneasy voyage through life had found no gentler place to lay their heads.

A quarter of an hour later the trolley car rumbled toward them, a clanking eye of light in the distance. There were only three other passengers, dozing unhappily on the wood seats, and Noah sat formally beside the girl, feeling, in the lighted car, creaking along the dark streets, like a man on a raft, wrecked with strangers, relics of a poor ship that had foundered on a cold run among northern islands. The girl sat primly, staring straight ahead, her hands crossed in her lap, and Noah felt as though he did not know her at all, as though if he ventured to speak to her she would cry out for a policeman and demand to be protected against him.

"All right," she said, and stood up. Once more he followed her to the door. The car stopped and the door wheezed open. They stepped down to the wet pavement. The car pulled away, a mass of protesting bearings, clashing at the meager sleep of the natives, packed into their leaning houses. Noah and the girl walked away from the trolley tracks. Here and there along the mean streets there was a tree, fretted with green in surprising evidence that spring had come to this place this year.

The girl turned into a small concrete yard, under a high stone stoop.

There was a barred iron door. She opened the lock with her key and the door swung open.

"There," she said, coldly. "We're home," and turned to face him.

Noah took off his hat. The girl's face bloomed palely out of the darkness. She had taken off her hat, too, and her hair made a wavering line around the ivory gleam of her cheeks and brow. Noah felt like weeping, as though he had lost everything that he had ever held dear, as he stood close to her in the poor shadow of the house in which she lived.

"I . . . I want to say . . ." he said, whispering, "that I do not object . . . I mean I am please . . . pleased, I mean, to have brought you home."

"Thank you," she said. She was whispering, too, but her voice was noncommittal.

"Complex," he said. He waved his hands vaguely. "If you only knew how complex. I mean, I'm very pleased, really . . ."

She was so close, so poor, so young, so frail, deserted, courageous, lonely . . . He put out his hands in a groping blind gesture and took her head delicately in his hands and kissed her.

Her lips were soft and firm and a little damp from the mist.

Then she slapped him. The noise echoed meanly under the stone steps. His cheek felt a little numb. How strong she is, he thought dazedly, for such a frail-looking girl.

"What made you think," she said coldly, "that you could kiss me?"

"I . . . I don't know," he said, putting his hand to his cheek to assuage the smarting, then pulling it away, ashamed of showing that much weakness at a moment like this. "I . . . I just did."

"You do that with your other girls," Hope said crisply. "Not with me."

"I don't do it with other girls," Noah said unhappily.

"Oh," Hope said. "Only with me. I'm sorry I look so easy."

"Oh, no," said Noah, mourning within him. "That isn't what I mean." Oh, God, he thought, if only there were some way to explain to her how I feel. Now she thinks I am a lecherous fool on the loose from the corner drugstore, quick to grab any girl who'll let me. He swallowed dryly, the English language clotted in his throat.

"Oh," he said, weakly. "I'm so sorry."

"I suppose you think," the girl began cuttingly, "you're so wonderfully attractive, so bright, so superior that any girl would just fall all over herself to let you paw her . . ."

"Oh, God." He backed away painfully, and nearly stumbled against the two steps that led down from the cement yard.

"I never in all my days," said the girl, "have come across such an arrogant, opinionated, self-satisfied young man."

"Stop . . ." Noah groaned. "I can't stand it."

"I'll say good night now," the girl said bitingly. "Mr. Ackerman."

"Oh, no," he whispered. "Not now. You can't."

She moved the iron gate with a tentative, forbidding gesture, and the hinges creaked in his ears.

"Please," he begged, "listen to me . . . "

"Good night." With a single, swift movement, she was behind the gate. It slammed shut and locked. She did not look back, but opened the wooden door to the house and went through it. Noah stared stupidly at the two dark doors, the iron and the wood, then slowly turned, and brokenly started down the street.

He had gone thirty yards, holding his hat absently in his hand, not noticing that the rain had begun again and a fine drizzle was soaking his hair, when he stopped. He looked around him uneasily, then turned and went back toward the girl's house. There was a light on there now, behind the barred window on the street level, and even through the drawn blinds he could see a shadow moving about within.

He walked up to the window, took a deep breath, and tapped at it. After a moment, the blind was drawn aside and he could see Hope's face peering out. He put his face as close to the window as he could and made vague, senseless gestures to indicate that he wanted to talk to her. She shook her head irritably and waved to him to go away, but he said, quite loudly, with his lips close to the window. "Open the door. I've got to talk to you. I'm lost. Lost. LOST!"

He saw her peering at him doubtfully through the rain-streaked glass. Then she grinned and disappeared. A moment later he heard the inside door being opened, and then she was at the gate. Involuntarily, he sighed.

"Ah," he said, "I'm so glad to see you."

"Don't you know your way?" she asked.

"I am lost," he said. "No one will ever find me again."

She chuckled.

"You're a terrible fool," she said, "aren't you?"

"Yes," he said humbly. "Terrible."

"Well," she said, very serious now, on the other side of the locked gate, "you walk two blocks to your left and you wait for the trolley, the one that comes from your left, and you take that to Eastern Parkway and then . . ."

Her voice swept on, making a small music out of the directions for escaping to the larger world, and Noah noticed as she stood there that she had taken off her shoes and was much smaller than he had realized, much more delicate, and more dear.

"Are you listening to me?" she asked.

"I want to tell you something," he said loudly. "I am not arrogant, I am not opinionated . . ."

"Sssh," she said, "my aunt's asleep."

"I am shy," he whispered, "and I don't have a single opinion in the whole world, and I don't know why I kissed you. I . . . I just couldn't help it."

"Not so loud," she said. "My aunt."

"I was trying to impress you," he whispered. "I don't know any Continental women. I wanted to pretend to you that I was very smart and very sophisticated. I was afraid that if I just was myself you wouldn't look at me. It's been a very confusing night," he whispered brokenly. "I don't remember ever going through anything so confusing. You were perfectly right to slap me. Perfectly. A lesson," he said, leaning against the gate, his face cold against the iron, close to her face. "A very good lesson. I . . . I can't say what I feel about you at the moment. Some other time, maybe, but . . ." He stopped. "Are you Roger's girl?" he asked.

"No," she said. "I'm not anybody's girl."

He laughed, an insane, creaking laugh.

"My aunt," she warned.

"Well," he whispered, "the trolley to Eastern Parkway. Good night. Thank you. Good night."

But he didn't move. They stared at each other in the shadowy, watery light from the lamppost.

"Oh, Lord," he said softly, full of anguish, "you don't know, you just don't know."

He heard the lock of the gate opening, and then the gate was open and he had taken the one step in. They kissed, but it wasn't like the first kiss. Somewhere within him something was thundering, but he couldn't help feeling that perhaps, in the middle of it, she would step back and hit him again.

She moved slowly away from him, looking at him with a dark smile. "Don't get lost," she said, "on the way home."

"The trolley," he whispered, "the trolley to Eastern Parkway and then . . . I love you," he said. "I love you."

"Good night," she said. "Thanks for taking me home."

He stepped back and the gate closed between them. She turned and padded gently through the door in her stockinged feet. Then the door was shut and the street was empty. He started toward the trolley car. It didn't occur to him until he was at the door of his own room nearly two hours later, but he had never before in all his twenty-one years said "I love you" to anyone.

The room was dark and he could hear Roger's measured sleeping breath. Noah undressed swiftly and silently and slid into bed across the room from his friend. He lay there staring at the ceiling, caught in alternate waves of pleasure and agony as he thought first of the girl and the kiss at the gate, and of Roger and what he would say in the morning.

He was dozing off to sleep when he heard his name.

"Noah!"

He opened his eyes. "Hello, Roger," he said.

"You all right?"

"Yes."

Silence.

"Take her home?"

"Yes."

Silence in the dark room.

"We went out to get some sandwiches," Roger said. "You must have missed us."

"Yes."

Silence again.

"Roger . . ."

"Yes?"

"I feel I have to explain. I didn't mean to . . . Honest. I started out by myself and then . . . I don't quite remember . . . Roger, are you awake?"

"Yes."

"Roger, she told me something . . ."

"What?"

"She told me she wasn't your girl."

"Did she?"

"She said she wasn't anybody's girl. But if she *is* your girl. Or if you want her to *be* your girl . . . I . . . I'll never see her again. I swear, Roger. Are you awake?"

"Yes. She's not my girl. I won't deny, from time to time the thought's crossed my mind, but who the hell could make that trip to Brooklyn three times a week?"

Noah wiped the sweat off his forehead in the dark. "Roger," he said.

"Yes."

"I love you."

"Go the hell to sleep." Then the chuckle across the shared dark room. Then silence again.

In the next two months Noah and Hope wrote each other forty-two letters. They worked near each other and met every day for lunch and almost every night for dinner, and they slipped away from their jobs on sunny afternoons to walk along the docks and watch the ships passing in and out of the harbor. Noah made the long, shuttling trip back and forth to Brooklyn thirty-seven times in the two months, but their real life was carried through the United States mails.

Sitting next to her, in no matter how dark and private a place, he could only manage to say, "You're so pretty," or "I love the way you smile," or "Will you go to the movies with me on Sunday night?" But with the heady freedom of blank paper, and through the impersonal agency of the letter-carrier, he could write, "Your beauty is with me day and night. When I look out in the morning at the sky, it is clearer because I know it is covering you, too; when I look up the river at the bridge, I believe it is a stronger bridge because you have once walked across it with me; when I look at my own face in the mirror, it seems to me it is a better face, because you have kissed it the night before."

And Hope, who had a dry, New England severity in her make-up that prevented her from offering any but the most guarded and reticent expressions of love in person, would write . . . "You have just left the house and I think of you walking down the empty street and waiting in the spring darkness for the trolley car, and riding in the train to your home. I will stay up with you tonight while you make your journey through the city. Darling, as you travel, I sit here in the sleeping house, with one lamp on, and think of all the things I believe about you. I believe that you are good and strong and just, and I believe that I love you. I believe that your eyes are beautiful and your mouth sad and your hands supple and lovely . . ."

And then, when they would meet, they would stare at each other, the glory of the written word trembling between them, and say, "I got two tickets for a show. If you're not doing anything tonight, want to go?"

Then, late at night, lightheaded with the dazzle of the theater, and love for each other, and lack of sleep, standing, embraced in the cold vestibule of Hope's house, not being able to go in, because her uncle had a dreadful habit of sitting up in the living room till all hours of the morning reading the Bible, they would hold each other desperately, kissing until their lips were numb, the life of their letters and their real life together fusing for the moment in a sorrowing burst of passion.

They did not go to bed with each other. First of all, there seemed to be no place in the whole brawling city, with all its ten million rooms, that they could call their own and go to in dignity and honor. Then, Hope had a stubborn religious streak, and every time they veered dangerously close to consummation, she pulled back, alarmed. "Some time, some time," she would whisper. "Not now . . ."

"You will just explode," Roger told him, grinning, "and blow away. It's unnatural. What's the matter with the girl? Doesn't she know she's the postwar generation?"

"Cut it out, Roger," Noah said sheepishly. He was sitting at the desk in their room, writing Hope a letter, and Roger was lying flat on his back on the floor, because the spring of the sofa had been broken five months ago and the sofa was very uncomfortable for a tall man.

"Brooklyn," Roger said. "That dark, mysterious land." Since he was on the floor anyway, he started doing some exercises for the abdomen, bringing his feet above his head and then letting them down slowly three times. "Enough," he said, "I feel healthier already. Sex," he said, "is like swimming. You either go in all the way or you stay out. If you just hang around the edge, letting the spray hit you, you get cold and nervous. One more month with that girl and you'll have to go to a psychoanalyst. Write her that and tell her I said so."

"Sure thing," said Noah. "I'm putting it down right now."

"If you're not careful," Roger said, "you're going to find yourself a married man."

Noah stopped typing. He had bought a typewriter on time payments when he found himself writing so many letters.

"No danger," he said. "I'm not going to get married." But the truth was he had thought about it again and again, and had even, in his letters, written tentatively about it to Hope.

"Maybe it wouldn't be so bad at that," Roger said. "She's a fine girl and it'd keep you out of the draft."

They had avoided thinking about the draft. Luckily, Noah's number was among the highest. The Army hung somewhere in the future, like a dark, distant cloud in the sky.

"No," said Roger, judiciously, from the floor, "I have only two things against the girl. One, she keeps you from getting any sleep. Two, you know what. Otherwise, she's done you a world of good."

Noah glanced at his friend gratefully.

"Still," Roger said, "she ought to go to bed with you."

"Shut up."

"Tell you what. I'll go away this week end and you can have the place." Roger sat up. "Nothing could be fairer than that."

"Thanks," Noah said. "If the occasion arises, I'll take your offer."

"Maybe," Roger said, "I'd better talk to her. In the role of best friend, concerned for his comrade's safety. 'My dear young lady, you may not realize it, but our Noah is on the verge of leaping out the window.' Give me a dime, I'll call her this minute."

"I'll manage it myself," Noah said, without conviction.

"How about this Sunday?" Roger asked. "Lovely month of June, etcetera, the full moon of summer, etcetera . . ."

"This Sunday is out," said Noah. "We're going to a wedding."

"Whose?" Roger asked. "Yours?"

Noah laughed falsely. "Some friend of hers in Brooklyn."

"You ought to get a wholesale rate," Roger said, "from the Transit System." He lay back. "I have spoken. I now hold my peace."

He remained quiet for a moment while Noah typed.

"One month," he said. "Then the psychoanalyst's couch. Mark my words."

Noah laughed and stood up. "I give up," he said. "Let's go down and I'll buy you a beer."

Roger sprang to his feet. "My good friend," he said, "the virgin Noah."

They laughed and went out of the house, into the soft, calm summer evening, toward the frightful saloon on Columbus Avenue that they frequented.

The wedding on Sunday was held in a large house in Flatbush, a house with a garden and a small lawn, leading down to a tree-shaded street. The bride was pretty and the minister was quick and there was champagne.

It was warm and sunny and everyone seemed to be smiling with the tender, unashamed sensuality of wedding guests. In corners of the large house, after the ceremony, the younger guests were pairing off in secret conversations. Hope had a new yellow dress. She had been out in the sun during the week and her skin was tanned. Noah kept watching her proudly and a little anxiously as she moved about, her hair dark and tumbled in a new coiffure, above the soft golden flash of her dress. Noah stood off to one side, sipping the champagne, a little shy, talking quietly again and again to the friendly guests, watching Hope, something inside his head saying, her hair, her lips, her legs, in a kind of loving shorthand.

He kissed the bride and there was a jumbled confusion of white satin and lace and lipstick taste and perfume and orange blossom. He looked past the bright, moist eyes and the parted lips of the bride to Hope, standing watching him across the room, and the shorthand within him noted her throat, her waist. Hope came over and he said, "There's something I've wanted to do," and he put out his hands to her waist, slender in the tight bodice of her new dress. He felt the narrow, girlish flesh and the intricate small motion of the hipbones. Hope seemed to understand. She leaned over gently and kissed him. He didn't mind, although several people were watching, because at a wedding everybody seemed licensed to kiss everyone else. Besides he had never before drunk champagne on a warm summer's afternoon.

They watched the bride and the groom go off in a car with streamers flying from it, the rice scattered around, the mother weeping softly at the doorstep, the groom grinning, red and self-conscious at the rear window. Noah looked at Hope and she looked at him and he knew they were thinking about the same thing.

"Why," he whispered, "don't we . . ."

"Sssh." She put her hand over his lips. "You've drunk too much champagne."

They made their good-bys and started off under the tall trees, between the lawns on which water sprinklers were whirling, the flashing fountains of water, brilliant and rainbow-like in the sun, making the green smell of the lawns rise into the waning afternoon. They walked slowly, hand in hand.

"Where are they going?" Noah asked.

"California," Hope said. "For a month. Monterey. He has a cousin there with a house."

They walked side by side among the fountains of Flatbush, thinking of the beaches of Monterey on the Pacific Ocean, thinking of the pale Mexican houses in the southern light, thinking of the two young people getting into their compartment on the train at Grand Central and locking the door behind them.

"Oh, God," Noah said. Then he grinned sourly. "I pity them," he said.

"What?"

"On a night like this. The first time. One of the hottest nights of the year."

Hope pulled her hand away. "You're impossible," she said sharply. "What a mean, vulgar thing to say. . ."

"Hope . . ." he protested. "It was just a little joke."

"I hate that attitude," Hope said loudly. "Everything's funny!" With surprise, he saw that she was crying.

"Please, darling." He put his arms around her, although two small boys and a large collie dog were watching him interestedly from one of the lawns.

She shrugged away. "Keep your hands off me," she said. She started swiftly away.

"Please." He followed her anxiously. "Please, let me talk to you."

"Write me a letter," she said, through her tears. "You seem to save all your romance for the typewriter."

He caught up with her and walked in troubled silence at her side. He was baffled and lost, adrift on the irrational, endless female sea, and he did not try to save himself, but merely let himself drift with the wind and tide, hoping they would not wreck him.

But Hope would not relent, and all the long way home on the trolley car she sat stubborn and silent, her mouth set in bitter rejection. Oh, God, Noah thought, peering at her timidly as the car rattled on. Oh, God, she is going to quit me.

But she let him follow her into the house when she opened the two doors with her key.

The house was empty. Hope's aunt and uncle had taken their two small children on a three-day holiday to the country, and an almost exotic air of peace hung over the dark rooms.

"You hungry?" Hope asked dourly. She was standing in the middle of the living room and Noah had thought he would kiss her until he saw the expression on her face.

"I think I'd better go home," he said.

"You might as well eat," she said. "I left some stuff in the icebox for supper."

He followed her meekly into the kitchen and helped as unobtrusively as possible. She got out some cold chicken and made a salad and poured a pitcherful of milk. She put everything on a tray and said, curtly, "Outside," like a sergeant commanding a platoon.

He took the tray out to the back garden, a twilit oblong now, that was bounded on two sides by a high board fence, and on the far end by the blank brick wall of a garage that had Virginia creeper growing all over it. There was a graceful acacia tree growing out of the garden. Hope's uncle had a small rock garden at one end and beds of common flowers, and there was a wood table with shielded candles and a long, sofa-like swing with a canopy. In the hazy blue light of evening, Brooklyn vanished like mist and rumor, and they were in a walled garden in England or France or the mountains of India.

Hope lit the candles and they sat gravely across from each other, eating hungrily. They hardly spoke while they ate, just polite requests for the salt and the milk pitcher. They folded their napkins and stood up on opposite sides of the table.

"We don't need the candles," Hope said. "Will you please blow out the one on your side?"

"Certainly," Noah said. He leaned over the small glass chimney that guarded the candle and Hope bent over the one on her side of the table. Their heads touched as they blew, together, and in the sudden darkness, Hope said, "Forgive me. I am the meanest female in the whole world."

Then it was all right. They sat side by side, in the swing, looking up at the darkening sky with the summer stars beginning to bloom above them one by one through the single tree. Far off the trolley, far off the trucks, far off the aunt, the uncle and the two children of the house, far off the newsboys crying beyond the garage, far off the world as they sat there in the walled garden in the evening.

Hope said, "No, we shouldn't" and "I'm afraid, afraid . . ." and "Darling, darling" and Noah was shy and triumphant and dazzled and humble and after it was over they lay there crushed and subdued by the wilderness of feeling through which they had blundered, and Noah was afraid that now that it was done she would hate him for it, and every moment of her silence seemed more and more foreboding and then she said, "See . . ." and she chuckled. "It wasn't too hot. Not too hot at all."

Much later, when it was time for him to go home, they went inside. They blinked in the light, and didn't quite look at each other. Noah bent over to turn the radio on because it gave him something to do.

They were playing Tchaikovsky on the radio, the piano concerto, and the music sounded rich and mournful, as though it had been especially composed and played for them, two people barely out of childhood, who had just loved each other for the first time. Hope came over and kissed the back of his neck as he stood above the radio. He turned to kiss her, when the music stopped, and a matter-of-fact voice said, "Special Bulletin from the Associated Press. The German advance is continuing along the Russian border at all points. Many new armored divisions have struck on a line extending from Finland to the Black Sea."

"What?" Hope said.

"The Germans," Noah said, thinking how often you say that word, how well known they've made themselves. "They've gone into Russia. That must have been what the newsboys were yelling . . ."

"Turn it off." Hope reached over and turned the radio off herself. "Tonight."

He held her, feeling her heart beating with sudden fierceness against him. All this afternoon, he thought, while we were at the wedding and walking down that street, and all this evening, in the garden, it was happening, the guns going, the men dying. From Finland to the Black Sea. His mind made no comment on it. It merely recorded the thought, like a poster on the side of the road which you read automatically as you speed by in a car.

They sat down on the worn couch in the quiet room. Outside it was very dark and the newsboys crying on the distant streets were remote and inconsequential. "What's the day?" Hope asked.

"Sunday." He smiled. "The day of rest."

"I don't mean that," she said. "I know that. The date."

"June," he said, "the twenty-second of June."

"June twenty-second," the girl whispered. "I'm going to remember that date. The first time you made love to me."

Roger was still up when Noah got home. Standing outside the doorway, in the dark house, trying to compose his face so that it would show nothing of what had gone on that night, Noah heard the piano being softly played within. It was a sad jazz tune, hesitant and blue, and Roger was improvising on it so that it was difficult to recognize the melody. Noah listened for two or three minutes in the little hallway before he opened the door and went in. Roger waved to him with one hand, without looking around, and continued playing. There was only one lamp lit, in the corner, and the room looked large and mysterious as Noah sank slowly into the battered leather chair near the window. Outside, the city was sleeping along the dark streets. The curtains moved at the open window in the soft wind. Noah closed his eyes, listening to the running, somber chords. He had a strange impression that he could feel every bone and muscle and pore of his body, alive and weary, in trembling balance under his clothes, reacting to the music.

In the middle of a passage Roger stopped. He sat at the piano with his long hands resting on the keyboard, staring at the scratched and polished old wood. Then he swung around.

"The house is yours," he said.

"What?" Noah opened his eyes.

"I'm going in tomorrow," Roger said. He spoke as though he were continuing a conversation with himself he had been conducting for hours.

"What?" Noah looked closely at his friend to see if he had been drinking.

"The Army. The party's over. Now they begin to collect the civilians."

Noah felt dazed, as though he couldn't quite understand the words Roger was using. Another night, he felt, and I could understand. But too much has happened tonight.

"I suppose," Roger said, "the news has reached Brooklyn."

"You mean about the Russians?"

"I mean about the Russians."

"Yes."

"I am going to spring to the aid of the Russians," Roger said.

"What?" Noah asked, puzzledly. "Are you going to join the Russian Army?"

Roger laughed and walked over to the window. He stood there, holding onto the curtain, staring out. "Not exactly," he said. "The Army of the United States."

"I'll go in with you," Noah said suddenly.

"Thanks," said Roger. "Don't be silly. Wait until they call you."

"They haven't called *you,*" said Noah.

"Not yet. But I'm in a hurry." Roger tied a knot reflectively in the curtain, then untied it. "I'm older than you. Wait until they come for you. It'll be soon enough."

"Don't sound," Noah said, "as though you're eighty years old."

Roger laughed and turned around. "Forgive me, son," he said. Then he grew more serious. "I ignored it just about as long as it could be ignored," he said. "Today, when I heard it over the radio, I knew I couldn't ignore it any more. From now on, the only way I can make any sense to myself is with a rifle in my hand. From Finland to the Black Sea," he said, and Noah remembered the voice on the radio. "From Finland to the Black Sea to the Hudson River to Roger Cannon. We're going to be in soon, anyway. I want to rush to it. I've waited around for things all my life. This thing I want to take a running broad jump at. What the hell, I come from an Army family, anyway." He grinned. "My grandfather deserted at Antietam, and my old man left three illegitimate children at Soissons."

"Do you think it'll do any good?" Noah said.

Roger grinned. "Don't ask me that, son," he said. "Never ask me that." Then he spoke more soberly. "It may be the making of me. Right now, as you may have noticed, I have no goal in life. That's a disease. In the beginning it's no worse than a pimple and you hardly notice it. Three years later the patient is paralyzed. Maybe the Army will give me a goal in life . . ." He grinned. "Like staying alive or making sergeant or winning some war. Do you mind if I play the piano some more?"

"Of course not," Noah said dully. He's going to die, a voice kept saying inside Noah's head, Roger is going to die, they're going to kill him.

Roger sat down at the piano once more and placed his hands reflectively on the keys. He played something Noah had never heard before.

"Anyway," said Roger above the music, "I'm glad to see you and the girl finally went and did it . . ."

"What?" Noah asked, hazily trying to remember if he had said anything. "What're you talking about?"

"It was sticking out all over your face," Roger said, grinning. "Like an electric sign." He played a long passage in the bass.

Roger disappeared into the Army the next day. He wouldn't let Noah go down to the recruiting station with him, and he left him all his belongings, all the furniture, all the books, and even all his clothes, although they were much too large for Noah. "I won't need any of this stuff," Roger said, looking around critically at the accumulation of the baggage of his twenty-six years. "It's just junk anyway." He stuffed a copy of the *New Republic* into his pocket to read on the subway ride down to Whitehall Street, smiling and saying, "Oh, what a frail weapon I have here," and waved at Noah and jammed his hat at his own private angle on the lean, close-cropped head, and once and for all left the room in which he had lived for five years. Noah watched him go, with a choked feeling in his throat, and a premonition that he would never have a friend again and that the best days of his life were past.

Occasionally Noah would get a dry, sardonic note from some camp in the South, and once a mimeographed company order announcing that Private Roger Cannon had been promoted to Private First Class, and then there was a long lapse until a two-page letter came from the Philippines, describing the red-light section of Manila and a half-Burmese, half-Dutch girl who had the S.S. *Texas* tattooed on her belly. There was a postscript, in Roger's sprawling handwriting. "P. S. Stay out of the Army. It is not for human beings."

There was, of course, one advantage, and Noah felt guiltily how much he was enjoying it. Now he and Hope had a place of their own. They were no longer night prowlers, famished for each other, waiting sadly in cold vestibules for Bible-reading uncles to go to bed, lovers lacking a couch to bed their love in, sad-eyed children comically frustrated on the public concrete of the city.

In the months after Roger's departure, Noah felt that he had finally, after all these years, made the discovery of his body. It was stronger than he had known and capable of more feelings than he had ever expected. He even took to looking at it in the long mirror behind the door, and with the blessing of Hope's approval on it, it appeared infinitely more graceful and useful than it had seemed to him before. Oh, he thought gratefully, looking at his bare chest, oh, how lucky it is I have no hair on it.

Hope, with a private place that was so securely their own, was unexpectedly wanton. In the warm familiar darkness of the city summer the cold hills of her Vermont puritanism vanished in riotous smoke, and they matched hunger for hunger, claim for claim on the other's flesh. In the dizzying ebb and flow of love, in the shabby room which had become the dearest and most profound secret of their lives, the noise of the streets below, the shouting on the corners, the calls in the Senate, the gunfire on other continents, dwindled to a remote murmur of background music, drums and bugles in the camp of another army far away in another war.

※

When Stage Designer Aline Bernstein met famous author Thomas Wolfe in New York in the early thirties, a fire was ignited that illuminated the entire literary world of the day. Indeed, the most intimate details of their intense and tortured relationship were revealed by the principals themselves.

The Thomas Wolfe selection reprinted here (the very last section of his novel *Of Time and the River,* published in 1935) and Miss Bernstein's story, taken from a short collection called *Three Blue Suits* (published in a limited edition only in 1933), are, I guess, the most indisputable "companion pieces" in this volume, detailing as they do the reactions of the two participants in the kind of tempestuous romance that flowers too seldom in these days of scientifically regulated emotions and behavior.

ED.

Faust and Helen

By THOMAS WOLFE

IMMENSE and sudden, and with abrupt nearness, the telescopic magic of a dream, the English ship appeared upon the coasts of France, and approached with the strange, looming immediacy of powerful and gigantic objects that move at great speed: there was no sense of continuous movement, of gradual and progressive enlargement, rather the visages of the ship melted rapidly from one bigness to another as do the visages of men in a cinema, which, by a series of fading sizes, brings these kinematic shapes of things, like genii unstoppered from a wizard's bottle, to an overpowering command above the spectator.

At first there was only the calm endlessness of the evening sea, the worn headlands of Europe, and the land, with its rich, green slopes, its striped patterns of minutely cultivated earth, its ancient fortresses and its town—the town of Cherbourg—which, from this distance, lay like a solid pattern of old chalk at the base of the coastal indentation.

Westward, a little to the south, against the darkening bulk of the headland, a long riband of smoke, black and low, told the position of the ship. She was approaching fast, her bulk widened; she had been a dot, a smudge, a shape—a tiny, hardly noticed point in the calm and immense geography of evening. Now she was there, sliding gently in beyond the ancient breakwater, inhabiting and dominating the universe with the presence of her sixty thousand tons, so that the vast setting of sky and sea and earth, in which formerly she had been only an inconspicuous but living mark, were now a background for her magnificence.

At this very moment of her arrival the sun rested upon the western wave like a fading coal: its ancient light fell over sea and land without violence or heat, with a remote, unearthly glow that had the delicate tinging of old bronze. Then, swiftly, the sun sank down into the sea, the uninhabited sky now burned with a fierce, an almost unbearable glory; the sun's old light had faded; and the ship was there outside the harbor, sliding softly through the water now, and quartering, in slow turn, upon the land as she came up for anchor.

The sheer wall of her iron plates scarcely seemed to move at all now in the water, it was as if she were fixed and foundered there among the tides, as implacable as the headlands of the coast; yet, over her solid bows the land was wheeling slowly. Water foamed noisily from her sides in thick, tumbling columns: the sea gulls swarmed around her, fluttering greedily and heavily to the water with their creaking and unearthly clamor. Then her anchors rushed out of her, and she stood still.

Meanwhile, the tenders, bearing the passengers who were going to board the ship, had put out from the town even before the ship's arrival, and were now quite near. They had, in fact, cruised slowly for some time about the outer harbor, for the ship was late and the commander had wirelessed asking that there be as little delay as possible when he arrived.

Now the light faded on the land: the fierce, hard brilliance of the western sky, full of bright gold and ragged flame, had melted to an orange afterglow, the subtle, grapy bloom of dusk was melting across the land; the town, far off, was half immersed in it, its moving shadow stole across the fields and slopes, it moved upon the waters like a weft. Above the land the sky was yet full of light—of that strange, phantasmal light of evening which reveals itself to people standing in the dusk below without touching them with any of its radiance: the material and physical property of light seems to have been withdrawn from it, and it remains briefly in the sky, without substance or any living power, like the ghost of light, its soul, its spirit.

In these late skies of France, this late, evening light of waning summer had in it a quality that was high and sad, remote and full of classic repose and dignity. Beneath it, it was as if one saw people grave and beautiful move slowly homeward through long aisles of planted trees: the light was soft, lucent, delicately empearled—and all great labor was over, all strong joy and hate and love had ended, all wild desire and hope, all maddening of the flesh and heart and brain, the fever and the tumult and the fret; and the grave-eyed women in long robes walked slowly with cut flowers in their arms among the glades of trees, and night had come, and they would go to the wood no more.

Now, in this light, all over the land of France the men were coming from the fields: they had used preciously the last light of day, summer was almost over, the fields were mown, the hay was raked and stacked, and in a thousand places, along the Rhine, and along the Marne, in Burgundy, in Touraine, in Provence, the wains were lumbering slowly down the roads.

In the larger towns the nervous and swarming activity of evening had begun: the terraces of the cafés were uncomfortably crowded with noisy people, the pavements were thronged with a chattering and gesticulating tide, the streets were loud with traffic, the clatter of trams, the heavy grinding of buses, the spiteful little horns of innumerable small taxis. But over all, over the opulence of the mown fields, and the untidy and distressful throngings of the towns, hung this high, sad light of evening.

A stranger, a visitor from some newer and more exultant earth—an American, perhaps—had he seen this coast thus for the first time, might have imagined the land as inhabited by a race far different from the one that really lived here: he would have felt the opulent austerity of this earth under its dying light, and he would have been deeply troubled by it.

For such a visitor, disturbed by the profound and subtle melancholy of this scene, for which his own experience had given him no adequate understanding or preparation, because it was steeped in peace without hope, in beauty without joy, in tranquil and brooding resignation without exultancy, the sight of the ship, as she lay now, immense and immovable at her anchor, would have pierced him suddenly with a thrill of victory, a sudden renewal of his faith and hope, a belief in the happy destiny of life.

She lay there, an alien presence in those waters; she had the reality of magic, the reality that is so living and magnificent that it seems unreal. She was miraculous and true—as one looked at her, settled like some magic luminosity upon that mournful coast, a strong cry of exultancy rose up in one's throat: the sight of the ship was as if a man's mistress had laid her hand upon his loins.

The ship was now wholly anchored: she lay there in the water with the living stillness of all objects that were made to move. Although entirely motionless, outwardly as fixed and permanent as any of the headlands of the coast, the story of her power and speed was legible in every line. She glowed and pulsed with the dynamic secret of life, and although her great sides towered immense and silent as a cliff, although the great plates of her hull seemed to reach down and to be founded in the sea's bed, and only the quietly flowing waters seemed to move and eddy softly at her sides, she yet had legible upon her the story of a hundred crossings, the memory of strange seas, of suns and moons and many different lights, the approach of April on far coasts, the change of wars and histories, and the completed dramas of all her voyages, charactered by the phantoms of many thousand passengers, the life, the hate, the love, the bitterness, the jealousy, the intrigue of six-day worlds, each one complete and separate in itself, which only a ship can have, which only the sea can bound, which only the earth can begin or end.

She glowed with the radiance of all her brilliant and luminous history; and besides this, she was literally a visitant from a new world. The stranger from the new world who saw the ship would also instantly have seen this. She had been built several years after the war and was entirely a product of European construction, engineering, navigation, and diplomacy. But her spirit, the impulse that communicated itself in each of her lines, was not European, but American. It is Europeans, for the most part, who have constructed these great ships, but without America they have no meaning. These ships are alive with the supreme ecstasy of the modern world, which is the voyage to America. There is no other experience that is remotely comparable to it, in its sense of joy, its exultancy, its drunken and magnificent hope which, against reason and knowledge, soars into a heaven of fabulous conviction, which believes in the miracle and sees it invariably achieved.

In this soft, this somewhat languid air, the ship glowed like an immense and brilliant jewel. All of her lights were on, they burned row by row straight across her nine hundred feet of length, with the small, hard twinkle of cut gems: it was as if the vast, black cliff of her hull, which strangely suggested the glittering nighttime cliff of the fabulous city that was her destination, had been sown with diamonds.

And above this, her decks were ablaze with light. Her enormous superstructure with its magnificent frontal sweep, her proud breast which was so full of power and speed, her storied decks and promenades as wide as city streets, the fabulous variety and opulence of her public rooms, her vast lounges and salons, her restaurants, grills, and cafés, her libraries, writing rooms, ballrooms, swimming pools, her imperial suites with broad beds, private decks, sitting rooms, gleaming baths—all of this, made to move upon the stormy seas, leaning against eternity and the gray welter of the Atlantic at twenty-seven knots an hour, tenanted by the ghosts, impregnated by the subtle perfumes of thousands of beautiful and expensive women, alive with the memory of the silken undulance of their long backs, with the naked, living velvet of their shoulders as they paced down the decks at night—all of this, with the four great funnels that in the immense drive and energy of their slant were now cut sharp and dark against the evening sky, burned with a fierce, exultant vitality in the soft melancholy of this coast.

The ship struck joy into the spinal marrow. In her intense reality she became fabulous, a visitant from another world, a creature monstrous and magical with life, a stranger, seeming strange, to these melancholy coasts, for she was made to glitter in the hard, sharp air of a younger, more exultant land.

She was made also to quarter on the coasts of all the earth, to range powerfully on the crest and the ridge of the globe, sucking continents toward her, devouring sea and land; she was made to enter European skies like some stranger from another world, to burn strangely and fabulously in the dull, gray air of Europe, to pulse and glow under the soft, wet European sky. But she was only a marvelous stranger there; she was a bright, jeweled thing; she came definitely, indubitably, wonderfully from but one place on earth, and in only that one place could she be fully seen and understood, in only that one place could she slide in to her appointed and imperial setting.

That place was America: that place was the reaches to the American coast: that place was the approaches to the American continent. That place, finally, and absolutely, was the port whither she was bound—the fabulous rock of life, the proud, masted city of the soaring towers, which was flung with a lion's port into the maw of ocean. And as the Americans who were now approaching the ship in the puffing little tender saw this mark upon her, they looked at her and knew her instantly; they felt a qualm along their loins, their flesh stirred.

"Oh, look!" cried a woman suddenly, pointing to the ship whose immense and glittering side now towered over them. "Isn't that lovely! God, but she's big! How do you suppose we're ever going to find the ocean?"

"The first thing I'm going to do, darling, is find my bed," said her companion, in a tone of languorous weariness. A tall and sensual-looking Jewess, she was seated on a pile of baggage, smoking a cigarette, her long legs indolently crossed: indifferently, with smoldering and arrogant glances, she surveyed the crowd of passengers on the tender.

The other woman could not be still: her rosy face was burning with the excitement of the voyage, she kept slipping the ring on and off her finger nervously, and moving around at her brisk little step among the heaped-up piles of baggage.

"Oh, here!" she cried out suddenly in great excitement, pointing to a bag buried at the bottom of one of the piles. "Oh, here!" she cried again to the general public. "This one's mine! Where are the others? Can't you find the others for me?" she said in a sharp, protesting voice to one of the porters, a little, brawny man with sprouting mustaches. "Hey?" she said, lifting her small hand complainingly to her ear as he answered her in a torrent of reassuring French. She turned to her companion protestingly:

"I can't get them to do anything. They don't pay a bit of attention to what I say! I can't find my trunk and two of my bags. I think it's the most dreadful thing I ever heard of. Don't you? Hey?" again she lifted her little hand to her ear, for she was somewhat deaf: her small, rosy face was crimson with excitement and earnestness—in her tone, her manner, her indignation, there was something irresistibly comic, and suddenly her companion began to laugh.

"Oh, Esther!" she said. "Lord!" and then paused abruptly, as if there were no more to say.

Esther was fair; she was fair; she had dove's eyes.

Now the woman's lovely face, like a rarer, richer, and more luminous substance, was glowing among all the other faces of the travelers, which, as the tender circled and came in close below the ship, were fixed with a single intentness upon the great hull that loomed over them with its overpowering immensity.

The great ship cast over them all her mighty spell: most of these people had made many voyages, yet the great ship caught them up again in her magic glow, she possessed and thrilled them with her presence as if they had been children. The travelers stood there silent and intent as the little boat slid in beside the big one, they stood there with uplifted faces; and for a moment it was strange and sad to see them thus, with loneliness, and longing in their eyes. Their faces made small, lifted whitenesses; they shone in the gathering dark with a luminous glimmer: there was something small, naked and lonely in the glimmer of those faces, around them was the immense eternity of sea and death. They heard time.

For if, as men be dying, they can pluck one moment from the darkness into which their sense is sinking, if one moment in all the dark and mysterious forest should then live, it might well be the memory of such a moment as this which, although lacking in logical meaning, burns for an instant in the dying memory as a summary and a symbol of man's destiny on earth. The fading memory has forgotten what was said then by the passengers, the thousand tones and shadings of the living moment are forgotten, but drenched in the strange, brown light of time, the scene glows again for an instant with an intent silence: darkness has fallen upon the eternal earth, the great ship like a monstrous visitant blazes on the waters, and on the tender the faces of the travelers are lifted up like flowers in a kind of rapt and mournful ecstasy—they are weary of travel, they have wandered in strange cities among strange tongues and faces, and they have left not even the print of their foot in any town.

Their souls are naked and alone, and they are strangers upon the earth, and many of them long for a place where those weary of travel may find rest, where those who are tired of searching may cease to search, where there will be peace and quiet living, and no desire. Where shall the weary find peace? Upon what shore will the wanderer come home at last? When shall it cease—the blind groping, the false desires, the fruitless ambitions that grow despicable as soon as they are reached, the vain contest with phantoms, the maddening and agony of the brain and spirit in all the rush and glare of living, the dusty tumult, the grinding, the shouting, the idiot repetition of the streets, the sterile abundance, the sick gluttony, and the thirst which goes on drinking?

Out of one darkness the travelers have come to be taken into another, but for a moment one sees their faces, awful and still, all uplifted toward the ship. This is all: their words have vanished, all memory of the movements they made then has also vanished: one remembers only their silence and their still faces lifted in the phantasmal light of lost time; one sees them ever, still and silent, as they slide from darkness on the river of time; one sees them waiting at the ship's great side, all silent and all damned to die, with their grave, white faces lifted in a single supplication to the ship, and toward the silent row of passengers along the deck, who for a moment return their gaze with the same grave and tranquil stare. The silent meeting is a summary of all the meetings of men's lives: in the silence one hears the slow, sad breathing of humanity, one knows the human destiny.

"Oh, look!" the woman cried again. "Oh, see! Was ever anything more beautiful?" The ship's great beetling cliff swept sheer above her. She turned the small, flushed flower of her face and saw the many men so little, so lonely, silent, and intent, that bent above her, looking from the ship's steep rail. She turned and saw the people all around her, the swift weave and patterned shifting of the forms, and she saw light then, ancient fading light, that fell upon the coasts of evening, and quiet waters reddened by fading day, and heard the unearthly creakings of a gull; and wonder filled her. And the strange and mortal ache of beauty, the anguish to pronounce what never could be spoken, to grasp what never could be grasped, to hold and keep forever what was gone the moment she put her hand upon it—

"Oh, these people here," she cried in a high tone—"The ship! . . . My God, the things that I could tell you all!" she cried indignantly. "The things I know—the things I have inside me here!"—she struck herself upon the breast with one clenched hand—"the way things are, the way they happen, and the beauty of the clear design—and no one ever asks me!" she cried out indignantly. "This wonderful thing is going on inside me all the time—and no one ever wants to know the way it happens!"— and stood staring at her friend accusingly a moment, a little figure of indignant loveliness until, becoming aware of people's smiles and her companion's laughter, her own face was suddenly suffused, and, casting back her head, she was swept with galelike merriment—a full, rich, woman's yell of triumph and delight.

And yet, even as she laughed, she was pierced again by the old ache of wonder, the old anguish of unspoken desire, and saw the many men, so lonely, silent, and intent, the ship immense and sudden there above her in old evening light, and so—remembering, "Canst thou draw out levia-

than with an hook? or his tongue with a cord which thou lettest down?"
—was still with wonder.

Ah, strange and beautiful, the woman thought, how can I longer bear
this joy intolerable, the music of this great song unpronounceable, the
anguish of this glory unimaginable, which fills my life to bursting and
which will not let me speak! It is too hard, and not to be endured, to feel
the great vine welling in my heart, the wild, strange music swelling in my
throat, the triumph of that final perfect song that aches forever there just
at the gateway of my utterance—and that has no tongue to speak! Oh
magic moment that are so perfect, unknown, and inevitable, to stand
here at this ship's great side, here at the huge last edge of evening and
return, with this still wonder in my heart and knowing only that somehow we are fulfilled of you, oh, time! And see how gathered there against
the rail high over us, there at the ship's great side, are all the people, silent,
lonely, and so beautiful, strange brothers of this voyage, chance phantoms
of the bitter briefness of our days—and you, oh, youth—for now she saw
him there for the first time—who bend there, lone and lean and secret, at
the rail of night, why are you there alone while these, your fellows, wait?
. . . Ah, secret and alone, she thought—how lean with hunger, and how
fierce with pride, and how burning with impossible desire he bends there
at the rail of night—and he is wild and young and foolish and forsaken,
and his eyes are starved, his soul is parched with thirst, his heart is famished with a hunger that cannot be fed, and he leans there on the rail and
dreams great dreams, and he is made for love and is athirst for glory, and
he is so cruelly mistaken—and so right! . . . Ah, see, she thought, how
that wild light flames there upon his brow—how bright, how burning and
how beautiful— Oh, passionate and proud!—how like the wild, lost soul
of youth you are, how like my wild lost father who will not return!

He turned, and saw her then, and so finding her, was lost, and so losing
self, was found, and so seeing her, saw for a fading moment only the
pleasant image of the woman that perhaps she was, and that life saw. He
never knew: he only knew that from that moment his spirit was impaled
upon the knife of love. From that moment on he never was again to lose
her utterly, never to wholly repossess unto himself the lonely, wild integrity of youth, which had been his. At that instant of their meeting, that
proud inviolability of youth was broken, not to be restored. At that moment of their meeting she got into his life by some dark magic, and before
he knew it, he had her beating in the pulses of his blood—somehow thereafter—how he never knew—to steal into the conduits of his heart, and to
inhabit the lone, inviolable tenement of his one life; so, like love's great
thief, to steal through all the adyta of his soul, and to become a part of
all he did and said and was—through this invasion so to touch all loveliness that he might touch, through this strange and subtle stealth of love

henceforth to share all that he might feel or make or dream, until there was for him no beauty that she did not share, no music that did not have her being in it, no horror, madness, hatred, sickness of the soul, or grief unutterable, that was not somehow consonant to her single image and her million forms—and no final freedom and release bought through the incalculable expenditure of blood and anguish and despair, that would not bear upon its brow forever the deep scar, upon its sinews the old mangling chains, of love.

After all the blind, tormented wanderings of youth, that woman would become his heart's center and the target of his life, the image of immortal oneness that again collected him to one, and hurled the whole collected passion, power and might of his one life into the blazing certitude, the immortal governance and unity, of love.

"Set me as a seal upon thine heart, as a seal upon thine arm: for love is strong as death; jealousy is cruel as the grave; the coals thereof are coals of fire, which hath a most vehement flame."

And now all the faces pass in through the ship's great side (the tender flower face among them). Proud, potent faces of rich Jews, alive with wealth and luxury, glow in rich, lighted cabins; the doors are closed, and the ship is given to the darkness and the sea.

Eugene

By ALINE BERNSTEIN

THE DAY was warm, it was nearly twelve o'clock, but sleep still clutched Eugene, pinned him to the bed where he lay helpless. Sleep covered him with a mossy blanket, great clots of sleep were in his brain, choking sleep layered his throat and nostrils. His face was spangled with sweat; it tightened the dark waves of his hair into hundreds of ringlets, and soaked the neck of his opened shirt.

His length filled the bed; he was sprawled diagonally above the bed clothes, arms hanging down on either side. His head lay twisted, the face in profile, face and features disproportionately delicate to the body. The only sign of life was the quick pulsing visible where the shirt fell away from his neck. One hand held a coat of blue serge by the sleeve, the coat dragging along the floor; the other hand lay on an open ledger, the pages covered with writing. A yellow pencil had fallen from his relaxed fingers, and beside the book was a coffee cup in a saucer that did not match it, and the saucer was filled with cigarette butts. All over the floor were more cigarette butts, sprinklings of ashes, odd socks, a collar or two, and several neckties. Beneath the coat, under his left hand, were books, some opened face down on the floor, some opened face up, some piled together, all bearing unmistakable signs of the wear and tear of continued reading.

An engagement to lunch with his publisher was trying to break through to consciousness, it was boring its way up, hardly strong enough to breast the waves of sleep. He must have heard a step coming up the stairs, for when she had let herself in with her key, his eyelids were partly open, though the eyes were still glazed and far away. He was trying so hard to come to life, to return from the land of dark magic that held him each day in thrall.

She tried to put her parcels on the table, but it was full of litter, like the floor; books face up and face down, books in stacks, coffee cups with black dregs and ashes and cigarette ends, sticky glasses, an old typewriter —it was a disgrace the way he left his letters around for everyone to read. She would read them herself, against her better judgment, and against her principles, and got many a heartache. The women were after him; there was a letter that would have cost a school principal her job if it had come to light. She turned to lay the things on her own drawing table, and found it piled with all kinds of newspapers—yesterday's, last night's, foreign ones, papers from his home town, books, books, letters, letters, and worst of all, burnt matches. She was ready to cry with vexation, but what was the use, he couldn't change, only he might have had some consideration for the drawing table. She went into the kitchenette to dispose of the things, and gave a despairing look at the used-up dishes and pots in the sink.

"My God, how does he do it?" she thought. "It was cleaned yesterday. If I tried, it would take me a week to get a place looking like this." She laid her hat and coat over a pile of his clothes on a chair. With the first kiss her vexation was gone.

"Your neck is all sweaty, you smell like a little baby out of its nap, you smell like musty books and I love them!"

He held her tight, tried to draw her back into sleep with him.

"You smell like goose grease, all Jews smell like goose grease, but you smell like a flower too, a fresh dewy flower just out of the bathtub."

"Who ever heard of a flower out of a bathtub? You're crazy! You're—"

"*You* have heard of a flower out of a bathtub. You heard it this minute, and very few people in this day and age have any such experience, hearing something entirely new. What's more, this flower grew out of a dung heap, it was nourished and rooted on a pile of Broadway refuse, it—"

"Yes, and see what it can do now, this flower can cook the tastiest meal you ever ate, it can design beautiful clothes, it can sew, it can create perfect backgrounds for playwriters' plays, it can do a day's work before it comes to fix an author's lunch, it can—"

"Lunch? Don't you know I have to go uptown? I have an engagement, I must go, here you are taking up my time as usual. You talk, talk, talk while the hands slip round the clock, and with all your talk you haven't said one word about my new suit. I have the pants on my legs, I have the vest on my chair and I have the coat on my floor."

"Yes, and I have a blue tie with white spots, in my coat pocket. This is my Easter present. Your own mother would never know you in this necktie, it's going to make that new blue suit hum, and all the lunch you don't spill on the suit, you can sop up with the tie. You tell your friend up on Fifth Avenue that he had better bring an extra fifty cents along to feed the clothes. Darling, I forgot that you were going uptown for lunch and I brought in all sorts of stuff, but it will keep for dinner. Would you like me to cook dinner for you? I saw a duck in the market, it was short and fat, and white as the driven snow; it might have been a little Jewish girl bleached in the sun."

"Don't be silly, Jewish girls get brown in the sun, I've seen a million of them on Long Beach."

"All right, my love, have it your own way, but tell me this, why did you have to sleep all night in your new trousers?"

"I did not sleep all night in my blue pants, nor in any thing else, I worked all night, and about five o'clock this morning I started to try on the new suit, when the bell rang and up came Thompson and Wilcox from Charleston. They were on a party all night and brought a bottle of villainous corn likker, so we had a few and it seemed only fair to show them my suit. I got into the pants and we had a couple more, Wilcox called up his girl and we had a couple more because she was angry—I had to speak to her. I said, 'Daisy, think of all the girls who are never called up at 5:30 A.M., all the girls who are never called up at all, how the hell would you like to be one of those girls?'

"She said, 'I get down on my bended knees every night and thank the Lord I am engaged to a drunken good-for-nothing.' She said, 'Tell him for me, I went out to dinner with his cousin, we had a quart of champagne, and we drove over the new bridge.'

"So I told him and he started to cry. By the time they left I was exhausted, I lay down to rest a moment before going to bed, I was reading. Listen to this, my dear, how beautiful, they can't do it any more. That ungainly minister in his country parsonage, writing about a little child, telling about the little child's faith."

She lay still, it was so lovely, lying here and hearing the beautiful poetry. It was twice beautiful, once in itself and again because it came on his voice. Her head against his chest could feel the vibration of voice and poetry together. Why couldn't they just freeze like this, turn to stone, never be forced to go on to some inevitable end. She knew she had to break it, to get him up and out to his engagement. He would read there for hours. She held up her hand with the wristwatch on it and put it before his eyes.

"You have to shave too," she said.

> "Then, as all my soules bee,
> Emparadised in you,"

She moved her arm so that her hand lay against the pulsing heart, and so made one more channel for him to flow to her. He finished. The poem was above and around them, held them together, touched off the inflammable material of their love. Finally she had to move, to make him go, he would be so angry because she kept him there, he would shout and rail at her for making him late for his appointment. It was really important, he had to go.

"My dear," she said, "please get up and dress. I'll make coffee while you bathe and shave. Would you like some eggs? No, I forgot, you are going to lunch, just a piece of toast. If you stay there another minute you can't even have coffee. Let me have your suit, it's a mess, that nice new suit, I must straighten it out for you. Wasn't he wonderful, the fellow who waited on us, did you notice the way he—"

Eugene sprang from the bed in a late but excessive fit of energy.

"Right you are, my girl, you're not often right but this is one of the occasions. Coffee is the correct word, coffee and no bath. The papers will carry tomorrow morning, 'Mr. Eugene Lyon introduced a novel custom for breakfast yesterday. He had coffee and no bath. Mr. Lyon is the son of Mrs. Frederick Lyon of Charleston, well known in real estate circles, and himself the author of that—' "

"What! No bath? They won't let you in, don't you know that is the most select and stylish publishing house in this broad land? Why, young men of good family deem it a privilege to work there for nothing, young women also, and if you will kindly move your great hulking frame away from the sink I will fill the kettle and make the first item of the new-style breakfast."

Eugene watched her while she cleared the sink, and wondered why there wasn't some way to make pots and dishes clean themselves up, and go neatly into the cupboard. He took his shaving brush in hand and looked at it a long time. He put it down and took up his toothbrush and looked at that. Then he saw his face in the mirror and looked at it for a long time and started to make funny grimaces, stretching his mouth, making grotesque expressions of emotion, finally striking a Napoleonic attitude.

"It's ten minutes to one, you idiot," she called.

He polished off his teeth and lathered his face. The coffee began to bubble and smell good. That will make him hurry a little, she thought. He made a long clean path from the top of his cheek to his chin with the razor, then looked through the door to see what she was doing. Gobs of lather dripped onto his trousers. He pointed the razor at her.

"I know what you are thinking, you think I am lazy, I sleep too much. I am not lazy, I am exhausted by the constant working of my brain, my mind beats out a thousand rhythms while you, poor fool, think I am wasting time. My mind isn't in tight little compartments like yours, each one with a label. You can always close up one and open up another and it makes no impression on you, it is the most extraordinary and irritating—"

"No, darling, it is not true. I love you so much that you overlay my being. It makes you angry that I can love you so and still do my work, but God made me that way and I can't help it. You know the work I do cannot compare to yours, it is not so deep, so great. I don't think you are lazy, but why do you ever make engagements for lunch? We go through this same performance every time."

"Because publishers desire my company for lunch, I entertain them, they love me. Why do you take lunch with me nine days a week? You begrudge the occasional lunch I throw to my publisher, you would like to lunch with me twelve days a week. I know, you want—"

"The lather is all drying out on your face as well as your trousers. It is one o'clock and how you are going to be at Fifty-eighth Street at quarter to one is a mystery to me, but possibly that great brain can solve it."

Eugene turned back to the steaming sink where he had left the hot-water tap running. The stream had caught the edge of a saucer and spurted fine beads down his left leg. He wanted to stay and lunch with her, he wanted to go uptown and lunch with Watkins, he wanted to walk uptown, he wanted to ride up on the bus, he wanted to take a taxi and dash up to the door, he wanted to stay home and write, he wanted to lie on the bed and hold her close to him, he wanted to tease and torment her and make her cry, he wanted her to go away and leave him alone, he wanted to stand by the window and let his mind float out into the infinite, he wanted to think about all the books he was going to write, he wanted a long drink of gin that was in the closet, where she would not be likely to see it, he wanted to live in everyone's house to see what they were like, he wanted to get inside her mind, he wanted to learn what a woman really thought. There were passages in a woman's mind, back ways and digressions that he never could find. Some day he'd get some woman down and make her tell him everything, if he broke every bone in her body. This one was always holding something back, she never gave up the last drop, she saved up for other things, for work. She was friendly with too many people; but he loved her; if only he was sure she was good.

The coffee boiled over, he cursed and turned out the gas below the pot. Two little rivers of coffee crept over the edge of the stove and fell into the upturned cuff of his trouser leg. He felt the moisture come through to his ankle, he cursed some more. She came running and cleaned up the coffee with a dish towel.

"Now listen, Eugene, this is ridiculous. I'm going to stand right here until you are dressed. Go on, finish your shaving. I'll get you out a clean shirt, don't tell me you will wear the one you have on, it reeks with liquor, sweat, all very well for me but how about those gentlemanly young workers uptown? I want you to look fine today."

He really started to hurry now, finished shaving, put his head under the tap to get all the soap off, and came out rosy, clean and damp all over, with more water and suds on his legs. The cuff of his coat on the floor had taken a little drink of coffee from one of the old saucers. She took a clean handkerchief and wiped the suit off to the best of her ability. His lethargy had left him.

He found his taxi jammed in traffic at Forty-eighth Street, his nerves jangled and tortured him as though he himself were wedged helpless. He decided to walk, it would be quicker and it would be better than sitting still.

When he reached the offices, he found he was only half an hour late, he could have stopped for another cup of coffee. She had made him hurry so that his tongue was burned by the first cup. Everybody was glad to see him, he was their best bet, the white hope of the young writers. His book, with all its power and beauty, would be a credit to the House; they had discovered him.

His friend took him to one of those magnificent gray stone houses with imposing iron gates, houses that never suspected in their dull and expensive beginning what an enchanting middle age they would enjoy. The bar was like a bargain counter, bright people crowding and laughing, spilling the overflow of cocktails, calling each other by their first names. Through the delicious lunch Eugene talked fully nine-tenths of the time. The rush of his temperament was turning out instead of inward, the good drinks had changed the current. They discussed everything, books, food, drinks, the trend of the times, his future, what he was to do with himself after publication, where he was to go to write the next book. Watkins had made a suggestion, and when they returned to the office, Eugene had written a letter. As the letter left his fingers and dropped into the box, a little cloud came to rest over his mind, a cloud that was to grow so large some day that it threw her entire life into cold black shadow.

He walked down Fifth Avenue, his head upturned, sniffing the springtime air. He stopped off at his club to see if there were letters from home. There were plenty of letters, and there was half a bottle of gin. The bartender mixed him a Tom Collins. It tasted good; he was thirsty and excited. Whoever Mr. Collins may have been, his soul is resting somewhere in peace, for Eugene used up the remainder of the gin in toasts to his memory. Drops of the Collins invention gleamed here and there on Eugene's coat and vest. He walked into the shadowy hall, cool, spacious and clean, up the stairs into the library. It was impossible to resist the deep leather couch. He would rest himself a while, he must think of how he would tell her.

He reached down some old volumes of London *Punch;* he could think while he looked at the pictures. She would enjoy these books; pity he couldn't take them home to show her. How calm it was in the dim light, how soothing, everybody should own a downy couch in a dim room, on an early spring afternoon.

"Mr. Lyon! Mr. Lyon! Mr. Lyon! Mr. Lyon!"

Eugene's sleeping mind responded to the call of his own name.

The boy stood looking down.

"I hated to call you, Mr. Lyon, but the lady phoned twice."

He looked at the clock. Seven, and he had promised to be home by three. The evening was fine, he would walk down and clear the cobwebs, he would stop off and get a pint of rye, she would like that and he needed a little drink. She was fine, no one like her, she knew how he had to live and what he liked. His heart was tender, and all his feeling about her was loving. But he wished he could pack her up in a trunk and take her out only when he felt like it. That would not do either, for sometimes when he didn't feel like seeing her at all, she would say something, do something, that would touch him to the quick. Possibly that was the reason for marriage. Only in marriage is the deep-rooted fecund love. Watkins was right, this relationship bore nothing but jealousy and pain in the end.

She was bending over the stove, stirring something in a pan. She made believe she did not hear him come in. She was humming as loud as she could and finally her voice broke into a giggle.

His face had a sheepish grin. He held up the bottle for her to see. "Giggle soup, my dear, it will create a giggle where it does not exist and prolong one already in being."

"Did you have a good time? Tell me what they said to you, was Watkins nice? I'm sure they are all crazy about you. Who can help it? You are the most enchanting person that ever lived, but I am the only woman in the world who can stand your ways. Look, I'll open the oven door and show you a picture. Did you ever in your life see a plumper, finer duck? You know, darling, I would rather cook a meal for you than anything in the world, I would rather listen to you than anything in the world when you tell me about things; it is much finer than the things themselves." She was flushed, and happy that he was here again. She had worked hard from early morning, and this her reward.

"I'll tell you about everything, but first I must sit and rest, I walked down from Forty-fourth Street. My dear, do you realize the number of questions you ask, they are utterly meaningless, you never wait for an answer."

"They are not meaningless, they are good questions, they show you what I want to know, and they convey my state of mind. Of course I don't expect an answer right away. I wouldn't get one if I did. I expect nothing whatsoever. All I get is so much velvet."

He had his arms around her, kissing her warm red face a hundred times. She struggled to free the hand that held the cooking spoon, but it was too late, the fat from the duck was already pressed close to his side. How stupid he was about things, but how wonderful.

"Go and rest, my dear, while the dinner is cooking, and then we can have a beautiful long evening. I'll tell you about all the things I saw in the street on the way downtown this morning, I'll tell you about how things were here in New York when I was a little girl, and you can tell me about your lunch and everything that happened. First, we'll drink each other's health, just a little one."

Eugene sat where he could watch her, the old easy chair had long ago molded itself into his form. He drank his whiskey, sniffing it and tasting it slowly. She was so sure, so swift at her work. Maybe the Guggenheim was all apportioned, maybe, after all, he would stay. She came with the steaming plates of duck and vegetables, the bowl of cool salad. They ate and laughed together until they could no more.

"Eugene, aren't you glad you're a swell author and a man, otherwise you'd have to do the dishes."

"Can't you leave the dishes? I'll do them, I'll help you, we'll clear them away and wash them later, we'll throw them out of the window if you prefer. I want to talk to you, dearest, I must talk to you about a . . ."

She stood still, there was something the matter, his voice was different. She turned toward him.

"Eugene, what is the matter, tell me at once, aren't they going to publish the book?"

"No, no, it isn't that, they are crazy about the book, it is something else. Come here, my dear, I'll . . ."

"Eugene, tell me at once, what is the matter." Her heart began to beat, it sounded in her ears. "What have those men uptown been saying to you?" She looked at him, her eyes wide with fright.

"Watkins suggested," he cleared his throat. "You see it will be six months before anything comes in from the book, even if it is a success, they all thought up there it would be a good idea—" He got up from his chair and went to her. "Watkins thought it would be a good idea if I went abroad on a Guggenheim fellowship, it would give me a year on the new one, quiet now, my dear."

The plates fell crashing to the floor, her hands caught at her throat, she moved a step away.

"How much?"

"Twenty-five hundred for the year, away from America, no more teaching—"

"So you'd let me down, sell me out for twenty-five hundred, would you!" Black wings beat freezing air upon her. "Darling, no, you can't mean it. What do they know up there about you, they are a lot of snobs, they don't know that I am here, have you ever told Watkins about me, about how we love each other? You are ashamed, you never have told him. You never would have me meet any of those people."

"I told him that I had a dear friend that I hated to leave, it would be hard for us both. Come, my dear, lie down beside me for a while, quiet now, quiet."

"How can you live and do such a thing, how can you take your food or breathe the air?" She could barely speak, sobs choked her. "How can you deny the Eugene I have loved? You promised you would never leave me, darling, you said as long as we both lived you would never—remember, remember all the times you have said it." Her sobs, her tears in great streams were on his shoulder. "This morning, here beside you, I wanted to turn to stone, to die, life without you—"

"Stop that, I hate people who want to die, I loathe all—"

"I do not want to die, I love life, but not on ugly terms. You know that no one finds life more rich than I do, but what use is it to me without you? My dear, how can you? What on God's earth can you find to balance my pain?"

"I am not gone, see, my dearest, Eugene's arms are holding you, here, now, I love you, my life will never know a love like this again. I will not stay away, I can manage to go for six months and then come back, I promise."

"Don't use the word promise, never again. You have no conception of its meaning, it is a golden word, but to you it is only an expedient, it fills in the gap where you are lacking. You think you can fool me once more with that word. You think you can make me quiet with it before you go."

It seemed to Eugene as though she would weep an ocean full. It was terrible. He tried to comfort her, but there was no comforting in this situation. Either he must stay or go, and his resolve was to go. She was becoming a little more quiet, but she was holding so tight to him that he could scarcely move. He hated it, he wished with all his heart that things could be always just the way he wanted them. He wanted a world where he could wander at his own sweet will, he wished that he could write in thought, he wished that his books would spring full printed from his brain, without the drudgery of pencil guided by his hand on paper, typing, cutting, revising. He wished that he could tell her of his deep love, and still make her see the necessity of his going. He wished he could do all this without having to do it. He wished that he was far away in space and time, far enough so that he could write the book about her. There was so much in his mind, he tried to reach his notebook. It was in the pocket of his coat. He moved and looked down at her face. The beauty was obliterated, sobs and tears and grief had made it red and swollen. It was like a battlefield plowed with the harrow of her pain. He wanted none of her grief, no pain but his own. He pulled his arm free, and wrenched the notebook from his pocket, tearing a long gash in the coat. He wrote in the book, "Can there be no revolution without bloodshed?"

She looked at what he had written. "No, no," she cried and her helpless hands beat blows upon his head and chest. She cried and beat until she had no more strength. They both sank back into the old embrace, and daylight found them, sleeping.

II

Yesterday

Indian Summer of a Forsyte

By JOHN GALSWORTHY

"And Summer's lease hath all too short a date."
SHAKESPEARE

TO
ANDRÉ CHEVRILLON

I

ON THE last day of May in the early nineties, about six o'clock of the evening, old Jolyon Forsyte sat under the oak tree below the terrace of his house at Robin Hill. He was waiting for the midges to bite him, before abandoning the glory of the afternoon. His thin brown hand, where blue veins stood out, held the end of a cigar in its tapering, long-nailed fingers —a pointed polished nail had survived with him from those earlier Victorian days when to touch nothing, even with the tips of the fingers, had been so distinguished. His domed forehead, great white mustache, lean cheeks, and long lean jaw were covered from the westering sunshine by an old brown Panama hat. His legs were crossed; in all his attitude was serenity and a kind of elegance, as of an old man who every morning put eau de Cologne upon his silk handkerchief. At his feet lay a woolly brown-and-white dog trying to be a Pomeranian—the dog Balthasar between whom and old Jolyon primal aversion had changed into attachment with the years. Close to his chair was a swing, and on the swing was seated one of Holly's dolls—called "Duffer Alice"—with her body fallen over her legs and her doleful nose buried in a black petticoat. She was never out of disgrace, so it did not matter to her how she sat. Below the oak tree the lawn dipped down a bank, stretched to the fernery, and, beyond that refinement, became fields, dropping to the pond, the coppice, and the prospect—"Fine, remarkable"—at which Swithin Forsyte, from under this very tree, had stared five years ago when he drove down with Irene to look at the house. Old Jolyon had heard of his brother's exploit—that drive which had become quite celebrated on Forsyte 'Change. Swithin! And the fellow had gone and died, last November, at the age of only seventy-nine, renewing the doubt whether Forsytes could live forever, which had first arisen when Aunt Ann passed away. Died! and left only Jolyon and James, Roger and Nicholas and Timothy, Julia, Hester, Susan! And old Jolyon thought: "Eighty-five! I don't feel it—except when I get that pain."

His memory went searching. He had not felt his age since he had bought his nephew Soames's ill-starred house and settled into it here at Robin Hill over three years ago. It was as if he had been getting younger every spring, living in the country with his son and his grandchildren— June, and the little ones of the second marriage, Jolly and Holly; living down here out of the racket of London and the cackle of Forsyte 'Change,' free of his boards, in a delicious atmosphere of no work and all play, with plenty of occupation in the perfecting and mellowing of the house and its twenty acres, and in ministering to the whims of Holly and Jolly. All the knots and crankiness, which had gathered in his heart during that long and tragic business of June, Soames, Irene his wife, and poor young Bosinney, had been smoothed out. Even June had thrown off her melancholy at last—witness this travel in Spain she was taking now with her father and her stepmother. Curiously perfect peace was left by their departure; blissful, yet blank, because his son was not there. Jo was never anything but a comfort and a pleasure to him nowadays—an amiable chap; but women, somehow—even the best—got a little on one's nerves, unless of course one admired them.

Far off a cuckoo called; a wood pigeon was cooing from the first elm tree in the field, and how the daisies and buttercups had sprung up after the last mowing! The wind had got into the sou'west, too—a delicious air, sappy! He pushed his hat back and let the sun fall on his chin and cheek. Somehow, today, he wanted company—wanted a pretty face to look at. People treated the old as if they wanted nothing. And with the un-Forsytean philosophy which ever intruded on his soul, he thought: "One's never had enough! With a foot in the grave one'll want something, I shouldn't be surprised!" Down here—away from the exigencies of affairs —his grandchildren, and the flowers, trees, birds of his little domain, to say nothing of sun and moon and stars above them, said, "Open, sesame," to him day and night. And sesame had opened—how much, perhaps, he did not know. He had always been responsive to what they had begun to call "Nature," genuinely, almost religiously responsive, though he had never lost his habit of calling a sunset a sunset and a view a view, however deeply they might move him. But nowadays Nature actually made him ache, he appreciated it so. Every one of these calm, bright, lengthening days, with Holly's hand in his, and the dog Balthasar in front looking studiously for what he never found, he would stroll, watching the roses open, fruit budding on the walls, sunlight brightening the oak leaves and saplings in the coppice, watching the water-lily leaves unfold and glisten, and the silvery young corn of the one wheatfield; listening to the starlings and skylarks, and the Alderney cows chewing the cud, flicking slow their tufted tails; and every one of these fine days he ached a little from sheer love of it all, feeling perhaps, deep down, that he had not very much longer to enjoy it. The thought that some day—perhaps not ten years hence, perhaps not five—all this world would be taken away from him, before he had exhausted his powers of loving it, seemed to him in the nature of an injustice brooding over his horizon. If anything came after this life, it wouldn't be what he wanted; not Robin Hill, and flowers and birds and pretty faces—too few, even now, of those about him! With the years his dislike of humbug had increased; the orthodoxy he had worn in the sixties, as he had worn side whiskers out of sheer exuberance, had long dropped off, leaving him reverent before three things alone—beauty, upright conduct, and the sense of property; and the greatest of these now was beauty. He had always had wide interests, and, indeed, could still read *The Times,* but he was liable at any moment to put it down if he heard a blackbird sing. Upright conduct, property—somehow, they were tiring; the blackbirds and the sunsets never tired him, only gave him an uneasy feeling that he could not get enough of them. Staring into the stilly radiance of the early evening and at the little gold and white flowers on the lawn, a thought came to him: This weather was like the music of *Orfeo,* which he had recently heard at Covent Garden. A beautiful opera, not like Meyerbeer, nor even quite Mozart, but, in its way, perhaps even more lovely; something classical and of the Golden Age about it, chaste and mellow, and the Ravogli "almost worthy of the old days"—highest praise he could bestow. The yearning of Orpheus for the beauty he was losing, for his love going down to Hades, as in life love and beauty did go—the yearning which sang and throbbed through the golden music, stirred also in the lingering beauty of the world that evening. And with the tip of his cork-soled, elastic-sided boot he involuntarily stirred the ribs of the dog Balthasar, causing the animal to wake and attack his fleas; for though he was supposed to have none, nothing could persuade him of the fact. When he had finished, he rubbed the place he had been scratching against his master's calf, and settled down again with his chin over the instep of the disturbing boot. And into old Jolyon's mind came a sudden recollection—a face he had seen at that opera three weeks ago—Irene, the wife of his precious nephew Soames, that man of property! Though he had not met her since the day of the "At Home" in his old house at Stanhope Gate, which celebrated his granddaughter June's ill-starred engagement to young Bosinney, he had remembered her at once, for he had always admired her—a very pretty creature. After the death of young Bosinney, whose mistress she had so reprehensibly become, he had heard that she had left Soames at once. Goodness only knew what she had been doing since. That sight of her face—a side view—in the row in front, had been literally the only reminder these three years that she was still alive. No one ever spoke of her. And yet Jo had told him something once—something which had upset him completely. The boy had got it from George Forsyte, he believed, who had seen Bosinney in the fog the day he was run over—something which explained the young fellow's distress—an act of Soames towards his wife—a shocking act. Jo had seen her, too, that afternoon, after the news was out, seen her for a moment, and his description had always lingered in old Jolyon's mind—"wild and lost" he had called her. And next day June had gone there—bottled up her feelings and gone there, and the maid had cried and told her how her mistress had slipped out in the night and vanished. A tragic business altogether! One thing was certain—Soames had never been able to lay hands on her again. And he was living at Brighton, and journeying up and down—a fitting fate, the man of property! For when he once took a dislike to anyone—as he had to his nephew—old Jolyon never got over it. He remembered still the sense of relief with which he had heard the news of Irene's disappearance. It had been shocking to think of her a prisoner in that house to which she must have wandered back, when Jo saw her, wandered back for a moment—like a wounded animal to its hole after seeing that news, "Tragic death of an Architect," in the street. Her face had struck him very much the other night—more beautiful than he had remembered, but like a mask, with something going on beneath it. A young woman still—twenty-eight perhaps. Ah, well! Very likely she had another lover by now. But at this subversive thought—for married women should never love: once, even, had been too much—his instep rose, and with it the dog Balthasar's head. The sagacious animal stood up and looked into old Jolyon's face. "Walk?" he seemed to say; and old Jolyon answered: "Come on, old chap!"

Slowly, as was their wont, they crossed among the constellations of buttercups and daisies, and entered the fernery. This feature, where very little grew as yet, had been judiciously dropped below the level of the lawn so that it might come up again on the level of the other lawn and give the impression of irregularity, so important in horticulture. Its rocks and earth were beloved of the dog Balthasar, who sometimes found a mole there. Old Jolyon made a point of passing through it because, though it was not beautiful, he intended that it should be, some day, and he would think: "I must get Varr to come down and look at it; he's better than Beech." For plants, like houses and human complaints, required the best expert consideration. It was inhabited by snails, and if accompanied by his grandchildren, he would point to one and tell them the story of the little boy who said: "Have plummers got leggers, Mother?" "No, sonny." "Then darned if I haven't been and swallowed a snileybob." And when they skipped and clutched his hand, thinking of the snileybob going down the little boy's "red lane," his eyes would twinkle. Emerging from the fernery, he opened the wicket gate, which just there led into the first field, a large and parklike area, out of which, within brick walls, the vegetable garden had been carved. Old Jolyon avoided this, which did not suit his mood, and made down the hill towards the pond. Balthasar, who knew a water rat or two, gamboled in front, at the gait which marks an oldish dog who takes the same walk every day. Arrived at the edge, old Jolyon stood, noting another water lily opened since yesterday; he would show it to Holly tomorrow, when "his little sweet" had got over the upset which had followed on her eating a tomato at lunch—her little arrangements were very delicate. Now that Jolly had gone to school—his first term— Holly was with him nearly all day long, and he missed her badly. He felt that pain too, which often bothered him now, a little dragging at his left side. He looked back up the hill. Really, poor young Bosinney had made an uncommonly good job of the house; he would have done very well for himself if he had lived! And where was he now? Perhaps, still haunting this, the site of his last work, of his tragic love affair. Or was Philip Bosinney's spirit diffused in the general? Who could say? That dog was getting his legs muddy! And he moved towards the coppice. There had been the most delightful lot of bluebells, and he knew where some still lingered like little patches of sky fallen in between the trees, away out of the sun. He passed the cow houses and the henhouses there installed, and pursued a path into the thick of the saplings, making for one of the bluebell plots. Balthasar, preceding him once more, uttered a low growl. Old Jolyon stirred him with his foot, but the dog remained motionless, just where there was no room to pass, and the hair rose slowly along the center of his woolly back. Whether from the growl and the look of the dog's stivered hair, or from the sensation which a man feels in a wood, old Jolyon also felt something move along his spine. And then the path turned, and there was an old mossy log, and on it a woman sitting. Her face was turned away, and he had just time to think: "She's trespassing—I must have a board put up!" before she turned. Powers above! The face he had seen at the opera—the very woman he had just been thinking of! In that confused moment he saw things blurred, as if a spirit—queer effect—the slant of sunlight perhaps on her violet-gray frock! And then she rose and stood smiling, her head a little to one side. Old Jolyon thought: "How pretty she is!" She did not speak, neither did he; and he realized why with a certain admiration. She was here no doubt because of some memory, and did not mean to try and get out of it by vulgar explanation.

"Don't let that dog touch your frock," he said; "he's got wet feet. Come here, you!"

But the dog Balthasar went on towards the visitor, who put her hand down and stroked his head. Old Jolyon said quickly:

"I saw you at the opera the other night; you didn't notice me."

"Oh, yes! I did."

He felt a subtle flattery in that, as though she had added: "Do you think one could miss seeing you?"

"They're all in Spain," he remarked abruptly. "I'm alone; I drove up for the opera. The Ravogli's good. Have you seen the cow houses?"

In a situation so charged with mystery and something very like emotion he moved instinctively towards that bit of property, and she moved beside him. Her figure swayed faintly, like the best kind of French figures; her dress, too, was a sort of French gray. He noticed two or three silver threads in her amber-colored hair, strange hair with those dark eyes of hers, and that creamy-pale face. A sudden sidelong look from the velvety brown eyes disturbed him. It seemed to come from deep and far, from another world almost, or at all events from someone not living very much in this. And he said mechanically:

"Where are you living now?"

"I have a little flat in Chelsea."

He did not want to hear what she was doing, did not want to hear anything; but the perverse word came out:

"Alone?"

She nodded. It was a relief to know that. And it came into his mind that, but for a twist of fate, she would have been mistress of this coppice, showing these cow houses to him, a visitor.

"All Alderneys," he muttered; "they give the best milk. This one's a pretty creature. Woa, Myrtle!"

The fawn-colored cow, with eyes as soft and brown as Irene's own, was standing absolutely still, not having long been milked. She looked round at them out of the corner of those lustrous, mild, cynical eyes, and from her gray lips a little dribble of saliva threaded its way towards the straw. The scent of hay and vanilla and ammonia rose in the dim light of the cool cow house; and old Jolyon said:

"You must come up and have some dinner with me. I'll send you home in the carriage."

He perceived a struggle going on within her; natural, no doubt, with her memories. But he wanted her company; a pretty face, a charming figure, beauty! He had been alone all the afternoon. Perhaps his eyes were wistful, for she answered: "Thank you, Uncle Jolyon. I should like to."

He rubbed his hands, and said:

"Capital! Let's go up, then!" And, preceded by the dog Balthasar, they ascended through the field. The sun was almost level in their faces now, and he could see, not only those silver threads, but little lines, just deep enough to stamp her beauty with a coinlike fineness—the special look of life unshared with others. "I'll take her in by the terrace," he thought: "I won't make a common visitor of her."

"What do you do all day?" he said.

"Teach music; I have another interest, too."

"Work!" said old Jolyon, picking up the doll from off the swing, and smoothing its black petticoat. "Nothing like it, is there? I don't do any now. I'm getting on. What interest is that?"

"Trying to help women who've come to grief." Old Jolyon did not quite understand. "To grief?" he repeated; then realized with a shock that she meant exactly what he would have meant himself if he had used that expression. Assisting the Magdalenes of London! What a weird and terrifying interest! And, curiosity overcoming his natural shrinking, he asked:

"Why? What do you do for them?"

"Not much. I've no money to spare. I can only give sympathy and food sometimes."

Involuntarily old Jolyon's hand sought his purse. He said hastily: "How d'you get hold of them?"

"I go to a hospital."

"A hospital! Phew!"

"What hurts me most is that once they nearly all had some sort of beauty."

Old Jolyon straightened the doll. "Beauty!" he ejaculated: "Ha! Yes! A sad business!" and he moved towards the house. Through a French window, under sun blinds not yet drawn up, he preceded her into the room where he was wont to study *The Times* and the sheets of an agricultural magazine, with huge illustrations of mangold wurzels, and the like, which provided Holly with material for her paintbrush.

"Dinner's in half an hour. You'd like to wash your hands! I'll take you to June's room."

He saw her looking round eagerly; what changes since she had last visited this house with her husband, or her lover, or both perhaps—he did not know, could not say! All that was dark, and he wished to leave it so. But what changes! And in the hall he said:

"My boy Jo's a painter, you know. He's got a lot of taste. It isn't mine, of course, but I've let him have his way."

She was standing very still, her eyes roaming through the hall and music room, as it now was—all thrown into one, under the great skylight. Old Jolyon had an odd impression of her. Was she trying to conjure somebody from the shades of that space where the coloring was all pearl-gray and silver? He would have had gold himself; more lively and solid. But Jo had French tastes, and it had come out shadowy like that, with an effect as of the fume of cigarettes the chap was always smoking, broken here and there by a little blaze of blue or crimson color. It was not *his* dream! Mentally he had hung this space with those gold-framed masterpieces of still and stiller life which he had bought in days when quantity was precious. And now where were they? Sold for a song! That something which made him, alone among Forsytes, move with the times had warned him against the struggle to retain them. But in his study he still had "Dutch Fishing Boats at Sunset."

He began to mount the stairs with her, slowly, for he felt his side.

"These are the bathrooms," he said, "and other arrangements. I've had them tiled. The nurseries are along there. And this is Jo's and his wife's. They all communicate. But you remember, I expect."

Irene nodded. They passed on, up the gallery and entered a large room with a small bed, and several windows.

"This is mine," he said. The walls were covered with the photographs of children and water-color sketches, and he added doubtfully:

"These are Jo's. The view's first-rate. You can see the Grand Stand at Epsom in clear weather."

The sun was down now, behind the house, and over the "prospect" a luminous haze had settled, emanation of the long and prosperous day. Few houses showed, but fields and trees faintly glistened, away to a loom of downs.

"The country's changing," he said abruptly, "but there it'll be when we're all gone. Look at those thrushes—the birds are sweet here in the mornings. I'm glad to have washed my hands of London."

Her face was close to the window pane, and he was struck by its mournful look. "Wish I could make her look happy!" he thought. "A pretty face, but sad!" And taking up his can of hot water he went out into the gallery.

"This is June's room," he said, opening the next door and putting the can down; "I think you'll find everything." And closing the door behind her he went back to his own room. Brushing his hair with his great ebony brushes, and dabbing his forehead with eau de Cologne, he mused. She had come so strangely—a sort of visitation, mysterious, even romantic, as if his desire for company, for beauty, had been fulfilled by—whatever it was which fulfilled that sort of thing. And before the mirror he straightened his still upright figure, passed the brushes over his great white mustache, touched up his eyebrows with eau de Cologne, and rang the bell.

"I forgot to let them know that I have a lady to dinner with me. Let cook do something extra, and tell Beacon to have the landau and pair at half-past ten to drive her back to Town tonight. Is Miss Holly asleep?"

The maid thought not. And old Jolyon, passing down the gallery, stole on tiptoe towards the nursery, and opened the door whose hinges he kept specially oiled that he might slip in and out in the evenings without being heard.

But Holly *was* asleep, and lay like a miniature Madonna, of that type which the old painters could not tell from Venus, when they had completed her. Her long dark lashes clung to her cheeks; on her face was perfect peace—her little arrangements were evidently all right again. And old Jolyon, in the twilight of the room, stood adoring her! It was so charming, solemn, and loving—that little face. He had more than his share of the blessed capacity of living again in the young. They were to him his future life—all of a future life—that his fundamental pagan sanity perhaps admitted. There she was with everything before her, and his blood—some of it—in her tiny veins. There she was, his little companion, to be made as happy as ever he could make her, so that she knew nothing but love. His heart swelled, and he went out, stifling the sound of his patent-leather boots. In the corridor an eccentric notion attacked him: To think that children should come to that which Irene had told him she was helping! Women who were all, once, little things like this one sleeping there! "I must give her a check!" he mused; "Can't bear to think of them!" They had never borne reflecting on, those poor outcasts; wounding too deeply the core of true refinement hidden under layers of conformity to the sense of property—wounding too grievously the deepest thing in him—a love of beauty which could give him, even now, a flutter of the heart, thinking of his evening in the society of a pretty woman. And he went downstairs, through the swinging doors, to the back regions. There, in the wine cellar, was a hock worth at least two pounds a bottle, a Steinberg Cabinet, better than any Johannisberg that ever went down throat; a wine of perfect bouquet, sweet as a nectarine—nectar indeed! He got a bottle out, handling it like a baby, and holding it level to the light, to look. Enshrined in its coat of dust, that mellow-colored, slender-necked bottle gave him deep pleasure. Three years to settle down again since the move from Town—ought to be in prime condition! Thirty-five years ago he had bought it—thank God he had kept his palate, and earned the right to drink it. She would appreciate this; not a spice of acidity in a dozen. He wiped the bottle, drew the cork with his own hands, put his nose down, inhaled its perfume, and went back to the music room.

Irene was standing by the piano; she had taken off her hat and a lace scarf she had been wearing, so that her gold-colored hair was visible, and the pallor of her neck. In her gray frock she made a pretty picture for old Jolyon, against the rosewood of the piano.

He gave her his arm, and solemnly they went. The room, which had been designed to enable twenty-four people to dine in comfort, held now but a little round table. In his present solitude the big dining table oppressed old Jolyon; he had caused it to be removed till his son came back. Here in the company of two really good copies of Raphael Madonnas he was wont to dine alone. It was the only disconsolate hour of his day, this summer weather. He had never been a large eater, like that great chap Swithin, or Sylvanus Heythorp, or Anthony Thornworthy, those cronies of past times; and to dine alone, overlooked by the Madonnas, was to him but a sorrowful occupation, which he got through quickly, that he might come to the more spiritual enjoyment of his coffee and cigar. But this evening was a different matter! His eyes twinkled at her across the little table and he spoke of Italy and Switzerland, telling her stories of his travels there, and other experiences which he could no longer recount to his son and granddaughter because they knew them. This fresh audience was precious to him; he had never become one of those old men who ramble round and round the fields of reminiscence. Himself quickly fatigued by the insensitive, he instinctively avoided fatiguing others, and his natural flirtatiousness towards beauty guarded him specially in his relations with a woman. He would have liked to draw her out, but though she murmured and smiled and seemed to be enjoying what he told her, he remained conscious of that mysterious remoteness which constituted half her fascination. He could not bear women who threw their shoulders and eyes at you, and chattered away; or hard-mouthed women who laid down the law and knew more than you did. There was only one quality in a woman that appealed to him—charm; and the quieter it was, the more he liked it. And this one had charm, shadowy as afternoon sunlight on those Italian hills and valleys he had loved. The feeling, too, that she was, as it were, apart, cloistered, made her seem nearer to himself, a strangely desirable companion. When a man is very old and quite out of the running, he loves to feel secure from the rivalries of youth, for he would still be first in the heart of beauty. And he drank his hock, and watched her lips, and felt nearly young. But the dog Balthasar lay watching her lips too, and despising in his heart the interruptions of their talk, and the tilting of those greenish glasses full of a golden fluid which was distasteful to him.

The light was just failing when they went back into the music room. And, cigar in mouth, old Jolyon said:

"Play me some Chopin."

By the cigars they smoke, and the composers they love, ye shall know the texture of men's souls. Old Jolyon could not bear a strong cigar or Wagner's music. He loved Beethoven and Mozart, Handel and Gluck, and Schumann, and, for some occult reason, the operas of Meyerbeer; but of late years he had been seduced by Chopin, just as in painting he had succumbed to Botticelli. In yielding to these tastes he had been conscious of divergence from the standard of the Golden Age. Their poetry was not that of Milton and Byron and Tennyson; of Raphael and Titian; Mozart and Beethoven. It was, as it were, behind a veil; their poetry hit no one in the face, but slipped its fingers under the ribs and turned and twisted, and melted up the heart. And, never certain that this was healthy, he did not care a rap so long as he could see the pictures of the one or hear the music of the other.

Irene sat down at the piano under the electric lamp festooned with pearl-gray, and old Jolyon, in an armchair, whence he could see her, crossed his legs and drew slowly at his cigar. She sat a few moments with her hands on the keys, evidently searching her mind for what to give him. Then she began and within old Jolyon there arose a sorrowful pleasure, not quite like anything else in the world. He fell slowly into a trance, interrupted only by the movements of taking the cigar out of his mouth at long intervals, and replacing it. She was there, and the hock within him, and the scent of tobacco; but there, too, was a world of sunshine lingering into moonlight, and pools with storks upon them, and bluish trees above, glowing with blurs of wine-red roses, and fields of lavender where milk-white cows were grazing, and a woman all shadowy, with dark eyes and a white neck, smiled, holding out her arms; and through air which was like music a star dropped and was caught on a cow's horn. He opened his eyes. Beautiful piece; she played well—the touch of an angel! And he closed them again. He felt miraculously sad and happy, as one does, standing under a lime tree in full honey flower. Not live one's own life again, but just stand there and bask in the smile of a woman's eyes, and enjoy the bouquet! And he jerked his hand; the dog Balthasar had reached up and licked it.

"Beautiful!" He said: "Go on—more Chopin!"

She began to play again. This time the resemblance between her and "Chopin" struck him. The swaying he had noticed in her walk was in her playing too, and the Nocturne she had chosen and the soft darkness of her eyes, the light on her hair, as of moonlight from a golden moon. Seductive, yes; but nothing of Delilah in her or in that music. A long blue spiral from his cigar ascended and dispersed. "So we go out!" he thought. "No more beauty! Nothing?"

Again Irene stopped.

"Would you like some Gluck? He used to write his music in a sunlit garden, with a bottle of Rhine wine beside him."

"Ah! yes. Let's have *Orfeo*." Round about him now were fields of gold and silver flowers, white forms swaying in the sunlight, bright birds flying to and fro. All was summer. Lingering waves of sweetness and regret flooded his soul. Some cigar ash dropped, and taking out a silk handkerchief to brush it off, he inhaled a mingled scent as of snuff and eau de Cologne. "Ah!" he thought, "Indian summer—that's all!" and he said: "You haven't played one *Che faro*."

She did not answer; did not move. He was conscious of something—some strange upset. Suddenly he saw her rise and turn away, and a pang of remorse shot through him. What a clumsy chap! Like Orpheus, she of course—she too was looking for her lost one in the hall of memory! And disturbed to the heart, he got up from his chair. She had gone to the great window at the far end. Gingerly he followed. Her hands were folded over her breast; he could just see her cheek, very white. And, quite emotionalized, he said: "There, there, my love!" The words had escaped him mechanically, for they were those he used to Holly when she had a pain, but their effect was instantaneously distressing. She raised her arms, covered her face with them, and wept.

Old Jolyon stood gazing at her with eyes very deep from age. The passionate shame she seemed feeling at her abandonment, so unlike the control and quietude of her whole presence was as if she had never before broken down in the presence of another being.

"There, there—there, there!" he murmured, and putting his hand out reverently, touched her. She turned, and leaned the arms which covered her face against him. Old Jolyon stood very still, keeping one thin hand on her shoulder. Let her cry her heart out—it would do her good! And the dog Balthasar, puzzled, sat down on his stern to examine them.

The window was still open, the curtains had not been drawn, the last of daylight from without mingled with faint intrusion from the lamp within; there was a scent of new-mown grass. With the wisdom of a long life old Jolyon did not speak. Even grief sobbed itself out in time; only Time was good for sorrow—Time who saw the passing of each mood, each emotion in turn; Time the layer-to-rest. There came into his mind the words: "As panteth the hart after cooling streams"—but they were of no use to him. Then, conscious of a scent of violets, he knew she was drying her eyes. He put his chin forward, pressed his mustache against her forehead, and felt her shake with a quivering of her whole body, as of a tree which shakes itself free of raindrops. She put his hand to her lips, as if saying: "All over now! Forgive me!"

The kiss filled him with a strange comfort; he led her back to where she had been so upset. And the dog Balthasar, following, laid the bone of one of the cutlets they had eaten at their feet.

Anxious to obliterate the memory of that emotion, he could think of nothing better than china; and moving with her slowly from cabinet to cabinet, he kept taking up bits of Dresden and Lowestoft and Chelsea, turning them round and round with his thin, veined hands, whose skin, faintly freckled, had such an aged look.

"I bought this at Jobson's," he would say; "cost me thirty pounds. It's very old. That dog leaves his bones all over the place. This old 'ship bowl' I picked up at the sale when that precious rip, the Marquis, came to grief. But you don't remember. Here's a nice piece of Chelsea. Now, what would you say *this* was?" And he was comforted, feeling that, with her taste, she was taking a real interest in these things; for, after all, nothing better composes the nerves than a doubtful piece of china.

When the crunch of the carriage wheels was heard at last, he said:

"You must come again; you must come to lunch, then I can show you these by daylight, and my little sweet—she's a dear little thing. This dog seems to have taken a fancy to you."

For Balthasar, feeling that she was about to leave, was rubbing his side against her leg. Going out under the porch with her, he said: "He'll get you up in an hour and a quarter. Take this for your proté-gées," and he slipped a check for fifty pounds into her hand. He saw her brightened eyes, and heard her murmur: "Oh! Uncle Jolyon!" and a real throb of pleasure went through him. That meant one or two poor crea-tures helped a little, and it meant that she would come again. He put his hand in at the window and grasped hers once more. The carriage rolled away. He stood looking at the moon and the shadows of the trees, and thought: "A sweet night! She—!"

II

Two days of rain, and summer set in bland and sunny. Old Jolyon walked and talked with Holly. At first he felt taller and full of a new vigor; then he felt restless. Almost every afternoon they would enter the coppice, and walk as far as the log. "Well, she's not there!" he would think, "of course not!" And he would feel a little shorter, and drag his feet walking up the hill home, with his hand clapped to his left side. Now and then the thought would move in him: "Did she come—or did I dream it?" and he would stare at space, while the dog Balthasar stared at him. Of course she would not come again! He opened the letters from Spain with less excitement. They were not returning till July; he felt, oddly, that he could bear it. Every day at dinner he screwed up his eyes and looked at where she had sat. She was not there, so he unscrewed his eyes again.

On the seventh afternoon he thought: "I must go up and get some boots." He ordered Beacon, and set out. Passing from Putney towards Hyde Park he reflected: "I might as well go to Chelsea and see her." And he called out: "Just drive me to where you took that lady the other night." The coachman turned his broad red face, and his juicy lips answered: "The lady in gray, sir?"

"Yes, the lady in gray." What other ladies were there! Stodgy chap!

The carriage stopped before a small three-storied block of flats, standing a little back from the river. With a practiced eye old Jolyon saw that they were cheap. "I should think about sixty pound a year," he mused; and entering, he looked at the name board. The name "Forsyte" was not on it, but against "First Floor, Flat C" were the words: "Mrs. Irene Heron." Ah! She had taken her maiden name again! And somehow this pleased him. He went upstairs slowly, feeling his side a little. He stood a moment, before ringing, to lose the feeling of drag and fluttering there. She would not be in! And then—Boots! The thought was black. What did he want with boots at his age? He could not wear out all those he had.

"Your mistress at home?"

"Yes, sir."

"Say Mr. Jolyon Forsyte."

"Yes, sir, will you come this way?"

Old Jolyon followed a very little maid—not more than sixteen one would say—into a very small drawing room where the sun blinds were drawn. It held a cottage piano and little else save a vague fragrance and good taste. He stood in the middle, with his top hat in his hand, and thought: "I expect she's very badly off!" There was a mirror above the fireplace, and he saw himself reflected. An old-looking chap! He heard a rustle, and turned round. She was so close that his mustache almost brushed her forehead, just under her hair.

"I was driving up," he said. "Thought I'd look in on you, and ask you how you got up the other night."

And, seeing her smile, he felt suddenly relieved. She was really glad to see him, perhaps.

"Would you like to put on your hat and come for a drive in the Park?"

But while she was gone to put her hat on, he frowned. The Park! James and Emily! Mrs. Nicholas, or some other member of his precious family would be there very likely, prancing up and down. And they would go and wag their tongues about having seen him with her, afterwards. Better not! He did not wish to revive the echoes of the past on Forsyte 'Change. He removed a white hair from the lapel of his closely buttoned-up frock coat, and passed his hand over his cheeks, mustache, and square chin. It felt very hollow there under the cheekbones. He had not been eating much lately—he had better get that little whippersnapper who attended Holly to give him a tonic. But she had come back and when they were in the carriage, he said:

"Suppose we go and sit in Kensington Gardens instead?" and added with a twinkle: "No prancing up and down there," as if she had been in the secret of his thoughts.

Leaving the carriage, they entered those select precincts, and strolled towards the water.

"You've gone back to your maiden name, I see," he said: "I'm not sorry."

She slipped her hand under his arm: "Has June forgiven me, Uncle Jolyon?"

He answered gently: "Yes—yes; of course, why not?"

"And have you?"

"I? I forgave you as soon as I saw how the land really lay." And perhaps he had; his instinct had always been to forgive the beautiful.

She drew a deep breath. "I never regretted—I couldn't. Did you ever love very deeply, Uncle Jolyon?"

At that strange question old Jolyon stared before him. Had he? He did not seem to remember that he ever had. But he did not like to say this to the young woman whose hand was touching his arm, whose life was suspended, as it were, by memory of a tragic love. And he thought: "If I had met *you* when I was young I—I might have made a fool of myself, perhaps." And a longing to escape in generalities beset him.

"Love's a queer thing," he said, "fatal thing often. It was the Greeks—wasn't it?—made love into a goddess; they were right, I dare say, but then they lived in the Golden Age."

"Phil adored them."

Phil! The word jarred him, for suddenly—with his power to see all round a thing, he perceived why she was putting up with him like this. She wanted to talk about her lover! Well! If it was any pleasure to her! And he said: "Ah! There was a bit of the sculptor in him, I fancy."

"Yes. He loved balance and symmetry; he loved the wholehearted way the Greeks gave themselves to art."

Balance! The chap had no balance at all, if he remembered; as for symmetry—clean-built enough he was, no doubt; but those queer eyes of his, and high cheekbones—Symmetry?

"You're of the Golden Age, too, Uncle Jolyon."

Old Jolyon looked round at her. Was she chaffing him? No, her eyes were soft as velvet. Was she flattering him? But if so, why? There was nothing to be had out of an old chap like him.

"Phil thought so. He used to say: 'But I can never tell him that I admire him.'"

Ah! There it was again. Her dead lover; her desire to talk of him! And he pressed her arm, half resentful of those memories, half grateful, as if he recognized what a link they were between herself and him.

"He was a very talented young fellow," he murmured. "It's hot; I feel the heat nowadays. Let's sit down."

They took two chairs beneath a chestnut tree whose broad leaves covered them from the peaceful glory of the afternoon. A pleasure to sit there and watch her, and feel that she liked to be with him. And the wish to increase that liking, if he could, made him go on:

"I expect he showed you a side of him I never saw. He'd be at his best with you. His ideas of art were a little new—to me." He had stifled the word "fangled."

"Yes: but he used to say you had a real sense of beauty." Old Jolyon thought: "The devil he did!" but answered with a twinkle: "Well, I have, or I shouldn't be sitting here with you." She was fascinating when she smiled with her eyes, like that!

"He thought you had one of those hearts that never grow old. Phil had real insight."

He was not taken in by this flattery spoken out of the past, out of a longing to talk of her dead lover—not a bit; and yet it was precious to hear, because she pleased his eyes and heart which—quite true!—had never grown old. Was that because—unlike her and her dead lover, he had never loved to desperation, had always kept his balance, his sense of symmetry. Well! It had left him power, at eighty-four, to admire beauty. And he thought, "If I were a painter or a sculptor! But I'm an old chap. Make hay while the sun shines."

A couple with arms entwined crossed on the grass before them, at the edge of the shadow from their tree. The sunlight fell cruelly on their pale, squashed, unkempt young faces. "We're an ugly lot!" said old Jolyon suddenly. "It amazes me to see how—love triumphs over that."

"Love triumphs over everything!"

"The young think so," he muttered.

"Love has no age, no limit, and no death."

With that glow in her pale face, her breast heaving, her eyes so large and dark and soft, she looked like Venus come to life! But this extravagance brought instant reaction, and, twinkling, he said: "Well, if it had limits, we shouldn't be born; for by George! it's got a lot to put up with."

Then, removing his top hat, he brushed it round with a cuff. The great clumsy thing heated his forehead; in these days he often got a rush of blood to the head—his circulation was not what it had been.

She still sat gazing straight before her, and suddenly she murmured: "It's strange enough that *I'm* alive."

Those words of Jo's "wild and lost" came back to him.

"Ah!" he said; "my son saw you for a moment—that day."

"Was it your son? I heard a voice in the hall; I thought for a second it was—Phil."

Old Jolyon saw her lips tremble. She put her hand over them, took it away again, and went on calmly: "That night I went to the Embankment; a woman caught me by the dress. She told me about herself. When one knows that others suffer, one's ashamed."

"One of *those?*"

She nodded, and horror stirred within old Jolyon, the horror of one who has never known a struggle with desperation. Almost against his will he muttered: "Tell me, won't you?"

"I didn't care whether I lived or died. When you're like that, Fate ceases to want to kill you. She took care of me three days—she never left me. I had no money. That's why I do what I can for them, now."

But old Jolyon was thinking: "No money!" What fate could compare with that? Every other was involved in it.

"I wish you had come to me," he said. "Why didn't you?" But Irene did not answer.

"Because my name was Forsyte, I suppose? Or was it June who kept you away? How are you getting on now?" His eyes involuntarily swept her body. Perhaps even now she was—! And yet she wasn't thin—not really!

"Oh! with my fifty pounds a year, I make just enough." The answer did not reassure him; he had lost confidence. And that fellow Soames! But his sense of justice stifled condemnation. No, she would certainly have died rather than take another penny from *him*. Soft as she looked, there must be strength in her somewhere—strength and fidelity. But what business had young Bosinney to have got run over and left her stranded like this!

"Well, you must come to me now," he said, "for anything you want, or I shall be quite cut up." And putting on his hat, he rose. "Let's go and get some tea. I told that lazy chap to put the horses up for an hour, and come for me at your place. We'll take a cab presently; I can't walk as I used to."

He enjoyed that stroll to the Kensington end of the gardens—the sound of her voice, the glancing of her eyes, the subtle beauty of a charming form moving beside him. He enjoyed their tea at Ruffel's in the High Street, and came out thence with a great box of chocolates swung on his little finger. He enjoyed the drive back to Chelsea in a hansom, smoking his cigar. She had promised to come down next Sunday and play to him again, and already in thought he was plucking carnations and early roses for her to carry back to town. It was a pleasure to give her a little pleasure, if it *were* pleasure from an old chap like him! The carriage was already there when they arrived. Just like that fellow, who was always late when he was wanted! Old Jolyon went in for a minute to say good-by. The little dark hall of the flat was impregnated with a disagreeable odor of patchouli, and on a bench against the wall—its only furniture—he saw a figure sitting. He heard Irene say softly: "Just one minute." In the little drawing room when the door was shut, he asked gravely: "One of your protégées?"

"Yes. Now thanks to you, I can do something for her."

He stood, staring, and stroking that chin whose strength had frightened so many in its time. The idea of her, thus actually in contact with this outcast, grieved and frightened him. What could she do for them? Nothing. Only soil and make trouble for herself, perhaps. And he said: "Take care, my dear! The world puts the worst construction on everything."

"I know that."

He was abashed by her quiet smile. "Well then—Sunday," he murmured: "Good-by."

She put her cheek forward for him to kiss.

"Good-by," he said again; "take care of yourself." And he went out, not looking towards the figure on the bench. He drove home by way of Hammersmith, that he might stop at a place he knew of and tell them to send her in two dozen of their best Burgundy. She must want picking up sometimes! Only in Richmond Park did he remember that he had gone up to order himself some boots, and was surprised that he could have had so paltry an idea.

III

The little spirits of the past which throng an old man's days had never pushed their faces up to his so seldom as in the seventy hours elapsing before Sunday came. The spirit of the future, with the charm of the unknown, put up her lips instead. Old Jolyon was not restless now, and paid no visits to the log, because she was *coming to lunch*. There is wonderful finality about a meal; it removes a world of doubts, for no one misses meals except for reasons beyond control. He played many games with Holly on the lawn, pitching them up to her who was batting so as to be ready to bowl to Jolly in the holidays. For she was not a Forsyte, but Jolly was—and Forsytes always bat, until they have resigned and reached the age of eighty-five. The dog Balthasar, in attendance, lay on the ball as often as he could, and the page boy fielded, till his face was like the harvest moon. And because the time was getting shorter, each day was longer and more golden than the last. On Friday night he took a liver pill, his side hurt him rather, and though it was not the liver side, there is no remedy like that. Anyone telling him that he had found a new excitement in life and that excitement was not good for him, would have been met by one of those steady and rather defiant looks of his deep-set iron-gray eyes, which seemed to say: "I know my own business best." He always had and always would.

On Sunday morning, when Holly had gone with her governess to church, he visited the strawberry beds. There, accompanied by the dog Balthasar, he examined the plants narrowly and succeeded in finding at least two dozen berries which were really ripe. Stooping was not good for him, and he became very dizzy and red in the forehead. Having placed the strawberries in a dish on the dining table, he washed his hands and bathed his forehead with eau de Cologne. There, before the mirror, it occurred to him that he was thinner. What a "threadpaper" he had been when he was young! It was nice to be slim—he could not bear a fat chap; and yet perhaps his cheeks were *too* thin! She was to arrive by train at half-past twelve and walk up, entering from the road past Drage's farm at the far end of the coppice. And, having looked into June's room to see that there was hot water ready, he set forth to meet her, leisurely, for his heart was beating. The air smelled sweet, larks sang, and the Grand Stand at Epsom was visible. A perfect day! On just such a one, no doubt, six years ago, Soames had brought young Bosinney down with him to look at the site before they began to build. It was Bosinney who had pitched on the exact spot for the house—as June had often told him. In these days he was thinking much about that young fellow, as if his spirit were really haunting the field of his last work, on the chance of seeing—her. Bosinney

—the one man who had possessed her heart, to whom she had given her whole self with rapture! At his age one could not, of course, imagine such things, but there stirred in him a queer vague aching—as it were the ghost of an impersonal jealousy; and a feeling, too, more generous, of pity for that love so early lost. All over in a few poor months! Well, well! He looked at his watch before entering the coppice—only a quarter past, twenty-five minutes to wait! And then, turning the corner of the path, he saw her exactly where he had seen her the first time, on the log; and realized that she must have come by the earlier train to sit there alone for a couple of hours at least. Two hours of her society—missed! What memory could make that log so dear to her? His face showed what he was thinking, for she said at once:

"Forgive me, Uncle Jolyon; it was here that I first knew."

"Yes, yes; there it is for you whenever you like. You're looking a little Londony; you're giving too many lessons."

That she should have to give lessons worried him. Lessons to a parcel of young girls thumping out scales with their thick fingers!

"Where do you go to give them?" he asked.

"They're mostly Jewish families, luckily."

Old Jolyon stared; to all Forsytes Jews seem strange and doubtful.

"They love music, and they're very kind."

"They had better be, by George!" He took her arm—his side always hurt him a little going uphill—and said:

"Did you ever see anything like those buttercups? They came like that in a night."

Her eyes seemed really to fly over the field, like bees after the flowers and the honey. "I wanted you to see them—wouldn't let them turn the cows in yet." Then, remembering that she had come to talk about Bosinney, he pointed to the clock tower over the stables:

"I expect *he* wouldn't have let me put that there—had no notion of time, if I remember."

But, pressing his arm to her, she talked of flowers instead, and he knew it was done that he might not feel she came because of her dead lover.

"The best flower I can show you," he said, with a sort of triumph, "is my little sweet. She'll be back from church directly. There's something about her which reminds me a little of you," and it did not seem to him peculiar that he had put it thus, instead of saying: "There's something about you which reminds me a little of her." Ah! And here she was!

Holly, followed closely by her elderly French governess, whose digestion had been ruined twenty-two years ago in the siege of Strasbourg, came rushing towards them from under the oak tree. She stopped about a dozen yards away, to pat Balthasar and pretend that this was all she had in her mind. Old Jolyon who knew better, said:

"Well, my darling, here's the lady in gray I promised you."

Holly raised herself and looked up. He watched the two of them with a twinkle, Irene smiling, Holly beginning with grave inquiry, passing into a shy smile too, and then to something deeper. She had a sense of beauty, that child—knew what was what! He enjoyed the sight of the kiss between them.

"Mrs. Heron, Mam'zelle Beauce. Well, Mam'zelle—good sermon?"

For, now that he had not much more time before him, the only part of the service connected with this world absorbed what interest in church remained to him. Mam'zelle Beauce stretched out a spidery hand clad in a black kid glove—she had been in the best families—and the rather sad eyes of her lean yellowish face seemed to ask: "Are you well brrred?" Whenever Holly or Jolly did anything unpleasing to her—a not uncommon occurrence—she would say to them: "The little Tayleurs never did that—they were such well-brrred little children." Jolly hated the little Tayleurs; Holly wondered dreadfully how it was she fell so short of them. "A thin rum little soul," old Jolyon thought her—Mam'zelle Beauce.

Luncheon was a successful meal, the mushrooms which he himself had picked in the mushroom house, his chosen strawberries, and another bottle of the Steinberg cabinet filled him with a certain aromatic spirituality, and a conviction that he would have a touch of eczema tomorrow. After lunch they sat under the oak tree drinking Turkish coffee. It was no matter of grief to him when Mademoiselle Beauce withdrew to write her Sunday letter to her sister, whose future had been endangered in the past by swallowing a pin—an event held up daily in warning to the children to eat slowly and digest what they had eaten. At the foot of the bank, on a carriage rug, Holly and the dog Balthasar teased and loved each other, and in the shade old Jolyon with his legs crossed and his cigar luxuriously savored, gazed at Irene sitting in the swing. A light, vaguely swaying, gray figure with a fleck of sunlight here and there upon it, lips just opened, eyes dark and soft under lids a little drooped. She looked content; surely it did her good to come and see him! The selfishness of age had not set its proper grip on him, for he could still feel pleasure in the pleasure of others, realizing that what he wanted, though much, was not quite all that mattered.

"It's quiet here," he said; "you mustn't come down if you find it dull. But it's a pleasure to see you. My little sweet's is the only face which gives me any pleasure, except yours."

From her smile he knew that she was not beyond liking to be appreciated, and this reassured him. "That's not humbug," he said. "I never told a woman I admired her when I didn't. In fact I don't know when I've told a woman I admired her, except my wife in the old days; and wives are funny." He was silent, but resumed abruptly:

"She used to expect me to say it more often than I felt it, and there we were." Her face looked mysteriously troubled, and, afraid that he had said something painful, he hurried on:

"When my little sweet marries, I hope she'll find someone who knows what women feel. I shan't be here to see it, but there's too much topsy-turvydom in marriage; I don't want her to pitch up against that." And, aware that he had made bad worse, he added: "That dog *will* scratch."

A silence followed. Of what was she thinking, this pretty creature whose life was spoiled; who had done with love, and yet was made for love? Some day when he was gone, perhaps, she would find another mate—not so disorderly as that young fellow who had got himself run over. Ah! but her husband?

"Does Soames never trouble you?" he asked.

She shook her head. Her face had closed up suddenly. For all her softness there was something irreconcilable about her. And a glimpse of light on the inexorable nature of sex antipathies strayed into a brain which, belonging to early Victorian civilization—so much older than this of his old age—had never thought about such primitive things.

"That's a comfort," he said. "You can see the Grand Stand today. Shall we take a turn round?"

Through the flower and fruit garden, against whose high outer walls peach trees and nectarines were trained to the sun, through the stables, the vinery, the mushroom house, the asparagus beds, the rosery, the summerhouse, he conducted her—even into the kitchen garden to see the tiny green peas which Holly loved to scoop out of their pods with her finger, and lick up from the palm of her little brown hand. Many delightful things he showed her, while Holly and the dog Balthasar danced ahead, or came to them at intervals for attention. It was one of the happiest afternoons he had ever spent, but it tired him and he was glad to sit down in the music room and let her give him tea. A special little friend of Holly's had come in—a fair child with short hair like a boy's. And the two sported in the distance, under the stairs, on the stairs, and up in the gallery. Old Jolyon begged for Chopin. She played studies, mazurkas, waltzes, till the two children, creeping near, stood at the foot of the piano—their dark and golden heads bent forward, listening. Old Jolyon watched.

"Let's see you dance, you two!"

Shyly, with a false start, they began. Bobbing and circling, earnest, not very adroit, they went past and past his chair to the strains of that waltz. He watched them and the face of her who was playing turned smiling towards those little dancers thinking: "Sweetest picture I've seen for ages." A voice said:

"Hollee! *Mais enfin—qu'est-ce que tu fais là—danser, le dimanche! Viens, donc!*"

But the children came close to old Jolyon, knowing that he would save them, and gazed into a face which was decidedly "caught out."

"Better the day, better the deed, Mam'zelle. It's all my doing. Trot along, chicks, and have your tea."

And, when they were gone, followed by the dog Balthasar, who took every meal, he looked at Irene with a twinkle and said:

"Well, there we are! Aren't they sweet? Have you any little ones among your pupils?"

"Yes, three—two of them darlings."

"Pretty?"

"Lovely!"

Old Jolyon sighed; he had an insatiable appetite for the very young. "My little sweet," he said, "is devoted to music; she'll be a musician some day. You wouldn't give me your opinion of her playing, I suppose?"

"Of course I will."

"You wouldn't like—" but he stifled the words "to give her lessons." The idea that she gave lessons was unpleasant to him; yet it would mean that he would see her regularly. She left the piano and came over to his chair.

"I would like, very much; but there is—June. When are they coming back?"

Old Jolyon frowned. "Not till the middle of next month. What does that matter?"

"You said June had forgiven me; but she could never forget, Uncle Jolyon."

Forget! She *must* forget, if he wanted her to.

But as if answering, Irene shook her head. "You know she couldn't; one doesn't forget."

Always that wretched past! And he said with a sort of vexed finality: "Well, we shall see."

He talked to her an hour or more, of the children, and a hundred little things, till the carriage came round to take her home. And when she had gone he went back to his chair, and sat there smoothing his face and chin, dreaming over the day.

That evening after dinner he went to his study and took a sheet of paper. He stayed for some minutes without writing, then rose and stood under the masterpiece "Dutch Fishing Boats at Sunset." He was not thinking of that picture, but of his life. He was going to leave her something in his Will; nothing could so have stirred the stilly deeps of thought and memory. He was going to leave her a portion of his wealth, of his aspirations, deeds, qualities, work—all that had made that wealth; going to leave her, too, a part of all he had missed in life, by his sane and steady pursuit of wealth. Ah! What had he missed? "Dutch Fishing Boats" responded blankly; he crossed to the French window, and drawing the curtain aside, opened it. A wind had got up, and one of last year's oak leaves, which had somehow survived the gardener's brooms, was dragging itself

with a tiny clicking rustle along the stone terrace in the twilight. Except
for that it was very quiet out there, and he could smell the heliotrope
watered not long since. A bat went by. A bird uttered its last "cheep."
And right above the oak tree the first star shone. Faust in the opera had
bartered his soul for some fresh years of ycuth. Morbid notion! No such
bargain was possible, that was *real* tragedy! No making oneself new again
for love or life or anything. Nothing left to do but enjoy beauty from
afar off while you could, and leave it something in your Will. But how
much? And, as if he could not make that calculation looking out into
the mild freedom of the country night, he turned back and went up to
the chimney piece. There were his pet bronzes—a Cleopatra with the asp
at her breast; a Socrates; a greyhound playing with her puppy; a strong
man reining in some horses. "They last!" he thought, and a pang went
through his heart. They had a thousand years of life before them!

"How much?" Well! enough at all events to save her getting old before
her time, to keep the lines out of her face as long as possible, and gray
from soiling that bright hair. He might live another five years. She would
be well over thirty by then. "How much?" She had none of his blood in
her! In loyalty to the tenor of his life for forty years and more, ever since
he married and founded that mysterious thing, a family, came this warning thought—None of his blood, no right to anything! It was a luxury
then, this notion. An extravagance, a petting of an old man's whim, one
of those things done in dotage. His real future was vested in those who
had his blood, in whom he would live on when he was gone. He turned
away from the bronzes and stood looking at the old leather chair in which
he had sat and smoked so many hundreds of cigars. And suddenly he
seemed to see her sitting there in her gray dress, fragrant, soft, dark-eyed,
graceful, looking up at him. Why! She cared nothing for him, really; all
she cared for was that lost lover of hers. But she was there, whether she
would or no, giving him pleasure with her beauty and grace. One had
no right to inflict an old man's company, no right to ask her down to
play to him and let him look at her—for no reward! Pleasure must be
paid for in this world. "How much?" After all, there was plenty; his son
and his three grandchildren would never miss that little lump. He had
made it himself, nearly every penny; he could leave it where he liked,
allow himself this little pleasure. He went back to the bureau. "Well, I'm
going to," he thought, "let them think what they like. I'm going to!" And
he sat down.

"How much?" Ten thousand, twenty thousand—how much? If only
with his money he could buy one year, one month of youth. And startled
by that thought, he wrote quickly:

DEAR HERRING—Draw me a codicil to this effect: "I leave to my niece Irene

Forsyte, born Irene Heron, by which name she now goes, fifteen thousand pounds free of legacy duty."

Yours faithfully,
JOLYON FORSYTE

When he had sealed and stamped the envelope, he went back to the window and drew in a long breath. It was dark, but many stars shone now.

IV

He woke at half-past two, an hour which long experience had taught him brings panic intensity to all awkward thoughts. Experience had also taught him that a further waking at the proper hour of eight showed the folly of such panic. On this particular morning the thought which gathered rapid momentum was that if he became ill, at his age not improbable, he would not see her. From this it was but a step to realization that he would be cut off, too, when his son and June returned from Spain. How could he justify desire for the company of one who had stolen—early morning does not mince words—June's lover? That lover was dead; but June was a stubborn little thing; warmhearted, but stubborn as wood, and—quite true—not one who forgot! By the middle of next month they would be back. He had barely five weeks left to enjoy the new interest which had come into what remained of his life. Darkness showed up to him absurdly clear the nature of his feeling. Admiration for beauty—a craving to see that which delighted his eyes. Preposterous, at his age! And yet—what other reason was there for asking June to undergo such painful reminder, and how prevent his son and his son's wife from thinking him very queer? He would be reduced to sneaking up to London, which tired him; and the least indisposition would cut him off even from that. He lay with eyes open, setting his jaw against the prospect, and calling himself an old fool, while his heart beat loudly, and then seemed to stop beating altogether. He had seen the dawn lighting the window chinks, heard the birds chirp and twitter, and the cocks crow, before he fell asleep again, and awoke tired but sane. Five weeks before he need bother, at his age an eternity! But that early morning panic had left its mark, had slightly fevered the will of one who had always had his own way. He would see her as often as he wished! Why not go up to town and make that codicil at his solicitor's instead of writing about it; she might like to go to the opera! But, by train, for he would not have that fat chap Beacon grinning behind his back. Servants were such fools; and, as likely as not, they had known all the past history of Irene and young Bosinney—servants knew everything, and suspected the rest. He wrote to her that morning:

MY DEAR IRENE—I have to be up in town tomorrow. If you would like to have a look in at the opera, come and dine with me quietly . . .

But where? It was decades since he had dined anywhere in London save at his Club or at a private house. Ah! that newfangled place close to Covent Garden . . .

Let me have a line tomorrow morning to the Piedmont Hotel whether to expect you there at seven o'clock.

Yours affectionately,
JOLYON FORSYTE

She would understand that he just wanted to give her a little pleasure; for the idea that she should guess he had this itch to see her was instinctively unpleasant to him; it was not seemly that one so old should go out of his way to see beauty, especially in a woman.

The journey next day, short though it was, and the visit to his lawyer's, tired him. It was hot too, and after dressing for dinner he lay down on the sofa in his bedroom to rest a little. He must have had a sort of fainting fit, for he came to himself feeling very queer; and with some difficulty rose and rang the bell. Why! it was past seven! And there he was and she would be waiting. But suddenly the dizziness came on again, and he was obliged to relapse on the sofa. He heard the maid's voice say:

"Did you ring, sir?"

"Yes, come here"; he could not see her clearly, for the cloud in front of his eyes. "I'm not well, I want some sal volatile."

"Yes, sir." Her voice sounded frightened.

Old Jolyon made an effort.

"Don't go. Take this message to my niece—a lady waiting in the hall— a lady in gray. Say Mr. Forsyte is not well—the heat. He is very sorry; if he is not down directly, she is not to wait dinner."

When she was gone, he thought feebly: "Why did I say a lady in gray —she may be in anything. Sal volatile!" He did not go off again, yet was not conscious of how Irene came to be standing beside him, holding smelling salts to his nose, and pushing a pillow up behind his head. He heard her say anxiously: "Dear Uncle Jolyon, what is it?" was dimly conscious of the soft pressure of her lips on his hand; then drew a long breath of smelling salts, suddenly discovered strength in them, and sneezed.

"Ha!" he said, "it's nothing. How did you get here? Go down and dine—the tickets are on the dressing table. I shall be all right in a minute."

He felt her cool hand on his forehead, smelled violets, and sat divided between a sort of pleasure and a determination to be all right.

"Why! You *are* in gray!" he said. "Help me up." Once on his feet he gave himself a shake.

"What business had I to go off like that!" And he moved very slowly to the glass. What a cadaverous chap! Her voice, behind him, murmured: "You mustn't come down, Uncle; you must rest."

"Fiddlesticks! A glass of champagne'll soon set me to rights. I can't have you missing the opera."

But the journey down the corridor was troublesome. What carpets they had in these newfangled places, so thick that you tripped up in them at every step! In the lift he noticed how concerned she looked, and said with the ghost of a twinkle:

"I'm a pretty host."

When the lift stopped he had to hold firmly to the seat to prevent its slipping under him; but after soup and a glass of champagne he felt much better, and began to enjoy an infirmity which had brought such solicitude into her manner towards him.

"I should have liked you for a daughter," he said suddenly; and watching the smile in her eyes, went on:

"You mustn't get wrapped up in the past at your time of life; plenty of that when you get to my age. That's a nice dress—I like the style."

"I made it myself."

Ah! A woman who could make herself a pretty frock had not lost her interest in life.

"Make hay while the sun shines," he said; "and drink that up. I want to see some color in your cheeks. We mustn't waste life; it doesn't do. There's a new Marguerite tonight; let's hope she won't be fat. And Mephisto—anything more dreadful than a fat chap playing the Devil I can't imagine."

But they did not go to the opera after all, for in getting up from dinner the dizziness came over him again, and she insisted on his staying quiet and going to bed early. When he parted from her at the door of the hotel, having paid the cabman to drive her to Chelsea, he sat down again for a moment to enjoy the memory of her words: "You *are* such a darling to me, Uncle Jolyon!" Why! Who wouldn't be! He would have liked to stay up another day and take her to the Zoo, but two days running of him would bore her to death. No, he must wait till next Sunday; she had promised to come then. They would settle those lessons for Holly, if only for a month. It would be something. That little Mam'zelle Beauce wouldn't like it, but she would have to lump it. And crushing his old opera hat against his chest he sought the lift.

He drove to Waterloo next morning, struggling with a desire to say: "Drive me to Chelsea." But his sense of proportion was too strong. Besides, he still felt shaky, and did not want to risk another aberration like that of last night, away from home. Holly, too, was expecting him, and what he had in his bag for her. Not that there was any cupboard love in his little sweet—she was a bundle of affection. Then, with the rather bitter cynicism of the old, he wondered for a second whether it was not cupboard love which made Irene put up with him. No, she was not that sort either. She had, if anything, too little notion of how to butter her bread, no sense of property, poor thing! Besides, he had not breathed a word about that codicil, nor should he—sufficient unto the day was the good thereof.

In the victoria which met him at the station Holly was restraining the dog Balthasar, and their caresses made "jubey" his drive home. All the rest of that fine hot day and most of the next he was content and peaceful, reposing in the shade, while the long lingering sunshine showered gold on the lawns and the flowers. But on Thursday evening at his lonely dinner he began to count the hours; sixty-five till he would go down to meet her again in the little coppice, and walk up through the fields at her side. He had intended to consult the doctor about his fainting fit, but the fellow would be sure to insist on quiet, no excitement and all that; and he did not mean to be tied by the leg, did not want to be told of an infirmity—if there were one, could not afford to hear of it at his time of life, now that this new interest had come. And he carefully avoided making any mention of it in a letter to his son. It would only bring them back with a run! How far this silence was due to consideration for their pleasure, how far to regard for his own, he did not pause to consider.

That night in his study he had just finished his cigar and was dozing off, when he heard the rustle of a gown, and was conscious of a scent of violets. Opening his eyes he saw her, dressed in gray, standing by the fireplace, holding out her arms. The odd thing was that, though those arms seemed to hold nothing, they were curved as if round someone's neck, and her own neck was bent back, her lips open, her eyes closed. She vanished at once, and there were the mantelpiece and his bronzes. But those bronzes and the mantelpiece had not been there when she was, only the fireplace and the wall! Shaken and troubled, he got up. "I must take medicine," he thought; "I can't be well." His heart beat too fast, he had an asthmatic feeling in the chest; and going to the window, he opened it to get some air. A dog was barking far away, one of the dogs at Gage's farm no doubt, beyond the coppice. A beautiful still night, but dark. "I dropped off," he mused, "that's it! And yet I'll swear my eyes were open!" A sound like a sigh seemed to answer.

"What's that?" he said sharply, "who's there?"

Putting his hand to his side to still the beating of his heart, he stepped out on the terrace. Something soft scurried by in the dark. "Shoo!" It was that great gray cat. "Young Bosinney was like a great cat!" he thought. "It was him in there, that she—that she was— He's got her still!" He walked to the edge of the terrace, and looked down into the darkness; he could just see the powdering of the daisies on the unmown lawn. Here today and gone tomorrow! And there came the moon, who saw all, young and old, alive and dead, and didn't care a dump! His own turn soon. For a single day of youth he would give what was left! And he turned again towards the house. He could see the windows of the night nursery up there. His little sweet would be asleep. "Hope that dog won't wake her!" he thought. "What is it makes us love, and makes us die! I must go to bed."

And across the terrace stones, growing gray in the moonlight, he passed back within.

V

How should an old man live his days if not in dreaming of his well-spent past? In that, at all events, there is no agitating warmth, only pale winter sunshine. The shell can withstand the gentle beating of the dynamos of memory. The present he should distrust; the future shun. From beneath thick shade he should watch the sunlight creeping at his toes. If there be sun of summer, let him not go out into it, mistaking it for the Indian summer sun! Thus peradventure he shall decline softly, slowly, imperceptibly, until impatient Nature clutches his windpipe and he gasps away to death some early morning before the world is aired, and they put on his tombstone: "In the fulness of years!" yea! If he preserve his principles in perfect order, a Forsyte may live on long after he is dead.

Old Jolyon was conscious of all this, and yet there was in him that which transcended Forsyteism. For it is written that a Forsyte shall not love beauty more than reason; nor his own way more than his own health. And something beat within him in these days that with each throb fretted at the thinning shell. His sagacity knew this, but it knew too that he could not stop that beating, nor would if he could. And yet, if you had told him he was living on his capital, he would have stared you down. No, no; a man did not live on his capital; it was not done! The shibboleths of the past are ever more real than the actualities of the present. And he, to whom living on one's capital had always been anathema, could not have borne to have applied so gross a phrase to his own case. Pleasure is healthful; beauty good to see; to live again in the youth of the young— and what else on earth was he doing!

Methodically, as had been the way of his whole life, he now arranged his time. On Tuesdays he journeyed up to town by train; Irene came and dined with him. And they went to the opera. On Thursdays he drove to town, and, putting that fat chap and his horses up, met her in Kensington Gardens, picking up the carriage after he had left her, and driving home again in time for dinner. He threw out the casual formula that he had business in London on those two days. On Wednesdays and Saturdays she came down to give Holly music lessons. The greater the pleasure he took in her society, the more scrupulously fastidious he became, just a matter-of-fact and friendly uncle. Not even in feeling, really, was he more —for, after all, there was his age. And yet, if she were late he fidgeted himself to death. If she missed coming, which happened twice, his eyes grew sad as an old dog's, and he failed to sleep.

And so a month went by—a month of summer in the fields, and in his heart, with summer's heat and the fatigue thereof. Who could have believed a few weeks back that he would have looked forward to his son's and his granddaughter's return with something like dread! There was such a delicious freedom, such recovery of that independence a man enjoys before he founds a family, about these weeks of lovely weather, and this new companionship with one who demanded nothing, and remained always a little unknown, retaining the fascination of mystery. It was like a draught of wine to him who has been drinking water for so long that he has almost forgotten the stir wine brings to his blood, the narcotic to his brain. The flowers were colored brighter, scents and music and the sunlight had a living value—were no longer mere reminders of past enjoyment. There was something now to live for which stirred him continually to anticipation. He lived in that, not in retrospection; the difference is considerable to any so old as he. The pleasures of the table, never of much consequence to one naturally abstemious, had lost all value. He ate little, without knowing what he ate; and every day grew thinner and more worn to look at. He was again a "threadpaper"; and to this thinned form his massive forehead, with hollows at the temples, gave more dignity than ever. He was very well aware that he ought to see the doctor, but liberty was too sweet. He could not afford to pet his frequent shortness of breath and the pain in his side at the expense of liberty. Return to the vegetable existence he had led among the agricultural journals with the life-size mangold wurzels, before this new attraction came into his life— no! He exceeded his allowance of cigars. Two a day had always been his rule. Now he smoked three and sometimes four—a man will when he is filled with the creative spirit. But very often he thought: "I must give up smoking, and coffee; I must give up rattling up to town." But he did not; there was no one in any sort of authority to notice him, and this was a priceless boon. The servants perhaps wondered, but they were, naturally, dumb. Mam'zelle Beauce was too concerned with her own digestion, and too "well brrred" to make personal allusions. Holly had not as yet an eye for the relative appearance of him who was her plaything and her god. It was left for Irene herself to beg him to eat more, to rest in the hot part of the day, to take a tonic, and so forth. But she did not tell him that she was the cause of his thinness—for one cannot see the havoc oneself is working. A man of eighty-five has no passions, but the Beauty which produces passion works on in the old way, till death closes the eyes which crave the sight of Her.

On the first day of the second week in July he received a letter from his son in Paris to say that they would all be back on Friday. This had always been more sure than Fate; but, with the pathetic improvidence given to the old, that they may endure to the end, he had never quite admitted it. Now he did, and something would have to be done. He had ceased to be able to imagine life without this new interest, but that which is not imagined sometimes exists, as Forsytes are perpetually finding to their cost. He sat in his old leather chair, doubling up the letter, and mumbling with his lips the end of an unlighted cigar. After tomorrow his Tuesday expeditions to town would have to be abandoned. He could still drive up, perhaps, once a week, on the pretext of seeing his man of business. But even that would be dependent on his health, for now they would begin to fuss about him. The lessons! The lessons must go on! She must swallow down her scruples, and June must put her feelings in her pocket. She had done so once, on the day after the news of Bosinney's death; what she had done then, she could surely do again now. Four years since that injury was inflicted on her—not Christian to keep the memory of old sores alive. June's will was strong, but his was stronger, for his sands were running out. Irene was soft, surely she would do this for him, subdue her natural shrinking, sooner than give him pain! The lessons must continue; for if they did, he was secure. And lighting his cigar at last, he began trying to shape out how to put it to them all, and explain this strange intimacy; how to veil and wrap it away from the naked truth—that he could not bear to be deprived of the sight of beauty. Ah! Holly! Holly was fond of her, Holly liked her lessons. She would save him—his little sweet! And with that happy thought he became serene, and wondered what he had been worrying about so fearfully. He must not worry, it left him always curiously weak, and as if but half present in his own body.

That evening after dinner he had a return of the dizziness, though he did not faint. He would not ring the bell, because he knew it would mean a fuss, and make his going up on the morrow more conspicuous. When one grew old, the whole world was in conspiracy to limit freedom, and for what reason?—just to keep the breath in him a little longer. He did not want it at such cost. Only the dog Balthasar saw his lonely recovery from that weakness; anxiously watched his master go to the sideboard and drink some brandy, instead of giving him a biscuit. When at last old Jolyon felt able to tackle the stairs he went up to bed. And, though still shaky next morning, the thought of the evening sustained and strengthened him. It was always such a pleasure to give her a good dinner—he suspected her of undereating when she was alone; and, at the opera to watch her eyes glow and brighten, the unconscious smiling of her lips. She hadn't much pleasure, and this was the last time he would be able to give her that treat. But when he was packing his bag he caught himself wishing that he had not the fatigue of dressing for dinner before him, and the exertion, too, of telling her about June's return.

The opera that evening was *Carmen,* and he chose the last *entr'-acte* to break the news, instinctively putting it off till the latest moment. She took it quietly, queerly; in fact, he did not know how she had taken it before the wayward music lifted up again and silence became necessary. The mask was down over her face, that mask behind which so much went on that he could not see. She wanted time to think it over, no doubt! He would not press her, for she would be coming to give her lesson tomorrow afternoon, and he should see her then when she had got used to the idea. In the cab he talked only of the Carmen; he had seen better in the old days, but this one was not bad at all. When he took her hand to say good night, she bent quickly forward and kissed his forehead.

"Good-by, dear Uncle Jolyon, you have been so sweet to me."

"Tomorrow then," he said. "Good night. Sleep well." She echoed softly: "Sleep well!" and from the cab window, already moving away, he saw her face screwed round towards him, and her hand put out in a gesture which seemed to linger.

He sought his room slowly. They never gave him the same, and he could not get used to these "spick-and-spandy" bedrooms with new furniture and gray-green carpets sprinkled all over with pink roses. He was wakeful and that wretched Habanera kept throbbing in his head. His French had never been equal to its words, but its sense he knew, if it had any sense, a gipsy thing—wild and unaccountable. Well, there *was* in life something which upset all your care and plans—something which made men and women dance to its pipes. And he lay staring from deep-sunk eyes into the darkness where the unaccountable held sway. You thought you had hold of life, but it slipped away behind you, took you by the scruff of the neck, forced you here and forced you there, and then, likely as not, squeezed life out of you! It took the very stars like that, he shouldn't wonder, rubbed their noses together and flung them apart; it had never done playing its pranks. Five million people in this great blunderbuss of a town, and all of them at the mercy of that Life Force, like a lot of little dried peas hopping about on a board when you struck your fist on it. Ah, well! Himself would not hop much longer—a good long sleep would do him good!

How hot it was up here!—how noisy! His forehead burned; she had kissed it just where he always worried; just there—as if she had known the very place and wanted to kiss it all away for him. But, instead, her lips left a patch of grievous uneasiness. She had never spoken in quite that voice, had never before made that lingering gesture or looked back at him as she drove away. He got out of bed and pulled the curtains aside; his room faced down over the river. There was little air, but the sight of that breadth of water flowing by, calm, eternal, soothed him. "The great thing," he thought, "is not to make myself a nuisance. I'll think of my little sweet, and go to sleep." But it was long before the heat and throbbing of the London night died out into the short slumber of the summer morning. And old Jolyon had but forty winks.

When he reached home next day he went out to the flower garden, and with the help of Holly, who was very delicate with flowers, gathered a great bunch of carnations. They were, he told her, for "the lady in gray" —a name still bandied between them; and he put them in a bowl in his study where he meant to tackle Irene the moment she came, on the subject of June and future lessons. Their fragrance and color would help. After lunch he lay down, for he felt very tired, and the carriage would not bring her from the station till four o'clock. But as the hour approached he grew restless, and sought the schoolroom, which overlooked the drive. The sun blinds were down, and Holly was there with Mademoiselle Beauce, sheltered from the heat of a stifling July day, attending to their silkworms. Old Jolyon had a natural antipathy to these methodical creatures, whose heads and color reminded him of elephants; who nibbled such quantities of holes in nice green leaves; and smelled, as he thought, horrid. He sat down on a chintz-covered window seat whence he could see the drive, and get what air there was; and the dog Balthasar who appreciated chintz on hot days, jumped up beside him. Over the cottage piano a violet dust sheet, faded almost to gray, was spread, and on it the first lavender, whose scent filled the room. In spite of the coolness here, perhaps because of that coolness the beat of life vehemently impressed his ebbed-down senses. Each sunbeam which came through the chinks had annoying brilliance; that dog smelled very strong; the lavender perfume was overpowering; those silkworms heaving up their gray-green backs seemed horribly alive; and Holly's dark head bent over them had a wonderfully silky sheen. A marvelous cruelly strong thing was life when you were old and weak; it seemed to mock you with its multitude of forms and its beating vitality. He had never, till those last few weeks, had this curious feeling of being with one half of him eagerly borne along in the stream of life, and with the other half left on the bank, watching that helpless progress. Only when Irene was with him did he lose this double consciousness.

Holly turned her head, pointed with her little brown fist to the piano— for to point with a finger was not "well brrred"—and said slyly:

"Look at the 'lady in gray,' Gran; isn't she pretty today?"

Old Jolyon's heart gave a flutter, and for a second the room was clouded; then it cleared, and he said with a twinkle:

"Who's been dressing her up?"

"Mam'zelle."

"Hollee! Don't be foolish!"

That prim little Frenchwoman! She hadn't yet got over the music lessons being taken away from her. That wouldn't help. His little sweet was the only friend they had. Well, they were her lessons. And he shouldn't budge—shouldn't budge for anything. He stroked the warm wool on Balthasar's head, and heard Holly say: "When Mother's home, there won't be any changes, will there? She doesn't like strangers, you know."

The child's words seemed to bring the chilly atmosphere of opposition about old Jolyon, and disclose all the menace to his newfound freedom. Ah! He would have to resign himself to being an old man at the mercy of care and love, or fight to keep this new and prized companionship; and to fight tired him to death. But his thin, worn face hardened into resolution till it appeared all jaw. This was his house, and his affair; he should not budge! He looked at his watch, old and thin like himself; he had owned it fifty years. Past four already! And kissing the top of Holly's head in passing, he went down to the hall. He wanted to get hold of her before she went up to give her lesson. At the first sound of wheels he stepped out into the porch, and saw at once that the victoria was empty.

"The train's in, sir; but the lady 'asn't come."

Old Jolyon gave him a sharp upward look, his eyes seemed to push away that fat chap's curiosity, and defy him to see the bitter disappointment he was feeling.

"Very well," he said, and turned back into the house. He went to his study and sat down, quivering like a leaf. What did this mean? She might have lost her train, but he knew well enough she hadn't. "Good-by, dear Uncle Jolyon." Why "Good-by" and not "Good night"? And that hand of hers lingering in the air. And her kiss. What did it mean? Vehement alarm and irritation took possession of him. He got up and began to pace the Turkey carpet, between window and wall. She was going to give him up! He felt it for certain—and he defenseless. An old man wanting to look on beauty! It was ridiculous! Age closed his mouth, paralyzed his power to fight. He had no right to what was warm and living, no right to anything but memories and sorrow. He could not plead with her; even an old man has his dignity. Defenseless! For an hour, lost to bodily fatigue, he paced up and down, past the bowl of carnations he had plucked, which mocked him with its scent. Of all things hard to bear, the prostration of will power is hardest, for one who has always had his way. Nature had got him in its net, and like an unhappy fish he turned and swam at the meshes, here and there, found no hole, no breaking point. They brought him tea at five o'clock, and a letter. For a moment hope beat up in him. He cut the envelope with the butter knife, and read:

DEAREST UNCLE JOLYON—I can't bear to write anything that may disappoint you, but I was too cowardly to tell you last night. I feel I can't come down and give Holly any more lessons, now that June is coming back. Some things go too deep to be forgotten. It has been such a joy to see you and Holly. Perhaps I shall still see you sometimes when you come up, though I'm sure it's not good for you; I can see you are tiring yourself too much. I believe you ought to rest quite quietly all this hot weather, and now you have your son and June coming back you will be so happy. Thank you a million times for all your sweetness to me.

Lovingly your IRENE

So, there it was! Not good for him to have pleasure and what he chiefly cared about; to try and put off feeling the inevitable end of all things, the approach of death with its stealthy, rustling footsteps. Not good for him! Not even she could see how she was his new lease of interest in life, the incarnation of all the beauty he felt slipping from him!

His tea grew cold, his cigar remained unlit; and up and down he paced, torn between his dignity and his hold on life. Intolerable to be squeezed out slowly, without a say of your own, to live on when your will was in the hands of others bent on weighing you to the ground with care and love. Intolerable! He would see what telling her the truth would do—the truth that he wanted the sight of her more than just a lingering on. He sat down at his old bureau and took a pen. But he could not write. There was something revolting in having to plead like this; plead that she should warm his eyes with her beauty. It was tantamount to confessing dotage. He simply could not. And instead, he wrote:

I had hoped that the memory of old sores would not be allowed to stand in the way of what is a pleasure and a profit to me and my little granddaughter. But old men learn to forego their whims; they are obliged to, even the whim to live must be foregone sooner or later; and perhaps the sooner the better.

My love to you,

JOLYON FORSYTE

"Bitter," he thought, "but I can't help it. I'm tired." He sealed and dropped it into the box for the evening post, and hearing it fall to the bottom, thought: "There goes all I've looked forward to!"

That evening after dinner which he scarcely touched, after his cigar which he left half-smoked for it made him feel faint, he went very slowly upstairs and stole into the night nursery. He sat down on the window seat. A night light was burning, and he could just see Holly's face, with one hand underneath the cheek. An early cockchafer buzzed in the Japanese paper with which they had filled the grate, and one of the horses in the stable stamped restlessly. To sleep like that child! He pressed apart two rungs of the venetian blind and looked out. The moon was rising, blood-red. He had never seen so red a moon. The woods and fields out there were dropping to sleep too, in the last glimmer of the summer light. And beauty, like a spirit, walked. "I've had a long life," he thought, "the best of nearly everything. I'm an ungrateful chap; I've seen a lot of beauty in my time. Poor young Bosinney said I had a sense of beauty. There's a man in the moon tonight!" A moth went by, another, another. "Ladies in gray!" He closed his eyes. A feeling that he would never open them again beset him; he let it grow, let himself sink; then, with a shiver, dragged the lids up. There was something wrong with him, no doubt, deeply wrong; he would have to have the doctor after all. It didn't much matter now! Into that coppice the moonlight would have crept; there would be shadows, and those shadows would be the only things awake. No birds, beasts, flowers, insects; just the shadows—moving; "Ladies in gray!" Over that log they would climb; would whisper together. She and Bosinney! Funny thought! And the frogs and little things would whisper too! How the clock ticked, in here! It was all eerie—out there in the light of that red moon; in here with the little steady night light and the ticking clock and the nurse's dressing gown hanging from the edge of the screen, tall, like a woman's figure. "Lady in gray!" And a very odd thought beset him: Did she exist? Had she ever come at all? Or was she but the emanation of all the beauty he had loved and must leave so soon? The violet-gray spirit with the dark eyes and the crown of amber hair, who walks the dawn and the moonlight, and at bluebell time? What was she, who was she, did she exist? He rose and stood a moment clutching the window sill, to give him a sense of reality again; then began tiptoeing towards the door. He stopped at the foot of the bed; and Holly, as if conscious of his eyes fixed on her, stirred, sighed, and curled up closer in defense. He tiptoed on and passed out into the dark passage; reached his room, undressed at once, and stood before a mirror in his nightshirt. What a scarecrow—with temples fallen in, and thin legs! His eyes resisted his own image, and a look of pride came on his face. All was in league to pull him down, even his reflection in the glass, but he was not down—yet! He got into bed, and lay a long time without sleeping, trying to reach resignation, only too well aware that fretting and disappointment were very bad for him.

He woke in the morning so unrefreshed and strengthless that he sent for the doctor. After sounding him, the fellow pulled a face as long as your arm, and ordered him to stay in bed and give up smoking. That was no hardship; there was nothing to get up for, and when he felt ill, tobacco always lost its savor. He spent the morning languidly with the sun blinds down, turning and returning *The Times,* not reading much, the dog Balthasar lying beside his bed. With his lunch they brought him a telegram, running thus: "Your letter received coming down this afternoon will be with you at four-thirty. Irene."

Coming down! After all! Then she did exist—and he was not deserted. Coming down! A glow ran through his limbs; his cheeks and forehead felt hot. He drank his soup, and pushed the tray table away, lying very quiet until they had removed lunch and left him alone; but every now and then his eyes twinkled. Coming down! His heart beat fast, and then did not seem to beat at all. At three o'clock he got up and dressed deliberately, noiselessly. Holly and Mam'zelle would be in the schoolroom, and the servants asleep after their dinner, he shouldn't wonder. He opened his door cautiously, and went downstairs. In the hall the dog Balthasar lay solitary, and, followed by him, old Jolyon passed into his study and out into the burning afternoon. He meant to go down and meet her in the coppice, but felt at once he could not manage that in this heat. He sat down instead under the oak tree by the swing, and the dog Balthasar, who also felt the heat, lay down beside him. He sat there smiling. What a revel of bright minutes! What a hum of insects, and cooing of pigeons! It was the quintessence of a summer day. Lovely! And he was happy— happy as a sandboy, whatever that might be. She was coming; she had not given him up! He had everything in life he wanted—except a little more breath, and less weight—just here! He would see her when she emerged from the fernery, come swaying just a little, a violet-gray figure passing over the daisies and dandelions and "soldiers" on the lawn—the soldiers with their flowery crowns. He would not move, but she would come up to him and say: "Dear Uncle Jolyon, I am sorry!" and sit in the swing and let him look at her and tell her that he had not been very well but was all right now; and that dog would lick her hand. That dog knew his master was fond of her; that dog was a good dog.

It was quite shady under the tree; the sun could not get at him, only make the rest of the world bright so that he could see the Grand Stand at Epsom away out there, very far, and the cows cropping the clover in the field and swishing at the flies with their tails. He smelled the scent of limes, and lavender. Ah! that was why there was such a racket of bees. They were excited—busy, as his heart was busy and excited. Drowsy, too, drowsy and drugged on honey and happiness; as his heart was drugged and drowsy. Summer—summer—they seemed saying; great bees and little bees, and the flies too!

The stable clock struck four; in half an hour she would be here. He would have just one tiny nap, because he had had so little sleep of late; and then he would be fresh for her, fresh for youth and beauty, coming towards him across the sunlit lawn—lady in gray! And settling back in his chair he closed his eyes. Some thistledown came on what little air there was, and pitched on his mustache more white than itself. He did not know; but his breathing stirred it, caught there. A ray of sunlight struck through and lodged on his boot. A bumblebee alighted and strolled on the crown of his Panama hat. And the delicious surge of slumber reached the brain beneath that hat, and the head swayed forward and rested on his breast. Summer—summer! So went the hum.

The stable clock struck the quarter past. The dog Balthasar stretched and looked up at his master. The thistledown no longer moved. The dog placed his chin over the sunlit foot. It did not stir. The dog withdrew his chin quickly, rose, and leaped on old Jolyon's lap, looked in his face, whined; then, leaping down, sat on his haunches, gazing up. And suddenly he uttered a long, long howl.

But the thistledown was still as death, and the face of his old master. Summer—summer—summer! The soundless footsteps on the grass!

1917.

The Bar Sinister

By RICHARD HARDING DAVIS

PREFACE

When this story first appeared, the writer received letters of two kinds, one asking a question and the other making a statement. The question was, whether there was any foundation of truth in the story; the statement challenged him to say that there was. The letters seemed to show that a large proportion of readers prefer their dose of fiction with a sweetening of fact. This is written to furnish that condiment, and to answer the question and the statement.

In the dog world, the original of the bull terrier in the story is known as Edgewood Cold Steel and to his intimates as "Kid." His father was Lord Minto, a thoroughbred bull terrier, well known in Canada, but the story of Kid's life is that his mother was a black-and-tan named Vic. She was a lady of doubtful pedigree. Among her offspring by Lord Minto, so I have been often informed by many Canadian dog fanciers, breeders, and exhibitors, was the only white puppy, Kid, in a litter of black-and-tans. He made his first appearance in the show world in 1900 in Toronto, where, under the judging of Mr. Charles H. Mason, he was easily first. During that year, when he came to our kennels, and in the two years following, he carried off many blue ribbons and cups at nearly every first-class show in the country. The other dog, "Jimmy Jocks," who in the book was his friend and mentor, was in real life his friend and companion, Woodcote Jumbo, or "Jaggers," an aristocratic son of a long line of English champions. He has gone to that place where some day all good dogs must go.

In this autobiography I have tried to describe Kid as he really is, and this year, when he again strives for blue ribbons, I trust, should the gentle reader see him at any of the bench shows, he will give him a friendly pat and make his acquaintance. He will find his advances met with a polite and gentle courtesy.

THE AUTHOR

THE Master was walking most unsteady, his legs tripping each other. After the fifth or sixth round, my legs often go the same way.

But even when the Master's legs bend and twist a bit, you mustn't think he can't reach you. Indeed, that is the time he kicks most frequent. So I kept behind him in the shadow, or ran in the middle of the street. He stopped at many public houses with swinging doors, those doors that are cut so high from the sidewalk that you can look in under them, and see if the Master is inside. At night, when I peep beneath them, the man at the counter will see me first and say, "Here's the Kid, Jerry, come to take you home. Get a move on you"; and the Master will stumble out and follow me. It's lucky for us I'm so white, for, no matter how dark the night, he can always see me ahead, just out of reach of his boot. At night the Master certainly does see most amazing. Sometimes he sees two or four of me, and walks in a circle, so that I have to take him by the leg of his trousers and lead him into the right road. One night, when he was very nasty-tempered and I was coaxing him along, two men passed us, and one of them says, "Look at that brute!" and the other asks, "Which?" and they both laugh. The Master he cursed them good and proper.

But this night, whenever we stopped at a public house, the Master's pals left it and went on with us to the next. They spoke quite civil to me, and when the Master tried a flying kick, they gives him a shove. "Do you want us to lose our money?" says the pals.

I had had nothing to eat for a day and a night, and just before we set out the Master gives me a wash under the hydrant. Whenever I am locked up until all the slop pans in our alley are empty, and made to take a bath, and the Master's pals speak civil and feel my ribs, I know something is going to happen. And that night, when every time they see a policeman under a lamppost, they dodged across the street, and when at the last one of them picked me up and hid me under his jacket, I began to tremble; for I knew what it meant. It meant that I was to fight again for the Master.

I don't fight because I like fighting. I fight because if I didn't the other dog would find my throat, and the Master would lose his stakes, and I would be very sorry for him, and ashamed. Dogs can pass me and I can pass dogs, and I'd never pick a fight with none of them. When I see two dogs standing on their hind legs in the streets, clawing each other's ears, and snapping for each other's windpipes, or howling and swearing and rolling in the mud, I feel sorry they should act so, and pretend not to notice. If he'd let me, I'd like to pass the time of day with every dog I meet. But there's something about me that no nice dog can abide. When I trot up to nice dogs, nodding and grinning, to make friends, they always tell me to be off. "Go to the devil!" they bark at me. "Get out!" And when I walk away they shout "Mongrel!" and "Gutter dog!" and sometimes, after my back is turned, they rush me. I could kill most of them with three shakes, breaking the backbone of the little ones and squeezing the throat of the big ones. But what's the good? They *are* nice dogs; that's why I try to make up to them: and, though it's not for them to say it, I *am* a street dog, and if I try to push into the company of my betters, I suppose it's their right to teach me my place.

Of course they don't know I'm the best fighting bull terrier of my weight in Montreal. That's why it wouldn't be fair for me to take notice of what they shout. They don't know that if I once locked my jaws on them I'd carry away whatever I touched. The night I fought Kelley's White Rat, I wouldn't loosen up until the Master made a noose in my leash and strangled me; and, as for that Ottawa dog, if the handlers hadn't thrown red pepper down my nose I *never* would have let go of him. I don't think the handlers treated me quite right that time, but maybe they didn't know the Ottawa dog was dead. I did.

I learned my fighting from my mother when I was very young. We slept in a lumber yard on the river front, and by day hunted for food along the wharves. When we got it, the other tramp dogs would try to take it off us, and then it was wonderful to see mother fly at them and drive them away. All I know of fighting I learned from mother, watching her picking the ash heaps for me when I was too little to fight for myself. No one ever was so good to me as mother. When it snowed and the ice was in the St. Lawrence, she used to hunt alone, and bring me back new bones, and she'd sit and laugh to see me trying to swallow 'em whole. I was just a puppy then; my teeth was falling out. When I was able to fight we kept the whole river range to ourselves. I had the genuine long "punishing" jaw, so mother said, and there wasn't a man or a dog that dared worry us. Those were happy days, those were; and we lived well, share and share alike, and when we wanted a bit of fun, we chased the fat old wharf rats! My, how they would squeal!

Then the trouble came. It was no trouble to me. I was too young to care then. But mother took it so to heart that she grew ailing, and wouldn't go abroad with me by day. It was the same old scandal that they're always bringing up against me. I was so young then that I didn't know. I couldn't see any difference between mother—and other mothers.

But one day a pack of curs we drove off snarled back some new names at her, and mother dropped her head and ran, just as though they had whipped us. After that she wouldn't go out with me except in the dark, and one day she went away and never came back, and, though I hunted for her in every court and alley and back street of Montreal, I never found her.

One night, a month after mother ran away, I asked Guardian, the old blind mastiff, whose Master is the night watchman on our slip, what it all meant. And he told me.

"Every dog in Montreal knows," he says, "except you; and every Master knows. So I think it's time you knew."

Then he tells me that my father, who had treated mother so bad, was a great and noble gentleman from London. "Your father had twenty-two registered ancestors, had your father," old Guardian says, "and in him was the best bull-terrier blood of England, the most ancientest, the most royal; the winning 'blue-ribbon' blood, that breeds champions. He had sleepy pink eyes and thin pink lips, and he was as white all over as his own white teeth, and under his white skin you could see his muscles, hard and smooth, like the links of a steel chain. When your father stood still, and tipped his nose in the air, it was just as though he was saying, 'Oh, yes, you common dogs and men, you may well stare. It must be a rare treat for you colonials to see real English royalty.' He certainly was pleased with hisself, was your father. He looked just as proud and haughty as one of them stone dogs in Victoria Park—them as is cut out of white marble. And you're like him," says the old mastiff—"by that, of course, meaning you're white, same as him. That's the only likeness. But, you see, the trouble is, Kid—well, you see, Kid, the trouble is—your mother—"

"That will do," I said, for then I understood without his telling me, and I got up and walked away, holding my head and tail high in the air.

But I was, oh, so miserable, and I wanted to see mother that very minute, and tell her that I didn't care.

Mother is what I am, a street dog; there's no royal blood in mother's veins, nor is she like that father of mine, nor—and that's the worst—she's not even like me. For while I, when I'm washed for a fight, am as white as clean snow, she—and this is our trouble—she, my mother, is a black-and-tan.

When mother hid herself from me, I was twelve months old and able to take care of myself, and as, after mother left me, the wharves were never the same, I moved uptown and met the Master. Before he came, lots of other menfolks had tried to make up to me, and to whistle me home. But they either tried patting me or coaxing me with a piece of meat; so I didn't take to 'em. But one day the Master pulled me out of a street fight by the hind legs, and kicked me good.

"You want to fight, do you?" says he. "I'll give you all the *fighting* you want!" he says, and he kicks me again. So I knew he was my Master, and I followed him home. Since that day I've pulled off many fights for him, and they've brought dogs from all over the province to have a go at me; but up to that night none, under thirty pounds, had ever downed me.

But that night, so soon as they carried me into the ring, I saw the dog was overweight, and that I was no match for him. It was asking too much of a puppy. The Master should have known I couldn't do it. Not that I mean to blame the Master, for when sober, which he sometimes was— though not, as you might say, his habit—he was most kind to me, and let me out to find food, if I could get it, and only kicked me when I didn't pick him up at night and lead him home.

But kicks will stiffen the muscles, and starving a dog so as to get him ugly-tempered for a fight may make him nasty, but it's weakening to his insides, and it causes the legs to wobble.

The ring was in a hall back of a public house. There was a red-hot whitewashed stove in one corner, and the ring in the other. I lay in the Master's lap, wrapped in my blanket, and, spite of the stove, shivering awful; but I always shiver before a fight: I can't help gettin' excited. While the menfolks were a-flashing their money and taking their last drink at the bar, a little Irish groom in gaiters came up to me and gave me the back of his hand to smell, and scratched me behind the ears.

"You poor little pup," says he; "you haven't no show," he says. "That brute in the taproom he'll eat your heart out."

"That's what *you* think," says the Master, snarling. "I'll lay you a quid the Kid chews him up."

The groom he shook his head, but kept looking at me so sorry-like that I begun to get a bit sad myself. He seemed like he couldn't bear to leave off a-patting of me, and he says, speaking low just like he would to a manfolk, "Well, good luck to you, little pup," which I thought so civil of him that I reached up and licked his hand. I don't do that to many men. And the Master he knew I didn't, and took on dreadful.

"What 'ave you got on the back of your hand?" says he, jumping up.

"Soap!" says the groom, quick as a rat. "That's more than you've got on yours. Do you want to smell of it?" and he sticks his fist under the Master's nose. But the pals pushed in between 'em.

"He tried to poison the Kid!" shouts the Master.

"Oh, one fight at a time," says the referee. "Get into the ring, Jerry. We're waiting." So we went into the ring.

I could never just remember what did happen in that ring. He give me no time to spring. He fell on me like a horse. I couldn't keep my feet against him, and though, as I saw, he could get his hold when he liked, he wanted to chew me over a bit first. I was wondering if they'd be able to pry him off me, when, in the third round, he took his hold; and I begun to drown, just as I did when I fell into the river off the Red C slip. He closed deeper and deeper on my throat, and everything went black and red and bursting; and then, when I were sure I were dead, the handlers pulled him off, and the Master give me a kick that brought me to. But I couldn't move none, or even wink, both eyes being shut with lumps.

"He's a cur!" yells the Master, "a sneaking, cowardly cur! He lost the fight for me," says he, "because he's a _____ _____ _____ cowardly cur." And he kicks me again in the lower ribs, so that I go sliding across the sawdust. "There's gratitude fer yer," yells the Master. "I've fed that dog, and nussed that dog and housed him like a prince; and now he puts his tail between his legs and sells me out, he does. He's a coward! I've done with him, I am. I'd sell him for a pipeful of tobacco." He picked me up by the tail, and swung me for the menfolks to see. "Does any gentleman here want to buy a dog," he says, "to make into sausage meat?" he says. "That's all he's good for."

Then I heard the little Irish groom say, "I'll give you ten bob for the dog."

And another voice says, "Ah, don't you do it; the dog's same as dead —mebbe he is dead."

"Ten shilling!" says the Master, and his voice sobers a bit; "make it two pounds and he's yours."

But the pals rushed in again.

"Don't you be a fool, Jerry," they say. "You'll be sorry for this when you're sober. The Kid's worth a fiver."

One of my eyes was not so swelled up as the other, and as I hung by my tail, I opened it, and saw one of the pals take the groom by the shoulder.

"You ought to give 'im five pounds for that dog, mate," he says; "that's no ordinary dog. That dog's got good blood in him, that dog has. Why, his father—that very dog's father—"

I thought he never would go on. He waited like he wanted to be sure the groom was listening.

"That very dog's father," says the pal, "is Regent Royal, son of Champion Regent Monarch, champion bull terrier of England for four years."

I was sore, and torn, and chewed most awful, but what the pal said sounded so fine that I wanted to wag my tail, only couldn't, owing to my hanging from it.

But the Master calls out: "Yes, his father was Regent Royal; who's saying he wasn't? but the pup's a cowardly cur, that's what his pup is. And why? I'll tell you why: because his mother was a black-and-tan street dog, that's why!"

I don't see how I got the strength, but, some way, I threw myself out of the Master's grip and fell at his feet, and turned over and fastened all my teeth in his ankle, just across the bone.

When I woke, after the pals had kicked me off him, I was in the smoking car of a railroad train, lying in the lap of the little groom, and he was rubbing my open wounds with a greasy yellow stuff, exquisite to the smell and most agreeable to lick off.

II

"Well, what's your name—Nolan? Well, Nolan, these references are satisfactory," said the young gentleman my new Master called "Mr. Wyndham, sir." "I'll take you on as second man. You can begin today."

My new Master shuffled his feet and put his finger to his forehead. "Thank you, sir," says he. Then he choked like he had swallowed a fish bone. "I have a little dawg, sir," says he.

"You can't keep him," says "Mr. Wyndham, sir," very short.

" 'E's only a puppy, sir," says my new Master; " 'e wouldn't go outside the stables, sir."

"It's not that," says "Mr. Wyndham, sir." "I have large kennel of very fine dogs; they're the best of their breed in America. I don't allow strange dogs on the premises."

The Master shakes his head, and motions me with his cap, and I crept out from behind the door. "I'm sorry, sir," says the Master. "Then I can't take the place. I can't get along without the dawg, sir."

"Mr. Wyndham, sir," looked at me that fierce that I guessed he was going to whip me, so I turned over on my back and begged with my legs and tail.

"Why, you beat him!" says "Mr. Wyndham, sir," very stern.

"No fear!" the Master says, getting very red. "The party I bought him off taught him that. He never learnt that from me!" He picked me up in his arms, and to show "Mr. Wyndham, sir," how well I loved the Master, I bit his chin and hands.

"Mr. Wyndham, sir," turned over the letters the Master had given him. "Well, these references certainly are very strong," he says. "I guess I'll let the dog stay. Only see you keep him away from the kennels—or you'll both go."

"Thank you, sir," says the Master, grinning like a cat when she's safe behind the area railing.

"He's not a bad bull terrier," says "Mr. Wyndham, sir," feeling my head. "Not that I know much about the smooth-coated breeds. My dogs are St. Bernards." He stopped patting me and held up my nose. "What's the matter with his ears?" he says. "They're chewed to pieces. Is this a fighting dog?" he asks, quick and rough-like.

I could have laughed. If he hadn't been holding my nose, I certainly would have had a good grin at him. Me the best under thirty pounds in the Province of Quebec, and him asking if I was a fighting dog! I ran to the Master and hung down my head modest-like, waiting for him to tell my list of battles; but the Master he coughs in his cap most painful. "Fightin' dawg, sir!" he cries. "Lor' bless you, sir, the Kid don't know the word. 'E's just a puppy, sir, same as you see; a pet dog, so to speak. 'E's a regular old lady's lapdog, the Kid is."

"Well, you keep him away from my St. Bernards," says "Mr. Wyndham, sir," "or they might make a mouthful of him."

"Yes, sir; that they might," says the Master. But when we gets outside he slaps his knee and laughs inside hisself, and winks at me most sociable.

The Master's new home was in the country, in a province they called

Long Island. There was a high stone wall about his home with big iron gates to it, same as Godfrey's brewery; and there was a house with five red roofs; and the stables, where I lived, was cleaner than the aërated bakery shop. And then there was the kennels; but they was like nothing else in this world that ever I see. For the first days I couldn't sleep of nights for fear someone would catch me lying in such a cleaned-up place, and would chase me out of it; and when I did fall to sleep I'd dream I was back in the old Master's attic, shivering under the rusty stove, which never had no coals in it, with the Master flat on his back on the cold floor, with his clothes on. And I'd wake up scared and whimpering, and find myself on the new Master's cot with his hand on the quilt beside me; and I'd see the glow of the big stove, and hear the high-quality horses below stairs stamping in their straw-lined boxes, and I'd snoop the sweet smell of hay and harness soap and go to sleep again.

The stables was my jail, so the Master said, but I don't ask no better home than that jail.

"Now, Kid," says he, sitting on the top of a bucket upside down, "you've got to understand this. When I whistle it means you're not to go out of this 'ere yard. These stables is your jail. If you leave 'em I'll have to leave 'em too, and over the seas, in the County Mayo, an old mother will 'ave to leave her bit of a cottage. For two pounds I must be sending her every month, or she'll have naught to eat, nor no thatch over 'er head. I can't lose my place, Kid, so see you don't lose it for me. You must keep away from the kennels," says he; "they're not for the likes of you. The kennels are for the quality. I wouldn't take a litter of them woolly dogs for one wag of your tail, Kid, but for all that they are your betters, same as the gentry up in the big house are my betters. I know my place and keep away from the gentry, and you keep away from the champions."

So I never goes out of the stables. All day I just lay in the sun on the stone flags, licking my jaws, and watching the grooms wash down the carriages, and the only care I had was to see they didn't get gay and turn the hose on me. There wasn't even a single rat to plague me. Such stables I never did see.

"Nolan," says the head groom, "some day that dog of yours will give you the slip. You can't keep a street dog tied up all his life. It's against his natur'." The head groom is a nice old gentleman, but he doesn't know everything. Just as though I'd been a street dog because I liked it! As if I'd rather poke for my vittels in ash heaps than have 'em handed me in a washbasin, and would sooner bite and fight than be polite and sociable. If I'd had mother there I couldn't have asked for nothing more. But I'd think of her snooping in the gutters, or freezing of nights under the bridges, or, what's worst of all, running through the hot streets with her tongue down, so wild and crazy for a drink that the people would shout "mad dog" at her and stone her. Water's so good that I don't blame the menfolks for locking it up inside their houses; but when the hot days come, I think they might remember that those are the dog days, and leave a little water outside in a trough, like they do for the horses. Then we wouldn't go mad, and the policemen wouldn't shoot us. I had so much of everything I wanted that it made me think a lot of the days when I hadn't nothing, and if I could have given what I had to mother, as she used to share with me, I'd have been the happiest dog in the land. Not that I wasn't happy then, and most grateful to the Master, too, and if I'd only minded him, the trouble wouldn't have come again.

But one day the coachman says that the little lady they called Miss Dorothy had come back from school, and that same morning she runs over to the stables to pat her ponies, and she sees me.

"Oh, what a nice little, white little dog!" said she. "Whose little dog are you?" says she.

"That's my dog, miss," says the Master. "'Is name is Kid." And I ran up to her most polite, and licks her fingers, for I never see so pretty and kind a lady.

"You must come with me and call on my new puppies," says she, picking me up in her arms and starting off with me.

"Oh, but please, miss," cries Nolan, "Mr. Wyndham give orders that the Kid's not to go to the kennels."

"That'll be all right," says the little lady; "they're my kennels too. And the puppies will like to play with him."

You wouldn't believe me if I was to tell you of the style of them quality dogs. If I hadn't seen it myself I wouldn't have believed it neither. The Viceroy of Canada don't live no better. There was forty of them, but each one had his own house and a yard—most exclusive—and a cot and a drinking basin all to hisself. They had servants standing round waiting to feed 'em when they was hungry, and valets to wash 'em; and they had their hair combed and brushed like the grooms must when they go out on the box. Even the puppies had overcoats with their names on 'em in blue letters, and the name of each of those they called champions was painted up fine over his front door just like it was a public house or a veterinary's. They were the biggest St. Bernards I ever did see. I could have walked under them if they'd have let me. But they were very proud and haughty dogs, and looked only once at me, and then sniffed in the air. The little lady's own dog was an old gentleman bull dog. He'd come along with us, and when he notices how taken aback I was with all I see, 'e turned quite kind and affable and showed me about.

"Jimmy Jocks," Miss Dorothy called him, but, owing to his weight, he walked most dignified and slow, waddling like a duck, as you might say, and looked much too proud and handsome for such a silly name.

"That's the runway, and that's the trophy house," says he to me, "and that over there is the hospital, where you have to go if you get distemper, and the vet gives you beastly medicine."

"And which of these is your 'ouse, sir?" asks I, wishing to be respectful. But he looked that hurt and haughty. "I don't live in the kennels," says he, most contemptuous. "I am a house dog. I sleep in Miss Dorothy's room. And at lunch I'm let in with the family, if the visitors don't mind. They 'most always do, but they're too polite to say so. Besides," says he, smiling most condescending, "visitors are always afraid of me. It's because I'm so ugly," says he. "I suppose," says he, screwing up his wrinkles and speaking very slow and impressive, "I suppose I'm the ugliest bull dog in America"; and as he seemed to be so pleased to think hisself so, I said, "Yes, sir; you certainly are the ugliest ever I see," at which he nodded his head most approving.

"But I couldn't hurt 'em, as you say," he goes on, though I hadn't said nothing like that, being too polite. "I'm too old," he says; "I haven't any teeth. The last time one of those grizzly bears," said he, glaring at the big St. Bernards, "took a hold of me, he nearly was my death," says he. I thought his eyes would pop out of his head, he seemed so wrought up about it. "He rolled me around in the dirt, he did," says Jimmy Jocks, "an' I couldn't get up. It was low," says Jimmy Jocks, making a face like he had a bad taste in his mouth. "Low, that's what I call it—bad form, you understand, young man, not done in my set—and—and low." He growled way down in his stomach, and puffed hisself out, panting and blowing like he had been on a run.

"I'm not a street fighter," he says, scowling at a St. Bernard marked "Champion." "And when my rheumatism is not troubling me," he says, "I endeavor to be civil to all dogs, so long as they are gentlemen."

"Yes, sir," said I, for even to me he had been most affable.

At this we had come to a little house off by itself, and Jimmy Jocks invites me in. "This is their trophy room," he says, "where they keep their prizes. Mine." he says, rather grand-like, "are on the sideboard." Not knowing what a sideboard might be, I said, "Indeed, sir, that must be very gratifying." But he only wrinkled up his chops as much as to say, "It is my right."

The trophy room was as wonderful as any public house I ever see. On the walls was pictures of nothing but beautiful St. Bernard dogs, and rows and rows of blue and red and yellow ribbons; and when I asked Jimmy Jocks why they was so many more of blue than of the others, he laughs and says, "Because these kennels always win." And there was many shining cups on the shelves, which Jimmy Jocks told me were prizes won by the champions.

"Now, sir, might I ask you, sir," says I, "wot is a champion?"

At that he panted and breathed so hard I thought he would bust hisself. "My dear young friend!" says he, "wherever have you been educated? A champion is a—a champion," he says. "He must win nine blue ribbons in the 'open' class. You follow me—that is—against all comers. Then he has the title before his name, and they put his photograph in the sporting papers. You know, of course, that *I* am a champion," says he. "I am Champion Woodstock Wizard III, and the two other Woodstock Wizards, my father and uncle, were both champions."

"But I thought your name was Jimmy Jocks," I said.

He laughs right out at that.

"That's my kennel name, not my registered name," he says. "Why, certainly you know that every dog has two names. Now, for instance, what's your registered name and number?" says he.

"I've got only one name," I says. "Just Kid."

Woodstock Wizard puffs at that and wrinkles up his forehead and pops out his eyes.

"Who are your people?" says he. "Where is your home?"

"At the stable, sir," I said. "My Master is the second groom."

At that Woodstock Wizard III looks at me for quite a bit without winking, and stares all around the room over my head.

"Oh, well," says he at last, "you're a very civil young dog," says he, "and I blame no one for what he can't help," which I thought most fair and liberal. "And I have known many bull terriers that were champions," says he, "though as a rule they mostly run with fire engines and to fighting. For me, I wouldn't care to run through the streets after a hose cart, nor to fight," says he: "but each to his taste."

I could not help thinking that if Woodstock Wizard III tried to follow a fire engine he would die of apoplexy, and seeing he'd lost his teeth, it was lucky he had no taste for fighting; but, after his being so condescending, I didn't say nothing.

"Anyway," says he, "every smooth-coated dog is better than any hairy old camel like those St. Bernards, and if ever you're hungry down at the stables, young man, come up to the house and I'll give you a bone. I can't eat them myself, but I bury them around the garden from force of habit and in case a friend should drop in. Ah, I see my mistress coming," he says, "and I bid you good day. I regret," he says, "that our different social position prevents our meeting frequent, for you're a worthy young dog with a proper respect for your betters, and in this country there's precious few of them have that." Then he waddles off, leaving me alone and very sad, for he was the first dog in many days that had spoke to me. But since he showed, seeing that I was a stable dog, he didn't want my company, I waited for him to get well away. It was not a cheerful place to wait, the trophy house. The pictures of the champions seemed to scowl at me, and ask what right such as I had even to admire them, and the blue and gold ribbons and the silver cups made me very miserable. I had never won no blue ribbons or silver cups, only stakes for the old Master to spend in the publics; and I hadn't won them for being a beautiful high-quality dog, but just for fighting—which, of course, as Woodstock Wizard III says, is low. So I started for the stables, with my head down and my tail between my legs, feeling sorry I had ever left the Master. But I had more reason to be sorry before I got back to him.

The trophy house was quite a bit from the kennels, and as I left it I see Miss Dorothy and Woodstock Wizard III walking back toward them, and, also, that a big St. Bernard, his name was Champion Red Elfberg, had broke his chain and was running their way. When he reaches old Jimmy Jocks he lets out a roar like a grain steamer in a fog, and he makes three leaps for him. Old Jimmy Jocks was about a fourth his size; but he plants his feet and curves his back, and his hair goes up around his neck like a collar. But he never had no show at no time, for the grizzly bear, as Jimmy Jocks had called him, lights on old Jimmy's back and tries to break it, and old Jimmy Jocks snaps his gums and claws the grass, panting and groaning awful. But he can't do nothing, and the grizzly bear just rolls him under him, biting and tearing cruel. The odds was all that Woodstock Wizard III was going to be killed; I had fought enough to see that: but not knowing the rules of the game among champions, I didn't like to interfere between two gentlemen who might be settling a private affair, and, as it were, take it as presuming of me. So I stood by, though I was shaking terrible, and holding myself in like I was on a leash. But at that Woodstock Wizard III, who was underneath, sees me through the dust, and calls very faint, "Help, you!" he says. "Take him in the hind leg," he says. "He's murdering me," he says. And then the little Miss Dorothy, who was crying, and calling to the kennel men, catches at the Red Elfberg's hind legs to pull him off, and the brute, keeping his front pats well in Jimmy's stomach, turns his big head and snaps at her. So that was all I asked for, thank you. I went up under him. It was really nothing. He stood so high that I had only to take off about three feet from him and come in from the side, and my long "punishing jaw," as mother was always talking about, locked on his woolly throat, and my back teeth met. I couldn't shake him, but I shook myself, and every time I shook myself there was thirty pounds of weight tore at his windpipes. I couldn't see nothing for his long hair, but I heard Jimmy Jocks puffing and blowing on one side, and munching the brute's leg with his old gums. Jimmy was an old sport that day, was Jimmy, or Woodstock Wizard III, as I should say. When the Red Elfberg was out and down I had to run, or those kennel men would have had my life. They chased me right into the stables; and from under the hay I watched the head groom take down a carriage whip and order them to the right about. Luckily Master and the young grooms were out, or that day there'd have been fighting for everybody.

Well, it nearly did for me and the Master. "Mr. Wyndham, sir," comes raging to the stables. I'd half killed his best prize-winner, he says, and had oughter be shot, and he gives the Master his notice. But Miss Dorothy she follows him, and says it was his Red Elfberg what began the fight, and that I'd saved Jimmy's life, and that old Jimmy Jocks was worth more to her than all the St. Bernards in the Swiss mountains—wherever they may be. And that I was her champion, anyway. Then she cried over me most beautiful, and over Jimmy Jocks, too, who was that tied up in bandages he couldn't even waddle. So when he heard that side of it, "Mr. Wyndham, sir," told us that if Nolan put me on a chain we could stay. So it came out all right for everybody but me. I was glad the Master kept his place, but I'd never worn a chain before, and it disheartened me. But that was the least of it. For the quality dogs couldn't forgive my whipping their champion, and they came to the fence between the kennels and the stables, and laughed through the bars, barking most cruel words at me. I couldn't understand how they found it out, but they knew. After the fight Jimmy Jocks was most condescending to me, and he said the grooms had boasted to the kennel men that I was a son of Regent Royal, and that when the kennel men asked who was my mother they had had to tell them that too. Perhaps that was the way of it, but, however, the scandal got out, and every one of the quality dogs knew that I was a street dog and the son of a black-and-tan.

"These misalliances will occur," said Jimmy Jocks, in his old-fashioned way; "but no well-bred dog," says he, looking most scornful at the St. Bernards, who were howling behind the palings, "would refer to your misfortune before you, certainly not cast it in your face. I myself remember your father's father, when he made his début at the Crystal Palace. He took four blue ribbons and three specials."

But no sooner than Jimmy would leave me the St. Bernards would take to howling again, insulting mother and insulting me. And when I tore at my chain, they, seeing they were safe, would howl the more. It was never the same after that; the laughs and the jeers cut into my heart, and the chain bore heavy on my spirit. I was so sad that sometimes I wished I was back in the gutter again, where no one was better than me, and some nights I wished I was dead. If it hadn't been for the Master being so kind, and that it would have looked like I was blaming mother, I would have twisted my leash and hanged myself.

About a month after my fight, the word was passed through the kennels that the New York Show was coming, and such goings on as followed I never did see. If each of them had been matched to fight for a 'thousand pounds and the gate, they couldn't have trained more conscientious. But perhaps that's just my envy. The kennel men rubbed 'em and scrubbed 'em, and trims their hair and curls and combs it, and some dogs they fatted and some they starved. No one talked of nothing but the Show, and the chances "our kennels" had against the other kennels, and if this one of our champions would win over that one, and whether them as hoped to be champions had better show in the "open" or the "limit" class, and whether this dog would beat his own dad, or whether his little puppy sister couldn't beat the two of 'em. Even the grooms had their money up, and day or night you heard nothing but praises of "our" dogs, until I, being so far out of it, couldn't have felt meaner if I had been running the streets with a can to my tail. I knew shows were not for such as me, and so all day I lay stretched at the end of my chain, pretending I was asleep, and only too glad that they had something so important to think of that they could leave me alone.

But one day, before the Show opened, Miss Dorothy came to the stables with "Mr. Wyndham, sir," and, seeing me chained up and so miserable, she takes me in her arms.

"You poor little tyke!" says she. "It's cruel to tie him up so; he's eating his heart out, Nolan," she says. "I don't know nothing about bull terriers," says she, "but I think Kid's got good points," says she, "and you ought to show him. Jimmy Jocks has three legs on the Rensselaer Cup now, and I'm going to show him this time, so that he can get the fourth; and, if you wish, I'll enter your dog too. How would you like that, Kid?" says Maybe you'd meet a pal or two," says she. "It would cheer you up, she. "How would you like to see the most beautiful dogs in the world? wouldn't it, Kid?" says she. But I was so upset I could only wag my tail most violent. "He says it would!" says she, though, being that excited, I hadn't said nothing.

So "Mr. Wyndham, sir," laughs, and takes out a piece of blue paper and sits down at the head groom's table.

"What's the name of the father of your dog, Nolan?" says he. And Nolan says: "The man I got him off told me he was a son of Champion Regent Royal, sir. But it don't seem likely, does it?" says Nolan.

"It does not!" says "Mr. Wyndham, sir," short like.

"Aren't you sure, Nolan?" says Miss Dorothy.

"No, miss," says the Master.

"Sire unknown," says "Mr. Wyndham, sir," and writes it down.

"Date of birth?" asks "Mr. Wyndham, sir."

"I—I—unknown, sir," says Nolan. And "Mr. Wyndham, sir," writes it down.

"Breeder?" says "Mr. Wyndham, sir."

"Unknown," says Nolan, getting very red around the jaws, and I drops my head and tail. And "Mr. Wyndham, sir," writes that down.

"Mother's name?" says "Mr. Wyndham, sir."

"She was a—unknown," says the Master. And I licks his hand.

"Dam unknown," says "Mr. Wyndham, sir," and writes it down. Then he takes the paper and reads out loud: " 'Sire unknown, dam unknown, breeder unknown, date of birth unknown.' You'd better call him the 'Great Unknown,'" says he. "Who's paying his entrance fee?"

"I am," says Miss Dorothy.

Two weeks after we all got on a train for New York, Jimmy Jocks and me following Nolan in the smoking car, and twenty-two of the St. Bernards in boxes and crates and on chains and leashes. Such a barking and howling I never did hear; and when they sees me going, too, they laughs fit to kill.

"Wot is this—a circus?" says the railroad man.

But I had no heart in it. I hated to go. I knew I was no "show" dog, even though Miss Dorothy and the Master did their best to keep me from shaming them. For before we set out Miss Dorothy brings a man from town who scrubbed and rubbed me, and sandpapered my tail, which hurt most awful, and shaved my ears with the Master's razor, so they could 'most see clear through 'em, and sprinkles me over with pipe clay, till I shines like a Tommy's crossbelts.

"Upon my word!" says Jimmy Jocks when he first sees me. "Wot a swell you are! You're the image of your granddad when he made his début at the Crystal Palace. He took four firsts and three specials." But I knew he was only trying to throw heart into me. They might scrub, and they might rub, and they might pipe-clay, but they couldn't pipe-clay the insides of me, and they was black-and-tan.

Then we came to a garden, which it was not, but the biggest hall in the world. Inside there was lines of benches a few miles long, and on them sat every dog in America. If all the dog-snatchers in Montreal had worked night and day for a year, they couldn't have caught so many dogs. And they was all shouting and barking and howling so vicious that my heart stopped beating. For at first I thought they was all enraged at my presuming to intrude. But after I got in my place they kept at it just the same, barking at every dog as he come in: daring him to fight, and ordering him out, and asking him what breed of dog he thought he was, anyway. Jimmy Jocks was chained just behind me, and he said he never see so fine a show. "That's a hot class you're in, my lad," he says, looking over into my street, where there were thirty bull terriers. They was all as white as cream, and each so beautiful that if I could have broke my chain I would have run all the way home and hid myself under the horse trough.

All night long they talked and sang, and passed greetings with old pals, and the homesick puppies howled dismal. Them that couldn't sleep wouldn't let no others sleep, and all the electric lights burned in the roof, and in my eyes. I could hear Jimmy Jocks snoring peaceful, but I could only doze by jerks, and when I dozed I dreamed horrible. All the dogs in the hall seemed coming at me for daring to intrude, with their jaws red and open, and their eyes blazing like the lights in the roof. "You're a street dog! Get out, you street dog!" they yells. And as they drives me out, the pipe clay drops off me, and they laugh and shriek; and when I looks down I see that I have turned into a black-and-tan.

They was most awful dreams, and next morning, when Miss Dorothy comes and gives me water in a pan, I begs and begs her to take me home; but she can't understand. "How well Kid is!" she says. And when I jumps into the Master's arm and pulls to break my chain, he says, "If he knew all as he had against him, miss, he wouldn't be so gay." And from a book they reads out the names of the beautiful highbred terriers which I have got to meet. And I can't make 'em understand that I only want to run away and hide myself where no one will see me.

Then suddenly men comes hurrying down our street and begins to brush the beautiful bull terriers; and the Master rubs me with a towel so excited that his hands tremble awful, and Miss Dorothy tweaks my ears between her gloves, so that the blood runs to 'em, and they turn pink and stand up straight and sharp.

"Now, then, Nolan," says she, her voice shaking just like his fingers, "keep his head up—and never let the judge lose sight of him." When I hears that my legs breaks under me, for I knows all about judges. Twice the old Master goes up before the judge for fighting me with other dogs, and the judge promises him if he ever does it again he'll chain him up in jail. I knew he'd find me out. A judge can't be fooled by no pipe clay. He can see right through you, and he reads your insides.

The judging ring, which is where the judge holds out, was so like a fighting pit that when I come in it, and finds six other dogs there, I springs into position, so that when they lets us go I can defend myself. But the Master smooths down my hair and whispers, "Hold 'ard, Kid, hold 'ard. This ain't a fight," says he. "Look your prettiest," he whispers. "Please, Kid, look your prettiest"; and he pulls my leash so tight that I can't touch my pats to the sawdust, and my nose goes up in the air. There was millions of people a-watching us from the railings, and three of our kennel men, too, making fun of the Master and me, and Miss Dorothy with her chin just reaching to the rail, and her eyes so big that I thought she was a-going to cry. It was awful to think that when the judge stood up and exposed me, all those people, and Miss Dorothy, would be there to see me driven from the Show.

The judge he was a fierce-looking man with specs on his nose, and a red beard. When I first come in he didn't see me, owing to my being too quick for him and dodging behind the Master. But when the Master drags me round and I pulls at the sawdust to keep back, the judge looks at us careless-like, and then stops and glares through his specs, and I knew it was all up with me.

"Are there any more?" asks the judge to the gentleman at the gate, but never taking his specs from me.

The man at the gate looks in his book. "Seven in the novice class," says he. "They're all here. You can go ahead," and he shuts the gate.

The judge he doesn't hesitate a moment. He just waves his hand toward the corner of the ring. "Take him away," he says to the Master, "over there, and keep him away"; and he turns and looks most solemn at the six beautiful bull terriers. I don't know how I crawled to that corner. I wanted to scratch under the sawdust and dig myself a grave. The kennel men they slapped the rail with their hands and laughed at the Master like they would fall over. They pointed at me in the corner, and their sides just shaked. But little Miss Dorothy she presses her lips tight against the rail, and I see tears rolling from her eyes. The Master he hangs his head like he had been whipped. I felt most sorry for him than all. He was so red, and he was letting on not to see the kennel men, and blinking his eyes. If the judge had ordered me right out it wouldn't have disgraced us so, but it was keeping me there while he was judging the highbred dogs that hurt so hard. With all those people staring, too. And his doing it so quick, without no doubt nor questions. You can't fool the judges. They see inside you.

But he couldn't make up his mind about them highbred dogs. He scowls at 'em, and he glares at 'em, first with his head on the one side and then on the other. And he feels of 'em, and orders 'em to run about. And Nolan leans against the rails, with his head hung down, and pats me. And Miss Dorothy comes over beside him, but don't say nothing, only wipes her eye with her finger. A man on the other side of the rail he says to the Master, "The judge don't like your dog?"

"No," says the Master.

"Have you ever shown him before?" says the man.

"No," says the Master, "and I'll never show him again. He's my dog," says the Master, "and he suits me! And I don't care what no judges think." And when he says them kind words, I licks his hand most grateful.

The judge had two of the six dogs on a little platform in the middle of the ring, and he had chased the four other dogs into the corners, where they was licking their chops, and letting on they didn't care, same as Nolan was.

The two dogs on the platform was so beautiful that the judge hisself couldn't tell which was the best of 'em, even when he stoops down and holds their heads together. But at last he gives a sigh, and brushes the sawdust off his knees, and goes to the table in the ring, where there was a man keeping score, and heaps and heaps of blue and gold and red and yellow ribbons. And the judge picks up a bunch of 'em and walks to the two gentlemen who was holding the beautiful dogs, and he says to each, "What's his number?" and he hands each gentleman a ribbon. And then he turned sharp and comes straight at the Master.

"What's his number?" says the judge. And Master was so scared that he couldn't make no answer.

But Miss Dorothy claps her hands and cries out like she was laughing, "Three twenty-six," and the judge writes it down and shoves Master the blue ribbon.

I bit the Master, and I jumps and bit Miss Dorothy, and I waggled so hard that the Master couldn't hold me. When I get to the gate Miss Dorothy snatches me up and kisses me between the ears, right before millions of people, and they both hold me so tight that I didn't know which of them was carrying of me. But one thing I knew, for I listened hard, as it was the judge hisself as said it.

"Did you see that puppy I gave first to?" says the judge to the gentleman at the gate.

"I did. He was a bit out of his class," says the gate gentleman.

"He certainly was!" says the judge, and they both laughed.

But I didn't care. They couldn't hurt me then, not with Nolan holding the blue ribbon and Miss Dorothy hugging my ears, and the kennel men sneaking away, each looking like he'd been caught with his nose under the lid of the slop can.

We sat down together, and we all three just talked as fast as we could. They was so pleased that I couldn't help feeling proud myself, and I barked and leaped about so gay that all the bull terriers in our street stretched on their chains and howled at me.

"Just look at him!" says one of those I had beat. "What's he giving hisself airs about?"

"Because he's got one blue ribbon!" says another of 'em. "Why, when I was a puppy I used to eat 'em, and if that judge could ever learn to know a toy from a mastiff, I'd have had this one."

But Jimmy Jocks he leaned over from his bench and says, "Well done, Kid. Didn't I tell you so?" What he 'ad told me was that I might get a "commended," but I didn't remind him.

"Didn't I tell you," says Jimmy Jocks, "that I saw your grandfather make his début at the Crystal—"

"Yes, sir, you did, sir," says I, for I have no love for the men of my family.

A gentleman with a showing leash around his neck comes up just then and looks at me very critical. "Nice dog you've got, Miss Wyndham," says he; "would you care to sell him?"

"He's not my dog," says Miss Dorothy, holding me tight. "I wish he were."

"He's not for sale, sir," says the Master, and I was *that* glad.

"Oh, he's yours, is he?" says the gentleman, looking hard at Nolan. "Well, I'll give you a hundred dollars for him," says he, careless-like.

"Thank you, sir; he's not for sale," says Nolan, but his eyes get very big. The gentleman he walked away; but I watches him, and he talks to a man in a golf cap, and by and by the man comes along our street, looking at all the dogs, and stops in front of me.

"This your dog?" says he to Nolan. "Pity he's so leggy," says he. "If he had a good tail, and a longer stop, and his ears were set higher, he'd be a good dog. As he is, I'll give you fifty dollars for him."

But, before the Master could speak, Miss Dorothy laughs and says: "You're Mr. Polk's kennel man, I believe. Well, you tell Mr. Polk from me that the dog's not for sale now any more than he was five minutes ago, and that when he is, he'll have to bid against me for him."

The man looks foolish at that, but he turns to Nolan quick-like. "I'll give you three hundred for him," he says.

"Oh, indeed!" whispers Miss Dorothy, like she was talking to herself. "That's it, is it?" And she turns and looks at me just as though she had never seen me before. Nolan he was a-gaping, too, with his mouth open. But he holds me tight.

"He's not for sale," he growls, like he was frightened; and the man looks black and walks away.

"Why, Nolan!" cried Miss Dorothy, "Mr. Polk knows more about bull terriers than any amateur in America. What can he mean? Why, Kid is no more than a puppy! Three hundred dollars for a puppy!"

"And he ain't no thoroughbred, neither!" cries the Master. "He's 'Unknown,' ain't he? Kid can't help it, of course, but his mother, miss—"

I dropped my head. I couldn't bear he should tell Miss Dorothy. I couldn't bear she should know I had stolen my blue ribbon.

But the Master never told, for at that a gentleman runs up, calling, "Three twenty-six, three twenty-six!" And Miss Dorothy says, "Here he is; what is it?"

"The Winners' class," says the gentleman. "Hurry, please; the judge is waiting for him."

Nolan tries to get me off the chain onto a showing leash, but he shakes so, he only chokes me. "What is it, miss?" he says. "What is it?"

"The Winners' class," says Miss Dorothy. "The judge wants him with the winners of the other classes—to decide which is the best. It's only a form," says she. "He has the champions against him now."

"Yes," says the gentleman, as he hurries us to the ring. "I'm afraid it's only a form for your dog, but the judge wants all the winners, puppy class even."

We had got to the gate, and the gentleman there was writing down my number.

"Who won the open?" asks Miss Dorothy.

"Oh, who would?" laughs the gentleman. "The old champion, of course. He's won for three years now. There he is. Isn't he wonderful?"

says he; and he points to a dog that's standing proud and haughty on the platform in the middle of the ring.

I never see so beautiful a dog—so fine and clean and noble, so white like he had rolled hisself in flour, holding his nose up and his eyes shut, same as though no one was worth looking at. Aside of him we other dogs, even though we had a blue ribbon apiece, seemed like lumps of mud. He was a royal gentleman, a king, he was. His master didn't have to hold his head with no leash. He held it hisself, standing as still as an iron dog on a lawn, like he knew all the people was looking at him. And so they was, and no one around the ring pointed at no other dog but him.

"Oh, what a picture!" cried Miss Dorothy. "He's like a marble figure by a great artist—one who loved dogs. Who is he?" says she, looking in her book. "I don't keep up with terriers."

"Oh, you know him," says the gentleman. "He is the champion of champions, Regent Royal."

The Master's face went red.

"And this is Regent Royal's son," cries he, and he pulls me quick into the ring, and plants me on the platform next my father.

I trembled so that I near fell. My legs twisted like a leash. But my father he never looked at me. He only smiled the same sleepy smile, and he still kept his eyes half shut, like as no one, no, not even his own son, was worth his lookin' at.

The judge he didn't let me stay beside my father, but, one by one, he placed the other dogs next to him and measured and felt and pulled at them. And each one he put down, but he never put my father down. And then he comes over and picks me up and sets me back on the platform, shoulder to shoulder with the Champion Regent Royal, and goes down on his knees, and looks into our eyes.

The gentleman with my father he laughs, and says to the judge, "Thinking of keeping us here all day, John?" But the judge he doesn't hear him, and goes behind us and runs his hand down my side, and holds back my ears, and takes my jaws between his fingers. The crowd around the ring is very deep now, and nobody says nothing. The gentleman at the score table, he is leaning forward, with his elbows on his knees and his eyes very wide, and the gentleman at the gate is whispering quick to Miss Dorothy, who has turned white. I stood as stiff as stone. I didn't even breathe. But out of the corner of my eye I could see my father licking his pink chops, and yawning just a little, like he was bored.

The judge he had stopped looking fierce and was looking solemn. Something inside him seemed a-troubling him awful. The more he stares at us now, the more solemn he gets, and when he touches us he does it gentle, like he was patting us. For a long time he kneels in the sawdust, looking at my father and at me, and no one around the ring says nothing to nobody.

Then the judge takes a breath and touches me sudden. "It's his," he says. But he lays his hand just as quick on my father. "I'm sorry," says he. The gentleman holding my father cries:

"Do you mean to tell me—"

And the judge he answers, "I mean the other is the better dog." He takes my father's head between his hands and looks down at him most sorrowful. "The king is dead," says he. "Long live the king! Good-by, Regent," he says.

The crowd around the railings clapped their hands, and some laughed scornful, and everyone talks fast, and I start for the gate, so dizzy that I can't see my way. But my father pushes in front of me, walking very daintily, and smiling sleepy, same as he had just been waked, with his head high, and his eyes shut, looking at nobody.

So that is how I "came by my inheritance," as Miss Dorothy calls it; and just for that, though I couldn't feel where I was any different, the crowd follows me to my bench, and pats me, and coos at me, like I was a baby in a baby carriage. And the handlers have to hold 'em back so that the gentlemen from the papers can make pictures of me, and Nolan walks me up and down so proud, and the men shake their heads and says, "He certainly is the true type, he is!" And the pretty ladies ask Miss Dorothy, who sits beside me letting me lick her gloves to show the crowd what friends we is, "Aren't you afraid he'll bite you?" And Jimmy Jocks calls to me, "Didn't I tell you so? I always knew you were one of us. Blood will out, Kid; blood will out. I saw your grandfather," says he, "make his début at the Crystal Palace. But he was never the dog you are!"

After that, if I could have asked for it, there was nothing I couldn't get. You might have thought I was a show dog, and they was afeard I'd melt. If I wet my pats, Nolan gave me a hot bath and chained me to the stove; if I couldn't eat my food, being stuffed full by the cook—for I am a house dog now, and let in to lunch, whether there is visitors or not—Nolan would run to bring the vet. It was all tommyrot, as Jimmy says, but meant most kind. I couldn't scratch myself comfortable, without Nolan giving me nasty drinks, and rubbing me outside till it burnt awful; and I wasn't let to eat bones for fear of spoiling my "beautiful" mouth, what mother used to call my "punishing jaw"; and my food was cooked special on a gas stove; and Miss Dorothy gives me an overcoat, cut very stylish like the champions', to wear when we goes out carriage driving.

After the next Show, where I takes three blue ribbons, four silver cups, two medals, and brings home forty-five dollars for Nolan, they gives me a "registered" name, same as Jimmy's. Miss Dorothy wanted to call me "Regent Heir Apparent"; but I was *that* glad when Nolan says, "No; Kid don't owe nothing to his father, only to you and hisself. So, if you please, miss, we'll call him Wyndham Kid." And so they did, and you can see it on my overcoat in blue letters, and painted top of my kennel.

It was all too hard to understand. For days I just sat and wondered if I was really me, and how it all come about, and why everybody was so kind. But oh, it was so good they was, for if they hadn't been I'd never have got the thing I most wished after. But, because they was kind, and not liking to deny me nothing, they gave it me, and it was more to me than anything in the world.

It came about one day when we was out driving. We was in the cart they calls the dogcart because it's the one Miss Dorothy keeps to take Jimmy and me for an airing. Nolan was up behind, and me, in my new overcoat, was sitting beside Miss Dorothy. I was admiring the view, and thinking how good it was to have a horse pull you about so that you needn't get yourself splashed and have to be washed, when I hears a dog calling loud for help, and I pricks up my ears and looks over the horse's head. And I sees something that makes me tremble down to my toes. In the road before us three big dogs was chasing a little old lady dog. She had a string to her tail, where some boys had tied a can, and she was dirty with mud and ashes, and torn most awful. She was too far done up to get away, and too old to help herself, but she was making a fight for her life, snapping her old gums savage, and dying game. All this I see in a wink, and then the three dogs pinned her down, and I can't stand it no longer, and clears the wheel and lands in the road on my head. It was my stylish overcoat done that, and I cursed it proper, but I gets my pats again quick, and makes a rush for the fighting. Behind me I hear Miss Dorothy cry: "They'll kill that old dog. Wait, take my whip. Beat them off her! The Kid can take care of himself"; and I hear Nolan fall into the road, and the horse come to a stop. The old lady dog was down, and the three was eating her vicious; but as I come up, scattering the pebbles, she hears, and thinking it's one more of them, she lifts her head, and my heart breaks open like someone had sunk his teeth in it. For, under the ashes and the dirt and the blood, I can see who it is, and I know that my mother has come back to me.

I gives a yell that throws them three dogs off their legs.

"Mother!" I cries. "I'm the Kid," I cries. "I'm coming to you. Mother, I'm coming!"

And I shoots over her at the throat of the big dog, and the other two they sinks their teeth into that stylish overcoat and tears it off me, and that sets me free, and I lets them have it. I never had so fine a fight as that! What with mother being there to see, and not having been let to mix up in no fights since I become a prize-winner, it just naturally did me good, and it wasn't three shakes before I had 'em yelping. Quick as a wink, mother she jumps in to help me, and I just laughed to see her. It was so like old times. And Nolan he made me laugh, too. He was like a hen on a bank, shaking the butt of his whip, but not daring to cut in for fear of hitting me.

"Stop it, Kid," he says, "stop it. Do you want to be all torn up?" says he. "Think of the Boston show," says he. "Think of Chicago. Think of Danbury. Don't you never want to be a champion?" How was I to think of all them places when I had three dogs to cut up at the same time? But in a minute two of 'em begs for mercy, and mother and me lets 'em run away. The big one he ain't able to run away. Then mother and me we dances and jumps, and barks and laughs, and bites each other and rolls each other in the road. There never was two dogs so happy as we. And Nolan he whistles and calls and begs me to come to him; but I just laugh and play larks with mother.

"Now, you come with me," says I, "to my new home, and never try to run away again." And I shows her our house with the five red roofs, set on the top of the hill. But mother trembles awful, and says: "They'd never let me in such a place. Does the Viceroy live there, Kid?" says she. And I laugh at her. "No; I do," I says. "And if they won't let you live there, too, you and me will go back to the streets together, for we must never be parted no more." So we trots up the hill side by side, with Nolan trying to catch me, and Miss Dorothy laughing at him from the cart.

"The Kid's made friends with the poor old dog," says she. "Maybe he knew her long ago when he ran the streets himself. Put her in here beside me, and see if he doesn't follow."

So when I hears that I tells mother to go with Nolan and sit in the cart; but she says no—that she'd soil the pretty lady's frock; but I tells her to do as I say, and so Nolan lifts her, trembling still, into the cart, and I runs alongside, barking joyful.

When we drives into the stables I takes mother to my kennel, and tells her to go inside it and make herself at home. "Oh, but he won't let me!" says she.

"Who won't let you?" says I, keeping my eye on Nolan, and growling a bit nasty, just to show I was meaning to have my way.

"Why, Wyndham Kid," says she, looking up at the name on my kennel.

"But I'm Wyndham Kid!" says I.

"You!" cries mother. "You! Is my little Kid the great Wyndham Kid the dogs all talk about?" And at that, she being very old, and sick, and nervous, as mothers are, just drops down in the straw and weeps bitter.

Well, there ain't much more than that to tell. Miss Dorothy she settled it.

"If the Kid wants the poor old thing in the stables," says she, "let her stay.

"You see," says she, "she's a black-and-tan, and his mother was a black-and-tan, and maybe that's what makes Kid feel so friendly toward her," says she.

"Indeed, for me," says Nolan, "she can have the best there is. I'd never drive out no dog that asks for a crust nor a shelter," he says. "But what will Mr. Wyndham do?"

"He'll do what I say," says Miss Dorothy, "and if I say she's to stay, she will stay, and I say—she's to stay!"

And so mother and Nolan and me found a home. Mother was scared at first—not being used to kind people; but she was so gentle and loving that the grooms got fonder of her than of me, and tried to make me jealous by patting of her and giving her the pick of the vittles. But that was the wrong way to hurt my feelings. That's all, I think. Mother is so happy here that I tell her we ought to call it the Happy Hunting Grounds, because no one hunts you, and there is nothing to hunt; it just all comes to you. And so we live in peace, mother sleeping all day in the sun, or behind the stove in the head groom's office, being fed twice a day regular by Nolan, and all the day by the other grooms most irregular. And as for me, I go hurrying around the country to the bench shows, winning money and cups for Nolan, and taking the blue ribbons away from father.

While the Automobile Ran Down

By CHARLES BATTELL LOOMIS

IT WAS a letter to encourage a hesitating lover, and certainly Orville Thornton, author of *Thoughts for Non-Thinkers,* came under that head. He received it on a Tuesday, and immediately made up his mind to declare his intentions to Miss Annette Badeau that evening.

But perhaps the contents of the letter will help the reader to a better understanding of the case.

DEAR ORVILLE: Miss Badeau sails unexpectedly for Paris on the day after Christmas, her aunt Madge having cabled her to come and visit her. Won't you come to Christmas dinner? I've invited the Joe Burtons, and of course Mr. Marten will be there, but no others—except Miss Badeau.

Dinner will be at sharp seven. Don't be late, although I know you won't, you human timetable.

I do hope that Annette will not fall in love in Paris. I wish that she would marry some nice New Yorker and settle near me.

I've always thought that you have neglected marriage shamefully.

Remember tomorrow night, and Annette sails on Thursday. Wishing you a Merry Christmas, I am,

Your old friend,
HENRIETTA MARTEN

Annette Badeau had come across the line of Orville's vision three months before. She was Mrs. Marten's niece, and had come from the West to live with her aunt at just about the time that the success of Thornton's book made him think of marriage.

She was pretty and bright and expansive in a Western way, and when Thornton met her at one of the few afternoon teas that he ever attended he fell in love with her. When he learned that she was the niece of his lifelong friend, Mrs. Marten, he suddenly discovered various reasons why he should call at the Marten house once or twice a week.

But a strange habit he had of putting off delightful moments in order to enjoy anticipation to its fullest extent had caused him to refrain from disclosing the state of his heart to Miss Badeau, and so that young woman, who had fallen in love with him even before she knew that he was the

From *Araminta and the Automobile* by Charles Battell Loomis, published by T. Y. Crowell & Co.

gifted author of *Thoughts for Non-Thinkers,* often wished to herself that she could in some way give him a hint of the state of *her* heart.

Orville received Mrs. Marten's letter on Christmas Eve, and its contents made him plan a schedule for the next evening's running. No power on earth could keep him away from that dinner, and he immediately sent a telegram of regret to the Bellwether of the Wolves' Club, although he had been anticipating the Christmas gorge for a month.

He also sent a messenger with a note of acceptance to Mrs. Marten. . . .

Then he joined the crowd of persons who always wait until Christmas Eve before buying the presents that stern and unpleasant duty makes it necessary to get.

It would impart a characteristic Christmas flavor if it were possible to cover the ground with snow, and to make the air merry with the sound of flashing belts of silvery sleighbells on prancing horses; but although Christmases in stories are always snowy and frosty and sparkling with ice crystals, Christmases in real life are apt to be damp and humid. Let us be thankful that this Christmas was merely such a one as would not give a ghost of a reason for a trip to Florida. The mercury stood at 58, and even light overcoats were not things to be put on without thought.

Orville knew what he wished to get and where it was sold, and so he had an advantage over ninety-nine out of a hundred of the anxious-looking shoppers who were scuttling from shop to shop, burdened with bundles, and making the evening the worst in the year for tired salesgirls and -men.

Orville's present was not exactly Christmassy, but he hoped that Miss Badeau would like it, and it was certainly the finest one on the velvet tray. Orville, it will be seen, was of a sanguine disposition.

He did not hang up his stocking; he had not done that for several years; but he did dream that Santa Claus brought him a beautiful doll from Paris, and just as he was saying, "There must be some mistake," the doll turned into Miss Badeau and said: "No, I'm for you. Merry Christmas!" Then he woke up and thought how foolish and yet how fascinating dreams are.

Christmas morning was spent in polishing up an old essay on "The Value of the Summer as an Invigorator." It had long been a habit of his to work over old stuff on his holidays, and if he was about to marry he would need to sell everything he had—of a literary marketable nature. But this morning a vision of a lovely girl who on the morrow was going to sail thousands of miles away came between him and the page, and at last he tossed the manuscript into a drawer and went out for a walk.

It was the draggiest Christmas he had ever known, and the warmest. He dropped in at the club, but there was hardly anyone there; still, he did manage to play a few games of billiards, and at last the clock announced that it was time to go home and dress for the Christmas dinner.

It was half-past five when he left the club. It was twenty minutes to six when he slipped on a piece of orange peel, and measured his length on the sidewalk. He was able to rise and hobble up the steps on one foot, but the hallboy had to help him to the elevator and thence to his room. He dropped upon his bed, feeling white about the gills.

Orville was a most methodical man. He planned his doings days ahead and seldom changed his schedule. But it seemed likely that unless he was built of sterner stuff than most of the machines called men, he would not run out of the roundhouse tonight. His fall had given his foot a nasty wrench.

Some engineers, to change the simile, would have argued that the engine was off the track, and that therefore the train was not in running condition; but Orville merely changed engines. His own steam having been cut off, he ordered an automobile for twenty minutes to seven; and after he had bathed and bandaged his ankle he determined, with a grit worthy of the cause that brought it forth, to attend that dinner even if he paid for it in the hospital, with Annette as special nurse.

Old Mr. Nickerson, who lived across the hall, had heard of his misfortune, and called to proffer his services.

"Shall I help you get to bed?" said he.

"I am not due in bed, Mr. Nickerson, for many hours; but if you will give me a few fingers of your excellent old Scotch with the bouquet of smoked herring, I will go on dressing for dinner."

"Dear boy," said the old gentleman almost tearfully, "it is impossible for you to venture on your foot with such a sprain. It is badly swollen."

"Mr. Nickerson, my heart has received a worse wrench than any foot has, therefore I go out to dine." At sound of which enigmatical declaration Mr. Nickerson hurried off for the old Scotch, and in a few minutes Orville's faintness had passed off, and with help from the amiable old man he got into his evening clothes—with the exception of his left foot, which was encased in a flowered slipper of sunset red.

"Now, my dear Mr. Nickerson, I'm a thousand times obliged to you, and if I can get you to help me hop downstairs I will wait for the automobile on the front stoop." (Orville had been born in Brooklyn, where they still have "stoops.") "I'm on time so far."

But if Orville was on time, the automobile was not, the driver not being a methodical man; and when it did come, it was all the motorman could do to stop it. It seemed restive.

"You ought to shut off on the oats," said Orville gaily, from his seat on the lowest step of the "stoop."

The picture of a gentleman in immaculate evening clothes with the exception of a somewhat rococo carpet slipper, seemed to amuse some street children who were passing. If they could have followed the "auto" they would have been even more diverted, but such was not to be their fortune. Mr. Nickerson helped his friend into the vehicle, and the driver started at a lively rate for Fifth Avenue.

Orville lived in Seventeenth Street, near Fifth Avenue; Mrs. Marten lived on Fifth Avenue, near Fortieth Street. Thirty-eighth Street and Thirty-ninth Street were reached and passed without further incident than the fact that Orville's ankle pained him almost beyond the bearing point; but, as it is not the history of a sprained ankle that I am writing, if the vehicle had stopped at Mrs. Marten's my pen would not have been set to paper.

But the motor wagon did not even pause. It kept on as if the Harlem River were to be its next stop.

Orville had stated the number of his destination with distinctness, and he now rang the annunciator and asked the driver why he did not stop.

Calmly, in the even tones that clearheaded persons use when they wish to inspire confidence, the chauffeur said: "Don't be alarmed, sir, but I can't stop. There's something out of kilter, and I may have to run some time before I can get the hang of it. There's no danger as long as I can steer."

"Can't you slacken up in front of the house, so that I can jump?"

"With that foot, sir? Impossible, and, anyway, I can't slacken up. I think we'll stop soon. I don't know when it was charged, but a gentleman had it before I was sent out with it. It won't be long, I think. I'll run around the block, and maybe I can stop the next time."

Orville groaned for a twofold reason: his ankle was jumping with pain, and he would lose the pleasure of taking Miss Badeau in to dinner, for it was a minute past seven.

He sat and gazed at his carpet slipper, and thought of the daintily shod feet of the adorable Annette, as the horseless carriage wound around the block. As they approached the house again, Orville imagined that they were slackening up, and he opened the door to be ready. It was now three minutes past seven, and dinner had begun beyond a doubt. The driver saw the door swing open, and said: "Don't jump, sir. I can't stop yet. I'm afraid there's a good deal of run in the machine."

Orville looked up at the brownstone front of the house with an agonized stare, as if he would pull Mrs. Marten to the window by the power of his eyes. But Mrs. Marten was not in the habit of pressing her nose against the pane in an anxious search for tardy guests. In fact, it may be asserted with confidence that it is not a Fifth Avenue custom.

At that moment the purée was being served to Mrs. Marten's guests, and to pretty Annette Badeau, who really looked disconsolate with the vacant chair beside her.

"Something has happened to Orville," said Mrs. Marten, looking over her shoulder toward the hall door, "for he is punctuality itself."

Mr. Joe Burton was a short, red-faced little man, with black muttonchop whiskers of the style of '76, and a way of looking in the most cheerful manner upon the dark side of things. "Dessay he's been run over," said he choppily. "Wonder anyone escapes. Steam-, gasoline-, electric-, horseflesh-, man-propelled juggernauts. Ought to be prohibited."

Annette could not repress a shudder. Her aunt saw it and said: "Orville will never be run over. He's too wide-awake. But it is very singular."

"He may have been detained by an order for a story," said Mr. Marten, also with the amiable purpose of consoling Annette, for both of the Martens knew how she felt toward Mr. Thornton.

"Maybe he's lying on the front sidewalk, hit by a sign or bitten by a dog. Dogs ought not to be allowed in the city; they only add to the dangers of metropolitan existence," jerked out Mr. Burton, in blithe tones, totally unaware that his remarks might worry Annette.

"Dear me! I wish you'd send someone out to see, Aunt Henrietta."

"Nonsense, Annette. Mr. Burton is always an alarmist. But, Marie, you might step to the front door and look down the avenue. Mr. Thornton is always so punctual that it is peculiar."

Marie went to the front door and looked down the street just as Thornton, gesticulating wildly, disappeared around the corner of Fortieth Street.

"Oh, why didn't she come sooner!" said he aloud to himself. "At least they would know why I'm late. And she'll be gone before I come round again. Was there ever such luck? Oh for a good old horse that could stop, a dear old nag that would pause and not go round and round like a blamed carrousel! Say, driver, isn't there any way of stopping this cursed thing? Can't you run it into a fence or a house? I'll take the risk."

"But *I* won't, sir. These automobiles are very powerful, and one of them turned over a newsstand not long since and upset the stove in it, and nearly burned up the newsman. But there's a plenty of time for it to stop. I don't have to hurry back."

"That's lucky," said Orville. "I thought maybe you'd have to leave me alone with the thing. But, say, she may run all night. Here I am due at a dinner. I'm tired of riding. This is no way to spend Christmas. Slacken up, and I'll jump when I get around there again."

"I tell you I can't slacken up, and she's going ten miles an hour. You'll break your leg if you jump, and then where'll you be?"

"I might be on their sidewalk, and then you could ring their bell, and they'd take me in."

"And have you suing the company for damages? Oh, no, sir. I'm sorry, but it can't be helped. The company won't charge you for the extra time."

"No, I don't think it will," said Thornton savagely, the more so as his foot gave a twinge of pain just then.

"There was no one in sight, ma'am," said Marie, when she returned.

"Probably he had an order for a story and got absorbed in it and forgot us," said Mr. Marten; but this conjecture did not seem to suit Annette, for it did not fit what she knew of his character.

"Possibly he was dropped in an elevator," said Mr. Burton. "Strain on elevators, particularly these electrical ones, is tremendous. Some of 'em have got to drop. And a dropping elevator is no respecter of persons. You and I may be in one when it drops. Probably he was. Sure, I hope not, but as he is known to be the soul of punctuality, we must put forward some accident to account for his lateness. People aren't always killed in elevator accidents. Are they, my dear?"

"Mr. Burton," said his wife, "I wish you would give your morbid thoughts a rest. Don't you see that Annette is sensitive?"

"Sensitive—with someone dying every minute? It's merely because she happens to know Orville that his death would be unpleasant. If a man in the Klondike were to read of it in the paper he wouldn't remember it five minutes. But I don't say he was in an elevator. Maybe someone sent him an infernal machine for a Christmas present. May have been blown up in a manhole or jumped from his window to avoid flames. Why, there are a million ways to account for his absence."

Marie had opened the parlor windows a moment before, as the house was warm, and now there came the humming of a rapidly moving automobile. Mingled with it they heard distinctly, although faintly, "Mr. Marten, here I go."

It gave them all an uncanny feeling. The fish was left untouched, and for a moment silence reigned. Then Mr. Marten sprang from the table and ran to the front door. He got there just in time to see an automobile dashing around a corner and to hear a distinctly articulated imprecation in the well-known voice of Orville Thornton.

In the evening clothes and bareheaded, Mr. Marten ran to Fortieth Street, and saw the vehicle approaching Sixth Avenue, its occupant still hurling strong language upon the evening air. Mr. Marten is something of a sprinter, although he has passed the fifty mark, and he resolved to solve the mystery. But before he had covered a third of the block in Fortieth Street he saw that he could not hope to overtake the runaway automobile, so he turned and ran back to the house, rightly surmising that the driver would circle the block.

When he reached his own doorstep, badly winded, he saw the automobile coming full tilt up the avenue from Thirty-ninth Street.

The rest of the diners were on the steps. "I think he's coming," he panted. "The driver must be intoxicated."

A moment later they were treated to the spectacle of Orville, still hurling imprecations as he wildly gesticulated with both arms. Several boys were trying to keep up with the vehicle, but the pace was too swift. No policeman had yet discovered its rotary course.

As Orville came near the Marten mansion he cried "Ah-h-h!" in the relieved tones of one who has been falling for half an hour and at last sees ground in sight.

"What's the matter?" shouted Mr. Marten wonderingly, as the carriage, instead of stopping, sped along the roadway.

"Sprained foot. Can't walk. Auto out of order. Can't stop. Good-by till I come round again. Awful hungry. Merry Christmas!"

"Ah ha!" said Joe Burton. "I told you that it was an accident. Sprained his foot and lost power over vehicle. I don't see the connection, but let us be thankful that he isn't under the wheels, with a broken neck, or winding round and round the axle."

"But what's to be done?" said Mrs. Marten. "He says he's hungry."

"Tell you what!" said Mr. Burton, in his explosive way. "Put some food on a plate, and when the carriage comes round again I'll jump aboard, and he can eat as he travels."

"He loves purée of celery," said Mrs. Marten.

"Very well. Put some in a clean lard pail or a milk pail. Little out of the ordinary, but so is the accident, and he can't help his hunger. Hunger is no disgrace. I didn't think he'd ever eat soup again, to tell the truth. I was making up my mind whether a wreath or a harp would be better."

"Oh, you are so morbid, Mr. Burton," said his wife, while Mrs. Marten told the maid to get a pail and put some purée into it.

When Thornton came around again he met Mr. Marten near Thirty-ninth Street.

"Open the door, Orville, and Joe Burton will get aboard with some soup. You must be starved."

"There's nothing like exercise for getting up an appetite. I'll be ready for Burton," said Orville. "Awfully sorry I can't stop and talk; but I'll see you again in a minute or two."

He opened the door as he spoke, and then, to the great delight of at least a score of people who had realized that the automobile was running away, the rubicund and stout Joe Burton, a pail of purée in one hand and some table cutlery and silverware and a napkin in the other, made a dash at the vehicle, and with help from Orville effected an entrance.

"Merry Christmas!" said Orville.

"Merry Christmas! Awfully sorry, old man, but it might be worse. Better drink it out of the pail. They gave me a knife and fork, but they neglected to put in a spoon or a dish. I thought that you were probably killed, but I never imagined this. Miss Badeau was terribly worked up. I think that she had decided on white carnations. Nice girl. You could easily jump, old man, if you hadn't sprained your foot. Hurt much?"

"Like the devil; but I'm glad it worried Miss Badeau. No, I don't mean that. But you know."

"Yes, I know," said Burton, with a sociable smile. "Mrs. Marten told me. Nice girl. Let her in next time. Unusual thing, you know. People are very apt to jump *from* a runaway vehicle, but it seldom takes up passengers. Let her get in, and you can explain matters to her. You see, she sails early in the morning, and you haven't much time. You can tell her what a nice fellow you are, you know, and I'm sure you'll have Mrs. Marten's blessing. Here's where I get out."

With an agility admirable in one of his stoutness, Mr. Burton leaped to the street and ran up the steps to speak to Miss Badeau. Orville could see her blush, but there was no time for her to become a passenger that trip, and the young man once more made the circuit of the block, quite alone, but strangely happy. He had never ridden with Annette, except once on the elevated road, and then both Mr. and Mrs. Marten were of the company.

Round sped the motor, and when the Martens appeared in sight, Annette was on the sidewalk with a covered dish in her hand and a look of excited expectancy on her face that added a hundredfold to its charms.

"Here you are—only ten cents a ride. Merry Christmas!" shouted Orville gaily, and leaned half out of the automobile to catch her. It was a daring, almost an impossible jump, yet Annette made it without accident, and, flushed and excited, sat down in front of Mr. Thornton without spilling her burden, which proved to be sweetbreads.

"Miss Badeau—Annette, I hadn't expected it to turn out this way, but of course your aunt doesn't care, or she wouldn't have let you come. We're really in no danger. This driver has had more experience dodging teams in this last hour than he'd get in an ordinary year. They tell me you're going to Europe early tomorrow to leave all your friends. Now, I've something very important to say to you before you go. No, thanks, I don't want anything more. That purée was very filling. I've sprained my ankle, and I need to be very quiet for a week or two, perhaps until the machine runs down, but at the end of that time would you—"

Orville hesitated, and Annette blushed sweetly. She set the sweetbreads down upon the seat beside her. Orville had never looked so handsome before to her eyes.

He hesitated. "Go on," said she.

"Would you be willing to go to Paris on a bridal trip?"

Annette's answer was drowned in the hurrah of the driver as the automobile, gradually slackening, came to a full stop in front of the Martens'.

But Orville read her lips, and as he handed his untouched sweetbreads to Mrs. Burton, and his sweetheart to her uncle, his face wore a seraphically happy expression; and when Mr. Marten and the driver helped him up the steps at precisely eight o'clock, Annette's hand sought his, and it was a jolly party that sat down to a big though somewhat dried-up Rhode Island turkey.

"Marriage also is an accident," said Mr. Burton.

The Life and Death of Vaudeville

By FRED ALLEN

VAUDEVILLE is dead. The acrobats, the animal acts, the dancers, the singers, and the old-time comedians have taken their final bows and disappeared into the wings of obscurity. For fifty years—from 1875 to 1925—vaudeville was the popular entertainment of the masses. Nomadic tribes of nondescript players roamed the land. The vaudeville actor was part gypsy and part suitcase. With his brash manner, flashy clothes, capes and cane, and accompanied by his gaudy womenfolk, the vaudevillian brought happiness and excitement to the communities he visited. He spent his money freely and made friends easily. In the early days, the exact degree of prosperity the smalltimer was enjoying could be determined by taking inventory of the diamonds that adorned his person. If he was doing well, the smalltimer wore a large diamond horseshoe in his tie and two or three solitaires or clusters on his fingers; his wife, dripping with necklaces, rings, earrings, and bracelets, looked as though she had been pelted with ice cubes that had somehow stuck where they landed. The smalltimer's diamonds didn't have to be good. They just had to be big. What difference if the eight-karat ring was the color of a menthol cough drop as long as the stone sparkled in the spotlight during the act? To the smalltimer, a diamond represented security. It impressed the booker, the manager, and the audience, but, more important, the diamond was collateral. Confronted with a financial crisis in a strange community, the smalltimer didn't have to embarrass himself by attempting to convince a tradesman or a hotel manager that his credentials were valid. To obtain emergency funds, he merely stepped into the nearest pawnshop, slipped the ring from his finger, and consummated a legitimate routine business transaction. When his diamonds were temporarily on location, the smalltimer avoided his friends and his usual haunts, knowing that the absence of his Kimberley gravel was an admission that the panic was on. The instant his luck changed, the diamonds were redeemed and returned to their customary places. Back in the spotlight, with the horseshoe pin and the rings sparkling, the smalltimer's necktie and his ring fingers resumed strutting their stuff.

The herd instinct was a dominant impulse in the vaudeville actor's behavior pattern. When the season closed, the smalltimers congregated at vacation resorts to revel in each other's company. The smalltimer lived in another world. He thought and talked only about his act and about show business. Nothing else interested him. If you said to him, "Do you remember the Johnstown flood?" he would probably reply, "Remember the Johnstown flood? Are you kidding? I and the wife were playing Pittsburgh that week. Eva Tanguay was the star. Walter Kelly was next to closing. After the first show the manager comes running back and says, 'You kids is the hit of the bill!' He moves us down to next to closing for the rest of the week. Kelly is blowing his top. All week long I and the wife murder them!" Everybody in Johnstown could have been swept out of town: the smalltimer wouldn't know or care. He had nothing in common with anybody who was not in his profession.

The two vaudeville centers of the country were New York and Chicago. During the summer layoff season—theaters had no air conditioning then, and many closed during the hotter months—vaudeville colonies were formed. The Chicago acts rented or bought cottages near the lakes in Wisconsin or Michigan; the New York vaudevillians huddled together in Connecticut and down on Long Island. The most famous of the actors' colonies was founded at Freeport, Long Island. The stars first established summer homes at Freeport, and then the smalltimers precipitated a real-estate boom fighting to buy property and houses to make their home in Freeport to let the stars see how the other half lived.

The Long Island Good Hearted Thespians Society was formed. This was a social club whose members reduced the name to the Lights. The first president was Victor Moore. One of the traditional Lights Club functions was the celebration of Christmas on the Fourth of July. In December, most of the vaudeville actors were on the road, away from their homes, their families, and their friends. They spent their Christmas Days on trains, in dingy dressing rooms, or in drab hotels. Members of the Lights ignored the conventional Yule season and saved their Christmas greetings and presents until the return to Freeport. On July Fourth, though the temperature be in the nineties, the Lights' Christmas tree was decorated and lighted, Santa Claus was dressed in his heavy suit with the ermine trimmings, presents were placed under the tree, and the members and their children arrived in their furs, mittens, and earlaps, some even clattering into the club on snowshoes.

A vaudeville actor could relax and enjoy himself only in the company of another vaudeville actor. You could sit a vaudeville actor in front of a mirror and he would stay there contentedly for days on end. In cities on the road, the vaudeville performers congregated at the same boarding-houses or cheaper hotels. There was a time when the actor was *persona non grata* at the better inns, and this was especially true of vaudevillians, who were presumed to be irresponsible from the very fact that their profession was uncertain and their living precarious. It was generally understood that vaudeville performers went in for wild parties in their homes and that their domestic habits were rarely awarded the Good Housekeeping Seal of Approval. Accordingly it was deemed best for hotel clerks to smile blandly when they were asked for rooms and inform the vaudevillian that the hotel was "full up." Stage folk, except for those who had attained stellar rank, were pretty much pariahs around the decent hotels.

Duke Pohl, the manager of the Breevort Hotel in St. Louis, once told me that he was traveling in a special train to attend an annual convention of the Greeters of America, the official organization of the hotel men. Each man was asked to name his hotel and tell something about it. Duke later told me that when he announced that his Breevort catered to stage folks, "I could almost hear the gasp that went around the circle. I told them I considered stage people the most maligned persons on earth. I said that my experience with vaudevillians had been uniformly pleasant, that they paid their bills, were quiet in their rooms, were sober, sedate, and serious people trying to make a living."

Duke defended the profession at a time when many hotel and rooming-house owners were complaining that some vaudeville people were stealing towels. This practice was so common that jokes were being told about it. One joke was about the vaudeville actor who died and left an estate of eight hundred hotel and Pullman towels. Then there was the charge that actors checked into their hotels with heavy suitcases, stayed a week or two, then disappeared without paying their bills. Credit had been extended because the manager had seen the heavy suitcases; when, later, these were pried open, they were found to contain nothing but a collection of bricks and old telephone books. Indigent vaudeville actors were known to lower their suitcases out the window in the back of the hotel, then walk through the lobby empty handed, reclaim their cases, and leave town. An actor who had a trunk in his room received an extension of credit. When the bill mounted, the actor, anticipating that the manager would tip the trunk to ascertain its contents and to try to find out if clothing had been pawned, took the precaution of nailing the trunk to the floor. Ted Healy, a comedian, once owed a sizable bill at the Lincoln Hotel in New York. Ted brought the three stooges he used in his act up to his room and ordered each stooge to don two or three sets of his underwear, two complete suits of clothes, and an overcoat. Healy followed the stooges out of the Lincoln lobby wearing three suits and one topcoat, and carrying a raincoat with every pocket bulging. Healy left the Lincoln Hotel with two mementos of his stay: an empty room and an empty trunk. Things of this kind took place occasionally, and hotel owners were suspicious, but Duke Pohl believed in befriending actors, and they showed their appreciation. As Duke used to say, "I've never lost anything by it. They all paid me eventually."

Vaudeville could not vouch for the honesty, the integrity, or the mentality of the individuals who collectively made up the horde the medium embraced. All the human race demands of its members is that they be born. That is all vaudeville demanded. You just had to be born. You could be ignorant and be a star. You could be a moron and be wealthy. The elements that went to make up vaudeville were combed from the jungles, the four corners of the world, the intelligentsia and the subnormal. An endless, incongruous swarm crawled over the countryside dragging performing lions, bears, tigers, leopards, boxing kangaroos, horses, ponies, mules, dogs, cats, rats, seals, and monkeys in their wake. Others rode bicycles, did acrobatic and contortion tricks, walked wires, exhibited sharpshooting skills, played violins, trombones, cornets, pianos, concertinas, xylophones, harmonicas, and any other known instrument. There were hypnotists, iron-jawed ladies, one-legged dancers, one-armed cornetists, mind readers, female impersonators, male impersonators, Irish comedians, Jewish comedians, blackface, German, Swedish, Italian, and rube comedians, dramatic actors, Hindu conjurors, ventriloquists, bag punchers, singers and dancers of every description, clay modelers, and educated geese: all traveling from hamlet to town to city, presenting their shows. Vaudeville asked only that you own an animal or an instrument, or have a minimum of talent or a maximum of nerve. With these dubious assets vaudeville offered fame and riches. It was up to you.

Vaudeville families endured for generations. The female of the species foaled on trains, in dressing rooms, in tank towns, and in the big cities. The show must go on. At the theater the baby slept in the top of the trunk in the dressing room. At the hotel a crib was improvised by removing a large bureau drawer and placing it on the bed or between two chairs. A large blanket filled the drawer nicely; the baby, wrapped in its quilt, rested serene in his drawer bassinet. The vaudeville baby carried its own baggage. A small valise contained milk bottles, nipples, safety pins, and emergency diapers. On a sleeper jump, vaudeville couples with a baby always had the same routine: at 1 A.M., with the train thundering through the night, a tiny cry is heard. In two berths, an upper and a lower, lights snap on instantly. The husband jumps down from his upper berth into the aisle. The curtains of the lower berth part just a crack, muted voices are heard, the clasps on the miniature valise click open, and a nippled bottle, filled with milk, appears through the curtains. The husband steadies himself as he sways down the aisle on his way to arouse the porter to warm the precious quota of milk. In the lower berth, the sounds of the mother's soothing voice and the baby's cries persist until the husband returns. The warm milk bottle is passed in, the baby gurgles and stops crying, the curtains close, the husband crawls back up into his berth. The lights go off in both berths, and it is dark and silent once again; the train hurries ahead into the night.

Arriving in the next town, and safe in their room, the family goes to work. The husband removes a small drawer from the dresser, places a rubber sheet over the drawer, and pokes it snugly down into the four corners. Then he fills the drawer half full of tepid water. The mother lowers the baby gently into the drawer to enjoy its bath after the train trip.

The smalltime vaudeville mother had the endurance of a doorknob. She did three or four shows a day as part of the act. She cared for her baby on the road and prepared its food. She did the family washing: there was always a clothesline hanging and dripping away in the dressing room and the boardinghouse, and the sinks were filled with diapers. As the family grew larger, the kids were packed like sardines into upper berths. (Midgets often traveled in clusters in upper berths; an actor in a lower berth once complained that he had been kept awake all night by a midget with insomnia who had been walking up and down in the upper berth.)

Many wives cooked the family meals in the dressing room; before electricity became promiscuous, vaudeville wives carried tin plates, cups, knives and forks, and prepared tasty meals over flaming gas jets and blazing Sterno cans in dressing and hotel rooms. Then there was a special theatrical trunk, made by the Herkert and Meisel Trunk Company of St. Louis, which was constantly adding new features to lighten the burden of the vaudeville wife. The H & M wardrobe trunk had such special innovations as a metal compartment in one drawer to hold an electric iron; a small rubber-lined compartment which enabled actors to pack wet sponges, washcloths, and soap on hurried closing nights; a hat compartment for man or woman; a flat drawer under the wardrobe section to hold shoes; a jewel box; an ironing board that could be attached securely to the trunk to enable women to iron in the theater. These, and many other features of this trunk, made life easier for the vaudeville mother.

Vaudeville families flourished. The babies teethed on greasepaint, and their sitters were other acts on the bill who watched the tots while the parents were on stage. When the babies were able to walk, they were led on stage to take their first bows. Later, they learned to imitate their parents and many other acts who played on the different bills. After completing their schooling, most of the children grew up and went into vaudeville, and had children who grew up and went into vaudeville.

The smalltimer plying his profession was exposed to many irritations. When his act laid an egg in one town, he couldn't wait to leave for the next town, where, he hoped, things would be better. When the audience was bad, the whole community was terrible; the hotel, the restaurants, the food, the newspapers, and the people all became impossible. When the smalltimer was a riot, his environment was perfect. Using the smalltimer's psychology, if his act went badly in Detroit, Detroit as a metropolis was a bust. If his act went big in Eureka, Eureka was Utopia.

Next to the audience, in its importance to the smalltimer, stood the theater orchestra. If the orchestra could not play his wife's ballad properly, if the tempo of his dance music was too fast or too slow, if the drummer didn't catch his pratfalls with a well-timed roll and crash or tear the cloth on cue as he pretended to rip his trousers, the actor fought with his wife and sulked in his dressing room until the next show. Vaudeville orchestras varied from one piece—a piano—to seven or eight pieces. The usual smalltime theater had piano, cornet, and drums. The drums were very important: they accentuated the falls and crashes of the comedians and played long rolls for the aerialists' sensational slides. For his music, the smalltimer carried eight or nine parts in cardboard or leather covers. Playing the cheaper theaters, which had only a piano and drum, only the piano and drum parts were used. After the smalltimer had played several weeks in dumps, and was then booked into a big theater, he would occasionally brag at rehearsal in order to leave the musicians with the impression that he was accustomed to playing good theaters. He couldn't fool the musicians, however, because the minute they saw the smalltimer's music they knew where the act had been playing. The violin, clarinet, cornet, and bass parts were brand-new; the piano and drum parts were filthy. At rehearsal in a new town, the smalltimer, sensing that the orchestra wasn't too friendly, examined his music. It explained everything. The drummer in the last town had written on the drum part, "This act is lousy." The clarinet player had written, "He died here." The cornet player had summed everything up by simply writing one words: "Stinks."

The smalltimer's billing was a matter of great concern. Before the opening show at each theater he examined the front of the theater to check on the size of his name and his position in the list of acts. The vaudeville headliner often had a clause in his contract assuring him of top billing. The smalltimer's billing depended on the whim of the local manager or the man who printed or painted the theater signs. Seeing his name in runt letters could catapult the smalltimer into a three-day funk. His position on the bill was of major importance. If his act had been next to closing and he suddenly found himself second on the bill, wires were dispatched to the booking office and his agent, and the theater manager was summoned to the dressing room before the smalltimer deigned to do the first show. Headliners had clauses in their contracts that entitled them to the best dressing rooms. The smalltimer dressed where he was told. If he used the same dressing room as his wife, the smalltimer immediately examined all walls and connecting doors for holes. A few depraved actors carried gimlets and bits around with them, and drilled holes in the walls to watch the sister act or the single woman in the next room undress. If holes were discovered, the stage manager was notified and the apertures were filled with shoemaker's wax. One worry less for the smalltimer.

The censoring of his act also upset the smalltimer. When Paul Keith, after running a museum on Washington Street in Boston, opened his first theater, the Bijou Dream, he insisted on clean entertainment. Mrs. Keith instigated the chaste policy, for she would tolerate no profanity, no suggestive allusions, *double-entendres,* or off-color monkey business. As the Keith circuit grew, every theater carried a sign on the bulletin board:

NOTICE
TO PERFORMERS

Don't say "slob" or "son-of-a-gun" or "hully gee" on this stage unless you want to be canceled peremptorily. Do not address anyone in the audience in any manner. If you have not the ability to entertain Mr. Keith's audiences without risk of offending them, do the best you can. Lack of talent will be less open to censure than would be an insult to a patron. If you are in doubt as to the character of your act, consult the local manager before you go on the stage, for if you are guilty of uttering anything sacrilegious or even suggestive, you will be immediately closed and will never again be allowed in a theater where Mr. Keith is in authority.

Long after Mr. Keith's death the circuit was still waging its campaign against suggestive material. For many months *Variety* published a column called "You Mustn't Say That" which featured deletions in stage material ("Hell" or "Lord Epsom, Secretary of the Interior," or "An old maid taking a tramp through the woods," and so on) made by the Keith censorship bureau. As most of the gamy lines and jokes were his biggest laughs, the smalltimer would fight to the death to keep them in his act.

Many smaller acts who used one or two jokes, or a few comedy lines, and could not buy special material subscribed to *Madison's Budget.* For twenty years—from 1898 to 1918—a man named James Madison published an annual collection of monologues, cross-fire jokes, sketches, minstrel-show afterpieces, and parodies. This assortment of humorous matter sold for one dollar and was known as *Madison's Budget.* If a comedian found six or eight jokes in the *Budget* that he could adapt to his act, his dollar investment had returned a hearty dividend.

Comedy acts were always the targets of the pirates. If a comedian was original and wrote his own material, or if he frequently bought new routines and songs to keep his act up to date, he soon found that other comedians were stealing parts of his act. For many years performers had no way to protect their gags, parodies, or bits of business. Copyright laws were ignored, and good gags spread like bad news. One blackface comedian on the big time stole so much material that he couldn't use it all in his act; he hired another blackface act and paid him a salary to play the smalltime using the stolen material he had left over. There was a young comedian whose father regularly attended the opening show at the Palace. If any of the acts had new lines, jokes, or song titles, the father copied them down and wired them to his son. The act continued convulsing the Palace audience in New York, little dreaming that its best jokes were being told in Omaha, San Francisco, or wherever the son happened to be playing.

Original material was spread around in many ways. For instance, when blackface acts and other comedy teams split up, many times the men or women took new partners, and both new acts continued to do the same routines. After a series of splittings it was not unusual to find four or five teams all doing the same act. Burlesque shows lifted scenes bodily from Broadway revues. Social directors at summer camps spent the winter copying down anything they found in the Broadway theaters which they thought they could use at the camps next summer. Johnny Neff, a monologist, used to explain to his audiences how crazy comedians were to buy jokes. Johnny would relate how Frank Tinney had paid a hundred dollars for a certain joke. Johnny would then tell the joke to prove that Tinney was insane. When Johnny had finished explaining how much money Raymond Hitchcock, Ed Wynn, Jack Donahue, Leon Errol, and Richard Carle had paid for their jokes, and after he had told all these jokes himself, Johnny had a hilarious monologue that hadn't cost him a penny. And Milton Berle for years has been bragging to audiences that he has stolen jokes from other comedians. There has been no reason to doubt his word.

When Mr. Albee founded the National Vaudeville Artists, Inc., after breaking the White Rats' strike (the White Rats had been the original vaudeville performers' association), one of the inducements to attract members was the new organization's Protected Material Department. Any member could protect his act. All he had to do was to enclose a copy of his material in a sealed envelope and deliver it to the N.V.A. office. The envelope was placed in the Protected Material files. Later, if a plagiarist was brought to bay, the act preferred charges, the sealed envelope was opened, and the N.V.A. officials dispensed justice. Hundreds of acts protected their material through this service. After Mr. Albee's death, vaudeville started over the hill and took the N.V.A. club with it. Before the members vacated the clubhouse on Forty-sixth Street, some official, by whose authority nobody will ever know, sold the entire contents of the N.V.A. Protected Material Department files to Olsen and Johnson.

Superstitions and irrational beliefs influenced the vaudevillian as he made his decisions and planned his daily activities. Many credulous omens the performer treated with respect. He thought bad luck ensued if he whistled in the dressing room, found peacock feathers anywhere in the theater, saw a bird on the window sill, threw away his old dancing shoes, and so forth. There were many other bad omens, but there were only two portents that assured the performer future happiness. Good luck was sure to follow if an actor put his undershirt on inside out, or if he touched a humpbacked person.

Vaudeville acts often assumed strange names to attract attention. An unusual name was easily remembered by bookers, managers, and audiences. A few uniquely named acts were: Fyne and Dandy (acrobats), Sharp and Flat (musicians), Willie Rolls (roller skater), Amazon and Nile (contortionists), Nip and Tuck (acrobats), North and South (musical act), Worth and While (sister act), Possum Welch (dancer), and Darn, Good, and Funny (comedy trio).

The early vaudeville performers were inventive; they had to create the unusual specialties they performed. Vaudeville grew, and new acts came along to help themselves to the ideas of the originators, and to elaborate on and embellish them. Many specialty artists, in constructing their acts, came up with some weird innovations. One of these was Orville Stamm. Not long ago I got a letter from Orville, asking if I remembered him. It was not easy to forget Orville. He billed himself as the "Strongest Boy in the World." To demonstrate his great strength, Orville played the violin; as he played, he had suspended from the crook of his bow arm an enormous English bulldog. The bulldog made graceful arcs in the air as Orville pizzicatoed and manipulated his bow. For the finish of his act, Orville lay flat on the stage and arched his back; in the better acrobat circles, this was known as "bending the crab." When Orville's chest and abdomen attained the correct altitude, a small upright piano was placed across his stomach. An assistant stood on Orville's thigh and played the piano accompaniment as Orville, in his "crab" position, sang "Ireland Must Be Heaven, 'Cause My Mother Came from There." This finish was a sensation, and I'm sure it was Orville's own idea.

Raymonde, a female impersonator, also originated an unusual finish. After doing his entire act as a girl, Raymonde took a bow and removed his wig. The audience, seeing man's hair, was amazed to find that the girl was a boy. As the applause continued, Raymonde removed the man's wig, and blond tresses tumbled down over his shoulders. The boy was now a girl again. The audience, again duped, was frantic. Raymonde took another bow or two to thunderous applause, then removed the girl's wig and was a boy again. Raymonde, emulating the manner of a female impersonator's conception of a truck driver, swaggered off the stage to absolute bedlam.

A man named Willard was billed as the "Man Who Grows." As he talked, he stretched his arms out a foot or more beyond their normal length. For his finish Willard grew four or five inches in height. I watched Willard many times backstage without being able to discover his secret. He must have been able to telescope his skin.

An inventive monologist in Chicago featured a singing goat. Following a dull fifteen minutes of talk, the monologist would introduce his partner, the Singing Goat. The orchestra would play "Mammy"; when the monologist finished the verse and started the chorus, the goat would join him in singing "Ma-a-a-a-my! Ma-a-a-a-my!" The act stopped the show. One matinee, a representative of the S.P.C.A. called at the theater and removed the goat from the premises. When the theater manager remonstrated, the S.P.C.A. man showed him the goat's lacerated buttocks; the monologist had been prodding his rump with a sharp-pointed nail.

This sort of thing often happened in animal acts. Trainers who exhibited lions and tigers could seemingly cause them to growl and snarl on cue. The audience little suspected that the beasts worked on metal flooring, and that the lions and tigers would naturally growl or snarl after this metal flooring had been charged with electricity. Similarly, dog acts often astounded audiences when the little white terrier climbed the ladder, rung by rung, hesitated on the top rung for a second, and then jumped into space, landing in its master's arms. Little did the audience know that the top rung of the high ladder was electrified. When the little white terrier hesitated on this top rung, he wasn't kidding; he was frightened. A short shock through the rung, however, and the dog jumped.

Another great inventive act was that of Will Mahoney, who danced to his own melodies by attaching xylophone hammers to the toes of his shoes, and then danced atop the xylophone. If Will had spent the same amount of effort in thinking that he did on his xylophone, he might have discovered penicillin. I am sure that if all the hours vaudeville performers spent trying to improve their acts had been donated to science, automation would have been here fifty years sooner.

Vaudeville old-timers may not be wallowing in affluence in later life, but each smalltimer has his store of memories that will help him to escape from the unhappy present into the happy past. When the time comes that I find myself confined to the rubbish heap of humanity, I can temper my plight by conjuring up random recollections from my smalltime years. I can recall . . .

The manager of the vaudeville theater at Sandusky, Ohio. The audience there was so bad that he felt sorry for the acts. He invented an applause machine and installed it in the back of the theater. The machine manufactured applause by slapping a series of wooden paddles together. When an act finished and the audience sat there in its customary silence, the manager turned on his applause machine. To the sound of the wooden clatter, the act returned, took one or two bows, and withdrew.

The manager at Sherbrooke, Ontario, who was in the raincoat business. I remember that on the last night of my stay there he tried to talk the actors into taking their salaries in raincoats.

The manager at Torrington, Connecticut, who, on closing night, was driving me and a contortionist back to New York. Speeding through one small Connecticut town at midnight, the car was overtaken and stopped by the local policeman. The manager stepped out of the car to explain. He said, "I'm sorry, officer. I'm the manager of the theater at Torrington."

"I don't know nothin' about that," said the rube. "You was doin' sixty-five."

"I've got to get to New York," pleaded the manager. "I've got a contortionist in the car. He has to catch a train."

"You got what in the car?"

"A contortionist."

"A *contortionist?*"

"Yes."

"What's a contortionist?"

The contortionist couldn't stand it any longer. He jumped out of the car in the dark, ran around in front of the headlights, and ripped his coat off. He did a handstand, twined his legs around his neck, and ran around in circles on his hands.

The rube watched him for a few minutes and said, "That's a contortionist, eh?"

"Yes," said the manager.

"I'll be damned," the policeman said. "Go ahead!"

I can remember, too, the little theater at Lancaster, Pennsylvania, that had the bowling alley upstairs. Just as I came to the punch line of my joke, somebody in the bowling alley made a strike and the audience heard nothing but the awful crash.

And then there was the butcher in the small Ohio town who converted his shop into a theater at night and showed pictures and Gus Sun smalltime vaudeville acts. In the window of the butcher shop he hung a sign:

> Hamburger — 10¢ lb.
> Pork chops — 20¢ lb.
> Veal — 25¢ lb.
> Theater tonight — 20¢

There was a theater at Bayonne, New Jersey, where, during my act, a cat came down the aisle, emitted a series of bloodcurdling cries, and delivered a litter on the carpet. An usher rushed down the aisle with a coal shovel, scooped up the kittens, and returned, followed by the mother, to the back of the house. The audience was in a tumult. All I could do in feeble rebuttal was to coin the line "I thought my act was a monologue, not a catalogue."

The Jefferson Theatre, on Fourteenth Street in New York, had a mongrel audience: the theater was going to the dogs. Situated between Second and Third Avenues, it attracted patrons of all nationalities. Third Avenue at Fourteenth Street was an uptown Skid Row, and should have been renamed the Bowery-Plaza. Alcoholics of all sizes and in varying conditions frequented the neighborhood and used the Jefferson as a haven from the elements and a slumber sanctuary. At some performances the Jefferson took on the appearance of a flophouse that had put in vaudeville. At one supper show, during my monologue I heard a sort of "clunk!" noise that was repeated at regular intervals. It sounded like someone dropping wet wedges into a bathtub. I'd talk for thirty seconds—then a clunk. Another thirty seconds—and another clunk. Finally I located the source of the clunks. On the aisle, in the third row, sat a simian-faced specimen. Between his feet he was holding a wooden bucket; on the seat next to him he had a bag filled with oysters. As I was struggling through my monologue, this combination bivalve addict and theater patron was shucking his oysters and dropping the shells into the bucket.

I can remember, too, *l'affaire* midget at the depot at Quincy, Illinois. The headline act, a midget troupe, was leaving to open at Galesburg. One midget on the platform was berating the manager of the act, and demanding in squeaky words that he be given a raise in salary. The train started, but the midget refused to get aboard unless he was assured of more money. As the baggage car went by, the manager calmly picked up the midget and threw him in through the open door.

When I try to clamp the lid tightly on the past, names keep popping up. There was Eddie Borden, who did an English act with a partner called Sir James Dwyer. Eddie read a magazine ad for a preparation guaranteed to cure skin blemishes. The ad claimed that you could save the expense of a trip to Hot Springs by buying a bottle of the company's elixir and taking your own curative baths at home. Eddie, who was concerned about an acne condition, mailed in the coupon. At Minneapolis, the fluid arrived with full directions. To enjoy the Hot Springs bath at home, the patient had to close the bathroom door tightly, fill the tub with steaming hot water, pour in a given amount of the magic fluid, and lie in the tub to soak for an hour or more. Eddie followed the directions implicitly, finished his soaking, and went to bed. The next morning he opened the bathroom door, and instead of the pure white bathroom he had entered the night before, he now found a room with a brown ceiling, brown walls, brown tub, brown toilet seat and bowl, brown medicine cabinet, and a brown door. The Hot Springs elixir had contained sulfur, and the steam had transformed Eddie's suite into mahogany.

Jack Inglis was a funny nut comedian. One season, work was scarce. Jack lived in a rented house in Jersey with his wife and four children. A butcher friend of his knew that things were bad, and that the family wouldn't have a very happy Thanksgiving. Early in October, he gave Jack a live turkey. He told him he could keep it out in the yard in Jersey, and when the time came, he could kill the turkey for the family's Thanksgiving dinner. Jack took the turkey—a plump specimen—home, and turned it loose in the back yard. Every day for six weeks Jack's kids played with the turkey and chased it around. By the time Thanksgiving arrived, the turkey, after running away from the kids for six weeks, had lost some twenty pounds. For their Thanksgiving Day dinner that year the Inglis family had what looked like a tall sparrow.

The Billy Doss Revue was a smalltime girl act featuring Bill, a blackface comedian. I played on the bill with this act in Kansas City, Florence, Topeka, and Wichita in Kansas, and some dry oil wells in Oklahoma. The last chorus number of the revue was sung on a Southern dock with a river boat tied up in the background. On the dock there were bales of cotton, and on one of the bales sat a buxom mammy. For the act's finale the mammy jumped off the cotton bale and did an agile wooden-shoe dance to great applause. The mammy was really a boy in blackface wearing a bandanna and a well-stuffed calico dress. The boy sat on his bale for three or four shows a day, looking at audiences, and with audiences looking at him. The only thing unusual about this is that the boy was wanted by the police. When they finally caught up with the blackface mammy, he was washed up for ten years, which he spent in the Ohio Penitentiary.

Nelson's Cats and Rats were a big-time act. The cats and rats, traditional enemies, performed together to the astonishment of audiences. One time, on a bill in Chicago, Fanny Brice was the headliner. As she arrived at the theater one evening and opened her dressing-room door, she shrieked. The stage manager rushed over to her and said, "What's wrong, Miss Brice?" Fanny gasped, "A rat! There's a big rat in my dressing room!" The stage manager, no fool, called Nelson, the cat and rat authority. Nelson rushed in, cornered the rat, caught him in a heavy towel, and took the rat out of the dressing room. A few weeks later, I was on the bill with Nelson's Cats and Rats. I asked Nelson what had happened to the rat he had caught in Fanny Brice's dressing room. He said, "The next show, watch the finish of my act." I watched the finish, and saw a big black rat walk across the tiny platform carrying an American flag. "That," said Nelson, "is the rat."

The smalltimer, as he trudged through the seasons, always felt that he was getting closer to his goal. Every vaudeville actor dreamed of his personal utopia. Weekly sums were banked or mailed home against the day the smalltimer "quit the business." Then he would open his restaurant, filling station, real-estate office, chicken farm, dancing school, or other project that he had envisioned supporting him through his remaining years. Very few smalltimers saw their dreams take dimension. As the vaudeville monologist would explain it, "A funny thing happened to my savings on the way to my utopia." Sickness, relatives, going into businesses he didn't understand, meeting real-estate salesmen, joining collapsible building and loan clubs, gambling, lending money to other actors who never repaid him, playing the stock market, and a thousand other mishaps dissipated the smalltimer's savings and shattered his hopes. The few that did realize their ambitions found that after the travel and excitement of vaudeville, the dull and sedentary routine imposed on them as they tried to run some picayune enterprise in a small town was boring.

One vaudeville actor I knew couldn't wait to retire and start his own chicken farm. After he had bought a farm in California and tried to operate it for a few months, he was very unhappy. I went out to visit him one afternoon and found him sitting out in the yard under a tree, griping. Scampering around in a large wire enclosure were hundreds of White Wyandottes. The bottoms of these white hens had red circles on them; scooting by, they looked like little Japanese flags with legs on them. I asked the actor if his chickens had unusual markings. He said no, that he had seen an ad for Lay or Bust Feed that would increase the size of any hen's eggs, and that he had been giving his hens plenty of it. The hens started laying eggs that were too large for their disposal equipment. Laying the big economy-size eggs had sprung the hens' hips and split their sphincters. "That accounts for the red circles on the bottoms of the hens?" I asked. "Yes," he answered. "I had to catch every lousy hen and dab her with mercurochrome!"

The smalltimer was never happy in retirement. Had it been within his power, the vaudeville performer would have been a timeless wanderer, spanning the generations by using the bridge of his talents.

But vaudeville is dead. Vaudeville was more a matter of style than of material. It was not so much what the two- and three-a-day favorites said and did, as how they said and did it. For fifty years vaudeville's minstrels found their way into all lands, preaching their gospel of merriment and song, and rousing the rest of the world to laughter and to tears. A few diehards who knew and enjoyed vaudeville hover over their television sets, hoping for a miracle. They believe that this electronic device is a modern oxygen tent that in some mysterious way can revive vaudeville and return its colorful performers of yesteryear to the current scene. The optimism of these day and night dreamers is wasted. Their vigils are futile. Vaudeville is dead. Period.

III

Far Places

The Climax of the Ascent

By MAURICE HERZOG

ON THE third of June, 1950, the first light of dawn found us still clinging to the tent poles at Camp V. Gradually the wind abated, and with daylight, died away altogether. I made desperate attempts to push back the soft, icy stuff which stifled me, but every movement became an act of heroism. My mental powers were numbed: thinking was an effort, and we did not exchange a single word.

What a repellent place it was! To everyone who reached it, Camp V became one of the worst memories of their lives. We had only one thought —to get away. We should have waited for the first rays of the sun, but at half-past five we felt we couldn't stick it any longer.

"Let's go, Biscante," I muttered. "Can't stay here a minute longer."

"Yes, let's go," repeated Lachenal.

Which of us would have the energy to make tea? Although our minds worked slowly we were quite able to envisage all the movements that would be necessary—and neither of us could face up to it. It couldn't be helped—we would just have to go without. It was quite hard enough work to get ourselves and our boots out of our sleeping bags—and the boots were frozen stiff so that we got them on only with the greatest difficulty. Every movement made us terribly breathless. We felt as if we were being stifled. Our gaiters were stiff as a board, and I succeeded in lacing mine up; Lachenal couldn't manage his.

"No need for the rope, eh, Biscante?"

"No need," replied Lachenal laconically.

That was two pounds saved. I pushed a tube of condensed milk, some nougat and a pair of socks into my sack; one never knew; the socks might come in useful—they might even do as Balaclavas. For the time being I stuffed them with first-aid equipment. The camera was loaded with a black and white film; I had a color film in reserve. I pulled the movie camera out from the bottom of my sleeping bag, wound it up and tried letting it run without film. There was a little click, then it stopped and jammed.

From *Annapurna,* by Maurice Herzog. Copyright 1952, by E. P. Dutton & Co., Inc. Reprinted by permission of E. P. Dutton & Co., Inc. and Jonathan Cape, Ltd.

"Bad luck after bringing it so far," said Lachenal.

In spite of our photographer, Ichac's, precautions taken to lubricate it with special grease, the intense cold, even inside the sleeping bag, had frozen it. I left it at the camp rather sadly: I had looked forward to taking it to the top. I had used it up to 24,600 feet.

We went outside and put on our crampons, which we kept on all day. We wore as many clothes as possible; our sacks were very light. At six o'clock we started off. It was brilliantly fine, but also very cold. Our super-lightweight champons bit deep into the steep slopes of ice and hard snow up which lay the first stage of our climb.

Later the slope became slightly less steep and more uniform. Sometimes the hard crust bore our weight, but at others we broke through and sank into soft powder snow which made progress exhausting. We took turns in making the track and often stopped without any word having passed between us. Each of us lived in a closed and private world of his own. I was suspicious of my mental processes; my mind was working very slowly and I was perfectly aware of the low state of my intelligence. It was easiest just to stick to one thought at a time—safest, too. The cold was penetrating; for all our special eiderdown clothing we felt as if we'd nothing on. Whenever we halted, we stamped our feet hard. Lachenal went as far as to take off one boot which was a bit tight; he was in terror of frostbite.

"I don't want to be like Lambert," he said. Raymond Lambert, a Geneva guide, had to have all his toes amputated after an eventful climb during which he got his feet frostbitten.[1] While Lachenal rubbed himself hard, I looked at the summits all around us; already we overtopped them all except the distant Dhaulagiri. The complicated structure of these mountains, with which our many laborious explorations had made us familiar, was now spread out plainly at our feet.

The going was incredibly exhausting, and every step was a struggle of mind over matter. We came out into the sunlight, and by way of marking the occasion made yet another halt. Lachenal continued to complain of his feet. "I can't feel anything. I think I'm beginning to get frostbite." And once again he undid his boot.

I began to be seriously worried. I realized very well the risk we were running; I knew from experience how insidiously and quickly frostbite can set in if one is not extremely careful. Nor was Lachenal under any illusions. "We're in danger of having frozen feet. Do you think it's worth it?"

This was most disturbing. It was my responsibility as leader to think of the others. There was no doubt about frostbite being a very real danger.

[1] In May, 1952, Lambert, with the Sherpa Ang-Tsering, reached 28,215 feet on Mount Everest, possibly the highest point yet attained. (Translator's note.)

Did Annapurna justify such risks? That was the question I asked myself; it continued to worry me.

Lachenal had laced his boots up again, and once more we continued to force our way through the exhausting snow. The whole of the Sickle glacier was now in view, bathed in light. We still had a long way to go to cross it, and then there was that rock band—would we find a gap in it?

My feet, like Lachenal's, were very cold and I continued to wriggle my toes, even when we were moving. I could not feel them, but that was nothing new in the mountains, and if I kept on moving them it would keep the circulation going.

Lachenal appeared to me as a sort of specter—he was alone in his world, I in mine. But—and this was odd enough—any effort was slightly *less* exhausting than lower down. Perhaps it was hope lending us wings. Even through dark glasses the snow was blinding—the sun beating straight down on the ice. We looked down upon precipitous ridges which dropped away into space, and upon tiny glaciers far, far below. Familiar peaks soared arrow-like into the sky. Suddenly Lachenal grabbed me:

"If I go back, what will you do?"

A whole sequence of pictures flashed through my head: the days of marching in sweltering heat, the hard pitches we had overcome, the tremendous efforts we had all made to lay siege to the mountain, the daily heroism of all my friends in establishing the camps. Now we were nearing our goal. In an hour or two, perhaps, victory would be ours. Must we give up? Impossible! My whole being revolted against the idea. I had made up my mind, irrevocably. Today we were consecrating an ideal, and no sacrifice was too great. I heard my voice clearly:

"I should go on by myself."

I would go alone. If he wished to go down it was not for me to stop him. He must make his own choice freely.

"Then I'll follow you."

The die was cast. I was no longer anxious. Nothing could stop us now from getting to the top. The psychological atmosphere changed with these few words, and we went forward now as brothers.

I felt as though I were plunging into something new and quite abnormal. I had the strangest and most vivid impressions, such as I had never before known in the mountains. There was something unnatural in the way I saw Lachenal and everything around us. I smiled to myself at the paltriness of our efforts, for I could stand apart and watch myself making these efforts. But all sense of exertion was gone, as though there were no longer any gravity. This diaphanous landscape, this quintessence of purity—these were not the mountains I knew: they were the mountains of my dreams.

The snow, sprinkled over every rock and gleaming in the sun, was of a radiant beauty that touched me to the heart. I had never seen such complete transparency, and I was living in a world of crystal. Sounds were indistinct, the atmosphere like cotton wool.

An astonishing happiness welled up in me, but I could not define it. Everything was so new, so utterly unprecedented. It was not in the least like anything I had known in the Alps, where one feels buoyed up by the presence of others—by people of whom one is vaguely aware, or even by the dwellings one can see in the far distance.

This was quite different. An enormous gulf was between me and the world. This was a different universe—withered, desert, lifeless; a fantastic universe where the presence of man was not foreseen, perhaps not desired. We were braving an interdict, overstepping a boundary, and yet we had no fear as we continued upward. I thought of the famous ladder of St. Theresa of Avila. Something clutched at my heart.

Did Lachenal share these feelings? The summit ridge drew nearer, and we reached the foot of the ultimate rock band. The slope was very steep and the snow interspersed with rocks.

"Couloir!"

A finger pointed. The whispered word from one to another indicated the key to the rocks—the last line of defense.

"What luck!"

The couloir up the rocks though steep was feasible.

The sky was a deep sapphire blue. With a great effort we edged over to the right, avoiding the rocks; we preferred to keep to the snow on account of our crampons and it was not long before we set foot in the couloir. It was fairly steep, and we had a minute's hesitation. Should we have enough strength left to overcome this final obstacle?

Fortunately the snow was hard, and by kicking steps we were able to manage, thanks to our crampons. A false move would have been fatal. There was no need to make handholds—our axes, driven in as far as possible, served us for an anchor.

Lachenal went splendidly. What a wonderful contrast to the early days! It was a hard struggle here, but he kept going. Lifting our eyes occasionally from the slope, we saw the couloir opening out onto . . . well, we didn't quite know, probably a ridge. But where was the top—left or right? Stopping at every step, leaning on our axes, we tried to recover our breath and to calm down our racing hearts, which were thumping as though they would burst. We knew we were there now—that nothing could stop us. No need to exchange looks—each of us would have read the same determination in the other's eyes. A slight detour to the left, a few more steps—the summit ridge came gradually nearer—a few rocks to avoid. We dragged ourselves up. Could we possibly be there?

Yes!

A fierce and savage wind tore at us.

We were on top of Annapurna! 8,075 meters, 26,493 feet.

Our hearts overflowed with an unspeakable happiness.
"If only the others could know. . . ."
If only everyone could know!
The summit was a corniced crest of ice, and the precipices on the far side which plunged vertically down beneath us were terrifying, unfathomable. There could be few other mountains in the world like this. Clouds floated halfway down, concealing the gentle, fertile valley of Pokhara, 23,000 feet below. Above us there was nothing!
Our mission was accomplished. But at the same time we had accomplished something infinitely greater. How wonderful life would now become! What an inconceivable experience it is to attain one's ideal and, at the very same moment, to fulfill oneself. I was stirred to the depths of my being. Never had I felt happiness like this—so intense and yet so pure. That brown rock, the highest of them all, that ridge of ice—were these the goals of a lifetime? Or were they, rather, the limits of man's pride?
"Well, what about going down?"
Lachenal shook me. What were his own feelings? Did he simply think he had finished another climb, as in the Alps? Did he think one could just go down again like that, with nothing more to it?
"One minute, I must take some photographs."
"Hurry up!"
I fumbled feverishly in my sack, pulled out the camera, took out the little French flag which was right at the bottom, and the pennants. Useless gestures, no doubt, but something more than symbols—eloquent tokens of affection and good will. I tied the strips of material—stained by sweat and by the food in the sacks—to the shaft of my ice ax, the only flagstaff at hand. Then I focused my camera on Lachenal.
"Now, will you take me?"
"Hand it over—hurry up!" said Lachenal.
He took several pictures and then handed me back the camera. I loaded a color film and we repeated the process to be certain of bringing back records to be cherished in the future.
"Are you mad?" asked Lachenal. "We haven't a minute to lose: we must go down at once."
And in fact a glance round showed me that the weather was no longer gloriously fine as it had been in the morning. Lachenal was becoming impatient.
"We must go down!"
He was right. His was the reaction of the mountaineer who knows his own domain. But I just could not accustom myself to the idea that we had won our victory. It seemed inconceivable that we should have trodden those summit snows.
It was impossible to build a cairn; there were no stones; everything was

frozen. Lachenal stamped his feet; he felt them freezing. I felt mine freezing too, but paid little attention. The highest mountain to be climbed by man lay under our feet! The names of our predecessors on these heights raced through my mind: Mummery, Mallory and Irvine, Bauer, Welzenbach, Tilman, Shipton. How many of them were dead—how many had found on these mountains what, to them, was the finest end of all?

My joy was touched with humility. It was not just one party that had climbed Annapurna today, but a whole expedition. I thought of all the others in the camps perched on the slopes at our feet, and I knew it was because of their efforts and their sacrifices that we had succeeded. There are times when the most complicated actions are suddenly summed up, distilled, and strike you with illuminating clarity; so it was with this irresistible upward surge which had landed us two here.

Pictures passed through my mind—the Chamonix valley, where I had spent the most marvelous moments of my childhood; Mont Blanc, which so tremendously impressed me! I was a child when I first saw "the Mont Blanc people" coming home, and to me there was a queer look about them; a strange light shone in their eyes.

"Come on, straight down," called Lachenal.

He had already done up his sack and started going down. I took out my pocket aneroid: 8,500 meters. I smiled. I swallowed a little condensed milk and left the tube behind—the only trace of our passage. I did up my sack, put on my gloves and my glasses, seized my ice ax; one look around and I, too, hurried down the slope. Before disappearing into the couloir I gave one last look at the summit which would henceforth be all our joy and all our consolation.

Lachenal was already far below; he had reached the foot of the couloir. I hurried down in his tracks. I went as fast as I could, but it was dangerous going. At every step one had to take care that the snow did not break away beneath one's weight. Lachenal, going faster than I thought he was capable of, was now on the long traverse. It was my turn to cross the area of mixed rock and snow. At last I reached the foot of the rock band. I had hurried and I was out of breath. I undid my sack. What had I been going to do? I couldn't say.

"My gloves!"

Before I had time to bend over, I saw them slide and roll. They went further and further straight down the slope. I remained where I was, quite stunned. I watched them rolling down slowly, with no appearance of stopping. The movement of those gloves was engraved in my sight as something irredeemable, against which I was powerless. The consequences might be most serious. What was I to do?

"Quickly, down to Camp V."

Rebuffat and Terray would be there. My concern dissolved like magic. I now had a fixed objective again: to reach the camp. Never for a minute did it occur to me to use as gloves the socks which I always carry in reserve for just such a mishap as this.

On I went, trying to catch up with Lachenal. It had been two o'clock when we reached the summit; we had started out at six in the morning, but I had to admit that I had lost all sense of time. I felt as if I were running, whereas in actual fact I was walking normally, perhaps rather slowly, and I had to keep stopping to get my breath. The sky was now covered with clouds, everything had become gray and dirty-looking. An icy wind sprang up, boding no good. We must push on! But where was Lachenal? I spotted him a couple of hundred yards away, looking as if he was never going to stop. And I had thought he was in indifferent form!

The clouds grew thicker and came right down over us; the wind blew stronger, but I did not suffer from the cold. Perhaps the descent had restored my circulation. Should I be able to find the tents in the mist? I watched the rib ending in the beaklike point which overlooked the camp. It was gradually swallowed up by the clouds, but I was able to make out the spearhead rib lower down. If the mist should thicken I would make straight for that rib and follow it down, and in this way I should be bound to come upon the tent.

Lachenal disappeared from time to time, and then the mist was so thick that I lost sight of him altogether. I kept going at the same speed, as fast as my breathing would allow.

The slope was now steeper; a few patches of bare ice followed the smooth stretches of snow. A good sign—I was nearing the camp. How difficult to find one's way in thick mist! I kept the course which I had set by the steepest angle of the slope. The ground was broken; with my crampons I went straight down walls of bare ice. There were some patches ahead—a few more steps. It was the camp all right, but there were *two tents!*

So Rebuffat and Terray had come up. What a mercy! I should be able to tell them that we had been successful, that we were returning from the top. How thrilled they would be!

I got there, dropping down from above. The platform had been extended, and the two tents were facing each other. I tripped over one of the guy ropes of the first tent; there was movement inside, they had heard me. Rebuffat and Terray put their heads out.

"We've made it. We're back from Annapurna!"

Big Game Hunting in Africa

By J. A. HUNTER

FOR MANY years clients have been asking me, "Hunter, what do you consider the most dangerous big game animal in Africa?" No man can answer this question exactly, but at the risk of some repetition, I will summarize my own thought about it. Much depends on circumstances. An animal that may be most dangerous in bush can often be easily shot on open veldt. Also, hunters vary considerably in their individual abilities, and an animal that one man would consider dangerous would not cause another sportsman much concern. For example, a man who can take quick "snapshots" with a rifle would find a charging lion less formidable than a hunter whose reactions are slower. Again, much depends on the hunter's past experience. Some hunters have specialized in one type of game and, knowing the animal's habits, are apt to consider it a fairly easy quarry. The same hunter, confronted by a different type of animal, will probably have a series of narrow escapes and naturally conclude that this new beast is very cunning and aggressive. Thus a man may have been a professional hunter for many years and still find it difficult to judge correctly the abilities of different types of big game.

Owing to constant hunting, many game animals have completely changed their character in the last fifty years. Around the turn of the century, some animals were easy to hunt. Today, they are much more cunning and dangerous. I am thinking particularly of elephants. They have learned that man is their enemy and are not as trusting as they once were.

Some years ago, a friend of mine formed a partnership with a famous old-time ivory hunter who had killed well over two thousand elephants in his day. These two men were starting out on an ivory-hunting safari and my friend wanted me to accompany them, taking as my share one-third of the ivory shot. I refused. The old hunter was famous for shooting elephants with a very light-caliber rifle. I felt that the old man would simply anger and panic the elephants without helping us get any ivory.

My friend looked at me as though I were mad. "Hunter, this man has shot twice as many elephants as you'll ever kill," he told me. "Surely he knows more about the matter than you do."

"He made his reputation as an ivory hunter thirty or forty years ago," I explained. "In those days, elephants lived mainly in open country. As they had never been hunted, they had little fear of man. A hunter could lie out in the veldt with a light rifle and pick his shots. There was little danger of a charge. Now elephants live in bush. They know more about guns than many hunters and have learned how to set ambushes. Elephant hunting is far more dangerous today than it used to be."

My friend would not be convinced. He set out with the old hunter. Several months later he returned to Nairobi. They had not taken enough ivory even to pay for the expenses of the trip.

Later, my friend confessed to me that there had been so many close calls with elephants that he considered himself lucky to get back alive.

I have hunted every type of big game in Africa, both as a white hunter and as an employee of the game department doing control work. I have not specialized in any one type of hunting. Yet, because I lived during a period when it was necessary to shoot large numbers of game animals to make way for the rapidly expanding population, I have established records of one kind and another with several of the big game animals. I do not say this boastfully, as any experienced white hunter could, given my opportunities, have done as well or better. I mention the fact because I believe I have acquired more general experience with big game than most men. So, in giving my idea of the five most dangerous big game animals, I speak as a man who has hunted them all extensively. Yet I most certainly am not dogmatic in my listing, for, as I have said, much depends on time, place and the individual man or animal.

First, let me say that any animal can be dangerous when cornered or wounded. I have seen water buck, sable antelope, and warthogs put up a desperate fight under such circumstances. So I confine my remarks to the "big five"—the outstanding big game animals of Africa. They are the elephant, the rhino, the buffalo, the lion and the leopard. These animals have been the cause of the vast majority of hunting fatalities on this continent.

The elephant is by far the most intelligent of this group. But unless he is a rogue, his very intelligence tends to keep him from being a menace to hunters. An elephant knows he is no match against a man armed with a rifle and so does everything possible to avoid man rather than attack him. I am not speaking now of an irritable cow elephant with a young calf or a herd that has been so badgered by hunters that they will charge anything on sight. I am talking about the average animal. In elephant hunting, the great problem is generally getting near enough to make the shot possible, not having to stop a charge.

Naturally there are exceptions. When an elephant knows he is being hunted and finds that he cannot throw the man off his spoor, he may set out to "hunt the hunter." At such times, an elephant is exceedingly dangerous, especially if he has been hunted before and knows something of men and their ways.

It did happen once that an elephant waited for me beside a trail after I had killed his two companions. I was lucky to kill him before he killed me. Also—and in my opinion this is of prime importance—a charging elephant will nearly always turn away from a shot, even if not seriously wounded. Few elephants will push a charge home once they feel the impact of a bullet. For these two reasons, I class the average elephant as the least dangerous of the "big five."

Now let us consider the rhino. Unlike an elephant, a rhino will frequently charge with no provocation whatsoever. In my opinion, this makes them a more dangerous animal. But a rhino will also generally turn away from a shot.

I have met with three rhinos in a simultaneous charge, killed the middle one (a cow), and watched her escort (two bulls) disappear into the bush on either side of me so rapidly that I could hardly see them go. If those rhinos had been buffalo, they would have pressed their attack home and one or the other would surely have tossed me.

I do not mean to say that rhinos will *always* turn from a shot. On another occasion, I was again charged by three rhinos under very similar conditions. I was using a .500 double-barreled express rifle at the time. I dropped the two leading animals with a left and right, then turned to grab my second gun from the bearer. The man had vanished. He had bolted when the rhinos charged, taking my spare gun with him.

The third rhino was on me. I have a vivid memory of the animal's face. His eyes were closed and seemed mere slits. At the last moment, I tried to jump aside. As I did so, I was shot into the air with a suddenness that surprised me. Fortunately, the rhino kept on going and did not return to gore me. In general, rhinos are one-way beasts. I have heard that rhinos close their eyes at the moment of a charge and my observations at that time would seem to bear out this theory. However, I have strictly guarded against any further investigations.

I mention this incident to show that no one can tell exactly what an animal may do, but I still claim that few rhinos will press home a charge in the face of gunfire. I, therefore, class them fourth on my list; more dangerous than elephant because of their aggressive natures but less dangerous than buffalo, lion or leopard.

Many sportsmen have classed the buffalo as the most dangerous big game animal in Africa. There is much to be said for this point of view. The buffalo will push home a charge in spite of a gunshot wound. He is often most aggressive and will charge with comparatively little provocation. When he charges, he presents his great boss to the hunter and only a very heavy-caliber bullet will stop him. If he knocks a man down, he will almost always come back to gore his victim. Also, the buffalo is a cunning antagonist. He will circle and stand by his back trail, waiting for the hunter. This trick is usually played by a wounded buffalo that knows he can go no further.

Unlike other big game, a buffalo has all his senses equally well developed. As I have said, elephant and rhino have excellent scent but poor sight. Lions and leopards have good sight but, for an animal, indifferent powers of scent. A buffalo can see, hear, and scent equally well. A terrible combination.

Why, then, do I not consider the buffalo Africa's most dangerous big game animal? The buffalo's very size counts against him. No beast weighing well over two thousand pounds can effectively conceal himself except in the very thickest bush. Also, a charging buffalo offers such a large target that a man is reasonably sure of hitting him somewhere. If you use a heavy enough gun, you are sure to knock him down. Then you can plaster him with your second barrel.

There is another consideration. When a buffalo charges, he seems to come like the wind but actually he cannot do over thirty-five m.p.h. Nor can he reach the top of his speed immediately. This gives a man time to get his gun up and take aim. For these reasons, I class the buffalo as the third most dangerous animal in Africa.

We now come to the great cats—lions and leopards. I consider the lion the second most dangerous game animal in Africa. His ability to conceal himself in the sparsest cover, and his great speed, which requires no build-up—he hits high gear at the first bound—are both factors. Moreover, he is a small target compared with a buffalo. Also, he comes at you in a series of great leaps that make it difficult to draw a bead on him. He is as courageous as a buffalo and will not flinch away from a shot. He comes all out, either kill or be killed. If he hits a man with the full force of his charge behind him, the man will probably be knocked unconscious. This is lucky for the hunter, for then he will not feel the subsequent mauling.

Lions are exactly what you make them. A man can shoot lions from a lorry with virtually no trouble or danger. The same is true of killing them from a boma or machan. But following lions through bush is a very different matter. Here the lion has all the advantage. He knows where you are but you have no idea of his position. You must come to him—he will not come to you. Elephant, rhino, and buffalo can often be coaxed into charging, thus giving the hunter an advantage. A crouching lion waits until he is certain of getting his man. The reader must remember that I am talking now of a single hunter following a single lion. If you have beaters who will drive the animal out into the open, the whole affair becomes far more simple. I am also assuming that the lion knows he is being hunted and has not suddenly been bolted out of a donga by stones. But to go into the bush after lions with only your gun-bearer is a very difficult and dangerous sport.

The courage and strength of a fine lion can hardly be overestimated. I once saw a lion charge a three-ton lorry. This animal was ten feet from the lorry when he sprang for us. He made a wonderful leap. His whole body was stretched out to the fullest and gave the impression of being streamlined. I have often had lions leap at me but never had such an opportunity to see their grace and perfect co-ordination. He hit the back of the lorry with such force that the entire vehicle shuddered.

From my position in the driver's seat, I could not see what was going on in the back. Taking my 30-06 Springfield that I use to shoot antelope, I got out of the cab and went around behind. There was the lion walking away from the lorry, obviously dejected and disillusioned.

If, hunted under fair conditions, the lion is the second most dangerous animal in Africa, what animal is the most dangerous? In my opinion, the leopard. I know that many white hunters will not agree with me, yet I hold to my verdict. I have shot a great many of these animals—how many I do not know because we used to hunt them for their hides and kept no records. Shooting leopards was considered a praiseworthy occupation when I first came to Kenya, because they were most detrimental to stock. Wounds made by a leopard's claws invariably become infected, as his talons, like a lion's, are coated with putrid meat from his kills. Even if a sheep or cow were only lightly scratched, the animal almost always sickened and died. Leopards also showed no hesitation about attacking any rancher who came to the defense of his herds. Many of the early settlers in Kenya had lost an eye or part of their face as a result of leopard attacks. A charging leopard always leaps for a man's face, trying to tear out his victim's eyes with his germ-laden foreclaws while his rear talons are equally busy. At the same time, he usually fastens his teeth in the neck or shoulder.

A friend and I were once hunting leopard in the Masai Reserve. We saw one of the creatures running up a steep, stony slope. My friend fired, hitting the cat in the flank. The leopard gave a bound and vanished among the boulders. We picked up the blood spoor and began working our way slowly up the hill, walking a few yards apart with rifles held at the ready. This is nerve-racking work, for we knew that the cat was waiting for us somewhere among the great stones and was sure to charge.

We had gone about twenty yards when the leopard suddenly burst from behind a boulder and leaped on my friend. The creature simply whizzed through the air—he was nothing but a yellow flash of light. My friend was a quick shot but he did not even have time to bring his rifle up before the cat was on him. I fired while the leopard was still in the air, "snap-shooting" as though my rifle were a shotgun. By great luck the bullet broke both of the leopard's shoulders and he fell dead on my friend. Later, we measured the length of his spring. My friend had been twelve feet from the boulder when the cat leaped on him.

If a leopard is to be hunted in any kind of cover, I prefer to use a twelve-gauge shotgun charged with heavy shot. When a leopard leaps for you, his strung-out body makes a very difficult target indeed. I have said that a charging lion is a difficult target but a leopard weighs less than half as much as a lion. Being smaller than a lion, he can conceal himself even more thoroughly.

Many people think that an animal is dangerous only in relation to its size and that a bull elephant is naturally a more formidable enemy than a two-hundred-pound leopard. Not at all. Man is a delicate creature, easily killed by any decently aggressive wild beast. A man being hunted by any one of the great game animals is like a rat being pursued by a dog. A small, quick little terrier is more dangerous to a rat than is a big, clumsy Great Dane or St. Bernard. A leopard is not so powerful as a lion but he is quite strong enough to inflict a mortal wound on a man, and that is a hunter's only consideration.

A leopard is a smart beast. When a leopard knows he is being spoored, he will often climb a tree and lie out on a limb overhanging the trail. If the hunter does not see him, the leopard will usually let him pass. But if the hunter happens to glance up and their eyes meet, the leopard is on him like a flash. Most animals when they find themselves discovered will grunt or snarl and run on again. Not so with the leopard. The instant he sees a look of recognition cross the hunter's face, he charges instantly.

Twice I have been with hunters who walked under a tree where a leopard was crouching. In both cases, the cats gave no sign until the men happened to look up. Then the leopards sprang. Only the quickest of quick shooting saved the hunters from mutilation or worse.

Because leopards are as much at home in trees as on the ground, you must not only watch the cover on either side of the trail but also the limbs overhead. This more than doubles your difficulties.

A leopard's bushcraft is deficient in one notable respect. Although he may conceal his body perfectly in a mass of foliage, he often leaves his tail hanging down. I have shot a number of leopards that were waiting for me in ambush simply because they forgot to hide their tails.

In most other respects, leopards are very crafty. Their method of catching domestic dogs is a good example of their intelligence.

While leopards have a passion for dog meat, it is a curious fact that a leopard will run from a pack of dogs. Half a dozen little curs can hold the biggest of leopards up a tree indefinitely. But a leopard will go to any extremes to catch and kill a single dog, often actually enticing the dog into its power.

When a dog scents a leopard, he usually begins barking furiously, but takes care not to leave the safety of his master's tent or front porch. The leopard moves to a patch of open ground and lies down, apparently completely indifferent to the yapping dog. Then he begins to purr, waving his tail gently from side to side, and holding his head close to the ground as another dog would if he wanted to play. After a few minutes, the dog becomes curious. He moves closer to investigate, sniffing cautiously and still on the alert. The leopard, with hind legs tucked under him, is in a perfect position for a spring. But he does not appear to be crouching. He pays only occasional notice to the dog, looking around him and purring contentedly. Finally the dog is lured within range. Suddenly, and without the slightest warning, the leopard leaps for the unfortunate animal like a released spring. No dog, even the largest or fiercest, has any chance against a leopard. The cat has inch-long fangs and his claws as well. The leopard grabs the dog's throat, at the same instant fastening his talons in the dog's belly. As soon as the dog is dead, the leopard carries the carcass into the nearest thicket and devours it.

A leopard will almost always put the remains of a kill in the fork of a tree limb to protect it from scavengers. A large leopard can carry an animal weighing a hundred pounds up a tree trunk even though there are no branches to aid him. During the day, he will sleep in a tree some distance from the tree where he has left his kill, returning to feed on it after dark.

This fierce cat has at least one good trait. Unlike lions, leopards are not polygamous and have only one mate. There is strong affection between the couple. I once put out poisoned bait for a female leopard that had been killing a settler's stock. The next morning, I visited the bait and found the leopardess lying dead across the kill. Beside the dead animal was her mate, his head resting on her body in a caressing attitude. When he saw me he sprang up. He died beside his beloved consort.

Hunting a leopard in long grass, although not so dangerous as spooring the beast through jungle, is none the less a thrilling business. A leopard cannot be bolted out of grass with stones; he will not move even if you chance to hit him. A lion will nearly always betray his presence by growling, while a leopard remains absolutely silent until the moment of attack.

The elders of a Masai village once sent for me to destroy a cattle-killing leopard that had caused them great losses. Two young moran had spoored him down, only to be badly mauled. When I arrived at the village, I was astonished by the amount of damage this one animal had done. He would often kill five or six calves during the night, never touching the flesh but apparently killing merely for sport.

I set about tracking the animal. Near the village were several rock kopjes, made of colossal boulders that rested on top of each other in perfect balance, looking for all the world as if placed in position by mechanical means. With no frost or thaw to shake their balance, they had remained there for centuries and would, no doubt, continue to remain there for all time although it seemed that a puff of wind could topple them over. Between these great boulders were deep fissures, ideal dens for a leopard. I could see where he had walked among the huge, oblong rocks but I could not spoor him to his den. I lost his pug marks among the stones and returned to the village unsuccessful.

During the night there was a great commotion in the kraal. Cattle were stampeding and the natives yelling. When morning came, another calf had been killed, bitten through the throat as on other occasions.

I persuaded the owner of the calf to let me have the body as bait. My boys built me a machan in a convenient tree and I sat up to await the leopard's return.

At ten o'clock that night I saw a moving form loom up in the semi-darkness and creep cautiously toward the bait. It made no sound and its tread was deadly still. It was so large that I actually thought it was a lioness. It moved onto the bait and then squatted down. I could hardly see it against the earth. I decided to shoot as soon as it stood up again. Half an hour later, the cat rose and I could see his tail flicking from side to side. Taking aim, I fired low, as in the darkness you are apt to overshoot. The animal gave a tremendous bound and disappeared. I was satisfied he was hit but the light was so poor that I could only hope for the best. Taking no risks, I stayed in my perch until daylight.

When the dawn came, I examined the ground and found blood. The spoor was undoubtedly that of the cattle-killing leopard for I had examined his pug marks carefully while tracking him. My aim had not been good, otherwise he would have lain down within the first hundred yards. There was nothing for it but track him down to his den among the kopjes.

I set out with four moran, all carrying their spears and shields, and we tracked the blood spoor to the entrance of a small cave. Two of the moran cut a long sapling and began to probe in the hole while the other Masai stood by me with their spears at the ready. Suddenly a deep, coarse growl came from the cave, reverberating off the rocky sides. Immediately the leopard burst out like a bullet from a gun. As the leopard charged us he continued to utter a series of grunts, made by his breath's intake and output. He knocked down the two Masai with the pole and then leaped for one of the armed moran. The man met the charge with a spear thrust. He missed. In an instant the leopard was on top of his shield, mauling him about the face with his forepaws and biting him in the shoulder. The man fell to the ground with the animal still clinging to him. The other moran stabbed at the leopard, his spear passing so close to me that the razorlike head cut my trousers. Instantly the cat turned on him and seized the man by the arm. Down he went, with the leopard ripping him open with both forepaws and hind legs, his teeth still buried in the man's arm.

All this took but seconds, far less time than it takes to tell it. I pushed my rifle muzzle against the thick neck of the leopard and fired, blowing a hole through the mass of snarling savagery. So ended the worst cattle killer in that area.

I was astonished at the amount of damage this leopard had been able to inflict on the two Masai in a matter of moments. Knowing how rapidly wounds made by a leopard's teeth and claws infect, I lost no time in attending to them. The deep fang wounds on the moran's shoulder I syringed with T.C.P. disinfectant. The claw wounds I simply rinsed out with the same disinfectant. A week later both moran had gotten over their mauling.

All in all, I know of no beast that I would less like to hunt in cover than the fast, savage, cunning leopard.

In many parts of Africa, the use of traps, poisons, and dogs has virtually exterminated the leopard. In my youth, we thought that the only good leopard was a hide stretched out for drying. But now we are discovering that the leopard played an important part in maintaining nature's balance. Leopards used to kill thousands of baboons every year, and now that the leopards have been largely wiped out baboons are proving to be a major control problem in many parts of the colony. The perfect way to keep them in check is by allowing their natural enemy, the leopard, to destroy them. So leopards are now widely protected and allowed to increase in numbers. Such is the strange way that man works—first he virtually destroys a species and then does everything in his power to restore it.

Fish Are Such Liars

By ROLAND PERTWEE

THERE had been a fuss in the pool beneath the alders, and the small rainbow trout, with a skitter of his tail, flashed upstream, a hurt and angry fish. For three consecutive mornings he had taken the rise in that pool, and it injured his pride to be jostled from his drift just when the Mayfly was coming up in numbers. If his opponent had been a half-pounder like himself, he would have stayed and fought, but when an old hen fish weighing fully three pounds, with a mouth like a rat hole and a carnivorous, cannibalistic eye rises from the reed beds and occupies the place, flight is the only effective argument.

But Rainbow was very much provoked. He had chosen his place with care. Now the Mayfly was up, the little French chalk stream was full of rising fish, and he knew by experience that strangers are unpopular in that season. To do one's self justice during a hatch, one must find a place where the fly drifts nicely overhead with the run of the stream, and natural drifts are scarce even in a chalk stream. He was not content to leap at the fly like an hysterical youngster who measured his weight in ounces and his wits in milligrams. He had reached that time of life which demanded that he should feed off the surface by suction rather than exertion. No living thing is more particular about his table manners than a trout, and Rainbow was no exception.

"It's a sickening thing," he said to himself, "and a hard shame." He added: "Get out of my way," to a couple of fat young chub with negroid mouths who were bubbling the surface in the silly, senseless fashion of their kind.

"Chub indeed!"

But even the chub had a home and he had none—and the life of a homeless river dweller is precarious.

"I will not and shall not be forced back to midstream," he said.

For, save at eventide or in very special circumstances, trout of personality do not frequent open water where they must compete for every insect with the wind, the lightning-swift sweep of swallows and martins and even the laborious pursuit of predatory dragonflies with their bronze wings and bodies like rods of colored glass. Even as he spoke he saw a three-ouncer leap at a dapping Mayfly which was scooped out of his jaws by a passing swallow. Rainbow heard the tiny click as the Mayfly's body cracked against the bird's beak. A single wing of yellowy gossamer floated downward and settled upon the water. Under the shelving banks to right and left, where the fly, discarding its nymph and still too damp for its virgin flight, drifted downstream, a dozen heavy trout were feeding thoughtfully and selectively.

"If only some angler would catch one of them, I might slip in and occupy the place before it gets known there's a vacancy."

But this uncharitable hope was not fulfilled, and with another whisk of his tail he propelled himself into the unknown waters upstream. A couple of strands of rusty barbed wire, relic of the War, spanned the shallows from bank to bank. Passing beneath them he came to a narrow reach shaded by willows, to the first of which was nailed a board bearing the words, *Pêche Reservée*. He had passed out of the communal into private water—water running languidly over manes of emerald weed between clumps of alder, willow herb, tall crimson sorrel and masses of yellow iris. Ahead, like an apple-green rampart, rose the wooded heights of a forest; on either side were flat meadows of yellowing hay. Overhead, the vast expanse of blue June sky was tufted with rambling clouds. "My scales!" said Rainbow. "Here's water!"

But it was vain to expect any of the best places in such a reach would be vacant, and to avoid a recurrence of his unhappy encounter earlier in the morning, Rainbow continued his journey until he came to a spot where the river took one of those unaccountable right-angle bends which result in a pool, shallow on the one side, but slanting into deeps on the other. Above it was a water break, a swirl, smoothing, as it reached the pool, into a sleek, swift run, with an eddy which bore all the lighter floating things of the river over the calm surface of the little backwater, sheltered from above by a high shelving bank and a tangle of bramble and herb. Here in this backwater the twig, the broken reed, the leaf, the cork, the fly floated in suspended activity for a few instants until drawn back by invisible magnetism to the main current.

Rainbow paused in admiration. At the tail of the pool two sound fish were rising with regularity, but in the backwater beyond the eddy the surface was still and unbroken. Watching open-eyed, Rainbow saw not one but a dozen Mayflies, fat, juicy and damp from the nymph, drift in, pause and be carried away untouched. It was beyond the bounds of possibility that such a place could be vacant, but there was the evidence of his eyes to prove it; and nothing if not a trier, Rainbow darted across the stream and parked himself six inches below the water to await events.

It so happened that at the time of his arrival the hatch of fly was temporarily suspended, which gave Rainbow leisure to make a survey of his new abode. Beyond the eddy was a submerged snag—the branch of an apple tree borne there by heavy rains, water-logged, anchored and intricate—an excellent place to break an angler's line. The river bank on his right was riddled under water with old rat holes, than which there is no better sanctuary. Below him and to the left was a dense bed of weeds brushed flat by the flow of the stream.

"If it comes to the worst," said Rainbow, "a smart fish could do a get-away here with very little ingenuity, even from a cannibalistic old hen like—hullo!"

The exclamation was excited by the apparition of a gauzy shadow on the water, which is what a Mayfly seen from below looks like. Resisting a vulgar inclination to leap at it with the violence of a youngster, Rain-bow backed into the correct position which would allow the stream to present the morsel, so to speak, upon a tray. Which it did—and scarcely a dimple on the surface to tell what had happened.

"Very nicely taken, if you will accept the praise of a complete stran-ger," said a low, soft voice, one inch behind his line of sight.

Without turning to see by whom he had been addressed, Rainbow flicked a yard upstream and came back with the current four feet away. In the spot he had occupied an instant before lay a great old trout of the most benign aspect, who could not have weighed less than four pounds.

"I beg your pardon," said Rainbow, "but I had no idea that anyone—that is, I just dropped in *en passant,* and, finding an empty house, I made so bold—"

"There is no occasion to apologize," said Old Trout seductively. "I did not come up from the bottom as early today as is my usual habit at this season. Yesterday's hatch was singularly bountiful and it is possible I did myself too liberally."

"Yes, but a gentleman of your weight and seniority can hardly fail to be offended at finding—"

"Not at all," Old Trout broke in. "I perceive you are a well-conducted fish who does not advertise his appetite in a loud and splashing fashion."

Overcome by the charm of Old Trout's manner and address, Rainbow reduced the distance separating them to a matter of inches.

"Then you do not want me to go?" he asked.

"On the contrary, dear young sir, stay by all means and take the rise. You are, I perceive, of the rainbow or, as they say here in France, of the *Arc en ciel* family. As a youngster I had the impression that I should turn out a rainbow, but events proved it was no more than the bloom, the natural sheen of youth."

"To speak the truth, sir," said Rainbow, "unless you had told me to the contrary, I would surely have thought you one of us."

Old Trout shook his tail. "You are wrong," he said. "I am from Dulverton, an English trout farm on the Exe, of which you will have heard. You are doubtless surprised to find an English fish in French waters."

"I am indeed," Rainbow replied, sucking in a passing Mayfly with such excellent good manners that it was hard to believe he was feeding. "Then you, sir," he added, "must know all about the habits of men."

"I may justly admit that I do," Old Trout agreed. "Apart from being hand-reared, I have in my twelve years of life studied the species in moods of activity, passivity, duplicity, and violence."

Rainbow remarked that such must doubtless have proved of invaluable service. It did not, however, explain the mystery of his presence on a French river.

"For, sir," he added, "Dulverton, as once I heard when enjoying 'A Chat about Rivers' delivered by a much traveled sea trout, is situated in the West of England, and without crossing the Channel I am unable to explain how you arrived here. Had you belonged to the salmon family, with which, sir, it is evident you have no connection, the explanation would be simple, but in the circumstances it baffles my understanding."

Old Trout waved one of his fins airily. "Yet cross the Channel I certainly did," said he, "and at a period in history which I venture to state will not readily be forgotten. It was during the War, my dear young friend, and I was brought in a can, in company with a hundred yearlings, to this river, or rather the upper reaches of this river, by a young officer who wished to further an entente between English and French fish even as the War was doing with the mankind of these two nations."

Old Trout sighed a couple of bubbles and arched his body this way and that.

"There was a gentleman and sportsman," he said. "A man who was acquainted with our people as I dare to say very few are acquainted. Had it ever been my lot to fall victim to a lover of the rod, I could have done so without regret to his. If you will take a look at my tail, you will observe that the letter *W* is perforated on the upper side. He presented me with this distinguishing mark before committing me, with his blessing, to the water."

"I have seldom seen a tail more becomingly decorated," said Rainbow. "But what happened to your benefactor?"

Old Trout's expression became infinitely sad. "If I could answer that," said he, "I were indeed a happy trout. For many weeks after he put me into the river I used to watch him in what little spare time he was able to obtain, casting a dry fly with the most exquisite precision and likeness to nature in all the likely pools and runs and eddies near his battery position. Oh, minnows! It was a pleasure to watch that man, even as it was his pleasure to watch us. His bravery too! I call to mind a dozen times when he fished unmoved and unstartled while bullets from machine guns were pecking at the waters like herons and thudding into the mud banks upon which he stood."

"An angler!" remarked Rainbow. "It would be no lie to say I like him the less on that account."

Old Trout became unexpectedly stern.

"Why so?" he retorted severely. "Have I not said he was also a gentleman and a sportsman? My officer was neither a pot hunter nor a beast of prey. He was a purist—a man who took delight in pitting his knowledge of nature against the subtlest and most suspicious intellectual forces of the wild. Are you so young as not yet to have learned the exquisite enjoyment of escaping disaster and avoiding error by the exercise of personal ingenuity? Pray, do not reply, for I would hate to think so hard a thing of any trout. We, as a race, exist by virtue of our brilliant intellectuality and hypersensitive selectivity. In waters where there are no pike and only an occasional otter, but for the machinations of men, where should we turn to school our wits? Danger is our mainstay, for I tell you, Rainbow, that trout are composed of two senses—appetite, which makes of us fools, and suspicion, which teaches us to be wise."

Greatly chastened not alone by what Old Trout had said but by the forensic quality of his speech, Rainbow rose short and put a promising Mayfly on the wing.

"I am glad to observe," said Old Trout, "that you are not without conscience."

"To tell the truth, sir," Rainbow replied apologetically, "my nerve this morning has been rudely shaken, but for which I should not have shown such want of good sportsmanship."

And with becoming brevity he told the tale of his eviction from the pool downstream. Old Trout listened gravely, only once moving, and that to absorb a small blue dun, an insect which he keenly relished.

"A regrettable affair," he admitted, "but as I have often observed, women, who are the gentlest creatures under water in adversity, are a thought lacking in moderation in times of abundance. They are apt to snatch."

"But for a turn of speed she would certainly have snatched me," said Rainbow.

"Very shocking," said Old Trout. "Cannibals are disgusting. They destroy the social amenities of the river. We fish have but little family life and should therefore aim to cultivate a freemasonry of good fellowship among ourselves. For my part, I am happy to line up with other well-conducted trout and content myself with what happens along my own particular drift. Pardon me!" he added, breasting Rainbow to one side. "I invited you to take the rise of Mayfly, but I must ask you to leave the duns alone." Then, fearing this remark might be construed to reflect adversely upon his hospitality, he proceeded: "I have a reason which I will explain later. For the moment we are discussing the circumstances that led to my presence in this river."

"To be sure—your officer. He never succeeded in deluding you with his skill?"

"That would have been impossible," said Old Trout, "for I had taken up a position under the far bank where he could only have reached me with a fly by wading in a part of the river which was in view of a German sniper."

"Wily!" Rainbow chuckled. "Cunning work, sir."

"Perhaps," Old Trout admitted, "although I have since reproached myself with cowardice. However, I was at the time a very small fish and a certain amount of nervousness is forgivable in the young."

At this gracious acknowledgment the rose-colored hue in Rainbow's rainbow increased noticeably—in short, he blushed.

"From where I lay," Old Trout went on, "I was able to observe the maneuvers of my officer and greatly profit thereby."

"But excuse me, sir," said Rainbow, "I have heard it said that an angler of the first class is invisible from the river."

"He is invisible to the fish he is trying to catch," Old Trout admitted, "but it must be obvious that he is not invisible to the fish who lie beside or below him. I would also remind you that during the War every tree, every scrap of vegetation, and every vestige of natural cover had been torn up, trampled down, razed. The river banks were as smooth as the top of your head. Even the buttercup, that very humorous flower that tangles up the back cast of so many industrious anglers, was absent. Those who fished on the Western Front had little help from nature."

Young Rainbow sighed, for, only a few days before, his tongue had been badly scratched by an artificial alder which had every appearance of reality.

"It would seem," he said, "that this war had its merits."

"My young friend," said Old Trout, "you never made a greater mistake. A desire on the part of our soldiery to vary a monotonous diet of bully beef and biscuit often drove them to resort to villainous methods of assault against our kind."

"Nets?" gasped Rainbow in horror.

"Worse than nets—bombs," Old Trout replied. "A small oval black thing called a Mills bomb, which the shameless fellows flung into deep pools."

"But surely the chances of being hit by such a—"

"You reveal a pathetic ignorance," said Old Trout. "There is no question of being hit. The wretched machine exploded under water and burst our people's insides or stunned us so that we floated dead to the surface. I well remember my officer coming upon such a group of marauders one evening—yes, and laying about him with his fists in defiance of King's

Regulations and the Manual of Military Law. Two of them he seized by the collar and the pants and flung into the river. Spinning minnows, that was a sight worth seeing! 'You low swine,' I heard him say; 'you trash, you muck! Isn't there enough carnage without this sort of thing?' Afterward he sat on the bank with the two dripping men and talked to them for their souls' sake.

"'Look ahead, boys. Ask yourselves what are we fighting for? Decent homes to live in at peace with one another, fields to till and forests and rivers to give us a day's sport and fun. It's our rotten job to massacre each other, but, by gosh, don't let's massacre the harmless rest of nature as well. At least, let's give 'em a running chance. Boys, in the years ahead, when all the mess is cleared up, I look forward to coming back to this old spot, when there is alder growing by the banks, and willow herb and tall reeds and the drone of insects instead of the rumble of those guns. I don't want to come back to a dead river that I helped to kill, but to a river ringed with rising fish—some of whom were old comrades of the War.' He went on to tell of us hundred Dulverton trout that he had marked with the letter *W*. 'Give 'em their chance,' he said, 'and in the years to come those beggars will reward us a hundred times over. They'll give us a finer thrill and put up a cleaner fight than old Jerry ever contrived.' Those were emotional times, and though you may be reluctant to believe me, one of those two very wet men dripped water from his eyes as well as his clothing.

"'Many's the 'appy afternoon I've 'ad with a roach pole on Brentford Canal,' he sniffed, 'though I've never yet tried m' hand against a trout.' 'You shall do it now,' said my officer, and during the half hour that was left of daylight that dripping soldier had his first lesson in the most delicate art in the world. I can see them now—the clumsy, wet fellow, and my officer timing him, timing him—'one and two, and one and two, and—' The action of my officer's wrist with its persuasive flick was the prettiest thing I have ever seen."

"Did he carry out his intention and come back after the War?" Rainbow asked.

"I shall never know," Old Trout replied. "I do not even know if he survived it. There was a great battle—a German drive. For hours they shelled the river front, and many falling short exploded in our midst with terrible results. My own bank was torn to shreds and our people suffered. How they suffered! About noon the infantry came over—hordes in field gray. There were pontoons, rope bridges and hand-to-hand fights on both banks and even in the stream itself."

"And your officer?"

"I saw him once, before the water was stamped dense into liquid mud and dyed by the blood of men. He was in the thick of it, unarmed, and a German officer called on him to surrender. For answer he struck him in the face with a light cane. Ah, that wrist action! Then a shell burst, smothering the water with clods of fallen earth and other things."

"Then you never knew?"

"I never knew, although that night I searched among the dead. Next day I went downstream, for the water in that place was polluted with death. The bottom of the pool in which I had my place was choked with strange and mangled tenants that were not good to look upon. We trout are a clean people that will not readily abide in dirty houses. I am a Dulverton trout, where the water is filtered by the hills and runs cool over stones."

"And you have stayed here ever since?"

Old Trout shrugged a fin. "I have moved with the times. Choosing a place according to the needs of my weight."

"And you have never been caught, sir, by any other angler?"

"Am I not here?" Old Trout answered with dignity.

"Oh, quite, sir. I had only thought, perhaps, as a younger fish enthusiasm might have resulted to your disadvantage, but that, nevertheless, you had been returned."

"Returned! Returned!" echoed Old Trout. "Returned to the frying pan! Where on earth did you pick up that expression? We are in France, my young friend; we are not on the Test, the Itchen, or the Kennet. In this country it is not the practice of anglers to return anything, however miserable in size."

"But nowadays," Rainbow protested, "there are Englishmen and Americans on the river who show us more consideration."

"They may show you consideration," said Old Trout, "but I am of an importance that neither asks for nor expects it. Oblige me by being a little more discreet with your plurals. In the impossible event of my being deceived and caught, I should be introduced to a glass case with an appropriate background of rocks and weeds."

"But, sir, with respect, how can you be so confident of your unassailability?" Rainbow demanded, edging into position to accept an attractive Mayfly with yellow wings that was drifting downstream toward him.

"How?" Old Trout responded. "Because—" Then suddenly: "Leave it, you fool!"

Rainbow had just broken the surface when the warning came. The yellow-winged Mayfly was wrenched off the water with a wet squeak. A tangle of limp cast lapped itself round the upper branches of a willow far upstream and a raw voice exclaimed something venomous in French. By common consent the two fish went down.

"Well, really," expostulated Old Trout, "I hoped you were above that kind of thing! Nearly to fall victim to a downstream angler. It's a little too much! And think of the effect it will have on my prestige. Why, that incompetent fool will go about boasting that he rose me. Me!"

For some minutes Rainbow was too crestfallen even to apologize. At last:

"I am afraid," he said, "I was paying more heed to what you were saying than to my own conduct. I never expected to be fished from above. The fly was an uncommonly good imitation and it is a rare thing for a Frenchman to use Four-X gut."

"Rubbish," said Old Trout testily. "These are mere half-pound arguments. Four-X gut, when associated with a fourteen-stone shadow, should deceive nothing over two ounces. I saved your life, but it is all very provoking. If that is a sample of your general demeanor, it is improbable that you will ever reach a pound."

"At this season we are apt to be careless," Rainbow wailed. "And nowadays it is so hard, sir, to distinguish the artificial fly from the real."

"No one expects you to do so," was the answer, "but common prudence demands that you should pay some attention to the manner in which it is presented. A Mayfly does not hit the water with a splash, neither is it able to sustain itself in midstream against the current. Have you ever seen a natural insect leave a broadening wake of cutwater behind its tail? Never mind the fly, my dear boy, but watch the manner of its presentation. Failure to do that has cost many of our people their lives."

"You speak, sir," said Rainbow, a shade sulkily, "as though it were a disgrace for a trout ever to suffer defeat at the hands of an angler."

"Which indeed it is, save in exceptional circumstances," Old Trout answered. "I do not say that a perfect upstream cast from a well-concealed angler when the fly alights dry and cocked and dances at even speed with the current, may not deceive us to our fall. And I would be the last to say that a grasshopper skilfully dapped on the surface through the branches of an overhanging tree will not inevitably bring about our destruction. But I do most emphatically say that in such a spot as this, where the slightest defect in presentation is multiplied a hundredfold by the varying water speeds, a careless rise is unpardonable. There is only one spot—and that a matter of twelve yards downstream—from which a fly can be drifted over me with any semblance to nature. Even so, there is not one angler in a thousand who can make that cast with success, by reason of a willow which cramps the back cast and the manner on which these alders on our left sprawl across the pool."

Rainbow did not turn about to verify these statements because it is bad form for a trout to face downstream. He contented himself by replying, with a touch of acerbity:

"I should have thought, sir, with the feelings you expressed regarding sportsmanship, you would have found such a sanctuary too dull for your entertainment."

"Every remark you make serves to aggravate the impression of your ignorance," Old Trout replied. "Would you expect a trout of my intelligence to put myself in some place where I am exposed to the vulgar assaults of every amateur upon the bank? Of the green boy who lashes the water into foam, of the purblind peasant who slings his fly at me with a clod of earth or a tail of weed attached to the hook? In this place I invite attention from none but the best people—the expert, the purist."

"I understood you to say that there were none such in these parts," grumbled Rainbow.

"There are none who have succeeded in deceiving me," was the answer. "As a fact, for the last few days I have been vastly entranced by an angler who, by any standard, is deserving of praise. His presentation is flawless and the only fault I can detect in him is a tendency to overlook piscine psychology. He will be with us in a few minutes, since he knows it is my habit to lunch at noon."

"Pardon the interruption," said Rainbow, "but there is a gallant hatch of fly going down. I can hear your two neighbors at the tail of the pool rising steadily."

Old Trout assumed an indulgent air. "We will go up if you wish," said he, "but you will be well advised to observe my counsel before taking the rise, because if my angler keeps his appointment you will most assuredly be *meuniered* before nightfall."

At this unpleasant prophecy Rainbow shivered. "Let us keep to weed," he suggested.

But Old Trout only laughed, so that bubbles from the river bed rose and burst upon the surface.

"Courage," said he; "it will be an opportunity for you to learn the finer points of the game. If you are nervous, lie nearer to the bank. The natural fly does not drift there so abundantly, but you will be secure from the artificial. Presently I will treat you to an exhibition of playing with death you will not fail to appreciate." He broke off and pointed with his eyes. "Over you and to the left."

Rainbow made a neat double rise and drifted back into line. "Very mellow," he said—"very mellow and choice. Never tasted better. May I ask, sir, what you meant by piscine psychology?"

"I imply that my angler does not appreciate the subtle possibilities of our intellect. Now, my officer concerned himself as vitally with what we were thinking as with what we were feeding upon. This fellow, secure in the knowledge that his presentation is well-nigh perfect, is content to offer me the same variety of flies day after day, irrespective of the fact that I have learned them all by heart. I have, however, adopted the practice of rising every now and then to encourage him."

"Rising? At an artificial fly? I never heard such temerity in all my life," gasped Rainbow.

Old Trout moved his body luxuriously. "I should have said, appearing to rise," he amended. "You may have noticed that I have exhibited a predilection for small duns in preference to the larger *Ephemeridæ*. My procedure is as follows: I wait until a natural dun and his artificial Mayfly are drifting downstream with the smallest possible distance separating them. Then I rise and take the dun. Assuming I have risen to him, he strikes, misses, and is at once greatly flattered and greatly provoked. By this device I sometimes occupy his attention for over an hour and thus render a substantial service to others of my kind who would certainly have fallen victim to his skill."

"The river is greatly in your debt, sir," said Young Rainbow, with deliberate satire.

He knew by experience that fish as well as anglers are notorious liars, but the exploit his host recounted was a trifle too strong. Taking a sidelong glance, he was surprised to see that Old Trout did not appear to have appreciated the subtle ridicule of his remark. The long, lithe body had become almost rigid and the great round eyes were focused upon the surface with an expression of fixed concentration.

Looking up Rainbow saw a small white-winged Mayfly with red legs and a body the color of straw swing out from the main stream and describe a slow circle over the calm surface above Old Trout's head. Scarcely an inch away a tiny blue dun, its wings folded as closely as the pages of a book, floated attendant. An upward rush, a sucking kerr-rop, and when the broken water had calmed, the dun had disappeared and the Mayfly was dancing away downstream.

"Well," said Old Trout, "how's that, my youthful skeptic? Pretty work, eh?"

"I saw nothing in it," was the impertinent reply. "There is not a trout on the river who could not have done likewise."

"Even when one of those two flies was artificial?" Old Trout queried tolerantly.

"But neither of them was artificial," Rainbow retorted. "Had it been so the angler would have struck. They always do."

"Of course he struck," Old Trout replied.

"But he didn't," Rainbow protested. "I saw the Mayfly go down with the current."

"My poor fish!" Old Trout replied. "Do you presume to suggest that I am unable to distinguish an artificial from a natural fly? Are you so blind that you failed to see the prismatic colors in the water from the paraffin in which the fly had been dipped? Here you are! Here it is again!"

Once more the white-winged insect drifted across the backwater, but this time there was no attendant dun.

"If that's a fake I'll eat my tail," said Rainbow.

"If you question my judgment," Old Trout answered, "you are at liberty to rise. I dare say, in spite of a shortage of brain, that you would eat comparatively well."

But Rainbow, in common with his kind, was not disposed to take chances.

"We may expect two or three more casts from this fly and then he will change it for a bigger. It is the same program every day without variation. How differently my officer would have acted. By now he would have discovered my little joke and turned the tables against me. Aye me, but some men will never learn! Your mental outfit, dear Rainbow, is singularly like a man's," he added. "It lacks elasticity."

Rainbow made no retort and was glad of his forbearance, for every word Old Trout had spoken was borne out by subsequent events. Four times the white-winged Mayfly described an arc over the backwater, but in the absence of duns Old Trout did not rise again. Then came a pause, during which, through a lull in the hatch, even the natural insect was absent from the river.

"He is changing his fly," said Old Trout, "but he will not float it until the hatch starts again. He is casting beautifully this morning and I hope circumstances will permit me to give him another rise."

"But suppose," said Rainbow breathlessly, "you played this game once too often and were foul hooked as a result?"

Old Trout expanded his gills broadly. "Why, then," he replied, "I should break him. Once round a limb of that submerged apple bough and the thing would be done. I should never allow myself to be caught and no angler could gather up the slack and haul me into midstream in time to prevent me reaching the bough. Stand by."

The shadow of a large, dark Mayfly floated cockily over the backwater and had almost returned to the main stream when a small iron-blue dun settled like a puff of thistledown in its wake.

The two insects were a foot nearer the fast water than the spot where Old Trout was accustomed to take the rise. But for the presence of a spectator, it is doubtful whether he would have done so, but Young Rainbow's want of appreciation had excited his vanity, and with a rolling swoop he swallowed the dun and bore it downward.

And then an amazing thing happened. Instead of drifting back to his place as was expected, Old Trout's head was jerked sideways by an invisible force. A thin translucent thread upcut the water's surface and tightened irresistibly. A second later Old Trout was fighting, fighting, fighting to reach the submerged apple bough with the full weight of the running water and the full strength of the finest Japanese gut strained against him.

Watching, wide-eyed and aghast, from one of the underwater rat holes into which he had hastily withdrawn, Rainbow saw the figure of a man rise out of a bed of irises downstream and scramble upon the bank. In his right hand, with the wrist well back, he held a light split-cane rod whose upper joint was curved to a half-circle. The man's left hand was detaching a collapsible landing net from the ring of his belt. Every attitude and movement was expressive of perfectly organized activity. His mouth was shut as tightly as a steel trap, but a light of happy excitement danced in his eyes.

"No, you don't, my fellar," Rainbow heard him say. "No, you don't. I knew all about that apple bough before ever I put a fly over your pool. And the weed bed on the right," he added, as Old Trout made a sudden swerve half down and half across stream.

Tucking the net under his arm, the man whipped up the slack with a lightning-like action. The maneuver cost Old Trout dear, for when, despairing of reaching the weed and burrowing into it, he tried to regain his old position, he found himself six feet farther away from the apple bough than when the battle began.

Instinctively Old Trout knew it was useless to dash downstream, for a man who could take up slack with the speed his adversary had shown would profit by the expedient to come more quickly to terms with him. Besides, lower down there was broken water to knock the breath out of his lungs. Even where he lay straining and slugging this way and that, the water was pouring so fast into his open mouth as nearly to drown him. His only chance of effecting a smash was by a series of jumps, followed by quick dives. Once before, although he had not confessed it to Rainbow, Old Trout had saved his life by resorting to this expedient. It takes the strain off the line and returns it so quickly that even the finest gut is apt to sunder.

Meanwhile the man was slowly approaching, winding up as he came. Old Trout, boring in the depths, could hear the click of the check reel with increasing distinctness. Looking up, he saw that the cast was almost vertical above his head, which meant that the moment to make the attempt was at hand. The tension was appalling, for ever since the fight began his adversary had given him the butt unremittingly. Aware of his own weight and power, Old Trout was amazed that any tackle could stand the strain.

"Now's my time," he thought, and jumped.

It was no ordinary jump, but an aerial rush three feet out of the water, with a twist at its apex and a cutting lash of the tail designed to break the cast. But his adversary was no ordinary angler, and at the first hint of what was happening he dropped the point of the rod flush with the surface.

Once and once more Old Trout flung himself into the air, but after each attempt he found himself with diminishing strength and with less line to play with.

"It looks to me," said Rainbow mournfully, "as if my unhappy host

will lose this battle and finish up in that glass case to which he was referring a few minutes ago." And greatly affected, he burrowed his nose
in the mud and wondered, in the event of this dismal prophecy coming
true, whether he would be able to take possession of the pool without
molestation.

In consequence of these reflections he failed to witness the last phase of
the battle, when, as will sometimes happen with big fish, all the fight
went out of Old Trout, and rolling wearily over and over, he abandoned
himself to the clinging embraces of the net. He never saw the big man
proudly carry Old Trout back into the hayfield, where, before proceeding to remove the fly, he sat down beside a shallow dike and lit a cigarette and smiled largely. Then, with an affectionate and professional touch,
he picked up Old Trout by the back of the neck, his forefinger and thumb
sunk firmly in the gills.

"You're a fine fellar," he said, extracting the fly, "a good sportsman and
a funny fish. You fooled me properly for three days, but I think you'll
own I outwitted you in the end."

Rummaging in his creel for a small rod of hard wood that he carried
for the purpose of administering the quietus, he became aware of something that arrested the action. Leaning forward, he stared with open eyes
at a tiny *W* perforated in the upper part of Old Trout's tail.

"Shades of the War! Dulverton!" he exclaimed. Then with a sudden
warmth: "Old chap, old chap, is it really you? This is red-letter stuff. If
you're not too far gone to take another lease of life, have it with me."

And with the tenderness of a woman, he slipped Old Trout into the
dike and in a tremble of excitement hurried off to the *auberge* where the
fishermen lodged, to tell a tale no one even pretended to believe.

For the best part of an hour Old Trout lay in the shallow waters of
the dike before slowly cruising back to his own place beneath the overhanging bank. The alarming experience through which he had passed
had made him a shade forgetful, and he was not prepared for the sight
of Young Rainbow rising steadily at the hatch of fly.

"Pardon me, but a little more to your right," he said, with heavy
courtesy.

"Diving otters!" cried Young Rainbow, leaping a foot clear of the
water. "You, sir! You!"

"And why not?" Old Trout replied. "Your memory must be short if
you have already forgotten that this is my place."

"Yes, but—" Rainbow began and stopped.

"You are referring to that little circus of a few minutes ago," said Old
Trout. "Is it possible you failed to appreciate the significance of the affair?
I knew at once it was my dear officer when he dropped the artificial dun
behind the natural Mayfly. In the circumstances I could hardly do less
than accept his invitation. Nothing is more delightful than a reunion of

comrades of the war." He paused and added: "We had a charming talk, he and I, and I do not know which of us was the more affected. It is a tragedy that such friendship and such intellect as we share cannot exist in a common element."

And so great was his emotion that Old Trout dived and buried his head in the weeds. Whereby Rainbow did uncommonly well during the midday hatch.

You Can't Do That

By JOHN P. MARQUAND

SINCE the year 1806 a cloak of red-and-yellow feathers has hung in the hall-way of the March house on the Ridge, with a helmet made from the same plumage suspended above it. These two articles have always held the same position on the wall, except for such times as they have been put away in camphor to protect them from the moths. The cloak was brought there by John March and indicates very accurately the first venture of the March ships in the fur-and-sandalwood trade with China. It was hung there by John March when he returned as supercargo on the brig *Polly,* Moses March, owner, and Elihu Griggs, master. A single glance at that cloak in the shady, spacious hallway of that square Federalist house is startling to anyone who is even remotely familiar with the curiosities of the South Seas.

It hangs there, an alien object, and yet, through association, somehow strangely suitable to a house like the old March house in a New England seaport town. Granted that its presence there is known to many scholars, familiarity cannot avert a shock of surprise at a sight of that vivid garment, for it is one of the most beautiful objects ever conceived by the mind or executed by the hand of man. It is strange, too, to realize that if that cloak and the helmet above it were sold today, their price would probably equal the March profits in their precarious trade of another century. It is a long, fine cloak—and the Marches have always been careful of everything they have laid their hands on—one of the best of the hundred-and-some-odd feather garments which are known to be extant today, and there will never be another made. The o-o which supplied those yellow feathers, only one beneath each wing, a shy bird which once fluttered through the crimson-blossomed ohia and the tree-fern forest of the Hawaiian mountains, is virtually extinct, and the bird that wore the red plumage is in hardly a better case. He is vanishing from the face of this earth like the genial race whose ancestors collected and attached those feathers to their delicate base of fiber netting in a manner so admired by Captain Cook. Granted that the labor which went into the making of that garment is beyond all accurate calculation, the result was worth it. The reds and yellows are nearly as

Originally published in the *Saturday Evening Post.* Copyright 1935 by The Curtis Publishing Company. Reprinted by permission of the author.

vivid as when the coat was new. They glisten there in the hallway, jewel-like, with a depth of luster and lacy velvet texture that is more vital than inanimate. On an evening when the lights are lit, John March's cloak glows like flame and there is an element of awe in its splendor.

This is not odd, for it was intended to indicate greatness. The red lozenge pattern upon the yellow marks it as belonging not alone to one of the *alii* but to a Hawaiian chief of a royal lineage that was very near to kingship. Its size and the amount of yellow is a sufficient indication of its former owner's greatness. If the shadow of a commoner were to touch the shadow of the man who wore it, that commoner would suffer death, for the man who wore it was sublimated in the complicated feudal ritual of his islands into a being more than human. The feather kahili was carried behind him; an attendant bore his calabash of koa wood to preserve his spittle, his nail parings, and his fallen hair, so that they might not fall into the hands of enemies whose kahunas, or witch doctors, might use them in fatal incantations. When the man who wore that cloak walked abroad, the populace assumed a prone position on pain of death. Some trace of the majesty of its first owner's presence still seems to linger about that feather cloak, incongruously, in a New England town.

The cloak was owned by the chieftain Kualai, as his name is spelled, probably incorrectly, in the March letter books and the log of the brig *Polly,* since there were no missionaries then to bring order to the Hawaiian phonetics—no missionaries, no mosquitoes, no red ants to kill the kou trees, no colds, and no disease. Kualai ruled his share of the Kona coast on what is now known as the Big Island, under the protection of the great king Kamehameha in the days when John March was young. In Kualai's youth he had been one of the king's best warriors; in the war exercises he could evade six spears thrown at him simultaneously from varying directions; and he could trace his descent from one of the gods who had sailed with his attendants from the south.

Kualai gave his cloak and helmet to young John March when the *Polly* anchored in a bay on the Kona coast to exchange Yankee notions for sandalwood before proceeding to Canton. There is no doubt that John March valued the gift, for it is mentioned in his will. The clause reads:

"Item, the Feather Cloak that was given me by my friend Kualai on my first voyage to the Sandwich Islands, and the feather hat that goes with it, I leave to my daughter, Polly March, and I ask her to guard it carefully."

John March sailed other seas before he died and brought back other curious things, but there is every reason why the cloak should have had a value to him which was more than intrinsic; and his descendants have never sold that cloak because of the reason why it was given him, a reason that is closely connected with honor and integrity. John March was a shrewd trader, but he was an honest man.

In the New England harbor town which was the home port for the

March ships, a voyage around the world was not an unusual matter when John March was young. As long as John March could remember, his town had been a port of travelers, although a part of it was cast in the narrow mold of puritanical tradition. When John March was young, no music was allowed in the white church with the rooster on its spire where merchants and clerks and shipwrights and returned mariners listened for three hours each Sunday to discourses on original sin. Not even the note of a pipe was allowed, to indicate the pitch for the singing of the psalms, because such a concession was considered an encouragement to the idolatrous errors of papacy. Yet in such surroundings of a Sunday one could see from the square box of the March pew a distinctly cosmopolitan congregation, for the world across the seas was closer to the town in those days than it has ever been since. Nearly every man and boy and most of the women in the pews and the Reverend Thomas himself, who thundered forth his nasal sermon while the sands ran from his hourglass on the pulpit, knew their geography as well as they knew the intricacies of their catechism. They could talk familiarly of the Baltic ports and of St. Eustatius and St. Kitts. There were plenty who knew the ivory factories and the slave pens on the Grain Coast and the anchorages along Fernando Po. There were plenty who had seen the sand upon the lead from soundings off Madagascar. The weather off Cape Horn was common talk. A restless, burning energy that made the town a lively place, except on Saturday nights and Sunday, had driven others to the factories at Canton. The townspeople were familiar with nearly every world port where money could be gained, for the town lived from shipping. One had to go, of necessity, a long way to make money then, what with European wars and privateers and orders in council and blockades. It was a time for gambling with lives and ships, a time of huge losses and huge gains, and no one could judge which until the ships came in.

It seemed hardly more than a piece of everyday business to John March when his father called him into the square parlor of the March house on the Ridge. It was an evening in April; a bright, fresh fire was burning in the parlor, and the candles were lighted on the mahogany table in the center of the room. Moses March and a man whom John March had never seen before were seated somewhat stiffly by the table with a punch bowl between them. When John March saw the punch, he knew that they were discussing important business, for his father, particularly in his later years, was abstemious with liquor. Moses March had not changed much since John March could remember him. His brown hair, done in a queue, was heavily streaked with gray, and the shrewd lines around his eyes and mouth were deeper and more pronounced. There was an added stoop to his lanky shoulders, but his eyes were as bright as ever and his voice was vibrant, without any quaver of age.

"John," said Moses March, nodding at his guest, "this here is Captain

Griggs from Boston. Captain Griggs, he's been sailing for the Perkinses in the fur trade."

In many ways it seemed to John March that Captain Griggs was a younger replica of his father. The captain had the same bony facial contours and the same slouch to his shoulders. When he spoke he had the same flat voice, but his eyes were different—more mobile and less steady. The captain raised a hand before his tight-lipped mouth and coughed, then he rose from his chair with a creaking of his joints, a tall, somber man who might have been a deacon in a church. His eyes met John's and looked away toward some invisible object on the floor, then darted back and looked away again.

"Pleased to meet you," he said. . . . "I compliment you, Mr. March; he's handy looking, that's a fact."

"He's kind of peaked," said Moses March, "but John here's almighty quick at figures."

There was a silence. Captain Griggs ladled himself a fresh tumbler of punch, drank it at a gulp, and said, "He needs to be. It pays to be sharp, don't it, Mr. March?"

Moses March smiled in faint embarrassment. He had never been able to acquire a manner with his captains, nor to stop undue familiarity.

"Yes," he said, "I guess so. . . . John, Captain Griggs is taking out the *Polly*. You're sailing with him, supercargo."

John March looked at Captain Griggs again. The captain was staring intently at a lemon peel in the bottom of his glass. The news was entirely unexpected.

"Where to, Father?" he asked.

"Where you haven't been, son," said Moses March, "but you've heard the talk, I guess. Up along the Northwest Coast for sea otter, trading with the savages, then to these new islands you've heard Enoch Mayo talk about, to put aboard sandalwood, then the whole cargo sold at Canton for tea. The *Polly*, she's sailing the end of the month. You'll start in working over the cargo tomorrow. Your mother, she'll get your things packed."

John March nodded without speaking, and he showed no emotion. It was not the first time that his father had surprised him, because it was one of his father's maxims never to talk about what he proposed to do until he was ready. His father was always reaching for something new; his mind was always working. Probably he had been pondering over the matter all winter, and now, as though he were speaking about arrangements for hauling firewood, he was making plans to send one of his vessels where a March ship had never gone before.

It was strange to think that while he sat there, a homely, uncouth man, his mind could reach around the world and back. His life had never seemed so plain or matter-of-fact. The order of the March house, each piece of furniture exactly in its place, had never seemed so perfect as when he spoke of that voyage. That literal order of the letter books and the columns in the ledger were all a part of the business. There was no expression of doubt, because they all knew by then that a ship could go wherever there was water.

Captain Griggs ladled himself another tumbler of punch and blew his nose on a long blue handkerchief which seemed to have imparted some of its own color to his nose. Not having been asked to sit down, John March stood examining his new captain, comparing him with other seafaring men whom he had met. The captain was evidently a heavy and competent drinker and no doubt a capable master, but behind his lantern jaws and his high, narrow forehead there were hidden convolutions of character beyond John March's grasp. He only knew that by the time the voyage ended he would know the captain like a book. At the present time all John March could do was to stand staring at the pictures of his own imagination, striving to conjure up the sights which he and Captain Griggs would see. Captain Griggs was staring at him moodily across the brim of his glass.

"He'll do. He'll fill out," he said. "He'll be aft with the mate and me, of course. Does he know navigation, sir?"

"Yes," said Moses March; "he ain't a fool, but I hadn't aimed to make him a sailor. He'll handle this business ashore when I get through."

Captain Griggs nodded in a melancholy way. "I hope he ain't squeamish," he said. "He'll see some rough sights, like as not. We have a saying on the coast: 'You hang your conscience on the Horn.' "

"Yes," said Moses March, "I've heard it, but you, Captain, I'd like for you to keep your conscience on your ship."

"God bless you, sir," Captain Griggs said quickly, "no owner's ever complained of me. I'm always in my owner's interest. It's just dealing with these here savages, I mean. They've killed crews on the coast and they're murdering thieves on the islands." He rose stiffly. "You'll be satisfied, Mr. March. You'll be pleased as punch with me. There ain't no tricks in the trade that I don't know thereabouts. Four four-pounders and a bow chaser will be enough, and the grapeshot and plenty of small arms, and thanking you, I'll pick my own mate, and now I'll be under way, and I'll wish you a very good evening, and you, mister." He nodded to John March.

When the captain was gone, Moses March called to John March again. "John," he said, "set down. You've been to the Baltic; you've been to the Indies; and I'd proposed keeping you ashore, but I want for you to learn this trade when it's still new." Moses March paused and rubbed his jaw. "I hear tell there's money in it, and we're going where there's money."

"Yes sir," said John March.

"It seems," his father continued, staring at the fire, "as how these savages put aboard furs, and these other savages put aboard sandalwood, for nothing more than notions and novelties in trading goods. Well, I got 'em for you; you and Griggs can get the rest. He'll try hard. He has his money and more than the usual prerequisites."

"Yes sir," said John March.

"And sandalwood and furs are worth a mint of money in Canton."

"Yes sir," said John March.

"You know about it, do you?"

"Yes sir," said John March; "I've heard 'em talking."

His father smiled. "That's right," he said; "listen to 'em talk, but keep your own mouth shut. Have you anything to say?"

John March thought a moment. He had a number of things to say, but he kept them to himself. "No," he said. "I can obey orders, I guess. You know what you're doing, I guess, Father."

Moses March stroked his chin slowly, and then he asked a sudden question: "How did you like Griggs?"

"He looks too sharp to me," John March said, "but I guess we'll get along."

"Yes," said Moses March, "he's sharp, but maybe that's all right. But mind you watch him, John. I'm sharp, but I guess I'm honest. Mind you watch him."

Even when he was three thousand miles away from town and farther than that by water, something of the town was always with him. The *Polly* was a part of the town because she had been built in the yards by the river, a good tight brig of two hundred and fifty tons. The crew was a part of the town, because most of the men before the mast had been born within its limits. The sense of the nearness of things he knew gave John March a certain peace when everything else was strange. The emptiness of the Pacific coast, the incredible size of its fir trees, the frowning menace of its mountains, would have oppressed him if it had not been for that sense of home. As it was, everyone stood together and behaved, in order to keep reputations intact when they got home.

John March was used to work. He was satisfactory to Captain Griggs, and he was treated well because he was the owner's son. Once they began bartering for furs off the Northwest Coast, there was no doubt that the captain knew his business, and John March admired in silence the way the captain worked. Martin Sprague, the mate, knew his business, too, in caring for the ship. The men were armed; there was a sharp lookout day and night. The four-pounders were loaded with grapeshot, and the matches were kept burning. Only a definite number of the painted dugout canoes of the Indians were allowed alongside, and only a certain number of savages were permitted on deck to trade. There were very few ships off the coast that year, so that the selection of pelts was particularly fine.

Sea-otter pelts came aboard in great quantity in exchange for powder, shot, nails, muskets, beads, and blankets. It was a pretty sight to see the captain read faces and weigh the desire to sell. He seemed to have an intuitive sense of when to bargain and when to buy immediately.

"If there's any trade goods left after the islands," he said, "we'll stand back here again and use 'em up. It's a pity to see this fine fur wasting here. I wish we had six ships."

John March could feel the excitement as small goods turned suddenly into a valuable cargo. It was better than any figuring in the counting-house to see the fur pelts come aboard and to estimate their probable value in a Chinese port.

"Yes sir," said Captain Griggs, "it seems a pity to haul off and leave this. We ought to buy the villages out and to the devil with the islands and the wood."

They were in the cabin at the time, the captain and Sprague, the mate, a heavy muscular man, and John March, a thin blond boy.

"Mr. Sprague," said the captain, "pass the rum. What do you think, mister? Shall we do all the trading here and simply water at the islands?"

Martin Sprague rubbed the palm of his left hand over the knuckles of his right. "I never seen trading so easy," he said. "Yes sir, I think I should."

Then John March spoke up; it was the first time on the voyage that he'd made a positive statement. "We can't," he said.

Captain Griggs set down his glass and scowled. "Young man," he said, "I'm surprised at you. You ought to know better. You do know better. You've behaved yourself fine up till now, my boy. You've done your duty, and more, and I shall be pleased to report favorably to your father if you continue, but there's two things for you to get inside your head. The first is, you were sent here to learn to trade. You don't know this business, and don't you forget it. The second is, I'm captain, and this brig goes where I tell it to. I'm sorry to be obliged to tell you straight."

John March did not shift his position at the table. He knew that he was young and that he was green. He had interrupted solely from a con-scientious sense inherited from his race. It had come over him that he was a representative of the March family and of the March cargo. Now that the eyes of the older men were upon him, he found himself stam-mering, because he was shy in those days, but his hesitation only made him the more determined to speak out.

"Captain," he said, "I understand what you say. This is your ship, of course, but you are under owner's orders, just as I am. A portion of these trade goods was allotted for furs and the rest for sandalwood. The owner's orders are to stop and trade at the Sandwich Islands. There may be more profit here, but we are to establish relations there. We may send out another ship."

Captain Griggs leaned half across the table. "Young man," he inquired, "are you insinuating I'm not looking after owner's interests? Because if you are, I will not tolerate it. I'm thinking of my owner all the time, and a sight better than you are, maybe. We'll make for the islands tomorrow, and there's an end to that, but if there's any trade goods left when we're through there, why, then, with your kind permission, we'll come back here. I hope that satisfies you."

"Yes," said John March, "it does, and I ask your pardon, Captain."

Mr. Sprague rose. "I must be up with the watch," he said, "if you'll excuse me, sir. . . . Will you come with me, Mr. March?"

It was a fine night on deck, clear, with bright stars and a faint, quivering circle of the northern lights. The night was cool, without a breath of wind. The ship, with her own small lights, was like an insignificant fragment of a distant world anchored there in space. The mate took out his pipe and tinderbox. There was a flash of spark as he expertly hit the flint against the steel, and then the tinder glowed.

"Johnny March," he said, "I've kind of got to like you. Now you listen to what I say. This kind of spark's all right, but not the kind that you were striking in the cabin. You leave the old man be. He's as good a master as there is, and he's honest with the owners, and that's all we have to care for. I've sailed with Griggs before. I don't need to tell you that a master's king aboard his ship, and you know it makes 'em queer. I've never seen a skipper yet who liked to be crossed. You better leave him be."

"Yes sir," said John March.

"And listen, Johnny," the mate said, "the islands are a fine place. You'll like the islands. The islands are like heaven, pretty near. The captain will take you ashore, of course, to make the bargain. You'll see plenty of funny sights, but keep your mouth shut, Johnny, except to say 'Yes sir,' to the captain. We've got a long way yet to go."

"Yes sir," said John March.

"That's right," said Sprague, "that's right. I like a tight-lipped boy."

It was said in the forecastle of the *Polly,* just as it was said aft, that Johnny March was taciturn. As a supercargo he had no fixed duties in working the ship, and few knew much about him except that he was March's son. They only saw him as a thin, brown-faced, gray-eyed boy with yellow hair who made no trouble or complaint. They did not know the impression which strange sights made upon him, because he was studiously silent on that voyage to the islands, hardly ever venturing a remark, only answering courteously when addressed. No one on the *Polly* knew—and perhaps it was just as well—that his thoughts were poetic, because there was no room for poetry on a Yankee trading brig.

The evening before they sighted land, he had a sense of the land's nearness. The banks of clouds off the port bow as the sun went down were pink and gold, and were more like land clouds than sea clouds. The *Polly* was moving in the steady breath of the trades, and the setting sun struck the bellying sails forward, making their colors soft and golden. The only sounds were the creaking of wood, the straining of ropes, and the splash of waves on the bow. He had seen many evenings like that one, but subtly this was different. There was a mystery in the warmth of the air, an intangible unreality in the cloud banks. Captain Griggs came and stood beside him, smelling strongly of rum.

"Mr. Sprague," he said, "you've got everything locked up, I hope. To-morrow we'll be overrun by black thieves and their women. Clew up the courses and continue under topsails. Set a watch up in the crosstree and keep an eye out for breakers. We must not get in too close tonight. . . . And, Mr. March—"

"Yes sir," said John.

"You and I will go ashore."

"Yes sir," said Johnny March, and then he cleared his throat: "How will we speak to them, sir?"

"You'll soon learn, boy," said Captain Griggs. "You've got a lot to learn. These islands have kings, or chiefs, and the chiefs will have some-one who can speak trading English. The sandalwood is up in the moun-tains. It will be the property of the king, or chief. We will agree to purchase so many piculs, and he'll send his people to cut it. The chief will come aboard to see our goods, and we will make a bargain for the cargo, payable when the wood is safe aboard, you understand. There's no need to make our crew work when the chief will make his people load it. The islanders are handy men on ships. We'll go to see the chief, and we'll make the chief a present. Break out that clock that strikes the hour, and two cutlasses. That will be enough, and maybe"—Captain Griggs paused and hesitated—"three yards of bright print calico; he ought to like it—paper's all they dress in."

"Yes sir," said Johnny March. "Did you say that they dressed in paper?"

The hard lines of the captain's face wrinkled into an indulgent smile.

"Young man," he said, "it's a fact they dress in paper, when they dress at all, which isn't often. The women, they pound it out of the bark of a tree. They have nothing else on the islands, or almost nothing. Time was when they'd sell a pig for three tenpenny nails, and their women sell their virtue for less than that, which isn't strange, because they have no morals. Why, their menfolk bring 'em right aboard for the time we stay. Will you come below for a glass of rum?"

"No, thank you, sir," said Johnny March. "I'll stay on deck—that is, if you don't mind."

The sun had dipped out of sight behind a bank of clouds, and then suddenly the light was gone. Without a prelude of dusk, the dark came over them like a warm black garment. It seemed only a second before that the sky had been red and gold. Then, in another second, the sky was a void of darkness, filled with the trade wind and with stars. He stood for a while listening to the wind singing through the ropes, and then he went below. It was still dark when John March was awakened by a long-drawn-out call and by Mr. Sprague's voice shouting, "Where away?" and he knew that they had come in sight of land. Once he was up on deck, the topsails were slatting sleepily, and off the starboard bow there was a glow in the sky like fire.

"We've hit it to a second, sir," the mate was saying to Captain Griggs. "Yonder's the volcano; we're in the lee of the mountains."

Captain Griggs was a shadow in the starlight. It was too dark to see his face, but his voice was satisfied. "A pretty piece of navigating," he said, "if I do say so, mister. There'll be an inshore breeze by dawn, and then we'll make the bay." He sniffed the air. "We can't be far from land," he said, "but there's no use heaving lead. It shelves off here as deep as hell. There'll be an inshore breeze with dawn."

"Is that a light yonder, sir?" asked Johnny March.

Near the horizon there was a twinkling, glimmering point.

"Your eyesight's good," the captain said. "Yes, that will be a fire. We're close to land."

The dawn came as suddenly as the dark, in a swift rush of light, as though a hand had snatched away a veil, and John March saw the land. It was a solemn sight to see land which seemed to have risen out of nowhere. Off the bows of the *Polly* was a mountain, black and green, that rose in a gradual slope up into snow and clouds. The coast was dark from volcanic rock which made ugly black gashes between green forests. Close to the water's edge there was a fringe of palms and beeches between black lava headlands. The sea was smooth and calm and streaked with violet; the air was as soft as the air of spring at home and was subtly laden with the smells of land. All the colors were soft in a faint, early-morning haze. The black rocks merged into reds and purples. The greens of the upland forest blended subtly from shades of silver to emerald, and Captain Griggs was right—a soft breeze was filling the sails, moving the *Polly* gently along the coast.

"That's where the sandalwood comes from," Mr. Sprague was saying, "up yonder in the mountains. The coast hereabouts is the favorite place of the kings. Do you see the stone walls and the yellow thatch of the houses of the villages? The chiefs own straight from the tops of the mountains to the sea. How do you like it, son?"

The question made John March tongue-tied. "I think it's very handsome, sir," he said, "a very pleasant island."

The *Polly* was moving under topsails into a small bay. It opened out before them, a smooth amphitheater of water, surrounded by high cliffs. "Yonder's where the kings are buried," the mate said. "They scrape the flesh off their bones and tie them up in paper cloth and put them there in caves with their canoes."

At the head of the bay John March could see a beach fringed with tall palm trees, the leaves of which moved idly in the breeze, and he could see the thatch of houses beneath them. There was a dark crowd of people on the beach, pushing canoes into the water, log dugouts, balanced by an outrigger and manned by naked paddlers. Captain Griggs was wearing clean line and a black broadcloth coat, although the day was hot.

"Mister," he said, "we'll anchor. Let go falls and clew up lower top-sails and order the stern boat cleared. You can allow the women aboard, Mr. Sprague."

By the time the anchor struck the water, the *Polly* was surrounded by canoes and the water was full of swimmers who were pulling themselves up the anchor chain, smiling and laughing; men and women as beautiful as statues, their straight dark hair glistening with the water. Captain Griggs stared at his visitors sourly from the quarter-deck.

"They've got the minds of children," he said. "The chief's man should be here. Look at those shameless hussies, will you? There's no decency on these islands. They don't care for decency; no, they don't care."

As Captain Griggs finished speaking, a native pushed his way through the crowd at the waist and walked aft; evidently a man of importance, because the crowd gave way respectfully. He wore a pair of sailor's castoff trousers, and his skin was lighter than the others'. His voice rose above the babel of strange words in English.

"Mr. Captain," he called out, "I am Kualai's man."

"Who's he?" asked Captain Griggs. "The chief?"

The other nodded, bobbing his head up and down, still smiling. "Yes," he said, "yes, yes. And he sends me because I speak English good. I've been a sailor on a Boston boat. I speak English very good. Kualai sends me to say *aloha*. He is glad to see you. He asks you will you trade for wood?"

"Yes," said Captain Griggs, "we're here for wood. What's your name?"

"Moku," said the native. "Billy Adams Moku. Kualai ask what name."

The captain nodded condescendingly. "Captain Griggs," he said, "brig *Polly*. Moses March, owner. We're carrying very fine calicoes, ironware, tinware, lead and copper, and even a few muskets. Has your chief got wood?"

Moku nodded. "The wood is coming down. Kualai, he will see you." He pointed to a laden canoe. "Kualai sends you food."

Captain Griggs looked at the canoe carefully as it drew alongside. "Very good," he said. "When will he see me?"

"Mister," said Moku. "He waits on the shore."

"Mister," the captain called, "have the stern boat lowered. Mr. March and I will go ashore, and, Mr. March, give that man a pocketknife and bring along the presents."

The dark sand of the beach at the head of the bay seemed insecure under John March's feet, since he had been so long on the water. In the sunshine like a warm June day at home, every sight and sound was new. The crowd of natives standing on the beach drew back from them shyly and smiled, but their tongues kept chattering busily; commenting, probably, on the way these strangers looked. The chief's man walked first, then Captain Griggs, nonchalant and cool, and then John March behind him. They walked along a path beneath a grove of coconut palms and beneath large broad-leafed trees such as he had never seen. They were threading their way through a settlement of houses made of dried grass, past small gardens inclosed between walls of black volcanic rock. His memory of that day always brought back living green against dark rock, and dark smiling faces and red hibiscus flowers. In his memory of the place a soft breeze was always blowing and there was always a strange dry rattle from the leaves of the coconut palms. There was a group of larger houses not far back from the beach which evidently belonged to a man of importance. Natives were busying themselves about a fire in a pit; women and children were staring from open doorways. There was an open pavilion near the center of this group of buildings, and the chief's man led them toward it. Seated in a Cantonese armchair under the pavilion was one of the largest men that John March had ever seen. He was middle-aged, and so corpulent that the chair seemed to creak beneath his weight. A single look at his face was enough to indicate that he was the ruler, Kualai, of whom the man had spoken. The face was set in benign lines that could only have come upon it through suave and complete authority. It was all that was necessary to indicate his rank, but he also had the exterior show of office. He was wearing a yellow-and-red cloak of feathers, dazzlingly bright, which fell below his waist, and an attendant stood behind him holding a large stick which bore a tuft of colored feathers on the end. Moku stopped dead still at the entrance of the pavilion, and the great man rose from his chair and stepped slowly forward, gracefully, in spite of his heavy paunch. It was plain that he had seen other white men and knew something of their manners, because he smiled graciously and held out his right hand. At the same time he spoke melodiously in a language that was all vowels, so that his words sounded like rippling water.

"What's he saying?" asked Captain Griggs.

"Kualai," Moku translated, "he say he's, oh, very glad to see you."

"Well, I guess we're glad to see him too," said Captain Griggs as he shook hands. Then John March saw that Kualai was looking at him.

"He wants to know," said Moku, "who is the other man?"

"Tell him he's the son of the man who owns the vessel," said Captain Griggs.

"He wants to know," said Moku, "is he a chief's son?"

"Tell him yes," said Captain Griggs.

"He would like," said Moku, "to feel his hair. He would like to know if it is real."

"Take off your hat," said Captain Griggs, "and let him feel your hair. Don't be afraid of him. He won't hurt you."

"All right," said Johnny March. He felt very much like a child as he walked toward Kualai, for the man, now that he was standing, must have been close to seven feet in height. His skin was glistening with coconut oil. He was stretching out his arm. He touched Johnny March's hair gently and then he pulled it softly. Johnny March looked up at him and smiled, and Kualai smiled back.

"Break out the presents," said Captain Griggs, "bow to him and put 'em on the ground."

Kualai's face lighted up at the sight of the clock when John March held it toward him. It was evident that he had never seen such a mechanism—a battered ship's chronometer whose useful days were over. He touched it gingerly and imitated its sound.

"Tick-tick," he said, and John March nodded and repeated after him, "Tick-tick." That interchange of words always seemed to him ridiculous, but somehow there was an exchange of thought with the words which made them friends.

"He asks you to stay and eat," said Moku. "He will come on the ship tomorrow and see the goods, and he asks the young man to stay with him until the trade is over, to sleep inside his house."

Captain Griggs muttered something beneath his breath, and then he said, "March, you'd better stay."

"Yes sir," said John March, "I'd be very glad to stay." He turned to Moku. "Tell him I'll be glad."

Then Moku spoke again: "Kualai says he will trade with the young man."

"All right," said Captain Griggs, "as long as I'm there too. And tell him"—Captain Griggs's eyes shifted toward the bay and back—"you tell him I want the wood measured on the beach and put aboard by his people. Tell him my men are tired." And then he drew a bottle of rum from his pocket and added plaintively: "Ain't we had enough of this? Let's everybody have a drink, and bring on the dancing girls."

Some half-perceptible change in Captain Griggs's voice made John March turn to watch him. The captain's face was bleak and impassive, but his eyes were shifting from point to point, from the chief to John March, then away to the matting on the ground, then to the houses of the settlement. John March knew him well enough by then to know that the captain was turning over in his mind some thought which he wished entirely to conceal.

"Ah," he said suddenly, "here comes some wood," and he nodded toward a path which led upward to the mountains.

A dozen men and women were staggering down the path in single file, each bearing a burden of long sticks, and John March knew from hearsay that these were the chief's people, who had been sent to the upland forests where the sandalwood grew. The chief called out an order, which Moku ran to obey, and a few moments later a pile of the sandalwood lay on the matting before his chair, a heap of sticks which varied in size from a few inches to a foot in diameter. The bark had been stripped off, leaving a heavy wood of deep yellow which verged on orange. Captain Griggs ripped out his clasp knife, whittled at the sticks, and sniffed the shavings.

"It ain't bad," he said; "in fact, it's prime."

He was right that the wood was fine, since sandalwood was plentiful in the islands then, when the trade was new, and John March did not suspect that he would live to see the time when hardly a stick would be left standing on the entire island group. Captain Griggs stood there, staring at the pile of wood, apparently lost in thought.

"Tell him we'll pay him well for it," he said, and his voice was soft and almost kindly, "once he lands it on the deck."

But all the while John March was sure that Captain Griggs was concealing some other thought.

It took nearly two weeks to collect the wood and measure it, a space of time which moved in a peculiar series of days and nights, but it was strange to John March how soon the life there grew familiar. Though he could hardly understand a word which was spoken, though nearly every sight and sound in those two weeks was new, he became aware immediately of certain human values. Kualai, in his way, was a cultivated man of gentle breeding, who had developed his own taste for the arts, and qualities of understanding which were the same on that isolated island as they were elsewhere. He would sit for hours of an evening watching interpretive dances and listening to his minstrels sing of the exploits of his ancestors. He had a good eye for patterns in the tapa cloth, and a nice skill in various games of chance, which he played daily with his choice companions, but, above all, he had a sense of hospitality. He lost no occasion to make John March feel politely that he was a welcome guest. He took him fishing in his war canoe; he took him to the caves and the lava rocks; he took him to watch the young men perform feats of strength; he was even careful that John March's privacy should not be disturbed unduly. When he came aboard the *Polly,* he kept John March beside him. He was greatly pleased with the calico and nails and lead and copper in the trading cargo, but he went through the intricacies of the bargain in a detached way, like a gentleman. In those days trading was

easy on the islands, before the chiefs were glutted with material possessions.

"He say he want you to be happy," Moku said the last time Kualai
came aboard; "he want you to come again."

"Tell him we're happy," said Captain Griggs. "He understands when
all the wood's aboard that we'll give out the goods."

Moku nodded. "He understands," he said; "he knows you're good men."

Captain Griggs coughed slightly. "I shall want Mr. March back with
me," he said, "tomorrow morning. . . . Mr. March, you come here; I
want to speak with you in the cabin."

It occurred to John March, when they were in the cabin, that it was
the first time since they had been on the islands that he and Captain
Griggs had been alone. Captain Griggs rubbed his long hands together
and poured himself a glass of rum.

"Young man," he said, "you've done fine. You've kept that old heathen
happy, and that's all we needed—to keep him happy—and now we're all
finished shipshape. We'll get the wood stowed tonight"—Captain Griggs
smiled happily—"and tomorrow they can come and take off their goods,
but I want you aboard first, understand?"

"Yes sir," said John March, "but there's one thing I don't see. I don't
see why you haven't put the goods ashore before this, sir."

Captain Griggs poured himself a second tumbler of rum.

"Young man," he said, "when you take a few more voyages you'll understand you can't trust natives. How do you know we'd get the wood if
we put the goods ashore?"

"Because Kualai's honest," John March said.

Captain Griggs looked thoughtfully at the ceiling. "Maybe," he said,
"and maybe not. Anyways, we've got the wood. You come aboard tomorrow." And Captain Griggs smiled genially, but even when he smiled,
John March had a suspicion that something had been left unsaid, that
there was some thought in the captain's mind of which he had not spoken.

Mr. Sprague came up to get him the next morning, carrying a bundle
of small presents and perspiring in the heat of the early sun.

"Say good-by to the chief," he said. "The captain's orders are to leave
right now. You're to stay aboard until we sail. The quarter boat's waiting
at the beach."

John March was sorry, now that it was time to go. He walked to Kualai
and held out his hand. "Thank you very much," he said, and the interpreter, Moku, gave him back the chief's answer:

"He say for you to come back soon."

The canoes were gathering about the *Polly* already, by the time he
reached the beach. He and Mr. Sprague sat in the stern sheets of the
quarter boat while two men rowed, helped by a light breeze offshore.

It was only when they were halfway out that John March was aware of something disturbing.

"Look," he said; "they're setting the lower topsails!"

"Yes," said Mr. Sprague shortly, "so they are. We've got a fair breeze, haven't we?"

"But it'll take a good six hours to put off those goods," said Johnny March.

Mr. Sprague put a heavy hand on his knee and smiled. "Don't you worry, boy," he said. "Captain Griggs will see about those goods."

They were beside the companion ladder by that time, and even John March was puzzled, but nothing more. He was not aware of Captain Griggs's idea until he was on the poop, then he saw that the tarpaulins were off the guns and that men were beside them with matches, and then he saw that the decks were clear and that the sandalwood and the trade goods were all back in the hold. Captain Griggs grinned at him.

"Safe and sound," he said. "You've done very well, Mr. March; your father will be very pleased, I think. . . . Mister, you can man the capstan now."

John March found himself stammering: "But what about the goods, Captain? We haven't put the goods ashore."

"No, boy," said Captain Griggs, "we ain't, and we ain't going to. What's the use when we've got the wood aboard? Those goods are going to go for skins."

Even then John March did not entirely understand him. "But you can't do that," he said. "We owe the chief the goods."

"Listen boy," said Captain Griggs, "this ain't like home. There're plenty of other chiefs, and plenty of other islands. Let 'em come and get the goods, and I'll blow 'em out of water. There ain't no law out here. Now you be quiet, boy."

For a moment John March found it impossible to speak. Now that the whole matter was completely clear, he knew that he should have suspected long ago what must have been in the back of the captain's mind. Captain Griggs proposed sheer robbery, but he would not have called it that. He would have called it a clever piece of business in a place where there was no law.

"You see," Captain Griggs was saying, "it isn't as though they were white people, Mr. March. More fools they, that's all."

Then John March found his voice. "Captain," he said, "this is a March ship. You don't leave until you've set those goods on shore. We don't do things that way, Captain. You can't—"

Captain Griggs turned toward him quickly.

"That'll be enough from you," he said. "Who says I can't? I'm trying to make a profit on this voyage. I can, and I will, and I'm taking full responsibility. If you don't like it, get below."

John March's tongue felt dry and parched as he tried to speak. Even in that short while a hundred things were happening. The fore-and-aft staysails and the lower topsails were set by then, and the call came from forward, "Hawser short!" A glance toward the beach was enough to show him that the islanders were aware of the captain's trick. Men were running toward the water. He could hear the beating of a drum. Men in canoes were gesticulating and shouting. Men with spears and clubs and slings were hurrying to the beach.

"Break out anchor, mister," shouted Captain Griggs, "and stand by them guns! Forward there, pass out the small arms! By God, we'll show 'em!"

"Captain," said John March suddenly. He knew there was only one thing to do as he spoke. "If you go, you'll leave me here. I'm going back ashore."

Captain Griggs looked at him and laughed. "They'll kill you back ashore," he said. "Look at 'em on the beach."

John March spoke with difficulty. "You and I are different sorts of men," he said. "You can either set those goods ashore or I'm going."

"May I inquire," said Captain Griggs, "how you're going to go? Keep your mouth shut, boy!"

In the haste of getting under way, the quarter boat was still drifting alongside, and the captain must have perceived John March's intention from his glance.

He made a lunge at John March, but John March broke away, and then he went on the bulwarks.

"Get ahold of that damned fool!" shouted Captain Griggs. "Lay ahold of him!"

Two of the crew ran toward him, and he jumped crashing into the quarter boat. "Get in there after him!" Captain Griggs was shouting. "Don't let him go!"

And then John March cut the painter, and the quarter boat was drifting from the side.

"You damned fool!" shouted Captain Griggs. "You hear my orders! Come back here or they'll kill you, March!"

Once the boat was drifting from the side, John March was amazed at himself. His anger and his lack of fear amazed him. He was standing amidships in the quarter boat, shouting back at Captain Griggs.

"I'd rather be killed ashore," he shouted. "than stay aboard with you!" Then he picked up the oars and began to row ashore, slowly, because the boat was heavy for a single man to handle.

"You hear me?" Captain Griggs was shouting. "Stay there and be damned to you!"

John March saw that the anchor was aweigh and the *Polly* was standing slowly out to the open sea. His back was to the beach as he pulled toward it, but he heard the shouting and the beating of the drums. It must have been his anger at Captain Griggs that did not make him afraid, or an assurance within himself that he was right and Captain Griggs was wrong. A glance astern of the quarter boat as he strained at the oars showed him the *Polly* standing out to sea, but he did not look over his shoulder toward the beach. He did not look until the bottom of the quarter boat grated on the sand, then he shipped his oars carefully and stepped ashore. He found himself surrounded by shouting men who waved their spears and their fists in his face, but somehow they were not so real to him as the reality which lay inside himself. He only realized later that a single gesture of fear might have meant his death, but then he was so involved in his own preoccupation and with the single desire which was in him that he walked calmly enough across the beach toward the palm trees and the thatched houses; the crowd in front of him gave way as he walked, and then followed on his heels. He was taking the path to Kualai's house, and the shouting around him died away as he drew near it.

Then he saw Kualai walking toward him in the feather cloak which he had worn the first day they had met, carrying a light throwing spear in his right hand. Kualai was shouting something to him—obviously a question which he could not understand—and Moku was standing near him.

"Tell Kualai," John March said, "that I come from honest people. Tell him that I have come here to stay until he is paid for his wood." He saw Kualai listening intently to his answer, and then Kualai raised his right arm and drove his spear into the earth.

"He says you are his son," Moku said. "He asks you: Will you please to shake his hand?"

The reaction from what he had done came over him when Kualai grasped his hand. He knew the harsh and accurate consequences of his action then, as the smells and sounds of that Polynesian village came over him like a wave. Captain Griggs had left him, and every vestige of home was gone. He was a stranger among savages, and he might be there forever, for anything he knew, yet even then he knew that he had done the only proper thing. Suddenly he found that he was homesick, because the chief was kind.

"Ask him if I can be alone," he said. "Tell him I want to be alone."

He was given a house of his own that night, next to where the chief slept. He was given a pile of woven mats for his bed and a piece of tapa cloth to cover him. He was given baked pig and sweet potatoes and the gray paste made from the taro root, called poi, for his evening meal, and mullet from Kualai's fishpond. He was as comfortable as he could have hoped to be that night. For a moment, when he was awakened early the next morning, he thought he was at home, until he saw the rafters and the thatch above him. Moku was standing near him in his ragged sailor breeches, and Kualai himself was bending his head, just entering the door.

"Wake up!" Moku was saying. "The ship is back!"

John March sat up on his bed of mats and rubbed his arm across his face. Although he spoke to Moku, his eyes were on Kualai.

"The ship?" he asked. "What ship?"

"Your ship," said Moku. "She come back, and now the captain, he unloads the goods."

John March stood up. He had no great capacity for showing emotion. "Ask Kualai if he is satisfied," he said.

Moku nodded. "He says, 'Yes, very much,'" he said, and Kualai nodded back. "He asks for you to stay a long time—always."

"Thank him, please," said John March, "but tell him it's my ship. Tell him I must go to see that the goods are right."

"Kualai," Moku answered, "says he will go with you to the beach."

Mr. Sprague had landed in the longboat by the time they had reached the shore, and the beach was already covered with bolts of calico and small goods and ironware and lead and copper. Mr. Sprague nodded to John March formally, as though nothing had happened. "The captain sends his compliments," he said, "and asks you to come aboard, so that he can resume the voyage." And then Sprague grinned and added, "It's damned lucky for you, John March, that you're the owner's son."

John March looked at the goods upon the shore. "You can thank the captain for me for coming back," he answered. "You can tell him that I hope we both can forget what has happened, but the complete consignment is not landed yet. I'll stay here until the list is checked."

"You're an accurate man," said Sprague.

John March nodded. "I've been taught to be," he said, and he stayed there on the beach until every item was verified. Then he turned to Kualai and his interpreter.

"Tell the chief," he said, "that I believe that everything is right. Ask his pardon for the delay, but tell him our house will make any mistakes correct. Thank him, and tell him that I am going."

Moku spoke quickly in the musical language of the islands while Kualai stood, looking first at John March and then at the ship that brought him. After Kualai had listened, he stood silently for a moment. Then he smiled and spoke swiftly. He raised a hand and took off his feather helmet, and one of his men very carefully removed his feather cloak from his shoulders.

"He says there will always be wood for you," said Moku. "He asks you to take his coat."

Mr. Morgan

By JAMES A. MICHENER

WHEN I was a boy we lived in this manner. At six each morning the church bell summoned us to prayer and wardens stood by the entrance checking our names. If a man were missing other wardens were sent running to find him, and if a man and girl were both missing we trembled until they were found, for we knew what the penalty would be if they had been together.

After church we were allowed to go about our duties, except that wardens could summon us to jail at any time if we had broken rules. One day a week we had to work on church land making copra or we fished for pearl shell in the lagoon, turning over all we found to the pastor. We had also to keep careful records of any money we made from schooners, for of this the wardens collected one share in ten, as the Bible directs.

At sunset the bell rang again, and we gathered for prayer. After that we could eat when we wished, but in the evening began the most troublesome of our rules. All young men and all unmarried girls had to carry lighted lanterns wherever they went. This was to help the wardens keep track of what was happening on the island, and if two lanterns were seen heading toward the bush in back of Matareva, the wardens ran there to see that no indecencies took place. Of course, some young men were smart enough to put out their lights and wait for girls, but if they were caught the wardens beat them. The girl was further humiliated next morning in church, after which both the offenders were sent to jail.

At nine each night the church bell rang again and everyone had to be indoors. Sometimes it was very beautiful at that hour. The moon would shine down upon the lagoon and through the village of Matareva pale lights would move mysteriously from house to house. Those were the wardens, checking up to see that all families were behaving themselves properly. The wardens had a right to enter any house at any time for an accounting of what each person inside had been doing for the past day, but on week nights the wardens did not abuse this privilege, unless one of them became attracted to some girl, and then he would break into her house almost every night, whether she wished him to or not. It was useless to protest, for the pastor knew that his control of Matareva depended upon the absolute loyalty of his wardens, whom he excused of even the most brutal behavior.

On Saturday nights the wardens became especially active, for no frivolity was allowed from then until Monday at daybreak. No husband must sleep with his wife. There must be no kissing, no singing, no reading of books. The rules were strictly observed in most homes because on these nights the wardens gave no warning. There was a rush at the door, a clatter of clubs and people moaning from cracked heads.

On Sunday we prayed three times and had a procession led by the wardens. We marched from the lagoon to the church and stood at solemn attention while the pastor, in a black suit, walked slowly from his house to the church. Then we entered behind him. This took place only at the eleven-o'clock service, but even if it was pouring rain we marched as usual, the wardens with umbrellas, the pastor under a canopy held by four boys.

One Sunday, at the end of an unprecedented spell when fish deserted our lagoon, a school of tunny dashed in through the channel, driven by sharks. They arrived just as the procession started and fishermen who had been without food for days looked passionately at the leaping fish, but wardens dashed up and down striking the men with clubs to keep them from breaking line. On Monday the tunny were gone.

Our law, our parliament, our judge and our business dictator were all one man: the pastor. His name was Thomas Cobbett and he came from some unidentified rural village, perhaps in New Zealand or northern England. In appearance he was ordinary, a small man with watery blue eyes. Actually he was an inspired prophet right from the latter pages of the Old Testament with a penetrating voice and a sure faith that God personally guided him in the government of our atoll. He appeared always in a black suit and, when surrounded by his burly wardens, was a terrifying symbol of God's wrath in Matareva.

Often we puzzled why the Government permitted him to usurp its powers, but many years later an official explained that there had been so much clamor about Christianizing the islands that it was decided to leave one forgotten atoll exclusively to missionaries so as to test what they could accomplish.

Pastor Cobbett accomplished miracles. Even today many people will say there was never a finer island than Matareva in the old days. We were forced to bathe each afternoon. We had to kill the land crabs that burrowed in our gardens, buy screens for our kitchens and nail tin around our coconut trees to keep rats from eating the young nuts. We had to burn coral to make lime for painting our houses, and our walks had to be lined with white shells. Every woman worked one day a week at the church, so that the gardens there were the most beautiful in the Pacific.

The pastor was equally relentless regarding our spiritual lives. The old music, which everyone knows to have been lascivious, was forbidden and replaced by church hymns. Dancing was completely taboo and wardens could arrest anyone who dared to start the lewd old hulas. Everyone had to get married, widows must not talk with men except in the presence of other women and the number of illegitimate babies—a phrase never used on our island before Pastor Cobbett's time—was much reduced. There were some, of course, for in the old days girls had babies before they were married as proof that they would make good wives, but Pastor Cobbett raved against the practice and the penalties were brutally severe except when the father proved to be a warden. If the warden was unmarried, he had to marry the girl right away. If he already had a wife, he was reprimanded in private and the girl was publicly humiliated before the entire village on Sunday morning. She had to march from the rear of the big church up to the altar, fall upon the floor, put a black cloth over her head and walk back past all of us. It was always surprising to me that any girl would have the courage to risk such public shame, but many did and it was found that old women of the village supported them in their behavior, but as the old women died off, the girls found no consolation and some of them committed suicide, a thing never before heard of in our village.

Did no one revolt against this tyranny? As I said, some old women tried, because not even the wardens were cowardly enough to beat an old woman. Nor was the pastor able to quell them, for when he preached against them they stared back with implacable hatred. He solved the impasse by having his wardens spy on the family of the offending woman until a son or husband was detected breaking some trivial rule. Then the old women learned that no one could get the better of Pastor Cobbett. Once a man tried, but he was thrashed so often and spent so much time in jail that he fled to Tongareva, but his canoe was fragile. It capsized and he was eaten by sharks. After that Pastor Cobbett ruled our lives inflexibly.

But in 1919 a small schooner from Suva put into our lagoon and landed a man who was to revolutionize Matareva. He was a tall thin man with stooped shoulders and a dark complexion. He wore a dirty shirt, unbuttoned, and white cotton pants that seemed always about to slip off his hips. He had no shoes, a battered hat, a small suitcase. He stood on the wharf and stared at our village. Then he hitched up his pants with his wrists and said, "Just what I expected. I'll stop here."

The pastor hurried up and said, "There are no houses."

"I'll build one," the stranger replied.

"We have no materials. None."

"Those leaf huts look O.K. to me," the man said.

The pastor grew red in the face and said bluntly, "We don't want white men on this island."

So the stranger dropped his suitcase, planted his hands on his hips and growled, "You sound like a sergeant."

The pastor shouted for his wardens, who ran up with clubs, but the barefooted stranger sidestepped them, searching for some weapon of his own. An old woman kicked him a board, and with it he fairly flew at the astonished wardens, who were accustomed to punishing men afraid to strike back.

The stranger fought with such fury as we had not seen before, and soon the fat bullies retreated with bad bruises, leaving the amazed pastor alone by the wharf. The visitor walked up to him and said, "The name's Morgan. I'll build my house over here."

That night he stayed with my father, and at great risk to themselves, four men of the village crept into our house after midnight. "Morgan Tane," they whispered, "that was a good fight you did!"

"We were proud to see the wardens run," another whispered.

"Morgan Tane," said the spokesman, "you were brave to challenge the pastor. No one has ever been so brave before." There was a long silence and then the spokesman said in a hushed voice, "We have been waiting for a man like you. Will you help us to fight against the wardens?"

The stranger answered promptly. "Me? I didn't come down here to fight. I had enough of that."

"But Morgan Tane," the spokesman whispered, "here you will find no peace. The wardens will never let you spend one night in peace."

The stranger lit a cigarette, puffed on it several times and said, "Then I'll have to do something about it."

"Good!" the men cried. "We'll have a great rebellion."

"You don't understand," Mr. Morgan corrected them. "I'm not interested in trouble. I'm not going to be your leader. I'm not going to fight the wardens. I came down here for rest and quiet."

"But if the wardens . . ."

"It looks to me as if each man has got to handle them his own way. I'm going to bed."

He started building his house next day, and by Sunday he was completely involved in our struggle against the pastor, for as we prepared for the customary procession, it was noticed with hushed surprise that Mr. Morgan, bare to the waist, was hammering on his rooftree. Two wardens were sent to haul him into church, but they retreated in dismay when he produced a shotgun and said, "This thing is loaded."

They rushed off to report the crisis to the pastor, who came out into the road and studied the infidel from a safe distance. Then he wiped his face and waited for the congregation to reach the church. When the procession passed the uncompleted house, Mr. Morgan stopped his hammering and sat cross-legged on a barrel, weaving pandanus during the service. After the closing hymn he went back to the rooftree.

Pastor Cobbett knew that if he let this insult go unpunished, his hold upon Matareva was doomed, so when church was over he gathered his wardens and strode to the place where the white man was working.

"Mr. Morgan!" the pastor cried in his sepulchral voice. "Do you intend to desecrate the Sabbath?"

"Go away!" Mr. Morgan growled.

"You have spoken," Pastor Cobbett cried in terrible tones. "Now God shall destroy this sacrilege."

The pastor stepped up to the nearest pole and began to shake it as Samson shook the pillars of the temple. "Don't be a damned fool," Mr. Morgan called down from the rooftree.

"Come! Wardens! Everybody! Pull down the house of evil." The wardens, who knew of the shotgun, refused, but there were many natives who believed that Cobbett's voice was the voice of God, and these sprang into action, pulling down one of the posts so that a corner of the new house collapsed, tossing Mr. Morgan into the dust.

There was a moment of fateful silence as he slowly picked himself up, brushed off his pants and stood with his feet apart in the dust, studying the pastor. Finally he asked, "Reverend, are you crazy?"

"God has spoken," the missionary cried in his Old-Testament voice. "Men, destroy the blasphemy!"

The hypnotized natives rushed to the remaining poles and ripped them from the ground. Mr. Morgan remained with his head cocked to one side, staring with amazement at the impassioned scene. Still he did nothing and Pastor Cobbett exulted in victory, crying, "The devil in our midst has been cast out."

That was enough. Mr. Morgan looked at the pastor with disgust and said, "They shouldn't of let you out of the booby hatch." He rummaged among the ruins of his house and then walked doggedly to a spot some thirty feet away. There he raised his shotgun and with six cold, deliberate blasts destroyed each of the stained-glass windows in the church. They had been the glory of Matareva, and as they crashed an anguished sob arose from the watchers.

Pastor Cobbett stood like a man who has seen death striding across the motus. When he finally found strength to speak, a last fragment of window fell into the dust. He threw his hands over his face and gave an animal-like wail: "Sodom and Gomorrah have come! Surely God will strike this island with pestilence and evil." So powerful was his cry that true believers started to quake as if the day of judgment were at hand.

Mr. Morgan stalked back through the trembling crowd and hitched up his dirty pants. "Pastor," he said firmly, "if you want to hold prayer meeting, do it on your own land. Get off mine." He flourished the empty gun and the fearful natives drew back in horror as if he were truly cursed. Pastor Cobbett, still staring at the mutilated windows, made incoherent sounds and licked his parched lips.

"All right," Mr. Morgan said. "Who's going to help put these poles back in place?" No one moved. "Well, come on! You knocked them down."

Pastor Cobbett shrieked, "If anyone dares aid the infidel, God will strike him dead!"

"Please!" Mr. Morgan cried. "Shut up! Now you, Teofilo. Grab the pole." There was a deep silence. Many men must have wanted to aid the stranger, but they knew that when he left Matareva, Pastor Cobbett and the wardens would remain behind. No one would help.

"God be praised!" the pastor exulted.

Then a most memorable thing happened. In Matareva there was a girl named Maeva. Even on our island of beautiful girls she was handsome. She had very long hair that was envied by our women, strong arms and good teeth, but although she was already past twenty no man had married her because Pastor Cobbett said she was cursed of the devil because she refused to carry a lighted lantern at night.

Now she left the huddled crowd and crossed to where Mr. Morgan was waiting. "I will help you," she said.

"Wardens!" shouted the pastor. "Take that evil girl!"

"Reverend," the stranger said patiently. "For the last time, go home."

"Wardens! Wardens! Seize her!"

Mr. Morgan waved the empty shotgun at the crowd and said, "If you don't want to work, get out!"

Slowly the wardens withdrew. Now Pastor Cobbett stood alone, facing Mr. Morgan and the girl. "Maeva!" he cried in an ashen voice both commanding and pleading. "Your soul will rest in hell."

Mr. Morgan turned his back on the lonely, apocalyptic figure and said to the girl, "You? What's your name?"

"Maeva," she said.

"That's an odd name. Bring me the hammer."

That night in my father's kitchen a group of Matareva men assembled secretly. They said, "The wardens are afraid of this man. Even the pastor can do nothing. It's time for us to drive our persecutors from the island."

My father said, "It would be fatal to start a rebellion that didn't succeed."

"With Mr. Morgan it will have to succeed," another whispered.

A warden came to the door and the men hid under the porch. "Everybody here?" the warden asked.

"Yes," my father replied. Then he crept across the yard where my mother plants the crotons and hibiscus and in a few minutes he was back with Mr. Morgan.

"Morgan Tane," our oldest man said, "you are at war with the pastor. Good! May we join you?"

"Look, old man!" Mr. Morgan replied. "I'm at war with nobody. Now don't bother me any more."

He left us, but on Saturday he discovered that he had been wrong. He was at war. It began this way. Maeva, who had been working with Mr. Morgan, had slept each night at her brother's, but on Friday the wardens waited for her and had beaten her severely.

Next morning she limped up to the new house and sat upon the porch, her nose dripping blood. Some old women who hated the pastor gathered in bitter groups along the road. No one spoke. A warden went past and took the names of all who were watching.

Mr. Morgan rose late that day, for he had been working hard all week. The old women saw him stretch, sluice his head with a bucket of cold water and look at his tongue in a mirror. Then he came onto the front porch.

He looked with cold fury at Maeva's handsome face, all smeared with blood. Next he looked at the crowd of old women. It was a long time before he did anything. Then he fetched a basin of water and there on the front porch fixed Maeva's nose. It had been broken. After that he took her inside.

All that day there was whispered bitterness across Matareva. Word passed that any plans for rebellion must be stopped, for again the wardens had triumphed. It was said that what had happened to Maeva had finally convinced Mr. Morgan that resistance was useless.

On Saturday night, therefore, the wardens raided my father's home with new brutality and beat him for some minutes, adding, "We know you were talking with the white man. We know everything."

On Sunday we gathered as usual at the lagoon and lined up as the wardens directed. The bell rang strangely through the shattered windows and our procession started toward the imposing door.

At this moment Mr. Morgan appeared barefooted on the porch of his new house. Behind him stood the girl Maeva, her face bandaged. With long, careless steps, his toes kicking dust, the stranger walked along the dusty road and right up to the line of wardens. "Which one of them was it, Maeva?"

The handsome girl, her hair down to her waist, stepped from behind Mr. Morgan and pointed fearlessly at one of the worst wardens. "That one," she said.

The white man lifted his shotgun and there was a terrified gasp from the crowd, but he handed it to the girl and said, "I showed you how to use this. If anyone—a warden, the pastor, anyone comes at me, kill him."

Then slowly, like a wave about to crash upon the reef, he went to the warden who had beaten Maeva and with a sudden grab pulled the hulking man out of line. In silence, and in fearful efficiency, he beat the man until it seemed as if his small right hand could drive no more. The warden was fat, cowardly. Twice Mr. Morgan hauled him to his feet and waited until the bully got set. Then with merciless blows he knocked him down again. Blood was spattered across the white uniform.

So awesome was this cruel scene that no one in the procession moved, but we could see the beating from where we stood, and when it became apparent that Mr. Morgan was willing to fight the entire force of wardens, one after the other, a murmuring restlessness agitated the crowd and it appeared there might be a general uprising, but this was forestalled by the appearance of Pastor Cobbett.

"No one must move!" he cried in his great prophetic voice, but when he saw the ruined face of his leading warden he turned pale. Mr. Morgan, tired and breathless, stood back on his heels, blood across his dirty, sagging pants.

He spoke first. "The wardens told you I'd run away. Well, I like it here. I'll probably stay the rest of my life." He grabbed the shotgun from Maeva and walked slowly back to his house alone, and as we watched him go, barefooted and bent forward, we knew that even though he would not lead our rebellion, he was from that day on an atoll man.

We never called him by any name but Mr. Morgan. He received twelve letters a year, no more no less, each from the United States Government. Once when he cashed a batch of his pension checks with a passing trader he said, "It's good money. I earned it. Got shot up in France while the rich kids in our block stayed home." His only other reference to America came one night when the ocean hammered the reef in great violence, making thunder. "Sounds like the Third Avenue El," he said.

We were much surprised that after the fight he did not take the girl Maeva home with him. It was obvious that he could have any girl he wanted. He was brave and he had a regular income. At night pretty wahines began to drift by his house, but he took no notice of them. When curfew rang he usually went right to bed and twice when girls braver than the rest snuffed out their lanterns and hid upon his porch, he put on his sagging pants and led them boldly to their homes, where he delivered them to their mothers.

It may seem strange to people not of the islands, but we were all offended, men and women alike, that a stranger should have come amongst us and found our girls undesirable. My mother was commissioned to talk this over with Mr. Morgan, and she asked, "Are they not beautiful?"

"They're all right," Mr. Morgan said, his hands in his pockets.

"Then why don't you take one into your house? To mend your clothes? To cook?"

"Look," said the man gruffly. "I don't want any women around."

Yet it was he who finally ended the foolishness of the lanterns. It happened this way. My mother is not easily put off. She knew that every man needs a woman for cleaning up, if for nothing more. So she went to see Maeva, whose nose had now healed. She said, "Maeva, you must not let Morgan Tane live alone. It is no good." But Maeva replied that when she looked in the mirror she was ashamed. The wardens had beaten her so that she thought herself no longer pretty. But Mother knows well how love works and she said, "He will look at the hurts you received for him and he will let you stay."

So Maeva combed her hair, made a wreath of frangipani for her head and washed her feet. Then she went to the new house with her bed mats. She arrived when Mr. Morgan was on the reef and by the time he returned at sunset a fine meal was ready.

"That looks good," he said, and they ate together. Maeva had a face that men enjoyed to look at, so they spent a long time eating and finally Mr. Morgan stood up and ran his finger along her nose. "It's not much of a nose," he apologized.

"You fixed it well," she insisted.

"It's all right," he said. "Now you must go home."

Maeva allowed tears to come into her eyes and said, "Morgan Tane, it is no good for you to live alone. See, I have brought my things." With her brown foot she pushed open the door to the small room and there on the floor beside his large bed lay her sleeping mats.

Mr. Morgan studied them for a while and then stooped down and rolled them into a heap. He tossed them over his shoulder and started out the door. "Please, Morgan Tane!" the girl cried. "Not while it is still light. The village will laugh at me."

He dropped the mats and sat with Maeva while darkness crept over the lagoon. "Have you a wife?" she whispered. "In America?"

"Me? No."

"I am sorry," she said. "I am sorry you do not know that it is good for each man to have his wahine." She moved very close to him and that night he did not make her leave.

Of course the wardens noticed this and early next morning, when Mr. Morgan was out to buy some canned beef from the Chinaman, they descended on the house and arrested her, being very careful not to hurt her in any way, for they wished this affair to be completely legal.

At the jail Pastor Cobbett listened to the evidence and promptly sentenced her to three weeks at hard labor. The jail doors were locked and Maeva went to work.

When Mr. Morgan returned with the meat, he assumed that Maeva had gone back to her own home for a while, but when noon passed he felt a little relieved that he was not going to be bothered with a woman about the house. He preferred not to be bothered, so at dusk he carried Maeva's bed mats back to her mother,. Within a few minutes he learned what had happened.

In a blind rage he stormed up to the jail and demanded that Maeva be released. The jailer said Pastor Cobbett had the keys, so Mr. Morgan grabbed a chair and knocked the door down. Then he set Maeva free and when the girl stepped into the street she was surrounded by other girls, each with a lighted lantern. Angrily, Mr. Morgan took a big stick and broke every lantern. The wardens, seeing that he had no shotgun with him, started to close in on him all together, but he shouted for the men at Matareva, and at last the great rebellion was on.

We burned down the jail, ripped the handsome doors off the church and chased the wardens all across the island. Whenever we caught one we threw him back to the women who did many funny things to the fat men, I can tell you.

Under Mr. Morgan's direction all the wardens were finally herded together by the lagoon. Their uniforms were disgraced in the mud. Their heads were sore from women's fists. "You'll leave the island forever," Mr. Morgan said.

The men of Matareva then cried, "Where is the pastor?"

The mob rushed to his house, but he was waiting for us. He had been waiting since midnight, a small, watery-eyed man in a black suit. He appeared on the porch and slowly the rebellion stood at attention. Pastor Cobbett raised his eyes and moaned, "God will condemn the island of Matareva forever!" The men nearest the porch moved back.

Now Mr. Morgan came up and said, "Go on back to bed, Pastor."

"God will bring all the curses of Babylon upon you!" the prophetic voice cried.

"What do you know about God?" Mr. Morgan asked impatiently, jumping onto the porch and shoving the little missionary back into the safety of the house.

Then there was a shout at the lagoon, and Mr. Morgan had to hurry down there, for some women had got hold of the worst warden and were beating him up all over again. Mr. Morgan made my father's house the new jail and put three men to protect the wardens until a schooner could be sent to Tahiti.

The long night ended with everyone singing and shouting. Then suddenly there was a profound silence, for to the east, behind the church spire, the sun began to rise. It flooded Matareva with wonderful light, and it was a great majesty to all of us, for in my lifetime the people of my village had never before stayed up all night. An old woman began a few nimble steps, and soon the entire population was chanting the fine dirty songs of long ago. "Wahine! Tane!" The music grew louder and we danced.

In the soberness of daylight my father and the village leaders met with Mr. Morgan to discuss what must be done next. "Done?" he asked. "I guess we'll have to build a new jail."

"What we mean is, about the pastor?"

"Why do anything about him?" Mr. Morgan asked.

"We'll need a new government. We must report what has happened."

"We don't need a new government," Mr. Morgan said.

"But the pastor?"

"There's nothing wrong with him. You've just got to stand up to him, that's all."

"But, Morgan Tane, now that you have led us . . . We would like it if you agreed . . ."

"Don't take things too seriously," he said sleepily. "It's just like in France. We had a rotten sergeant. We argued with him. Then we beat the living hell out of him, After that things were all right."

"You mean you're willing to have Pastor Cobbett stay here?" my father asked in astonishment.

"Why not?" the tired man asked, and with that he went off to bed.

The effect of these events on Pastor Cobbett was unbelievable. When the wardens were banished we expected him to flee also. Instead, he became more active than ever. Shorn of his temporal power, he increased his spiritual dominion over us. We would see him night and day tirelessly tramping our atoll, exhorting people to mind the ways of God. He had no pride, no shame. He would burst upon unmarried lovers and stand there in the midst of their confusion, pleading with them to marry like decent Christians.

He was now in his sixties, a little man with a mass of white hair. He continued to wear black suits and his voice was more booming than ever. We were no longer required to attend church but most of us did for he changed the service to make it more inviting. He introduced twice as many songs and even fitted his own religious words to robust island tunes. I think he knew that our women mumbled the original verses about love-making by the lagoon, but he seemed not to care so long as they came to church. And always there was that small figure, thinner now, probing into every corner of island life.

For example, he went boldly to Mr. Morgan's house and said, "Morgan, you and Maeva ought to get married."

"Have a chair," Mr. Morgan said gruffly.

"I don't suppose you've ever thought about it," Pastor Cobbett said, "but Maeva would like it."

"I don't think she'd care," Mr. Morgan replied.

"Why not let her decide?" the pastor suggested.

"Hasn't she had enough of your religion? Broken nose? Public shame?"

"Mr. Morgan," the pastor cried as if he were in church, "where God is concerned things like that don't matter."

"You'd better go, Pastor. Such talk makes me sick."

"I'll call Maeva." Without waiting for permission the little man went to the door and shouted for the girl to come in. She was pregnant at the time and seemed one great, placid ball of humanity.

"Pull up a chair," Mr. Morgan said.

"Maeva," Pastor Cobbett began, "I've come here to ask Morgan Tane to marry you. In the church. Would that please you?"

The black-haired native girl looked at the two men, the one who had broken her nose, the one who had mended it with his own hands, and although she knew that she was offending the latter she said quietly, "Yes."

Pastor Cobbett rose dramatically and said, "You're right, Maeva. Any decent Christian woman wants to be married." With that he left.

There was a long discussion between Maeva and Mr. Morgan, but he finally said, "I understand how you feel, but I don't think I'll get married."

Nor did Pastor Cobbett content himself merely with religious matters. He performed all his old governmental functions, aided now by a council of native men, including my father, and he evolved the new plan whereby we made a better grade of copra for sale direct to Belgium.

Once, after a long meeting about health rules, he excused himself and went back to see Mr. Morgan, who never attended any discussions.

"I'm not going to argue with you, Morgan," he said bluntly. "I just want to tell you that I've seen lots of white men in the tropics. They all face three inevitable tests. One, have they the courage to marry the girl? Two, are they proud of her when she is pregnant for the first time? Three, and when the boat arrives from their own country—it always arrives, Morgan—do they introduce the woman and her dark children to their countrymen?"

That was all he said, and he must have known a great deal about Mr. Morgan, for the white man failed each test. He never married Maeva. Furthermore, he was ashamed and perplexed while she was pregnant, indifferent when the girl was born. And when schooners put into the atoll, Maeva and the baby were forbidden to appear in the front part of the house.

Once an American yacht sought refuge in our lagoon, but Mr. Morgan avoided the crew. Finally three of them forced their society upon him with loud cries of, "They say you're a real Yankee beachcomber!" He did not invite them into his house, but they came anyway with three cases of beer. When they were brave with drink one asked, "Is it true you're married to a beautiful native girl?"

"That's right," Mr. Morgan replied, his shoulders bent forward and his hands in the pockets of his sagging white pants.

We never understood what he did with his time. He didn't write. He never read books. He didn't like to fish nor did he sit and yarn with people about old times. He was a man who lived entirely within himself. He did not even take pleasure in his glowing wahine, who always walked five steps behind him when they went to the beach for a swim.

And yet we knew that here was a brave man, perhaps the bravest we had ever known. Because of this knowledge, our disappointment in him was trebled, for we had hoped that he might lead us to a better way of life, one with more purpose and happiness. He was not concerned with this, and painfully we discovered that he stood for nothing. He was a moral zero and we knew that such a man could never show us how to govern Matareva.

When I became the schoolteacher I understood why my father and the other old men returned at last to the pastor. He stood for something. Of course, when he ranted, "It's God's will!" we were no longer fooled. We knew that no man can say what God's will is, but we also knew it was important that we be led by someone who was at least concerned about what that will might be. We had hoped for a better man than the pastor to lead us, but failing that we had to make do with what was at hand.

The years passed and we forgot Mr. Morgan. Life passed him by and he walked the beach, a man of no consequence, a man loved by no one except perhaps Maeva. Then suddenly he was catapulted tragically back into the orbits of our village as he had been years before. Now the women of Matareva gathered before the white man's house and wept, saying to one another, "At least he's human, like the rest of us."

Maeva was deeply stricken with our most dreaded illness, tuberculosis. I am told that elsewhere this disease lingers in the patient's lungs for many years. It is not so with us. There is the racking cough, the pallor under our brown skins and the chest all caved away. There is nothing we can do against tuberculosis, nothing except die.

I often saw Maeva in the last stages of her illness. It was terrifying. Here was a strong woman who had fished off the reef in her own canoe, yet now she was thin as a ghost, her face fallen in. Here was a girl so beautiful that sailors from schooners would walk like schoolboys to her house, bringing gifts, yet now even her lovely lips were sunk into the gasping mouth. She lay on the floor where she had always slept, and no one could look at her without knowing that death must already be sailing his canoe at the reef's edge.

The effect on Mr. Morgan was something nobody could have predicted. He seemed to us never to have loved his wife, yet now he sat day after day with her, his unlighted pipe between his teeth. He had sent his daughter to a family down the beach while he sat in the silent house caring for the dying girl.

Once when Pastor Cobbett came to talk with Maeva, Mr. Morgan could bear no longer the sight of that vanished face and he burst from the house like a madman. He came rushing down to see my father and cried, "God! God! She just lies there!" My father took him for a walk along the lagoon, but the pounding waves that roared upon the reef reminded the shivering man of Maeva fishing. The stars coming out were like the candles she had burned in his house. He walked mechanically until my father had to leave him, and all that night Pastor Cobbett stayed with Maeva. In the morning Mr. Morgan returned, apparently reconciled to what must happen. When the pastor had trudged off, the white man said, "The lagoon with stars upon it is beautiful, Maeva." So far as we knew, he had never before commented in any way about the atoll he had shared for many years. Now he walked endlessly among us, hurrying back to Maeva to tell her how we looked, what we were doing that day. Once he stopped me and grabbed me by the arm. "Have you ever seen heron crashing down on a fish?" It was a common sight, the great black bill snipping the water, but he stood there transfixed.

The next day Pastor Cobbett asked Mr. Morgan if Maeva would like to have a few prayers. Mr. Morgan said he didn't think so, but Pastor Cobbett said he would come in anyway. He was there when Maeva died, quietly as if not knowing that this sleep was different. For a moment Mr. Morgan would not believe that she was dead, and then he stood by the bed crying, "No! No!"

All night he stood there by the wasted figure on the mat. Our old women came to dress the body and they thought it improper that he should watch them, but he would not leave. When the village keeners came to wail their penetrating lament for the dead soul on its vast journey, he fell into a chair and kept his hands over his ears. The weird cry of the mourners drove him mad and he shouted that they must stop, but they could no more forsake the dead than they could stop the sun from climbing at last above the trees of Matareva.

At the funeral Pastor Cobbett stood by the grave and preached great moving words so that we all wept for this good woman who was dead, but before the pastor ended Mr. Morgan left the graveyard and returned to the lagoon beach, where he walked for many hours. Finally the pastor said to me, "You must talk with him. He would be offended if I did."

I followed him until he turned and saw me unexpectedly. Again he grabbed my arm imploringly and asked in a hushed voice, "Have you ever seen a star like that? Casting a shadow across the lagoon?"

I said that at Matareva we often saw that star and he threw his hands across his face and cried, "There was so much Maeva could have shown me!" He walked off in agony and I watched him for a long time.

Finally I went up to him and said, "Morgan Tane, I think we should go to the Chinaman's and have a beer."

"That's a good idea," he said.

We went to Ah Kim's and opened two bottles, but after drinking only part of his Mr. Morgan said, "I think I'll go to bed."

We expected this upheaval of his world to bring Mr. Morgan at last into the heart of our village, but instead it drove him further from us. He did not even bother to recover his daughter from the house along the beach, and the family living there were very happy to keep the girl as their own, for they prized a white man's child.

So once more we forgot Mr. Morgan. He caused no trouble, spent his money cautiously. Sometimes from my school window I would see him shuffling barefooted along the beach, his shirt open, his pants hanging low upon his hips. Often he did not shave and for days on end we might not see him. His daughter Turia was growing up, a bright, fine-limbed girl like her mother. Once Pastor Cobbett, now seventy-six, found her with a sailor off an Australian ship and punished her on the spot. Mr. Morgan, when he heard of this, said she probably deserved it.

That is how things were in 1941, and then one day a schooner called to say that Honolulu had been bombed. We had an old radio on Matareva and under Pastor Cobbett's excited urgings a man from the schooner got it working. For days on end the pastor sat transfixed before it, piecing together the news of war in our ocean. He borrowed a map from my school and called the head men of the village together. He proved it inevitable that Japan would invade Matareva and to prevent this organized a complete lookout system, a line of fighters for the beaches and a hiding place for the radio.

Early in his operations the frenzied little missionary approached Mr. Morgan, who said, "The Japs'll never bother with this dump."

"But in war we must be prepared!" the pastor argued.

"I fought my war," Mr. Morgan replied.

"But it's your nation that is threatened!" Cobbett cried angrily.

"They're tough. They can look out for themselves."

He would take no part in the wild plans evolved by the pastor, but when the government destroyer put into our lagoon and reviewed what Cobbett had done the defense minister said, "Remarkable! Remarkable! All we need give you chaps is a radio for sending as well as receiving." Later the government had to impose strict rules about this radio, for Pastor Cobbett reported voluminously every four hours.

Yet it was this radio which finally brought Matareva full into the war. Pastor Cobbett was listening one rainy, wind-swept afternoon when he heard the lonely signal of an American plane, lost in a violent storm. He rushed into the road crying, "Plane trying to find Bora Bora!" We hurried to the radio and heard a plea for any kind of help.

I was handed the microphone, and for twenty minutes I repeated over and over, "C-47. C-47. This is Matareva. Bad storm outside the reef, but you can land in the lagoon." It was weird and haunting to be sending words that might never be heard. Then finally came the crackling whisper: "Matareva. Matareva. We cannot land on water. Have you level ground?" The men about me argued for a moment and I reported, "C-47. C-47. There is no land. Crash on calm water a hundred yards from shore. Our canoes will save you." I said this fifteen times and at last we heard the bewildered pilot: "I cannot get there before dark. Matareva. Matareva."

A tall figure stepped beside me, barefooted, stoop-shouldered, no shirt. Mr. Morgan said, "We'll put lights on the motus. Lights around the lagoon."

"C-47," I cried in the flat voice that betrays no hope, no fear. "We will light the lagoon as follows." I started to explain but the pilot broke in: "How will we know where the shore is?"

Mr. Morgan grabbed the microphone. "Come in, you damned fools," he snapped. "You've nowhere else to go. Head between the green lights. Land short of the red ones." And as I sat there, encouraging the pilot, Mr. Morgan dashed out into the rain and shouted for everyone on Matareva either to get into his canoe or take a light and stand along the reef. When the first lights blew out he cried above the storm, "Pastor! Didn't you have some extra lanterns in the church?" When a man near the lagoon cried, "No plane can land in this storm," Mr. Morgan snapped, "If we don't save them, they're too dumb to save themselves."

He took a motor boat and a dozen lanterns wrapped in whatever green cloth the women could provide. He called for volunteers and set out across the lagoon to where the great waves thundered on the reef. Night came, and about the entire lagoon you could see the thin ring of lights, green clusters to the west, a red cluster marking the landing course.

"C-47. C-47," I called. "Everything is ready. The canoes will be at your side within a minute after you land."

The pilot called back in an ashen voice, "The lights? All set?"

"Come in between the green. Finish at the red."

And then Pastor Cobbett took the microphone and said in a low, powerful voice, "Pilot! God will bring your plane in. God is riding with you."

The wind howled but above it we heard the droning of a crippled motor. We had never seen an airplane at Matareva, and everyone along the lagoon, those with beacons and those who tensely clutched their paddles, stared into the sky. A wavering light appeared and an astonished cry rose from all Matareva. The plane was so big. It was so low.

It came roaring in between the green lights. Its wing dipped perilously toward the water, then straightened. There was a long hiss, a flash of spray and gas tanks exploding in the night.

Instantly our canoes dashed in among the flames and our pearl divers leaped into the crackling waters. Not one American was lost.

We had a night of wild celebration. Each man of Matareva thought himself a true hero. We spoke endlessly of what we had done, whose canoe had been first among the flames, which man had stood knee-deep among the sharks, waving his green lantern.

There were six Americans and we were amazed at how young they were. Their navigator, no more than a boy, blubbered when he saw Mr. Morgan. "We had a million dollars' worth of medicine and radio in that plane. We lost it all."

"There's plenty more where that came from," Mr. Morgan said. He took the six men to his house and for the next three weeks Matareva knew such excitement as we had never experienced before. The talk was all of America, and slowly Mr. Morgan become involved. He said, "Forget Pearl Harbor. We lose lots of battles. But we win lots of wars." He stared pointedly at Pastor Cobbett and said, "We taught the British all about that."

Once the plane captain, Harry Faber, said, "It was almost a miracle! I was scared silly but when I got my last instructions from your radio I took off the headphones and said, 'Here we go!' Then I heard a voice as clear as I can hear yours saying, 'You are in God's care.' And even though the plane exploded, we all got out."

"What did the voice sound like?" Mr. Morgan asked.

"Deep. Powerful. Speaking right to me."

"It was a miracle all right," Mr. Morgan said disgustedly. But when the picket boat came to take the flyers on to Samoa, he followed them right to the tip end of the wharf and shouted, "Give those Japs hell!"

Now he was truly at war. The picket boat gave him a large map and some colored pins. He kept it at the Chinaman's, and there he and Pastor Cobbett would sit hour after hour making out the radio reports. We called them Churchill and Roosevelt, and when portentous things happened like El Alamein or the entry into Paris, the entire island would celebrate.

When the war ended, an American warship came to Matareva to give the island a scroll thanking us for our part in saving an American crew. The pastor had a big day! He arranged formal ceremonies and appeared in his black suit to give a long invocation. At the end of the prayer an American flag was hoisted over the church and the American officials gave Mr. Morgan a medal "for improvising a landing strip under extreme difficulties." They also left the flag, which to our surprise Mr. Morgan nailed on the wall of his front room. When boys of our village came to talk with him about America, he served citronade and said, "Now there's one country you ought to see!"

He lived in this way until 1946, when a schooner from Australia dropped by and landed a young man in khaki shorts. Before he had left the wharf our girls were screaming, "Harry Faber! American pilot! He come back!"

He hurried right to Mr. Morgan's house and clapped the tall man on the shoulders. "I swore I'd get back here to say thanks." He brought us six crates of things contributed by members of the crew we had saved. There were radios, ice boxes, many jazz records, books and more than a dozen fine Army blankets. "All stolen," he said proudly.

We made a great festivity for Harry, and the record player was set up in Mr. Morgan's front room, beneath the flag, where we gathered many nights to hear Bing Crosby.

But before long we noticed that Harry Faber was rarely at these pleasant sessions, and my mother, who always hears these things first, said that he was spending his nights with Turia Vanaavoa, as Mr. Morgan's daughter was now called.

Soon everyone on the island knew about the love affair, except Mr. Morgan, whom no one told such things. Then one day an old woman said approvingly, "Wouldn't it be wonderful if the American married your daughter?"

It took about a minute for the implication of this question to reach his brain. He looked very puzzled and asked, "Turia . . . Vanaavoa?" He seemed unable to remember that this girl whom he had rejected was his daughter. But next day he found a piece of paper and suddenly his life flamed into purposeful being, as if Turia, and dead Maeva, and lost America, and even the vanquished wardens had all thundered down upon him like stormy waves upon the reef.

He read the paper twice and said, "Damn such nonsense." Then he carried it straight to Pastor Cobbett and jammed it under his nose. "What do you make of that?" he growled.

The pastor lifted his spectacles, cleared his throat and read the following poem, which is now famous in Matareva:

SONG OF A TROPICAL TRAMP

I have wandered through the islands with hibiscus in my hair,
I've surrendered my ambitions for a life that laughs at care,
I have loved an island maiden when the nights were far and fair:
    And I've seen the constellations upside down.

I have watched canoes go gliding on a fairytale lagoon,
I have heard the sun come raging up a day, a year too soon.

Then I've waited for Turia and the rising of the moon:
    And I've heard the wild sharks twisting near the shore.

When the schooner fled outside the reef to run before the gale,
When palm trees bowed their heads to hear the hurricane's wild wail,
Then her lips on mine were golden brown and mine on hers were pale:
    For I've seen the stars surrender to the storm.

Sometimes within the city streets I hear a curlew cry,
I see the reef spume leaping up to meet a cobalt sky.
Then the island fever has me and I think that I must die:
    For I've seen the atolls baking in the sun.

Pastor Cobbett finished reading and put down his spectacles. "What's it mean?" Morgan asked.

"The usual bad poetry a young man writes," the pastor explained. "I never wrote any, but I recognize the stuff."

"Is it anything serious?"

Cobbett rose and stood with his hands behind his back as if about to deliver a sermon. Then he saw his friend's agnostic face and changed his mind. "Two kinds of men come to the atolls," he said simply. "You came here and made a life. You were one of us, and our problems were your problems. You helped us, for better or worse. But other men come like birds of passage. They think it's part of growing up. To see strange places. To love strange women. Maybe they're right, but it's hard on the places. It's very hard on the women."

"That's what I thought it meant," Mr. Morgan said grimly. "But I never found much time for reading." Clutching the poem in his hand he strode back to his house, where he found Harry Faber reading a book. "You write this?" he asked.

Harry looked at the poem and said yes.

"It's time you left Matareva," Mr. Morgan said.

"What do you mean?"

The old man began to shout, the only time we ever heard him raise his voice. "Damn it all. I didn't save your life so you could come back and make a fool of my daughter." We were dumbfounded! We had even forgotten that Turia Vanaavoa was his child, and now after all the years he trembled with fatherly concern!

"Wait a minute, sir!" the flier protested.

"I said it's time to go, Harry. You smart guys who come down here like birds of passage. There's a schooner out there. Get on it!" And that night Harry Faber was on his way to Tahiti.

The girl Turia was heartbroken. She had a copy of the poem and a guitar player set it to mournful music, which our wahines still sing with tears in their eyes. Mr. Morgan amazed us by insisting that Turia come back to live with him as his daughter. The Vanaavoas made no protest, for they had enjoyed the girl as she grew up and now it was time for her to have a life of her own. She started going with a young man of our village and when she became pregnant told her father that she wished to get married. "It's high time," he said.

The wedding was held in church, the last occasion on which Mr. Morgan ever wore a tie. Later he gave a reception in his house, but we noticed that the American flag had been taken down. He gave an embarrassed speech about his daughter's happiness and then disappeared. When I went home I saw him sitting on the sea wall, the solitary man whom life had subtly surrounded as the coral polyps working on our reef once surrounded a portion of the vast sea and made it habitable. I was inspired to rush up to this man and say that we were proud he had made Matareva his home, but as I moved to do so, I saw that he was sitting with Pastor Cobbett. What they were talking about I do not know.

IV

It Takes All Kinds

IV

* * * *

Mr. Know-All

By W. SOMERSET MAUGHAM

I WAS prepared to dislike Max Kelada even before I knew him. The war had just finished and the passenger traffic in the ocean-going liners was heavy. Accommodation was very hard to get and you had to put up with whatever the agents chose to offer you. You could not hope for a cabin to yourself and I was thankful to be given one in which there were only two berths. But when I was told the name of my companion my heart sank. It suggested closed portholes and the night air rigidly excluded. It was bad enough to share a cabin for fourteen days with anyone (I was going from San Francisco to Yokohama), but I should have looked upon it with less dismay if my fellow-passenger's name had been Smith or Brown.

When I went on board I found Mr. Kelada's luggage already below. I did not like the look of it; there were too many labels on the suitcases, and the wardrobe trunk was too big. He had unpacked his toilet things, and I observed that he was a patron of the excellent Monsieur Coty; for I saw on the washing stand his scent, his hair wash and his brilliantine. Mr. Kelada's brushes, ebony with his monogram in gold, would have been all the better for a scrub. I did not at all like Mr. Kelada. I made my way into the smoking room. I called for a pack of cards and began to play patience. I had scarcely started before a man came up to me and asked me if he was right in thinking my name was so-and-so.

"I am Mr. Kelada," he added, with a smile that showed a row of flashing teeth, and sat down.

"Oh, yes, we're sharing a cabin, I think."

"Bit of luck, I call it. You never know who you're going to be put in with. I was jolly glad when I heard you were English. I'm all for us English sticking together when we're abroad, if you understand what I mean."

I blinked.

"Are you English?" I asked, perhaps tactlessly.

"Rather. You don't think I look like an American, do you? British to the backbone, that's what I am."

To prove it, Mr. Kelada took out of his pocket a passport and airily waved it under my nose.

King George has many strange subjects. Mr. Kelada was short and of a sturdy build, clean-shaven and dark-skinned, with a fleshy, hooked nose and very large, lustrous and liquid eyes. His long black hair was sleek and curly. He spoke with a fluency in which there was nothing English and his gestures were exuberant. I felt pretty sure that a closer inspection of that British passport would have betrayed the fact that Mr. Kelada was born under a bluer sky than is generally seen in England.

"What will you have?" he asked me.

I looked at him doubtfully. Prohibition was in force and to all appearances the ship was bone-dry. When I am not thirsty I do not know which I dislike more, ginger ale or lemon squash. But Mr. Kelada flashed an oriental smile at me.

"Whisky and soda or a dry Martini, you have only to say the word."

From each of his hip pockets he fished a flask and laid them on the table before me. I chose the Martini, and calling the steward he ordered a tumbler of ice and a couple of glasses.

"A very good cocktail," I said.

"Well, there are plenty more where that came from, and if you've got any friends on board, you tell them you've got a pal who's got all the liquor in the world."

Mr. Kelada was chatty. He talked of New York and of San Francisco. He discussed plays, pictures, and politics. He was patriotic. The Union Jack is an impressive piece of drapery, but when it is flourished by a gentleman from Alexandria or Beirut, I cannot but feel that it loses somewhat in dignity. Mr. Kelada was familiar. I do not wish to put on airs, but I cannot help feeling that it is seemly in a total stranger to put mister before my name when he addresses me. Mr. Kelada, doubtless to set me at my ease, used no such formality. I did not like Mr. Kelada. I had put aside the cards when he sat down, but now, thinking that for this first occasion our conversation had lasted long enough, I went on with my game.

"The three on the four," said Mr. Kelada.

There is nothing more exasperating when you are playing patience than to be told where to put the card you have turned up before you have had a chance to look for yourself.

"It's coming out, it's coming out," he cried. "The ten on the knave."

With rage and hatred in my heart I finished. Then he seized the pack.

"Do you like card tricks?"

"No, I hate card tricks," I answered.

"Well, I'll just show you this one."

He showed me three. Then I said I would go down to the dining room and get my seat at table.

"Oh, that's all right," he said. "I've already taken a seat for you. I thought that as we were in the same stateroom we might just as well sit at the same table."

I did not like Mr. Kelada.

I not only shared a cabin with him and ate three meals a day at the same table, but I could not walk round the deck without his joining me. It was impossible to snub him. It never occurred to him that he was not wanted. He was certain that you were as glad to see him as he was to see you. In your own house you might have kicked him downstairs and slammed the door in his face without the suspicion dawning on him that he was not a welcome visitor. He was a good mixer, and in three days knew everyone on board. He ran everything. He managed the sweeps, conducted the auctions, collected money for prizes at the sports, got up quoit and golf matches, organized the concert and arranged the fancy dress ball. He was everywhere and always. He was certainly the best-hated man in the ship. We called him Mr. Know-All, even to his face. He took it as a compliment. But it was at meal times that he was most intolerable. For the better part of an hour then he had us at his mercy. He was hearty, jovial, loquacious and argumentative. He knew everything better than anybody else, and it was an affront to his overweening vanity that you should disagree with him. He would not drop a subject, however unimportant, till he had brought you round to his way of thinking. The possibility that he could be mistaken never occurred to him. He was the chap who knew. We sat at the doctor's table. Mr. Kelada would certainly have had it all his own way, for the doctor was lazy and I was frigidly indifferent, except for a man called Ramsay who sat there also. He was as dogmatic as Mr. Kelada and resented bitterly the Levantine's cocksureness. The discussions they had were acrimonious and interminable.

Ramsay was in the American Consular Service, and was stationed at Kobe. He was a great heavy fellow from the Middle West, with loose fat under a tight skin, and he bulged out of his ready-made clothes. He was on his way back to resume his post, having been on a flying visit to New York to fetch his wife, who had been spending a year at home. Mrs. Ramsay was a very pretty little thing, with pleasant manners and a sense of humor. The Consular Service is ill paid, and she was dressed always very simply; but she knew how to wear her clothes. She achieved an effect of quiet distinction. I should not have paid any particular attention to her but that she possessed a quality that may be common enough in women, but nowadays is not obvious in their demeanor. You could not look at her without being struck by her modesty. It shone in her like a flower on a coat.

One evening at dinner the conversation by chance drifted to the subject of pearls. There had been in the papers a good deal of talk about the culture pearls which the cunning Japanese were making, and the doctor remarked that they must inevitably diminish the value of real ones. They were very good already; they would soon be perfect. Mr. Kelada, as was his habit, rushed the new topic. He told us all that was to be known about pearls. I do not believe Ramsay knew anything about them at all, but he could not resist the opportunity to have a fling at the Levantine, and in five minutes we were in the middle of a heated argument. I had seen Mr. Kelada vehement and voluble before, but never so voluble and vehement as now. At last something that Ramsay said stung him, for he thumped the table and shouted:

"Well, I ought to know what I am talking about. I'm going to Japan just to look into this Japanese pearl business. I'm in the trade and there's not a man in it who won't tell you that what I say about pearls goes. I know all the best pearls in the world, and what I don't know about pearls isn't worth knowing."

Here was news for us, for Mr. Kelada, with all his loquacity, had never told anyone what his business was. We only knew vaguely that he was going to Japan on some commercial errand. He looked round the table triumphantly.

"They'll never be able to get a culture pearl that an expert like me can't tell with half an eye." He pointed to a chain that Mrs. Ramsay wore. "You take my word for it, Mrs. Ramsay, that chain you're wearing will never be worth a cent less than it is now."

Mrs. Ramsay in her modest way flushed a little and slipped the chain inside her dress. Ramsay leaned forward. He gave us all a look and a smile flickered in his eyes.

"That's a pretty chain of Mrs. Ramsay's, isn't it?"

"I noticed it at once," answered Mr. Kelada. "Gee, I said to myself, those are pearls all right."

"I didn't buy it myself, of course. I'd be interested to know how much you think it cost."

"Oh, in the trade somewhere round fifteen thousand dollars. But if it was bought on Fifth Avenue I shouldn't be surprised to hear that anything up to thirty thousand was paid for it."

Ramsay smiled grimly.

"You'll be surprised to hear that Mrs. Ramsay bought that string at a department store the day before we left New York, for eighteen dollars."

Mr. Kelada flushed.

"Rot. It's not only real, but it's as fine a string for its size as I've ever seen."

"Will you bet on it? I'll bet you a hundred dollars it's imitation."

"Done."

"Oh, Elmer, you can't bet on a certainty," said Mrs. Ramsay.

She had a little smile on her lips and her tone was gently deprecating.

"Can't I? If I get a chance of easy money like that I should be all sorts of a fool not to take it."

"But how can it be proved?" she continued. "It's only my word against Mr. Kelada's."

"Let me look at the chain, and if it's imitation I'll tell you quickly enough. I can afford to lose a hundred dollars," said Mr. Kelada.

"Take it off, dear. Let the gentleman look at it as much as he wants."

Mrs. Ramsay hesitated a moment. She put her hands to the clasp.

"I can't undo it," she said. "Mr. Kelada will just have to take my word for it."

I had a sudden suspicion that something unfortunate was about to occur, but I could think of nothing to say.

Ramsay jumped up.

"I'll undo it."

He handed the chain to Mr. Kelada. The Levantine took a magnifying glass from his pocket and closely examined it. A smile of triumph spread over his smooth and swarthy face. He handed back the chain. He was about to speak. Suddenly he caught sight of Mrs. Ramsay's face. It was so white that she looked as though she were about to faint. She was staring at him with wide and terrified eyes. They held a desperate appeal; it was so clear that I wondered why her husband did not see it.

Mr. Kelada stopped with his mouth open. He flushed deeply. You could almost *see* the effort he was making over himself.

"I was mistaken," he said. "It's a very good imitation, but of course as soon as I looked through my glass I saw that it wasn't real. I think eighteen dollars is just about as much as the damned thing's worth."

He took out his pocketbook and from it a hundred-dollar note. He handed it to Ramsay without a word.

"Perhaps that'll teach you not to be so cocksure another time, my young friend," said Ramsay as he took the note.

I noticed that Mr. Kelada's hands were trembling.

The story spread over the ship as stories do, and he had to put up with a good deal of chaff that evening. It was a fine joke that Mr. Know-All had been caught out. But Mrs. Ramsay retired to her stateroom with a headache.

Next morning I got up and began to shave. Mr. Kelada lay on his bed smoking a cigarette. Suddenly there was a small scraping sound and I saw a letter pushed under the door. I opened the door and looked out. There was nobody there. I picked up the letter and saw that it was addressed to Max Kelada. The name was written in block letters. I handed it to him.

"Who's this from?" He opened it. "Oh!"

He took out of the envelope, not a letter, but a hundred-dollar note.

He looked at me and again he reddened. He tore the envelope into little bits and gave them to me.

"Do you mind just throwing them out of the porthole?"

I did as he asked, and then I looked at him with a smile.

"No one likes being made to look a perfect damned fool," he said.

"Were the pearls real?"

"If I had a pretty little wife I shouldn't let her spend a year in New York while I stayed at Kobe," said he.

At that moment I did not entirely dislike Mr. Kelada. He reached out for his pocketbook and carefully put in it the hundred-dollar note.

"Vanity"

By FRANK O'CONNOR

THERE are a lot of things old bishops have to put up with besides old age, loneliness, and lack of domestic comforts, and the worst of these is co-adjutors. To be God Almighty—the just and moral Governor of the universe—for years and years, and then have an assistant God Almighty tagged on you to see that your justice and morality are of the proper kind, is a more than human ordeal. The Bishop of Moyle, the Most Reverend Dr. Gallogly, called his coadjutor the Stump, the Spy, or the Boy, according to the way he felt about him. Mostly the Boy. The Boy had nasty supercilious ways that the Bishop detested. He let on to know a lot about French history, gave himself out for an authority on food and wine, jeered at Dr. Gallogly's coffee—the best bottled coffee on the market—and mocked at Dr. Gallogly's statement that the best food and wine in the world were to be had on the train from Holyhead to Euston. It must be admitted that the Bishop was vulnerable to that sort of criticism. As a one-time Professor of Dogmatic Theology he tended to turn everything into a dogma.

What was worse than that, the coadjutor was a bit of a snob, and what was worst of all, he had the illusion that at eighty-six the Bishop was past his prime, whereas the Bishop knew well that he had never been brighter in his wits. Just to show Lanigan, he would suddenly order round the car, drive a couple of hundred miles to Dublin, stay at the best hotel, interview three Ministers and ask them all about their Departments, and then come home and tell Lanigan nothing. Lanigan let on to be amused at this as just another example of the old Bishop's irresponsibility, but, being an inquisitive man himself, the Bishop knew he was mad at not knowing what went on, and only pretended not to care out of vanity. Vanity—the besetting sin of people in religion, according to Dr. Gallogly—was Lanigan's as well, and at heart the Bishop knew he was wild.

Whenever the notion of going to Dublin struck the Bishop, he always made inquiries about people from Moyle who might be staying there, so that he could call. He knew they liked that; it was a thing they could brag about, and afterwards they came back and said what a wonderful old man he was—another thorn in Lanigan's flesh.

One morning before he set out, he discovered that one of his curates was in a nursing home in Dublin for a major operation.

"Father O'Brien?" he exclaimed in astonishment. "What's he doing with an operation? Sure, he's only—what is he, Father?"

"Forty-five, my Lord."

"Forty-five! And having operations! Sure, there's no sense in that. Remind me to go and see Father O'Brien, Paddy," he added to his chauffeur.

Even the Bishop's best friend wouldn't have pretended that this was pure kindness, though he had plenty of that. It was mainly wonder at himself, having reached the age of eighty-six without a surgeon's ever sticking a knife in him, while a whole generation of priests was growing up that couldn't even reach forty-five without an operation of some sort. Motorcars! It couldn't be anything else only motorcars.

And every step he climbed up to the first-floor room of the nursing home, the Bishop vacillated between good nature and complacency; good nature in being able to do a good turn for a lonesome young priest, far from his friends and family, and a furious complacency that it wasn't the young fellow of forty-five who was coming to visit the old man, but the fine, upstanding old man of eighty-six who was coming to visit the young fellow. And the two emotions mingled in the triumphant smile with which he opened the young priest's door and trumpeted joyously "Father O'Brien, do you want me to suspend you? Wouldn't you get up out of that and attend to your duties?" That would get back to Lanigan as well.

What at home might have been an ordeal for the curate became, because of the unfamiliar surroundings and the Bishop's excitement, a most enjoyable occasion for both. The Bishop was no fool, but because he was behaving rather foolishly, he talked with more freedom than he would otherwise have permitted himself about the Moyle clergy and their families. A bishop has to know everything, and he realized that you could never know a man unless you knew his family. You could never explain the extraordinary behavior of a man like Lanigan unless you knew about his brother, the parish priest, who not only had died young of a particularly wishy-washy disease that would never have killed anyone else but had suffered for two years before he died from scruples. Scruples!

"Nerves!" said the Bishop. "All that family were neurotic. You'll see, he'll go just the same way."

He returned to his hotel, saying to Paddy, his "man": "That'll show them, Paddy," and Paddy grinned because he knew well whom the Bishop was referring to. There is nobody who resents a coadjutor more than a Bishop's man. The lounge of the hotel was crowded and several people were waiting for the lift, but by this time the Bishop's complacency was contemptuous of every obstacle. "Ah, I can't be bothered waiting for that machine," he said, loud enough to be overheard by everyone; and went up the stairs "like a hare," as Paddy put it, though this was really comparison gone mad.

He negotiated the main stair successfully, but when he came to a flight of six steps leading disconcertingly from one level to another, he slipped. He had only six steps to fall, but he knew they might as well have been twenty. He was dished. He didn't move; he knew it wasn't safe. "Pride goeth before a fall," he thought. "I should have waited for that blooming old lift."

"I think I'm hurt," he said to the waiter who rushed to his aid. "Don't tell anyone. Get something to lift me in on and call Dr. Jameson."

It was agony being transferred to the stretcher and from the stretcher to the bed, but pain was the least of the Bishop's troubles, and the tears in his blue eyes were as much humiliation as anything else. After an irreproachable life of eighty-six years he was suddenly, because of what he now called "a mad vagary," no longer his own master, and as much subject to stretcher-bearers, doctors, and nurses as any poor curate. Lanigan's opportunity had come. No longer would they talk of him in Moyle as a wonderful old man. The shock of it was almost enough to make him lose his reason.

"Am I bad?" he asked the doctor bleakly.

"It looks as if you've broken your shoulder and leg," said the doctor, a brisk, moon-faced young man. "We'll have to get you to hospital and see if there's anything else."

"Am I going to die?" asked the Bishop almost hopefully. If he were really going to die, there would be no further problem.

"You must be pretty tough to have reached your age," said the doctor, who was privately convinced that the Bishop wouldn't leave the hospital outside a box.

"Ah, I'm tough enough," said the Bishop. "Couldn't you do whatever you have to do here?"

"I could not," said the doctor in alarm.

"Why couldn't you?" asked the Bishop angrily. He hated to be contradicted in that positive way—it is one of the drawbacks of having been Almighty God.

"Because I have to get an Xray at once."

"Couldn't you get it here? I'm a busy man. I haven't the time for going to hospital."

"But you have to go to hospital."

"If you were in my position, you'd see why I don't want to go to hospital," the Bishop said earnestly. "People think when a man has authority that he can do as he likes. He can't. He always has people after him, trying to make out he's not fit to look after himself. They want to treat you as if you were a child. If this gets round, it's going to be very awkward for me."

"But an accident can happen to anybody," protested the doctor.

"An accident can happen to a young man," the Bishop said, wincing. "What happens to an old man isn't supposed to be an accident. You'd think, the way they go on, that we did it out of spite. The manager here is an old friend of mine. I can trust him to keep his mind to himself."

"You're asking for impossibilities," the doctor said. "You needn't be worried about the nursing home. You'll be as comfortable there as you are here."

"I don't give a rap about comfort," said the Bishop with an indignant flash of his blue eyes. "But if I go into a nursing home, 'twill be all round Moyle by tomorrow."

"It'll be all round Moyle anyway."

"It will not be all round Moyle, if I can prevent it."

"But people will have to know."

"Why will they have to know?" the Bishop asked fiercely. It was bad enough to be enduring that pain and worse to be enduring complete helplessness, without being contradicted into the bargain. "What business is it of anyone's?" Then, as his mind began again to play with the possibilities, his voice grew milder. "Supposing I do go to hospital, can't I go under a false name?"

"But you'd have to tell the nuns," said the doctor aghast.

"I would *not* tell the nuns," the Bishop said with renewed irascibility. "You don't know what you're talking about. I know more about nuns than you do, and I wouldn't tell a nun anything."

"But they'd have to know you were a clergyman."

"I tell you you don't know what you're talking about, man. A clergyman in this country has no privacy. The first thing they'd want to know was what diocese I was from, and then there would be a nun or a nurse with a brother a priest in the same diocese. As a matter of fact, there's a curate there from my own diocese. There's too much curiosity about priests in this country."

"Let me give you something to ease that pain before you talk any more," said the doctor, seeing that the Bishop was on the point of collapse.

"I'm not going to be taking any drugs from you till I know where I stand," said the Bishop. "What sort of woman is the Reverend Mother in that place?"

"She's a nice, friendly woman."

"Never mind how friendly she is. Where is she from?"

"I never asked her."

"And isn't it a great wonder you wouldn't find out?" said the Bishop, who knew that if only he knew her father or her brother, he could guess how reliable she was. "Is she young or old?"

"Oldish."

"Ask her to come here and talk to me."

"Do you know, my Lord, you're a very obstinate old man?" said the doctor.

"Ah, if you had my responsibilities, you'd be the same," grunted the Bishop without rancor. He liked to be told he was obstinate. It showed that he was a man who knew his own mind. "Bring her here to me and I'll talk to her myself."

Ten minutes later the doctor returned with the nun. She was an oldish, soft-mannered, gigglesome woman who almost smothered the Bishop with her solicitude. He let her moan on, knowing it was only part of her stock in trade, and waited till the doctor left the room before putting his hand on hers.

"The doctor is a very bright young man, Mother," he said earnestly, "but he's not easy to talk to. 'Tisn't often you'll find a layman that can understand the difficulties of people in religion."

"Sure, how could he?" she asked.

"And the reason is," he said solemnly, "that every calling has its own graces and temptations. Now, the great temptation of religious people is vanity."

"I wonder, my Lord," she said coyly, as if she had noticed a few others.

"You needn't," replied the Bishop in the tone he used for proclaiming the merits of the Holyhead train. "That is what makes it so hard for people in religion to be growing old. You're a young woman yet," he went on with brazen flattery, "so you wouldn't know."

"Oh, indeed, I'm afraid, so far as that goes, I'm older than you give me credit for," she said, growing alarmingly girlish.

"Why then, indeed, you are not," said the Bishop confidently, knowing that he had won her ear. "But your own turn will come. You'll see the young people pushing you to make way for them, watching you and criticizing you; waiting for you to make a slip."

"Ah, indeed, my Lord, I've seen it already."

"I can see you're an understanding woman," said the Bishop solemnly. "Now, Mother, this is a thing I could not say to a lay person, but I can say it to you. I have a coadjutor, and we do not get on. I know this won't go any further. That young man takes too much on himself. He thinks I'm not fit to look after myself. If he knows I had an accident, it will give him a hold over me. He will say I am not fit to be taking decisions on my own. I do not like to be criticizing, but there is nothing he is not vain enough to think."

"My Lord," she said in alarm, "I don't think you know what you're asking."

"Mother," he said compellingly, "there is nothing an intelligent woman cannot do, if she puts her mind to it."

However, she gave her word to do her best. There had been, she admitted, certain private patients whose identity had had to be concealed for reasons of policy, and some distinguished patients whose delirium tremens had to be disguised as something else. She would do what she could. That evening the Bishop was comfortably settled in a room corridors away from the rest of the nursing home, with two old nuns to look after him. The old nuns had long ceased to be active; one of them was crippled with rheumatics and the other slightly gone in the head, but they rejoiced in their responsibility, exulted in the fact that at last they had been found indispensable, revenged themselves on those who had slighted their age and infirmity by a scornful silence, and guarded the Bishop with something approaching ferocity.

The Bishop was in great pain, but even the pain didn't hinder his feeling of complacency. He had arranged everything. The curate was in the same nursing home, and was probably lying awake marveling at the Bishop's sturdy health, while all the time the Bishop was lying near him, as helpless as himself, but content in the feeling that what Father O'Brien didn't know wouldn't harm him. The essence of authority consists in keeping your secrets.

But after the first day or two even the Bishop became aware of the atmosphere of mystery in which Reverend Mother had wrapped him. She was the only other nun permitted to visit him. The nurses weren't allowed into his room at all. But the trouble with the Bishop's gallant old watchdogs was that they had lost their teeth. They were easy game for the younger nuns and the nurses, because Sister Martha's bad head and Sister Dympna's bad legs meant that when they left his room there was no guarantee that they would ever get back. On the third day the door suddenly opened and a middle-aged, scraggy-looking nurse came in and looked at him in apparent astonishment.

"I'm sorry," she said, giving him a crooked smile. "Are you Mr. Murphy?"

"No," said the Bishop with a glare. "I'm Mr. Dempsey."

"You wouldn't be one of the Dempseys from Limerick?" she asked. "The motor people?"

"No," he replied brazenly. "My family came from Kanturk."

"We had a nurse one time from Kanturk," she said, screwing up her eyes. "Lucey, her name was. You wouldn't know her?"

"She must be from another part of Kanturk," said the Bishop.

"I dare say," she said, realizing that she had met her match. "From the other side of the post office. What happened you anyway?"

"A fall I got off my bicycle," said the Bishop.

An inquisitive man himself, the Bishop deeply resented inquisitiveness, but he had never met inquisitiveness to match that of the nurse. For a while after she left the room he was boiling with rage and decided that it was almost a matter for a pastoral letter. But as he thought of it, he realized that there was something about the nurse's air which he resented even more. The woman had been familiar with him. She had shown him no proper respect. As he thought of it his anger vanished and gave place to a feeling of his own guile. He realized now that Reverend Mother had really succeeded in baffling her staff, and that they thought he was probably a rich businessman or politician whose illness had to be concealed from his eneimes. It impressed him that even as such he had been treated with such little ceremony. As a young priest he had noticed how conversation changed when he entered a room. Now, in his old age, he was getting the real thing—the tone people adopted among themselves. The religious life was too sheltered. As a result he never reported the visit of the nurse and even waited impatiently for her to come back.

In her place there came a young and good-looking girl who didn't even pretend to have strayed into his room by accident. She looked at him with a guilty air, and then her small, keen eyes started to wander, looking for a clue.

"They say you were in America; were you?" she asked.

"What makes them think that?" asked the Bishop.

"I don't know. I suppose because you don't seem to have any family here."

"Well, I'll tell you the truth, girl," the Bishop said slyly. "I haven't a family. I was never what you'd call a marrying man."

"Why would you?" she asked with a shrug. "I suppose you can get them without."

For a moment the Bishop was so stunned that he almost gave himself away. He looked at the young nurse again, but her pretty face still remained vague and sweet and innocent.

"Isn't that a shocking thing for a girl like you to say?" he asked indignantly.

"What's shocking about it?" she asked ingenuously. "I suppose you're not going to pretend you did without them?"

It left the Bishop very thoughtful. There were apparently lots of things that had escaped him even in his eighty-six years. "Too sheltered," he muttered to himself again. "Too blooming sheltered. We don't know the half that's going on. We might as well have blinkers." What surprised him most was that he was becoming almost attached to his anonymity, and grew quite hopeful when he heard a woman's step outside his door that it might be another of the nurses coming to pump him. When the first nurse returned to test a new theory of his identity and told him a dirty story, he wasn't even shocked. It had never occurred to him before that women knew dirty stories. "We live and learn," he thought.

Reverend Mother arranged his departure as she had arranged his arrival. The two old nuns knelt for his blessing, and had a little bawl because they would again be regarded as old and useless. One of them guarded the landing and another the hall while Paddy took down the bags. They passed the door of the curate's room. He was still there, poor fellow, though beginning to come round.

"I suppose you'll go straight to the hotel?" said the doctor.

"I will not," replied the Bishop. "I want to know what's going on in Moyle. That coadjutor of mine only waits till my back is turned."

"I can tell you now you're a very lucky man," said the doctor. "I thought you were for the long road. I have a patient of twenty-two that the same thing happened to, and he'll never walk again."

"Poor fellow! Poor fellow!" said the Bishop perfunctorily. "I suppose a lot of it is having the stamina."

He was bitterly disappointed on reaching Moyle to discover that everyone knew of his accident, but surprised at the warmth of his welcome. Crowds gathered and knelt for his blessing in the street, and the second day, when he called at Cronin's Hotel, he was cheered as he emerged. It puzzled him a lot. As a dogmatic theologian he never enthused himself, and he didn't understand other people's enthusing. It wouldn't have occurred to him that in a small town even the presence of two bishops was nearly as good a tonic as a boxing match.

"What the blazes ails them?" he asked Jerry Cronin.

"Ah, well, people were very upset when they heard of the accident," said Jerry in surprise.

"And I suppose they knew all about it within twenty-four hours?" said the Bishop indignantly.

"Oh, sooner than that, my Lord, sooner than that," said Jerry with a shocked air.

"Nuns! Nuns! Nuns!" muttered the Bishop. "You can never trust nuns."

Revelations

By KATHERINE MANSFIELD

FROM eight o'clock in the morning until about half-past eleven Monica Tyrell suffered from her nerves, and suffered so terribly that these hours were—agonizing, simply. It was not as though she could control them. "Perhaps if I were ten years younger . . ."she would say. For now that she was thirty-three she had a queer little way of referring to her age on all occasions, of looking at her friends with grave, childish eyes and saying, "Yes, I remember how twenty years ago . . ." or of drawing Ralph's attention to the girls—real girls—with lovely youthful arms and throats and swift hesitating movements who sat near them in restaurants. "Perhaps if I were ten years younger . . ."

"Why don't you get Marie to sit outside your door and absolutely forbid anybody to come near your room until you ring your bell?"

"Oh, if it were as simple as that!" She threw her little gloves down and pressed her eyelids with her fingers in the way he knew so well. "But in the first place I'd be so conscious of Marie sitting there, Marie shaking her finger at Rudd and Mrs. Moon, Marie as a kind of cross between a wardress and a nurse for mental cases! And then, there's the post. One can't get over the fact that the post comes, and once it has come, who—who—could wait until eleven for the letters?"

His eyes grew bright; he quickly, lightly clasped her. "*My* letters, darling?"

"Perhaps," she drawled, softly, and she drew her hand over his reddish hair, smiling too, but thinking, "Heavens! What a stupid thing to say!"

But this morning she had been awakened by one great slam of the front door. Bang. The flat shook. What was it? She jerked up in bed, clutching the eiderdown; her heart beat. What could it be? Then she heard voices in the passage. Marie knocked, and, as the door opened, with a sharp tearing rip out flew the blind and the curtains, stiffening, flapping, jerking. The tassel of the blind knocked—knocked against the window. "Eh-h, *voilà!*" cried Marie, setting down the tray and running. "*C'est le vent, Madame. C'est un vent insupportable.*"

Up rolled the blind; the window went up with a jerk; a whitey-grayish light filled the room. Monica caught a glimpse of a huge pale sky and a cloud like a torn shirt dragging across before she hid her eyes with her sleeve.

"Marie! the curtains! Quick, the curtains!" Monica fell back into the bed and then "Ring-ting-a-ping-ping, ring-ting-a-ping-ping." It was the telephone. The limit of her suffering was reached; she grew quite calm. "Go and see, Marie."

"It is Monsieur. To know if Madame will lunch at Princes' at one-thirty today." Yes, it was Monsieur himself. Yes, he had asked that the message be given to Madame immediately. Instead of replying, Monica put her cup down and asked Marie in a small wondering voice what time it was. It was half-past nine. She lay still and half closed her eyes. "Tell Monsieur I cannot come," she said gently. But as the door shut, anger—anger suddenly gripped her close, close, violent, half strangling her. How dared he? How dared Ralph do such a thing when he knew how agonizing her nerves were in the morning! Hadn't she explained and described and even—though lightly, of course; she couldn't say such a thing directly—given him to understand that this was the one unforgivable thing?

And then to choose this frightful windy morning. Did he think it was just a fad of hers, a little feminine folly to be laughed at and tossed aside? Why, only last night, she had said: "Ah, but you must take me seriously, too." And he had replied: "My darling, you'll not believe me, but I know you infinitely better than you know yourself. Every delicate thought and feeling I bow to, I treasure. Yes, laugh! I love the way your lip lifts"— and he had leaned across the table—"I don't care who sees that I adore all of you. I'd be with you on a mountaintop and have all the searchlights of the world play upon us."

"Heavens!" Monica almost clutched her head. Was it possible he had really said that? How incredible men were! And she had loved him— how could she have loved a man who talked like that? What had she been doing ever since that dinner party months ago, when he had seen her home and asked if he might come and "see again that slow Arabian smile"? Oh, what nonsense—what utter nonsense—and yet she remembered at the time a strange deep thrill unlike anything she had ever felt before.

"Coal! Coal! Coal! Old iron! Old iron! Old iron!" sounded from below. It was all over. Understand her? He had understood nothing. That ringing her up on a windy morning was immensely significant. Would he understand that? She could almost have laughed. "You rang me up when the person who understood me simply couldn't have." It was the end. And when Marie said: "Monsieur replied he would be in the vestibule in case Madame changed her mind," Monica said: "No, not verbena, Marie. Carnations. Two handfuls."

A wild white morning, a tearing, rocking wind. Monica sat down before the mirror. She was pale. The maid combed back her dark hair—combed it all back—and her face was like a mask, with pointed eyelids and dark red lips. As she stared at herself in the bluish shadowy glass she suddenly felt—oh, the strangest, most tremendous excitement filling her slowly, slowly, until she wanted to fling out her arms, to laugh, to scatter everything, to shock Marie, to cry: "I'm free. I'm free as the wind." And now all this vibrating, trembling, exciting, flying world was hers. It was her kingdom. No, no, she belonged to nobody but Life.

"That will do, Marie," she stammered. "My hat, my coat, my bag. And now get me a taxi." Where was she going? Oh, anywhere. She could not stand this silent flat, noiseless Marie, this ghostly, quiet, feminine interior. She must be out; she must be driving quickly—anywhere, anywhere.

"The taxi is there, Madame." As she pressed open the big outer doors of the flats the wild wind caught her and floated her across the pavement. Where to? She got in, and smiling radiantly at the cross, cold-looking driver, she told him to take her to her hairdresser's. Whenever Monica had nowhere else to go to or nothing on earth to do she drove there. She might just have her hair waved, and by that time she'd have thought out a plan. The cross, cold driver drove at a tremendous pace, and she let herself be hurled from side to side. She wished he would go faster and faster. Oh, to be free of Princes' at one-thirty, of being the tiny kitten in the swansdown basket, of being the Arabian, and the grave, delighted child and the little wild creature. . . . "Never again," she cried aloud, clenching her small fist. But the cab had stopped, and the driver was standing holding the door open for her.

The hairdresser's shop was warm and glittering. It smelled of soap and burnt paper and wallflower brilliantine. There was Madame behind the counter, round, fat, white, her head like a powder puff rolling on a black satin pincushion. Monica always had the feeling that they loved her in this shop and understood her—the real her—far better than many of her friends did. She was her real self here, and she and Madame had often talked—quite strangely—together. Then there was George who did her hair, young, dark, slender George. She was really fond of him.

But today—how curious! Madame hardly greeted her. Her face was whiter than ever, but rims of bright red showed round her blue bead eyes, and even the rings on her pudgy fingers did not flash. They were cold, dead, like chips of glass. When she called through the wall telephone to George there was a note in her voice that had never been there before. But Monica would not believe this. No, she refused to. It was just her imagination. She sniffed greedily the warm, scented air, and passed behind the velvet curtain into the small cubicle.

Her hat and jacket were off and hanging from the peg, and still George did not come. This was the first time he had ever not been there to hold the chair for her, to take her hat and hang up her bag, dangling it in his fingers as though it were something he'd never seen before—something fairy. And how quiet the shop was! There was not a sound even from Madame. Only the wind blew, shaking the old house; the wind hooted, the portraits of Ladies of the Pompadour Period looked down and smiled, cunning and sly. Monica wished she hadn't come. Oh, what a mistake to have come! Fatal. Fatal. Where was George? If he didn't appear the next moment she would go away. She took off the white kimono. She didn't want to look at herself any more. When she opened a big pot of cream on the glass shelf her fingers trembled. There was a tugging feeling at her heart as though her happiness—her marvelous happiness—were trying to get free.

"I'll go. I'll not stay." She took down her hat. But just at that moment steps sounded, and, looking in the mirror, she saw George bowing in the doorway. How queerly he smiled! It was the mirror of course. She turned round quickly. His lips curled back in a sort of grin, and—wasn't he unshaved?—he looked almost green in the face.

"Very sorry to have kept you waiting," he mumbled, sliding, gliding forward.

Oh, no, she wasn't going to stay. "I'm afraid," she began. But he had lighted the gas and laid the tongs across, and was holding out the kimono. "It's the wind," he said. Monica submitted. She smelled his fresh young fingers pinning the jacket under her chin. "Yes, there is a wind," said she, sinking back into the chair. And silence fell. George took out the pins in his expert way. Her hair tumbled back, but he didn't hold it as he usually did, as though to feel how fine and soft and heavy it was. He didn't say it "was in a lovely condition." He let it fall, and, taking a brush out of a drawer, he coughed faintly, cleared his throat and said dully, "Yes, it's a pretty strong one, I should say it was."

She had no reply to make. The brush fell on her hair. Oh, oh, how mournful, how mournful! It fell quick and light, it fell like leaves; and then it fell heavy, tugging like the tugging at her heart. "That's enough," she cried, shaking herself free.

"Did I do it too much?" asked George. He crouched over the tongs. "I'm sorry." There came the smell of burnt paper—the smell she loved—and he swung the hot tongs round in his hand, staring before him. "I shouldn't be surprised if it rained." He took up a piece of her hair, when—she couldn't bear it any longer—she stopped him. She looked at him; she saw herself looking at him in the white kimono like a nun. "Is there something the matter here? Has something happened?" But George gave a half shrug and a grimace. "Oh, no, Madame. Just a little occurrence." And he took up the piece of hair again. But, oh, she wasn't deceived. That was it. Something awful had happened. The silence—really, the silence seemed to come drifting down like flakes of snow. She shivered. It was cold in the little cubicle, all cold and glittering. The nickel taps and jets and sprays looked somehow almost malignant. The wind rattled the windowframe; a piece of iron banged, and the young man went on changing the tongs, crouching over her. Oh, how terrifying Life was, thought Monica. How dreadful. It is the loneliness which is so appalling. We whirl along like leaves, and nobody knows—nobody cares where we fall, in what black river we float away. The tugging feeling seemed to rise into her throat. It ached, ached; she longed to cry. "That will do," she whispered. "Give me the pins." As he stood beside her, so submissive, so silent, she nearly dropped her arms and sobbed. She couldn't bear any more. Like a wooden man the gay young George still slid, glided, handed her her hat and veil, took the note, and brought back the change. She stuffed it into her bag. Where was she going now?

George took a brush. "There is a little powder on your coat," he murmured. He brushed it away. And then suddenly he raised himself and, looking at Monica, gave a strange wave with the brush and said: "The truth is, Madame, since you are an old customer—my little daughter died this morning. A first child"—and then his white face crumpled like paper, and he turned his back on her and began brushing the cotton kimono. "Oh, oh," Monica began to cry. She ran out of the shop into the taxi. The driver, looking furious, swung off the seat and slammed the door again. "Where to?"

"Princes'," she sobbed. And all the way there she saw nothing but a tiny wax doll with a feather of gold hair, lying meek, its tiny hands and feet crossed. And then just before she came to Princes' she saw a flower shop full of white flowers. Oh, what a perfect thought. Lilies-of-the-valley, and white pansies, double white violets and white velvet ribbon. . . . From an unknown friend. . . . From one who understands. . . . For a Little Girl. . . . She tapped against the window, but the driver did not hear; and, anyway, they were at Princes' already.

Eneas Africanus

By HARRY STILLWELL EDWARDS

Editor *Telegraph and Messenger,*
Macon, Ga.

Dear Sir: I am writing to invoke your kind assistance in tracing an old family Negro of mine who disappeared in 1864, between my stock farm in Floyd County and my home place, locally known as Tommeysville, in Jefferson County. The Negro's name was Eneas, a small gray-haired old fellow and very talkative. The unexpected movement of our army after the battle of Resaca, placed my stock farm in line of the Federal advance and exposed my family to capture. My command, Tommey's Legion, passing within five miles of the place, I was enabled to give them warning, and they hurriedly boarded the last southbound train. They reached Jefferson County safely but without any baggage, as they did not have time to move a trunk. An effort was made to save the family silver, much of it very old and highly prized, especially a silver cup known in the family as the "Bride's Cup" for some six or eight generations and bearing the inscription:

> Ye bryde whose lippes kysse myne
> And taste ye water an no wyne
> Shall happy live an hersel see
> A happy grandchile on each knee.

These lines were surrounded with a wreath and surmounted by a knight's head, visor down, and the motto: "SEMPER FIDELIS."

This cup was hurriedly packed with other silver in a hair trunk and intrusted to Eneas with verbal instructions as to travel. He drove an old-fashioned, flea-bitten, blooded mare to a one-horse wagon full of forage and carried all the Confederate money the family left, to pay his expenses. He was last seen, as I ascertained soon after the war from a wounded member of my command, about eight miles southeast of Atlanta, asleep in the wagon, the mare turning to the right instead of keeping the straight road to Macon. Eneas was a faithful Negro, born and raised in the Tommey family and our belief is he was murdered by army stragglers and robbed of the trunk. He had never been over the road he was traveling, as we always traveled to North Georgia by rail, shipping the horses likewise. His geographical knowledge consisted of a few names— places to which I had at different times taken him, and in the neighbor- hood, of my home, such as Macon, Sparta, Louisville, and the counties of Washington and Jefferson. If given a chance to talk he would probably confine himself to Lady Chain, the mare he was driving; Lightning, the noted four-mile stallion temporarily in my possession; the Tommey family and our settlement, Tommeysville. On these topics he could talk eighteen hours a day.

I have no hope of ever seeing Eneas again, for if living he would have gotten back if he had to travel all over the South to do it, but there is a bare chance that the cup may be found, and I am writing to gratify my daughter, whose wedding day is approaching. All brides in the family, since 1670, have used this cup on their wedding days. If the cup was stolen, doubtless the thieves sold it, and if so, the holder may read these lines if they are given publicity. I am willing to waive any question of ownership and purchase the cup at the holder's valuation, if within my power; or, if unwilling to sell, he may loan the cup for a few days.

I shall be greatly obliged if you will publish this letter with a request that all Southern papers, daily and weekly, copy the same. Thanking you in advance and with all good wishes for your happiness and pros- perity, I am, most respectfully,

Your obed't servant,
GEORGE E. TOMMEY,
Late Major, Tommey's Legion, C. S. A.
P. O., Louisville, Ga.

Althea Lodge, Fayette Co., Ga.
October 15, 1872
Maj. Geo. E. Tommey,
Louisville, Ga.

Dear Major Tommey: I read with deep interest and sympathy your letter in the *Telegraph and Messenger* inquiring of a Negro named Eneas. This man, I am sure, came to my house about twenty miles south of Atlanta in 1864. I remember the occasion perfectly, because he men- tioned your name and one of my boys was serving in your command. I gave him shelter for the night and food for himself and horse. He insisted on sleeping in his wagon. He told me that the mare was famous on the race track and very valuable and he was afraid to leave her. This struck me as singular, at the time, because she seemed old and broken down. I did not see any trunk, but his wagon was full of hay and fodder and he may have had one hidden under it. Eneas asked me to put him on the road to Thomasville—or so I understood him—and I gave him explicit directions as far as Newman, advising him to get more at that point. He was gone when I arose next morning. I do hope you will find the old man, as well as the cup. I took quite a fancy to him. He gave me a very vivid description of yourself—whom I had long wished to meet—and of your home, the twelve-room house, lawn with its three fountains, beautiful lake and your hundred Negroes in their painted cottages, etc.

Excuse this rambling letter. Your name has stirred an old woman's memories.

Sincerely your friend,
MARTHA HORTON

P. S.—My son, William, who served in your command, married a Connecticut girl. Think of it, Major! But she proved to be a noble-hearted woman and has influenced him to give up tobacco and stimulants in every form. He travels this territory for a New York house. His wife is well connected, and one of her ancestors came over in the *Mayflower*. She is with me now and sends you her regards. Billy has convinced her that next to General Joseph Johnston, you were the bravest man in the Georgia armies.   M. H.

Talbotton, Ga., Oct. 18, 1872

Major George Tommey, Louisville, Ga.

Sir: Read your letter in the *Columbus Enquirer*. I kept a livery stable here in '64 and saw the man you are hunting about that time. He drove a broken-down old speckled gray mare he called Lady Chain, now that you mention it, and claimed she was in foal to Lightning, the great four-mile horse. I took this for a joke along with some of the fairy stories he gave me about the Tommeys, but he was so polite and humble that I let him stay overnight in the stable. Offered to pay me next morning and seemed like he had about a bushel of Confedrit money; but I was long on Confed myself and didn't let him put any more on me. Don't remember seein' any trunk. He was on his way to Thomasville, so he said, and I giv' him as much directions as he could carry.

Very truly,   WILLIAM PETERS.

Thomas County, Oct. 19, 1872

Major George Tommey, Louisville, Ga.

Dear Sir: My wife remembered your old nigger as soon as she read your letter in the Macon paper, and so did I when she called it to my mind. He was a big talker all right, and sat on our back steps half the night talking about the Tommeys, their race horse, twenty-room house, yard with six fountains, and a whole tribe of niggers. We fed him, and he slept in his wagon. Next day he wanted to pay me in Confederate money; was using a corn sack for a pocketbook, and it was most full. He moved on to Thomasville, about six miles from here, but I don't think it was the place he was looking for. I reckon it must have been "Tommeysville" he was looking for. Major, I took a good look at Lady Chain and you ain't lost much if you never get her back, but if you don't find the nigger, you've lost the champion liar of Georgia. I hope you get him back, but it's hardly possible a man talking like he did could last seven years on the public road.

Respectfully, ABNER CUMMING

Thomasville, Ga., Oct. 19, 1872

Hon Sir and Major: Your man, Eneas, came to my home in Thomasville, in the winter of '65 or the fall of '64, in great distress. He said he had traveled a thousand miles to get to Thomasville, but it wasn't the right Thomasville. He had no idea of states, geography or direction, claimed he had lived in Jefferson County, next to Washington County, and as this describes two counties across the line in Florida, several people at different times had sent him over there. I gave him a letter to a friend over in Jefferson County near Tallahassee. He had an old gray mare he said was a famous race horse, but she didn't look it. Claimed she was in foal to the celebrated Lightning, whose four-mile race in the mud at New Orleans I witnessed. I thought the old nigger was loose in the upper story. He had no trunk when here.

Very truly,   ANDREW LOOMIS.

Tallahassee, Fla., Oct. 20, 1872

Major Geo. E. Tommey, Tommeysville, via
    Louisville, Ga.

My Dear Sir: Eneas, your old Negro, whose name I had forgotten until I read your letter in *The Atlanta Constitution,* was on my plantation near here in '65. He came here, very blue and utterly discouraged, from Thomasville, Ga. Said he was looking for a little Thomasville owned by Major George E. Tommey. He brought a letter from a friend of mine. There are no Tommeys in this county and no Thomasville, and not knowing what to do with him, I passed him along to Colonel Chairs, a friend in Washington County which is on the gulf coast. Chairs wrote me that he had had a great deal of fun out of Eneas. The gulf astonished him. He declared solemnly that he knew he was in the wrong Washington, because there were no oranges, or scrub palmettoes, or big, green spiders (crabs) in his, and the water had no salt in it. Eneas talked a good deal of Macon and Louisville, and there being a county and town so named, besides another Thomasville, to the north in Alabama, Chairs started him up that way. I am truly sorry the old man came to grief. He was a harmless old fellow, though a picturesque liar, as are many old Negroes when they talk of their white folks.

It is possible that Eneas had a trunk, but I have no recollection of seeing one in his possession.   Yours very truly,

RANDOLPH THOMAS

Louisville, Ala., Oct. 28, 1872

Major G. E. Tommey, Louisville, Ga.

Sir: A ole nigger name of enus come by hyar in the firs yer atter the war with er old mare and er colt he claim was by the lightnin. He was lokin for a tomusville an I tried to show him the way back to tomusville, in Georgia, but he got mad and wanted to fight me, and if he hadn't been er ole man I would have busted him open. Mr. tommy, you wont never see yo nigger no more less he mends his way of acktin when you are tryin to help him.

Respectfully, sir, yours,

POMPEY WILEY (Colored)

He lef hyar for Macon County.

Barton, Washington County, Ala.

Major G. E. Tommey, Louisville, Ga.

Dear Sir: Your Negro, Eneas, came to my place in this county in 1865, I think, from a little village named Thomasville to the northeast. He was very poor and his pathetic story appealed to my sympathies. I let him have some rations and a piece of land and he planted a cotton crop. He married a young mulatto woman on my place that year, and when he left here about Christmas, 1866, carried with him a young baby besides the old mare and her colt. The colt, by the way, was a beauty.

Eneas was a puzzle to me, though I have lived among Negroes all my life. His stories of you and your place were marvels. But for the fact that he held the mare and colt in your name, refusing dozens of offers for the latter when in dire need, I should have put him down a reckless romancer. He began preaching here among the Negroes and proved to be a most eloquent spiritual advocate. He claimed to be the pastor of a big congregation at home. I heard him on one occasion when he baptized forty converts and was thrilled by his imagery and power.

Eneas knew nothing of geography beyond the names of a few towns and counties. Hearing of a Macon and Louisville over in Mississippi, he gathered his household goods into his wagon in December, '66. I do hope you will yet find him. Suppose you make inquiries through the African Methodist Church—he ought to be a bishop by this time.

Very respectfully,

JAMES TALLEY,
Attorney at Law.

Sunshine Parsonage,
Washington County, Mississippi

Major Geo. E. Tommey, Louisville, Ga.

My Dear Sir: I was greatly interested in your letter copied into our county paper from the *Telegraph and Messenger,* concerning Eneas

Tommey. He was here in 1868 or 1869 with a wife and several children. They came in a one-horse wagon drawn by an old gray mare he called Lady Chain and followed by a splendid young colt he declared was from celebrated racing stock. An almost worn-out pass from his mistress, Mrs. Tommey, though it bore no date or address, saved the old man from arrest. His story, that he was lost and on his way home, though remarkable, was possible, and he was not molested. The narrative of his wanderings interested me greatly. He came up the river—the Mississippi—from Jefferson County, trying to find a ford. He had heard of a Washington parish and a Thomasville in Louisiana, and was trying to reach them. He rented a piece of land near here and raised a crop, leaving in 1869 for Jefferson County, Alabama. I gave him a letter to a minister in that county.

Very truly,
(Rev.) JOHN SIMMS

P. S.—I regret to say that after leaving here, Eneas, though an active minister of the Gospel, suffered the young horse to be entered in a county race. I understand that he won about seventy-five dollars. Allowance, however, must be made for the old man's necessities and distress.   J. S.

Idlewilde, Jefferson County, Ala.
October 26, 1872

Major Geo. E. Tommey, Louisville, Ga.

My Dear Sir: A Birmingham paper today gave me the explanation of a mystery that has puzzled my family for several years, when it reproduced your letter to the *Telegraph and Messenger*. Eneas—or the Rev. Eneas Tommey, as he called himself—came here in 1869 with a gray mare and a splendid young horse, which he claimed was of marvelous speed, and a letter from a friend of mine in Mississippi. He also brought a wife and two children. To the latter he added a third before leaving. My daughter was greatly interested in the old man's remarkable story and made an effort to help him. She took down a letter to you, which he dictated, made seven copies of it and sent one to every Thomasville in the South. They all came back to her. By good luck she retained one for her scrapbook, and I enclose it that you may see how the faithful old fellow was trying to reach you. He stayed around here farming and preaching until 1870 when, hearing from a horse trader of a Macon and a Sparta in Tennessee, he moved on. He had no trunk with him, and I am afraid your cup is gone.

Very truly,
(Rev.) AMOS WELLS

P. S.—I am informed that Eneas participated in a horse race in Birmingham after leaving here and won a great deal of money.

A. W.

The letter of Eneas enclosed in that of Rev. Mr. Wells:

Marse George: I am loss in er distric called Yallerhama, by a town name o' Burningham. Ef you knows whar Burningham is, fer God's sake come ter me fer I can't git ter you! Me and Lady Chain is plum wore out.

Marse George, I been ter first one an' den ernuther Thomasville, year in an' year out, tell thar ain't no sense in hit. An' I ain't hit de right one yit. Ev'y yuther place is name Thomasville er Macon er Washington er Jefferson. Everybody knows whar I wanter go but me, an' shows me de road; but all I kin do is ter keep movin. De firs Thomasville I got to I got back to fo' times. Hit was harder ter loose it than hit was ter find it!

Marse George, I come ter one pond I couldn't see ercross an' de water warn't no count. The last Thomasville was out most ter sundown an' I was headin' fer ernuther when I struck er creek a mile wide an' Lady Chain couldn't wade hit, so we turn back.

Marse George, Lady Chain's colt come, back in the secon' Jefferson, an' he sholy is old Lightnin's colt; long-legged, big-footed an' iron gray. I been tryin' him out hyar an' thar an' thar ain't nothin' kin tech him.

Marse George, I got ernuther wife down in de third Washington an' am bringin' her erlong. She weighs one hundred and sixty, an' picks fo' hundred pounds er cotton er day. She b'longs ter you, same as me an' Lady Chain an' de colt.

Marse George, er horse trader goin' by told me erbout some more Macons an' Spartas an' Jeffersons an' Washingtons up de country fum hyar an' ef I don't get word fum you by nex' month, I'm gointer move erlong.

Marse George, ef you knows whar I is fum dis hyar letter an' can't come yo'self, sen' fer me. I'm sick o' de road an' wanter git home. Do somp'n an' do hit quick!

> Yo' ole nigger,
> ENEAS

Macon, Tenn., Oct. 30, 1872

Maj. George E. Tommey, Louisville, Ga.

My Dear Sir: Eneas was here in 1869 or 1870 and remained about a year preaching at Mount Zion and other places in the county. I do not know when I ever met a more original and entertaining talker. His description of your colonial house with its forty rooms, white columns and splendid parks has aroused in me a strong desire to visit the place if I am ever able to come to Georgia. I know it must have suffered from the ravages of the war, but doubtless enough remains to show its former magnificence. I am especially anxious to see the great lake with its flocks of swans, and the twelve fountains on your lawn. My mother is a Georgian and I have often heard her describe the natural beauties of the state. There is a feeling with us all that at last it is "home" and that some day we shall all assemble in dear old Monroe County where Grandpa was born.

Eneas brought with him to this place a gray mare that was, he said, a famous race horse, and that the father of her colt was the greatest horse in the world. I had forgotten their names until I read your letters. Eneas insisted that you live at Thomasville next to Washington and Jefferson Counties, and near a town named Louisville. There are towns and counties of the same names in this state and he left to visit them. He seemed to have plenty of money. I hope you will hear from him yet, but I am afraid the trunk is gone. He had none when here.

Sincerely yours,

MARY ADKINS

Louisville, Tenn., Oct. 27, 1872

Sir: Don't you worry about old Eneas. He came here in or about '70 with a gray mare, a long-legged race horse; a young wife and three children, and give out that he was a minister of the Gospel. They stayed on my place and there were four children when they left. He was a preacher all right, 'cause I heard him time and again, but all the same he was the biggest liar in Tennessee at that time, and that's a great record for any man. Major, if half he said about you and your place is true, you ought to be President. You must have owned all the niggers in Georgia, and your home must be spread over all three of them counties he has been looking for ever since freedom. About that Lightning colt—he certainly looks it. Eneas slipped him into a free-for-all up here and him and a strange white man about busted the county. I offered him five hundred dollars for the colt, but he said your price was twenty thousand dollars. Considering you had never seen him, I thought that a little high and him and me didn't trade. Next day he was gone. I was away from home when he left. He owed me twenty dollars I had advanced him, taking a lien note on the crop. He sent me word that if the crop didn't pay out to send you the bill. Said he had plenty of money to pay the note, but didn't have time to wait for it to come due. Oh, you Eneas! Say, Major, if he ever gets back, and he will for you can't lose that kind of man for good, better nail down everything movable—including them twelve fountains.

Yours,

TOM JOHNSON

P. S.—I say; twelve fountains.
P. S. S.—Forty-four rooms! Gosh! is the Legion still with you?

Washington County, N. C., Oct. 20, 1872

Maj. George E. Tommey, Louisville, Ga.

My Dear Major: Your old Negro has been on my plantation for about a year farming and preaching and romancing. He came straight through

Tennessee and North Carolina, touching Sparta, Louisville, Washington and Jefferson Counties in the former, and the towns of Jefferson, Sparta and Macon in this state before he found me. I am affectionately known all over this section of the State as "Major Tommy," and as the old Negro was looking for "Major Tommy," somebody put him on my trail. He soon had me treed, but was greatly disappointed when he saw me. However, that did not keep him from paying me a year's visit. Eneas is a queer character—wisdom of the serpent and simplicity of a child. His story, probably growing with age, like the stories of some of our veterans, has beguiled many a lonely hour for me, but not until I read your letter in the Richmond *Dispatch* did I give him credit for many facts in it. The young race horse is certainly a fine animal and should you decide to sell him I trust you will give me the refusal. Eneas won several purses up here in local races. It seems he has a new name for his horse everywhere he goes. He says it keeps him from getting "too common." When Eneas was not plowing or racing, his favorite occupation was preaching, his subject usually being the wandering of the Hebrews in the desert. He left here for Jefferson, S. C. I am sorry to say I heard no mention of your lost cup, and if he had any trunk I was not informed of it.

With regards for yourself and all good wishes for the young bride, I am,   Very sincerely yours,

THOMAS BAILEY
(Late) Major 13th N. C. Volunteers,
C. S. A.

Extract from Columbia (S. C.) *Register,* October 27, 1872:

One of the surprises of yesterday's races came in the free-for-all two-mile dash, which was won by Chainlightning, entered by an old Negro man calling himself Eneas Tommey, who claims the horse was sired by the celebrated stallion Lightning, and that the dam, which he drives to a one-horse wagon on his way to Georgia, is Lady Chain. She was certainly a tired-looking old lady. Eneas arrived late and at once attracted attention by his unique appearance and his limitless faith in Chainlightning. His story and the splendid horse interested some stablemen and after a private demonstration they succeeded in getting him entered and a rider engaged. In the get-off Chainlightning took the lead and gave a marvelous exhibition of speed. He led the bunch by a hundred yards at the end of the first mile and by nearly three hundred at the end of the second. He was then going strong and the efforts of the rider to stop him resulted in a runaway. When he came around the third time the crowd blocked the track and brought him to a standstill, but his rider was thrown. Eneas won two hundred dollars. It is not known how his backers fared, but it is supposed that they cleaned up a good pile on the side. Eneas left yesterday, going toward Augusta, Ga. It was suggested afterward that this may have been the man advertised for in the *Telegraph and Messenger* by a Major Tommey, of Louisville, Ga., a few weeks ago. The matter will be brought to his attention. One reason for the sudden departure of the old Negro, who had become quite a hero among members of his race, is said to be a movement to elect him to the State Senate.

Louisville, Ga.—(Correspondence Macon *Telegraph and Messenger*, Oct. 31, '72)—Your correspondent on Thursday last was the favored guest

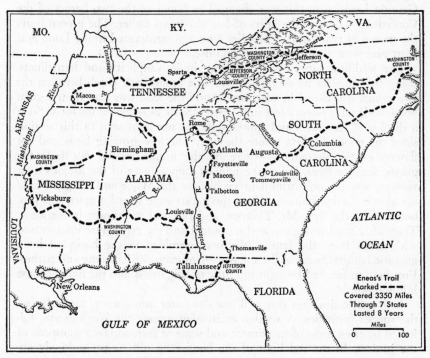

Eneas, it is said, started near Rome, Ga., in 1864 and arrived at his destination near Louisville, Ga., in 1872. This map will enable the reader to trace him.

of Major George E. Tommey, the famous commander of the Tommey Legion, which rendered conspicuous service to the Confederacy as a part of Johnston's—afterwards Hood's—army, in the Tennessee and North Georgia campaigns. The Major lives about twelve miles from this place at Tommeysville, as his plantation is called. His delightful residence is one of the old-fashioned, two-story houses with broad hall and verandas and two large wings, and is situated in a beautiful grove of oak and hickory. The broad lawn in front abounds with roses and among them is a tiny fountain with a spray. Beyond the house lie the barns and the Negro quarters and a small artificial lake where ducks abound. Sherman's army missed the charming spot and the only suggestion of the "late unpleasantness" is the Major's sword crossed with the colors of the Legion over the broad fireplace at the end of the hall.

The occasion of your correspondent's visit was the marriage of the Major's only daughter, Beauregarde Forrest, to Mirabeau Lamar Temple, of Dallas, Tex. The bride, a petite brunette of great beauty, entered life eighteen years ago, inheriting her mother's name, but by the act of the Georgia Legislature this was changed in honor of the two heroes of the Confederacy, dear to the heart of her illustrious father. The groom bears the names of two Georgia families long ago transported to the Lone Star State and is an attorney of great promise.

The wedding supper was charming in its simplicity and homeliness, using the word in its original sense. The broad back porch between the two wings was closed in with smilax and the feast was spread on a great homemade table twenty feet in diameter. Seats were placed for forty. Such a display of delicacies and substantials has not been seen in this section since the good old days before the war. The low-growing ferns and cut flowers of the decorations—there by the hundreds—did not hide the guests' smiling faces. Wine, the famous scuppernong of the Major's own vintage, was the only stimulant visible, for the Major and his good lady are almost total abstainers. When the guests were seated a grace was pronounced by the Rev. Mr. Thigpen, and fun and merriment broke loose. Toast after toast was given and sentiment and the poets were interspersed with songs from the family Negroes assembled in the backyard by a gigantic bonfire. Some of the songs were of exquisite harmony and pathos. Freedom, so far, had brought but little of brightness into the lives of these humble people.

A dramatic situation that will one day enter into a story, came during the supper festivities. A sudden excitement among the Negroes was followed by cries, some of merriment and some of fear, and by a stampede of the juniors. In the red light of the bonfire an old Negro suddenly appeared, reining up a splendid gray horse. The old man was seated in a red-wheeled road cart, enveloped in a flapping linen duster and wore a silk hat. His "Whoa, Chainlightnin!" resounded all over the place. Then he stood up and began to shout about Moses and the Hebrew children being led out of Egypt into the promised land. Major Tommey listened for a brief instant and rushed out. The newcomer met him with an equal rush and their loud greetings floated back to us clear as the notes of a plantation bell: "Eneas, you black rascal, where have you been?"

"Oh, Lord! Marse George! Glory be ter God! Out o' de wilderness! De projekin son am back again!"

"It's Eneas!" screamed the little bride, gathering up her skirts and rushing out. In the strong light, as the wedding party hurriedly followed, we could see the old Negro hanging to his master and filling the night with his weird cries. Catching the excitement, the Negroes around began to moan and chant, taking their text from the old man's words.

"Where have you been, sir?" The Major was trying to free himself and choking with tears and laughter.

"All over de blessed worl', Marse George! but I'm home ergin!—You hyar me, niggers?—home ergin!"

"Stop, sir!"

But suddenly the old man grew rigid in the grasp of a momentous thought. His voice sank to a whisper audible to only a few of us:

"Marse George, wha's Nancy?"

"Nancy is dead, Eneas," said the Major, sadly.

"Thank God!" said the old man fervently.

"Where is my trunk, Eneas?" The old Negro was making a horn of his hands and giving the plantation halloo. With his eyes set on the banking shadows beyond the fire, he waited, an inscrutable smile on his wrinkled face. Presently into the circle of light came an old gray mare, drawing a wagon in which sat a yellow woman, hovering a small colony of children.

"I done brought you a whole bunch o' new Yallerhama, Burningham niggers, Marse George! Some folks tell me dey is free, but I know dey b'long ter Marse George Tommey, des like Lady Chain and her colt! Marse George, you oughter see dat horse—"

"Where is the trunk?" repeated the Major, laughing and wiping his eyes. "Where did you leave it, Eneas?"

"I ain't lef' it," said Eneas indignantly. "Git out o' dat wagon, niggers, fo' I bus' somer you wide open!" The little colony fell over the wheels like cooters from a log, and drawing aside the hay that had held them, Eneas brought forth a time- and weather-defying hair trunk. He heaved a mighty sigh of relief as he dropped it on the ground:

"Dar 'tis, Marse George, an' I sho is glad to git shut o' dat ol' bunch o' hide an' har!" The bride danced and clapped her tiny hands: "My cup! My cup! Get it! Quick! O, please somebody, open the trunk."

Major Tommey picked up an ax and with one blow sliced off the ancient lock. From its snug nest in cotton batting, the bride lifted a shining cup, the cup, Mr. Editor, advertised in your columns a few weeks ago. A bucket rattled down in a nearby well and the bridegroom came with a great gourd of water. Then he read aloud the quaint inscription:

Ye bryde whose lippes kysse myne
An taste ye water an no wyne
Shall happy live an hersel see
A happy grandchile on each knee.

The little woman accepted the challenge with the cup, and smiling up to the face of her husband sipped of the crystal draught and handed him the cup. He, too, drank, but the slight flush on the bride's face was nothing to the fiery scarlet of his own, when a storm of applause greeted the act.

Eneas had drawn the Major aside and produced an old scrap pocket-book, stuffed with bills.

"Marse George," he began, "de bag o' yaller war money what dey gimme warn't no good over yonner whar I been. Countin' de c'llections I tuck up in de church an' what I winned on de track wid Chainlightnin' an' ain't spent—"

"Keep it, Eneas," said the Major, almost exploding with laughter, and patting the old man on the shoulder, "that bunch of Burningham Yaller-hama niggers more than square us."

They Grind Exceeding Small

By BEN AMES WILLIAMS

I TELEPHONED down the hill to Hazen Kinch. "Hazen," I asked, "are you going to town today?"

"Yes, yes," he said abruptly in his quick, harsh fashion. "Of course I'm going to town."

"I've a matter of business," I suggested.

"Come along," he invited brusquely. "Come along."

There was not another man within forty miles to whom he would have given that invitation.

"I'll be down in ten minutes," I promised him; and I went to pull on my Pontiacs and heavy half boots over them and started downhill through the sandy snow. It was bitterly cold; it had been a cold winter. The bay—I could see it from my window—was frozen over for a dozen miles east and west and thirty north and south; and that had not happened in close to a score of years. Men were freighting across to the islands with heavy teams. Automobiles had beaten a rough road along the course the steamers took in summer. A man who had ventured to stock one of the lower islands with foxes for the sake of their fur, counting on the water to hold them prisoners, had gone bankrupt when his stock in trade escaped across the ice. Bitterly cold and steadily cold, and deep snow lay upon the hills, blue-white in the distance. The evergreens were blue-black blotches on this whiteness. The birches, almost indistinguishable, were like trees in camouflage. To me the hills are never so grand as in this winter coat they wear. It is easy to believe that a brooding God dwells upon them. I wondered as I plowed my way down to Hazen Kinch's farm whether God did indeed dwell among these hills; and I wondered what He thought of Hazen Kinch.

This was no new matter of thought with me. I had given some thought to Hazen in the past. I was interested in the man and in that which should come to him. He was, it seemed to me, a problem in fundamental ethics; he was, as matters stood, a demonstration of the essential uprightness of things as they are. The biologist would have called him a sport, a deviation from type, a violation of all the proper laws of life. That such a man should live and grow great and prosper was not fitting; in a well-regulated world it could not be. Yet Hazen Kinch did live; he had grown—in his small way—great; and by our lights he had prospered. Therefore I watched him. There was about the man the fascination which clothes a tightrope walker above Niagara; an aeronaut in the midst of the nosedive. The spectator stares with half-caught breath, afraid to see and afraid to miss seeing the ultimate catastrophe. Sometimes I wondered whether Hazen Kinch suspected this attitude on my part. It was not impossible. There was a cynical courage in the man; it might have amused him. Certainly I was the only man who had in any degree his confidence.

I have said there was not another within forty miles whom he would have given a lift to town; I doubt if there was another man anywhere for whom he would have done this small favor.

He seemed to find a mocking sort of pleasure in my company.

When I came to his house he was in the barn harnessing his mare to the sleigh. The mare was a good animal, fast and strong. She feared and she hated Hazen. I could see her roll her eyes backward at him as he adjusted the traces. He called to me without turning:

"Shut the door! Shut the door! Damn the cold!"

I slid the door shut behind me. There was within the barn the curious chill warmth which housed animals generate to protect themselves against our winters.

"It will snow," I told Hazen. "I was not sure you would go."

He laughed crookedly, jerking at the trace.

"Snow!" he exclaimed. "A man would think you were personal manager of the weather. Why do you say it will snow?"

"The drift of the clouds—and it's warmer," I told him.

"I'll not have it snowing," he said, and looked at me and cackled. He was a little, thin, old man with meager whiskers and a curious precision of speech; and I think he got some enjoyment out of watching my expression at such remarks as this. He elaborated his assumption that the universe was conducted for his benefit, in order to see my silent revolt at the suggestion. "I'll not have it snowing," he said. "Open the door."

He led the mare out and stopped by the kitchen door.

"Come in," he said. "A hot drink."

I went with him into the kitchen. His wife was there, and their child. The woman was lean and frail; and she was afraid of him. The countryside said he had taken her in payment of a bad debt. Her father had owed him money which he could not pay.

"I decided it was time I had a wife," Hazen used to say to me.

The child was on the floor. The woman had a drink of milk and egg and rum, hot and ready for us. We drank, and Hazen knelt beside the child. A boy baby, not yet two years old. It is an ugly thing to say, but I hated this child. There was evil malevolence in his baby eyes. I have sometimes thought the gray devils must have left just such hate-bred babies as this in France. Also, he was deformed—a twisted leg. The women of the neighborhood sometimes said he would be better dead. But Hazen Kinch loved him. He lifted him in his arms now with a curious passion in his movement, and the child stared at him sullenly. When the mother came near the baby squalled at her, and Hazen said roughly:

"Stand away! Leave him alone!"

She moved back furtively; and Hazen asked me, displaying the child: "A fine boy, eh?"

I said nothing, and in his cracked old voice he mumbled endearments to the baby. I had often wondered whether his love for the child redeemed the man; or merely made him vulnerable. Certainly any harm that might come to the baby would be a crushing blow to Hazen.

He put the child down on the floor again and he said to the woman curtly: "Tend him well." She nodded. There was a dumb submission in her eyes; but through this blank veil I had seen now and then a blaze of pain.

Hazen went out of the door without further word to her, and I followed him. We got into the sleigh, bundling ourselves into the robes for the six-mile drive along the drifted road to town. There was a feeling of storm in the air. I looked at the sky and so did Hazen Kinch. He guessed what I would have said and he answered me before I could speak.

"I'll not have it snowing," he said, and leered at me.

Nevertheless, I knew the storm would come. The mare turned out of the barnyard and plowed through a drift and struck hard-packed road. Her hoofs beat a swift tattoo; our runners sang beneath us. We dropped to the little bridge and across and began the mile-long climb to the top of Rayborn Hill. The road from Hazen's house to town is compounded of such ups and downs.

At the top of the hill we paused for a moment to breathe the mare; paused just in front of the big old Rayborn house, that has stood there for more years than most of us remember. It was closed and shuttered and deserted; and Hazen dipped his whip toward it and said meanly:

"An ugly, improvident lot, the Rayborns were."

I had known only one of them—the eldest son. A fine man, I had thought him. Picking apples in his orchard, he fell one October and broke his neck. His widow tried to make a go of the place, but she borrowed of Hazen and he had evicted her this three months back. It was one of the lesser evils he had done. I looked at the house and at him, and he clucked to the mare and we dipped down into the steep valley below the hill.

The wind had a sweep in that valley and there was a drift of snow across it and across the road. This drift was well packed by the wind, but when we drove over its top our left-hand runner broke through the coaming and we tumbled into the snow, Hazen and I. We were well entangled in the rugs. The mare gave a frightened start, but Hazen had held the reins and the whip so that she could not break away. We got up together, he and I, and we righted the sleigh and set it upon the road again. I remember that it was becoming bitter cold and the sun was no longer shining. There was a steel-gray veil drawn across the bay.

When the sleigh was upright Hazen went forward and stood beside the mare. Some men, blaming the beast without reason, would have beaten her. They would have cursed, cried out upon her. That was not the cut of Hazen Kinch. But I could see that he was angry and I was not surprised when he reached up and gripped the horse's ear. He pulled the mare's head down and twisted the ear viciously. All in a silence that was deadly.

The mare snorted and tried to rear back and Hazen clapped the butt of his whip across her knees. She stood still, quivering, and he wrenched at her ear again.

"Now," he said softly, "keep the road."

And he returned and climbed to his place beside me in the sleigh. I said nothing. I might have interfered, but something had always impelled me to keep back my hand from Hazen Kinch.

We drove on and the mare was lame. Though Hazen pushed her, we were slow in coming to town and before we reached Hazen's office the snow was whirling down—a pressure of driving, swirling flakes like a heavy white hand.

I left Hazen at the stair that led to his office and I went about my business of the day. He said as I turned away:

"Be here at three."

I nodded. But I did not think we should drive home that afternoon. I had some knowledge of storms.

That which had brought me to town was not engrossing. I found time to go to the stable and see Hazen's mare. There was an ugly welt across her knees and some blood had flowed. The stablemen had tended the welt, and cursed Hazen in my hearing. It was still snowing, and the stable boss, looking out at the driving flakes, spat upon the ground and said to me:

"Them legs'll go stiff. That mare won't go home tonight."

"I think you are right," I agreed.

"The white-whiskered skunk!" he said, and I knew he spoke of Hazen.

At a quarter of three I took myself to Hazen Kinch's office. It was not much of an office; not that Hazen could not have afforded a better. But it was up two flights—an attic room ill lighted. A small airtight stove kept the room stifling hot. The room was also airtight. Hazen had a table and two chairs, and an iron safe in the corner. He put a pathetic trust in that safe. I believe I could have opened it with a screw driver. I met him as I climbed the stairs. He said harshly:

"I'm going to telephone. They say the road's impassable."

He had no telephone in his office; he used one in the store below. A small economy fairly typical of Hazen.

"I'll wait in the office," I told him.

"Go ahead," he agreed, halfway down the stairs.

I went up to his office and closed the drafts of the stove—it was red-hot —and tried to open the one window, but it was nailed fast. Then Hazen came back up the stairs grumbling.

"Damn the snow!" he said. "The wire is down."

"Where to?" I asked.

"My house, man! To my house!"

"You wanted to telephone home that you—"

"I can't get home tonight. You'll have to go to the hotel."

I nodded good-naturedly.

"All right. You, too, I suppose."

"I'll sleep here," he said.

I looked round. There was no bed, no cot, nothing but the two stiff chairs. He saw my glance and said angrily: "I've slept on the floor before."

I was always interested in the man's mental processes.

"You wanted to telephone Mrs. Kinch not to worry?" I suggested.

"Pshaw, let her fret!" said Hazen. "I wanted to ask after my boy." His eyes expanded, he rubbed his hands a little, cackling. "A fine boy, sir! A fine boy!"

It was then we heard Doan Marshey coming up the stairs. We heard his stumbling steps as he began the last flight and Hazen seemed to cock his ears as he listened. Then he sat still and watched the door. The steps climbed nearer; they stopped in the dim little hall outside the door and someone fumbled with the knob. When the door opened we saw who it was. I knew Marshey. He lived a little beyond Hazen on the same road. Lived in a two-room cabin—it was little more—with his wife and his five children; lived meanly and pitiably, groveling in the soil for daily bread, sweating life out of the earth—life and no more. A thin man, racking thin; a forward-thrusting neck and a bony face and a sad and drooping mustache about his mouth. His eyes were meek and weary.

He stood in the doorway blinking at us; and with his gloved hands— they were stiff and awkward with the cold—he unwound the ragged muffler that was about his neck and he brushed weakly at the snow upon his head and his shoulders. Hazen said angrily:

"Come in! Do you want my stove to heat the town?"

Doan shuffled in and he shut the door behind him. He said: "Howdy, Mr. Kinch." And he smiled in a humble and placating way.

Hazen said: "What's your business? Your interest is due."

Doan nodded.

"Yeah. I know, Mr. Kinch. I cain't pay it all."

Kinch exclaimed impatiently: "An old story! How much can you pay?"

"Eleven dollars and fifty cents," said Doan.

"You owe twenty."

"I aim to pay it when the hens begin to lay."

Hazen laughed scornfully.

"You aim to pay! Damn you, Marshey, if your old farm was worth taking I'd have you out in this snow, you old scamp!"

Doan pleaded dully: "Don't you do that, Mr. Kinch! I aim to pay."

Hazen clapped his hands on the table.

"Rats! Come! Give me what you've got! And, Marshey, you'll have to get the rest. I'm sick of waiting on you."

Marshey came shuffling toward the table. Hazen was sitting with the table between him and the man, and I was a little behind Hazen at one side. Marshey blinked as he came nearer, and his weak nearsighted eyes turned from Hazen to me. I could see that the man was stiff with the cold.

When he came to the table in front of Hazen he took off his thick gloves. His hands were blue. He laid the gloves on the table and reached into an inner pocket of his torn coat and drew out a little cloth pouch and he fumbled into this and I heard the clink of coins. He drew out two quarters and laid them on the table before Hazen, and Hazen picked them up. I saw that Marshey's fingers moved stiffly; I could almost hear them creak with the cold. Then he reached into the pouch again.

Something dropped out of the mouth of the little cloth bag and fell soundlessly on the table. It looked to me like a bill, a piece of paper currency. I was about to speak, but Hazen, without an instant's hesitation, had dropped his hand on the thing and drawn it unostentatiously toward him. When he lifted his hand the money—if it was money—was gone.

Marshey drew out a little roll of worn bills. Hazen took them out of his hand and counted them swiftly.

"All right," he said. "Eleven-fifty. I'll give you a receipt. But you mind me, Doan Marshey, you get the rest before the month's out. I've been too slack with you."

Marshey, his dull eyes watching Hazen write the receipt, was folding the little pouch and putting it away. Hazen tore off the bit of paper and gave it to him. Doan took it and he said humbly: "Thank'e, sir."

Hazen nodded.

"Mind now," he exclaimed, and Marshey said: "I'll do my best, Mr. Kinch."

Then he turned and shuffled across the room and out into the hall and we heard him descending the stairs.

When he was gone I asked Hazen casually: "What was it that he dropped upon the table?"

"A dollar," said Hazen promptly. "A dollar bill. The miserable fool!"

Hazen's mental processes were always of interest to me.

"You mean to give it back to him?" I asked.

He stared at me and he laughed. "No! If he can't take care of his own money—that's why he is what he is."

"Still it is his money."

"He owes me more than that."

"Going to give him credit for it?"

"Am I a fool?" Hazen asked me. "Do I look like so much of a fool?"

"He may charge you with finding it."

"He loses a dollar; I find one. Can he prove ownership? Pshaw!" Hazen laughed again.

"If there is any spine in him he will lay the thing to you as a theft," I suggested. I was not afraid of angering Hazen. He allowed me open speech; he seemed to find a grim pleasure in my distaste for him and for his way of life.

"If there were any backbone in the man he would not be paying me eighty dollars a year on a five-hundred-dollar loan—discounted."

Hazen grinned at me triumphantly.

"I wonder if he will come back," I said.

"Besides," Hazen continued, "he lied to me. He told me the eleven-fifty was all he had."

"Yes," I agreed. "There is no doubt he lied to you."

Hazen had a letter to write and he bent to it. I sat by the stove and watched him and considered. He had not yet finished the letter when we heard Marshey returning. His dragging feet on the stair were unmistakable. At the sound of his weary feet some tide of indignation surged up in me.

I was minded to do violence to Hazen Kinch. But—a deeper impulse held my hand from the man.

Marshey came in and his weary eyes wandered about the room. They inspected the floor; they inspected me; they inspected Hazen Kinch's table, and they rose at last humbly to Hazen Kinch.

"Well?" said Hazen.

"I lost a dollar," Marshey told him. "I 'lowed I might have dropped it here."

Hazen frowned.

"You told me eleven-fifty was all you had."

"This here dollar wa'n't mine."

The moneylender laughed.

"Likely! Who would give you a dollar? You lied to me, or you're lying now. I don't believe you lost a dollar."

Marshey reiterated weakly: "I lost a dollar."

"Well," said Hazen, "there's no dollar of yours here."

"It was to git medicine," Marshey said. "It wa'n't mine."

Hazen Kinch exclaimed: "By God, I believe you're accusing me!"

Marshey lifted both hands placatingly.

"No, Mr. Kinch. No, sir." His eyes once more wandered about the room. "Mebbe I dropped it in the snow," he said.

He turned to the door. Even in his slow shuffle there was a hint of trembling eagerness to escape. He went out and down the stairs. Hazen looked at me, his old face wrinkling mirthfully.

"You see?" he said.

I left him a little later and went out into the street. On the way to the hotel I stopped for a cigar at the drugstore. Marshey was there, talking with the druggist.

I heard the druggist say: "No, Marshey, I'm sorry. I've been stung too often."

Marshey nodded humbly.

"I didn't 'low you'd figure to trust me," he agreed. "It's all right. I didn't 'low you would."

It was my impulse to give him the dollar he needed, but I did not do it. An overpowering compulsion bade me keep my hands off in this matter. I did not know what I expected, but I felt the imminence of the fates. When I went out into the snow it seemed to me the groan of the gale was like the slow grind of millstones, one upon the other.

I thought long upon the matter of Hazen Kinch before sleep came that night.

Toward morning the snow must have stopped; and the wind increased and carved the drifts till sunrise, then abruptly died. I met Hazen at the post office at ten and he said: "I'm starting home."

I asked: "Can you get through?"

He laughed.

"I will get through," he told me.

"You're in haste."

"I want to see that boy of mine," said Hazen Kinch. "A fine boy, man! A fine boy!"

"I'm ready," I said.

When we took the road the mare was limping. But she seemed to work out the stiffness in her knees and after a mile or so of the hard going she was moving smoothly enough. We made good time.

The day, as often happens after a storm, was full of blinding sunlight. The glare of the sun upon the snow was almost unbearable. I kept my eyes all but closed, but there was so much beauty abroad in the land that I could not bear to close them altogether. The snow clung to twigs and to fences and to wires, and a thousand flames glinted from every crystal when the sun struck down upon the drifts. The pine wood upon the eastern slope of Rayborn Hill was a checkerboard of rich color. Green and blue and black and white, indescribably brilliant. When we crossed the bridge at the foot of the hill we could hear the brook playing beneath the ice that sheathed it. On the white pages of the snow wild things had writ here and there the fine-traced tale of their morning's adventuring. We saw once where a fox had pinned a big snowshoe rabbit in a drift.

Hazen talked much of that child of his on the homeward way. I said little. From the top of the Rayborn Hill we sighted his house and he laid the whip along the mare and we went down that last long descent at a speed that left me breathless. I shut my eyes and huddled low in the robes for protection against the bitter wind, and I did not open them again till we turned into Hazen's barnyard, plowing through the unpacked snow.

When we stopped Hazen laughed.

"Ha!" he said. "Now, come in, man, and warm yourself and see the baby! A fine boy!"

He was ahead of me at the door; I went in upon his heels. We came into the kitchen together.

Hazen's kitchen was also living room and bedroom in the cold of winter. The arrangement saved firewood. There was a bed against the wall opposite the door. As we came in a woman got up stiffly from this bed and I saw that this woman was Hazen's wife. But there was a change in her. She was bleak as cold iron and she was somehow strong.

Hazen rasped at this woman impatiently: "Well, I'm home! Where is the boy?"

She looked at him and her lips moved soundlessly. She closed them, opened them again. This time she was able to speak.

"The boy?" she said to Hazen. "The boy is dead!"

The dim-lit kitchen was very quiet for a little time. I felt myself breathe deeply, almost with relief. The thing for which I had waited—it had come. And I looked at Hazen Kinch.

He had always been a little thin man. He was shrunken now and very white and very still. Only his face twitched. A muscle in one cheek jerked and jerked and jerked at his mouth. It was as though he controlled a desire to smile. That jerking, suppressed smile upon his white and tortured countenance was terrible. I could see the blood drain down from his forehead, down from his cheeks. He became white as death itself.

After a little he tried to speak. I do not know what he meant to say. But what he did was to repeat—as though he had not heard her words—the question which he had flung at her in the beginning. He said huskily: "Where is the boy?"

She looked toward the bed and Hazen looked that way; and then he went across to the bed with uncertain little steps. I followed him. I saw the little twisted body there. The woman had been keeping it warm with her own body. It must have been in her arms when we came in. The tumbled coverings, the crushed pillows spoke mutely of a ferocious intensity of grief.

Hazen looked down at the little body. He made no move to touch it, but I heard him whisper to himself: "Fine boy."

After a while he looked at the woman. She seemed to feel an accusation in his eyes. She said: "I did all I could."

He asked: "What was it?"

I had it in me—though I had reason enough to despise the little man—to pity Hazen Kinch.

"He coughed," said the woman. "I knew it was croup. You know I asked you to get the medicine—ipecac. You said no matter—no need—and you had gone."

She looked out of the window.

"I went for help—to Annie Marshey. Her babies had had it. Her husband was going to town and she said he would get the medicine for me. She did not tell him it was for me. He would not have done it for you. He did not know. So I gave her a dollar to give him—to bring it out to me.

"He came home in the snow last night. Baby was bad by that time, so I was watching for Doan. I stopped him in the road and I asked for the medicine. When he understood he told me. He had not brought it."

The woman was speaking dully, without emotion.

"It would have been in time, even then," she said. "But after a while, after that, baby died."

I understood in that moment the working of the mills. And when I looked at Hazen Kinch I saw that he, too, was beginning to understand. There is a just mercilessness in an aroused God. Hazen Kinch was driven to questions.

"Why—didn't Marshey fetch it?" he asked.

She said slowly: "They would not trust him—at the store."

His mouth twitched, he raised his hands.

"The money!" he cried. "The money! What did he do with that?"

"He said," the woman answered, "that he lost it—in your office; lost the money there."

After a little the old moneylender leaned far back like a man wrenched with agony. His body was contorted, his face was terrible. His dry mouth opened wide.

He screamed!

Halfway up the hill to my house I stopped to look back and all around. The vast hills in their snowy garments looked down upon the land, upon the house of Hazen Kinch. Still and silent and inscrutable.

I knew now that a just and brooding God dwelt among these hills.

The Catbird Seat

By JAMES THURBER

MR. MARTIN bought the pack of Camels on Monday night in the most crowded cigar store on Broadway. It was theater time and seven or eight men were buying cigarettes. The clerk didn't even glance at Mr. Martin, who put the pack in his overcoat pocket and went out. If any of the staff at F & S had seen him buy the cigarettes, they would have been astonished, for it was generally known that Mr. Martin did not smoke, and never had. No one saw him.

It was just a week to the day since Mr. Martin had decided to rub out Mrs. Ulgine Barrows. The term "rub out" pleased him because it suggested nothing more than the correction of an error—in this case an error of Mr. Fitweiler. Mr. Martin had spent each night of the past week working out his plan and examining it. As he walked home now he went over it again. For the hundredth time he resented the element of imprecision, the margin of guesswork that entered into the business. The project as he had worked it out was casual and bold, the risks were considerable. Something might go wrong anywhere along the line. And therein lay the cunning of his scheme. No one would ever see in it the cautious, painstaking hand of Erwin Martin, head of the filing department at F & S, of whom Mr. Fitweiler had once said, "Man is fallible but Martin isn't." No one would see his hand, that is, unless it were caught in the act.

Sitting in his apartment, drinking a glass of milk, Mr. Martin reviewed his case against Mrs. Ulgine Barrows, as he had every night for seven nights. He began at the beginning. Her quacking voice and braying laugh had first profaned the halls of F & S on March 7, 1941 (Mr. Martin had a head for dates). Old Roberts, the personnel chief, had introduced her as the newly appointed special adviser to the president of the firm, Mr. Fitweiler. The woman had appalled Mr. Martin instantly, but he hadn't shown it. He had given her his dry hand, a look of studious concentration, and a faint smile. "Well," she had said, looking at the papers on his desk, "are you lifting the oxcart out of the ditch?" As Mr. Martin recalled that moment, over his milk, he squirmed slightly. He must keep his mind on her crimes as a special adviser, not on her peccadillos as a personality. This he found difficult to do, in spite of entering an objection and sustaining it. The faults of the woman as a woman kept chattering on in his mind like an unruly witness. She had, for almost two years now, baited him. In the halls, in the elevator, even in his own office, into which she romped now and then like a circus horse, she was constantly shouting these silly questions at him. "Are you lifting the oxcart out of the ditch? Are you tearing up the pea patch? Are you hollering down the rain barrel? Are you scraping around the bottom of the pickle barrel? Are you sitting in the catbird seat?"

It was Joey Hart, one of Mr. Martin's two assistants, who had explained what the gibberish meant. "She must be a Dodger fan," he had said. "Red Barber announces the Dodger games over the radio and he uses those expressions—picked 'em up down South." Joey had gone on to explain one or two. "Tearing up the pea patch" meant going on a rampage; "sitting in the catbird seat" meant sitting pretty, like a batter with three balls and no strikes on him. Mr. Martin dismissed all this with an effort. It had been annoying, it had driven him near to distraction, but he was too solid a man to be moved to murder by anything so childish. It was fortunate, he reflected as he passed on to the important charges against Mrs. Barrows, that he had stood up under it so well. He had maintained always an outward appearance of polite tolerance. "Why, I even believe you like the woman," Miss Paird, his other assistant, had once said to him. He had simply smiled.

A gavel rapped in Mr. Martin's mind and the case proper was resumed. Mrs. Ulgine Barrows stood charged with willful, blatant, and persistent attempts to destroy the efficiency and system of F & S. It was competent, material, and relevant to review her advent and rise to power. Mr. Martin had got the story from Miss Paird, who seemed always able to find things out. According to her, Mrs. Barrows had met Mr. Fitweiler at a party, where she had rescued him from the embraces of a powerfully built drunken man who had mistaken the president of F & S for a famous retired Middle Western football coach. She had led him to a sofa and somehow worked upon him a monstrous magic. The aging gentleman had jumped to the conclusion there and then that this was a woman of singular attainments, equipped to bring out the best in him and in the firm. A week later he had introduced her into F & S as his special adviser. On that day confusion got its foot in the door. After Miss Tyson, Mr. Brundage, and Mr. Bartlett had been fired and Mr. Munson had taken his hat and stalked out, mailing in his resignation later, old Roberts had been emboldened to speak to Mr. Fitweiler. He mentioned that Mr. Munson's department had been "a little disrupted" and hadn't they perhaps better resume the old system there? Mr. Fitweiler had said certainly not. He had the greatest faith in Mrs. Barrows' ideas. "They require a little seasoning, a little seasoning, is all," he had added. Mr. Roberts had given it up. Mr. Martin reviewed in detail all the changes wrought by Mrs. Barrows. She had begun chipping at the cornices of the firm's edifice and now she was swinging at the foundation stones with a pickax.

Mr. Martin came now, in his summing up, to the afternoon of Monday, November 2, 1942—just one week ago. On that day, at 3 P.M., Mrs. Barrows had bounced into his office. "Boo!" she had yelled. "Are you scraping around the bottom of the pickle barrel?" Mr. Martin had looked at her from under his green eyeshade, saying nothing. She had begun to wander about the office, taking it in with her great, popping eyes. "Do you really need *all* these filing cabinets?" she had demanded suddenly. Mr. Martin's heart had jumped. "Each of these files," he had said, keeping his voice even, "plays an indispensable part in the system of F & S." She had brayed at him, "Well, don't tear up the pea patch!" and gone to the door. From there she had bawled, "But you sure have got a lot of fine scrap in here!" Mr. Martin could no longer doubt that the finger was on his beloved department. Her pickax was on the upswing, poised for the first blow. It had not come yet; he had received no blue memo from the enchanted Mr. Fitweiler bearing nonsensical instructions deriving from the obscene woman. But there was no doubt in Mr. Martin's mind that one would be forthcoming. He must act quickly. Already a precious week had gone by. Mr. Martin stood up in his living room, still holding his milk glass. "Gentlemen of the jury," he said to himself, "I demand the death penalty for this horrible person."

The next day Mr. Martin followed his routine, as usual. He polished his glasses more often and once sharpened an already sharp pencil, but not even Miss Paird noticed. Only once did he catch sight of his victim; she swept past him in the hall with a patronizing "Hi!" At five-thirty he walked home, as usual, and had a glass of milk, as usual. He had never drunk anything stronger in his life—unless you could count ginger ale. The late Sam Schlosser, the S of F & S, had praised Mr. Martin at a staff meeting several years before for his temperate habits. "Our most efficient worker neither drinks nor smokes," he had said. "The results speak for themselves." Mr. Fitweiler had sat by, nodding approval.

Mr. Martin was still thinking about that red-letter day as he walked over to the Schrafft's on Fifth Avenue near Forty-sixth Street. He got there, as he always did, at eight o'clock. He finished his dinner and the financial page of the *Sun* at a quarter to nine, as he always did. It was his custom after dinner to take a walk. This time he walked down Fifth Avenue at a casual pace. His gloved hands felt moist and warm, his forehead cold. He transferred the Camels from his overcoat to a jacket pocket. He wondered, as he did so, if they did not represent an unnecessary note of strain. Mrs. Barrows smoked only Luckies. It was his idea to puff a few puffs on a Camel (after the rubbing out), stub it out in the ashtray holding her lipstick-stained Luckies, and thus drag a small red herring across the trail. Perhaps it was not a good idea. It would take time. He might even choke, too loudly.

Mr. Martin had never seen the house on West Twelfth Street where Mrs. Barrows lived, but he had a clear enough picture of it. Fortunately, she had bragged to everybody about her ducky first-floor apartment in the perfectly darling three-story red-brick. There would be no doorman or other attendants; just the tenants of the second and third floors. As he walked along, Mr. Martin realized that he would get there before nine-thirty. He had considered walking north on Fifth Avenue from Schrafft's to a point from which it would take him until ten o'clock to reach the house. At that hour people were less likely to be coming in or going out. But the procedure would have made an awkward loop in the straight thread of his casualness, and he had abandoned it. It was impossible to figure when people would be entering or leaving the house, anyway. There was a great risk at any hour. If he ran into anybody, he would simply have to place the rubbing out of Ulgine Barrows in the inactive file forever. The same thing would hold true if there were someone in her apartment. In that case he would just say that he had been passing by, recognized her charming house, and thought to drop in.

It was eighteen minutes after nine when Mr. Martin turned into Twelfth Street. A man passed him, and a man and a woman, talking. There was no one within fifty paces when he came to the house, halfway down the block. He was up the steps and in the small vestibule in no time, pressing the bell under the card that said "Mrs. Ulgine Barrows." When the clicking in the lock started, he jumped forward against the door. He got inside fast, closing the door behind him. A bulb in a lantern hung from the hall ceiling on a chain seemed to give a monstrously bright light. There was nobody on the stair, which went up ahead of him along the left wall. A door opened down the hall in the wall on the right. He went toward it swiftly, on tiptoe.

"Well, for God's sake, look who's here!" bawled Mrs. Barrows, and her braying laugh rang out like the report of a shotgun. He rushed past her like a football tackle, bumping her. "Hey, quit shoving!" she said, closing the door behind them. They were in her living room, which seemed to Mr. Martin to be lighted by a hundred lamps. "What's after you?" she said. "You're as jumpy as a goat." He found he was unable to speak. His heart was wheezing in his throat. "I—yes," he finally brought out. She was jabbering and laughing as she started to help him off with his coat. "No, no," he said. "I'll put it here." He took it off and put it on a chair near the door. "Your hat and gloves, too," she said. "You're in a lady's house." He put his hat on top of the coat. Mrs. Barrows seemed larger than he had thought. He kept his gloves on. "I was passing by," he said. "I recognized—is there anyone here?" She laughed louder than ever. "No," she said, "we're all alone. You're as white as a sheet, you funny man. Whatever *has* come over you? I'll mix you a toddy." She started toward a door across the room. "Scotch-and-soda be all right? But say, you don't drink, do you?" She turned and gave him her amused look. Mr. Martin pulled himself together. "Scotch-and-soda will be all right," he heard himself say. He could hear her laughing in the kitchen.

Mr. Martin looked quickly around the living room for the weapon. He had counted on finding one there. There were andirons and a poker and something in a corner that looked like an Indian club. None of them would do. It couldn't be that way. He began to pace around. He came to a desk. On it lay a metal paper knife with an ornate handle. Would it be sharp enough? He reached for it and knocked over a small brass jar. Stamps spilled out of it and it fell to the floor with a clatter. "Hey," Mrs. Barrows yelled from the kitchen, "are you tearing up the pea patch?" Mr. Martin gave a strange laugh. Picking up the knife, he tried its point against his left wrist. It was blunt. It wouldn't do.

When Mrs. Barrows reappeared, carrying two highballs, Mr. Martin, standing there with his gloves on, became acutely conscious of the fantasy he had wrought. Cigarettes in his pocket, a drink prepared for him—it was all too grossly improbable. It was more than that; it was impossible. Somewhere in the back of his mind a vague idea stirred, sprouted. "For heaven's sake, take off those gloves," said Mrs. Barrows. "I always wear them in the house," said Mr. Martin. The idea began to bloom, strange and wonderful. She put the glasses on a coffee table in front of a sofa and sat on the sofa. "Come over here, you odd little man," she said. Mr. Martin went over and sat beside her. It was difficult getting a cigarette out of the pack of Camels, but he managed it. She held a match for him, laughing. "Well," she said, handing him his drink, "this is perfectly marvelous. You with a drink and a cigarette."

Mr. Martin puffed, not too awkwardly, and took a gulp of the highball. "I drink and smoke all the time," he said. He clinked his glass against hers. "Here's nuts to that old windbag, Fitweiler," he said, and gulped again. The stuff tasted awful, but he made no grimace. "Really, Mr. Martin," she said, her voice and posture changing, "you are insulting our employer." Mrs. Barrows was now all special adviser to the president. "I am preparing a bomb," said Mr. Martin, "which will blow the old goat higher than hell." He had only had a little of the drink, which was not strong. It couldn't be that. "Do you take dope or something?" Mrs. Barrows asked coldly. "Heroin," said Mr. Martin. "I'll be coked to the gills when I bump that old buzzard off." "Mr. Martin!" she shouted, getting to her feet. "That will be all of that. You must go at once." Mr. Martin took another swallow of his drink. He tapped his cigarette out in the ashtray and put the pack of Camels on the coffee table. Then he got up. She stood glaring at him. He walked over and put on his hat and coat. "Not a word about this," he said, and laid an index finger against his lips. All Mrs. Barrows could bring out was "Really!" Mr. Martin put his hand on the doorknob. "I'm sitting in the catbird seat," he said. He stuck his tongue out at her and left. Nobody saw him go.

Mr. Martin got to his apartment, walking, well before eleven. No one saw him go in. He had two glasses of milk after brushing his teeth, and he felt elated. It wasn't tipsiness, because he hadn't been tipsy. Anyway, the walk had worn off all effects of the whiskey. He got in bed and read a magazine for a while. He was asleep before midnight.

Mr. Martin got to the office at eight-thirty the next morning, as usual. At a quarter to nine, Ulgine Barrows, who had never before arrived at work before ten, swept into his office. "I'm reporting to Mr. Fitweiler now!" she shouted. "If he turns you over to the police, it's no more than you deserve!" Mr. Martin gave her a look of shocked surprise. "I beg your pardon?" he said. Mrs. Barrows snorted and bounced out of the room, leaving Miss Paird and Joey Hart staring after her. "What's the matter with that old devil now?" asked Miss Paird. "I have no idea," said Mr. Martin, resuming his work. The other two looked at him and then at each other. Miss Paird got up and went out. She walked slowly past the closed door of Mr. Fitweiler's office. Mrs. Barrows was yelling inside, but she was not braying. Miss Paird could not hear what the woman was saying. She went back to her desk.

Forty-five minutes later, Mrs. Barrows left the president's office and went into her own, shutting the door. It wasn't until half an hour later that Mr. Fitweiler sent for Mr. Martin. The head of the filing department, neat, quiet, attentive, stood in front of the old man's desk. Mr. Fitweiler was pale and nervous. He took his glasses off and twiddled them. He made a small, bruffing sound in his throat. "Martin," he said, "you have been with us more than twenty years." "Twenty-two, sir," said Mr. Martin. "In that time," pursued the president, "your work and your—uh—manner have been exemplary." "I trust so, sir," said Mr. Martin. "I have understood, Martin," said Mr. Fitweiler, "that you have never taken a drink or smoked." "That is correct, sir," said Mr. Martin. "Ah, yes." Mr. Fitweiler polished his glasses. "You may describe what you did after leaving the office yesterday, Martin," he said. Mr. Martin allowed less than a second for his bewildered pause. "Certainly, sir," he said. "I walked home. Then I went to Schrafft's for dinner. Afterward I walked home again. I went to bed early, sir, and read a magazine for a while. I was asleep before eleven." "Ah, yes," said Mr. Fitweiler again. He was silent for a moment, searching for the proper words to say to the head of the filing department. "Mrs. Barrows," he said finally, "Mrs. Barrows has worked hard, Martin, very hard. It grieves me to report that she has suffered a severe breakdown. It has taken the form of a persecution complex accompanied by distressing hallucinations." "I am very sorry, sir," said Mr. Martin. "Mrs. Barrows is under the delusion," continued Mr. Fitweiler, "that you visited her last evening and behaved yourself in an—uh—unseemly manner." He raised his hand to silence Mr. Martin's little pained outcry. "It is the nature of these psychological diseases," Mr. Fitweiler said, "to fix upon the least likely and most innocent party as the—uh—source of persecution. These matters are not for the lay mind to grasp, Martin. I've just had my psychiatrist, Dr. Fitch, on the phone. He would not, of course, commit himself, but he made enough generalizations to substantiate my suspicions. I suggested to Mrs. Barrows, when she had completed her—uh—story to me this morning, that she visit Dr. Fitch, for I suspected a condition at once. She flew, I regret to say, into a rage, and demanded—uh—requested that I call you on the carpet. You may not know, Martin, but Mrs. Barrows had planned a reorganization of your department—subject to my approval, of course, subject to my approval. This brought you, rather than anyone else, to her mind—but again that is a phenomenon for Dr. Fitch and not for us. So, Martin, I am afraid Mrs. Barrows' usefulness here is at an end." "I am dreadfully sorry, sir," said Mr. Martin.

It was at this point that the door to the office blew open with the suddenness of a gas-main explosion and Mrs. Barrows catapulted through it. "Is the little rat denying it?" she screamed. "He can't get away with that!" Mr. Martin got up and moved discreetly to a point beside Mr. Fitweiler's chair. "You drank and smoked at my apartment," she bawled at Mr. Martin, "and you know it! You called Mr. Fitweiler an old windbag and said you were going to blow him up when you got coked to the gills on heroin!" She stopped yelling to catch her breath and a new glint came into her popping eyes. "If you weren't such a drab, ordinary little man," she said, "I'd think you'd planned it all. Sticking your tongue out, saying you were sitting in the catbird seat, because you thought no one would believe me when I told it! My God, it's really too perfect!" She brayed loudly and hysterically, and the fury was on her again. She glared at Mr. Fitweiler. "Can't you see how he has tricked us, you old fool? Can't you see his little game?" But Mr. Fitweiler had been surreptitiously pressing all the buttons under the top of his desk and employees of F & S began pouring into the room. "Stockton," said Mr. Fitweiler, "you and Fishbein will take Mrs. Barrows to her home. Mrs. Powell, you will go with them." Stockton, who had played a little football in high school, blocked Mrs. Barrows as she made for Mr. Martin. It took him and Fishbein together to force her out of the door into the hall, crowded with stenographers and office boys. She was still screaming imprecations at Mr. Martin, tangled and contradictory imprecations. The hubbub finally died out down the corridor.

"I regret that this has happened," said Mr. Fitweiler. "I shall ask you to dismiss it from your mind, Martin." "Yes, sir," said Mr. Martin, anticipating his chief's "That will be all" by moving to the door. "I will dismiss it." He went out and shut the door, and his step was light and quick in the hall. When he entered his department he had slowed down to his customary gait, and he walked quietly across the room to the W20 file, wearing a look of studious concentration.

Bread Alone

By JOHN O'HARA

IT WAS the eighth inning, and the Yankees had what the sportswriters call a comfortable lead. It was comfortable for them, all right. Unless a miracle happened, they had the ball game locked up and put away. They would not be coming to bat again, and Mr. Hart didn't like that any more than he was liking his thoughts, the thoughts he had been thinking ever since the fifth inning, when the Yanks had made their five runs. From the fifth inning on, Mr. Hart had been troubled with his conscience.

Mr. Hart was a car-washer, and what colored help at the Elbee Garage got paid was not much. It had to house, feed, and clothe all the Harts, which meant Mr. Hart himself; his wife, Lolly Hart; his son, Booker Hart; and his three daughters, Carrie, Linda, and the infant, Brenda Hart. The day before, Mr. Ginsburg, the bookkeeper who ran the shop pool, had come to him and said, "Well, Willie, you win the sawbuck."

"Yes sir, Mr. Ginsburg, I sure do. I was watchin' them newspapers all week," said Mr. Hart. He dried his hands with the chamois and extended the right.

"One, two, three, four, five, six, seven, eight, nine, anduh tenner. Ten bucks, Willie," said Mr. Ginsburg. "Well, what are you gonna do with all that dough? I'll bet you don't tell your wife about it."

"Well, I don't know, Mr. Ginsburg. She don't follow the scores, so she don't know I win. I don't know what to do," said Mr. Hart. "But say, ain't I suppose to give you your cut? I understand it right, I oughta buy you a drink or a cigar or something."

"That's the custom, Willie, but thinking it over, you weren't winners all year."

"No sir, that's right," said Mr. Hart.

"So I tell you, if you win another pool, you buy me *two* drinks or *two* cigars. Are you going in this week's pool?"

"Sure am. It don't seem fair, though. Ain't much of the season left and maybe I won't win again. Sure you don't want a drink or a cigar or something?"

"That's all right, Willie," said Mr. Ginsburg.

On the way home, Mr. Hart was a troubled man. That money belonged in the sugar bowl. A lot could come out of that money: a steak, stockings, a lot of stuff. But a man was entitled to a little pleasure in this life, the only life he ever had. Mr. Hart had not been to a ball game since about fifteen or twenty years ago, and the dime with which he bought his ticket in the pool every week was his own money, carfare money. He made it up by getting rides home, or pretty near home, when a truck driver or private chauffeur friend was going Harlem-ward; and if he got a free ride, or two free rides, to somewhere near home every week, then he certainly was entitled to use the dime for the pool. And this was the first time he had won. Then there was the other matter of who won it for him: the Yankees. He had had the Yankees and the Browns in the pool, the first time all season he had picked the Yanks, and it was they who made the runs that had made him the winner of the ten dollars. If it wasn't for those Yankees, he wouldn't have won. He owed it to them to go and buy tickets and show his gratitude. By the time he got home his mind was made up. He had the next afternoon off, and, by God, he was going to see the Yankees play.

There was, of course, only one person to take; that was Booker, the strange boy of thirteen who was Mr. Hart's only son. Booker was a quiet boy, good in school, and took after his mother, who was quite a little lighter complected than Mr. Hart. And so that night after supper he simply announced, "Tomorrow me and Booker's going over to see the New York Yankees play. A friend of mine happened to give me a choice pair of seats, so me and Booker's taking in the game." There had been a lot of talk, and naturally Booker was the most surprised of all—so surprised that Mr. Hart was not sure his son was even pleased. Booker was a very hard one to understand. Fortunately, Lolly believed right away that someone had really given Mr. Hart the tickets to the game; he had handed over his pay as usual, nothing missing, and that made her believe his story.

But that did not keep Mr. Hart from having an increasingly bad time from the fifth inning on. And Booker didn't help him to forget. Booker leaned forward and he followed the game all right but never said anything much. He seemed to know the game and to recognize the players, but never *talked*. He got up and yelled in the fifth inning when the Yanks were making their runs, but so did everybody else. Mr. Hart wished the game was over.

DiMaggio came to bat. Ball one. Strike one, called. Ball two. Mr. Hart wasn't watching with his heart in it. He had his eyes on DiMaggio, but it was the crack of the bat that made Mr. Hart realize that DiMaggio had taken a poke at one, and the ball was in the air, high in the air. Everybody around Mr. Hart stood up and tried to watch the ball. Mr. Hart stood up too. Booker sort of got up off the seat, watching the ball but not standing up. The ball hung in the air and then began to drop. Mr. Hart was judging it and could tell it was going to hit about four rows behind him. Then it did hit, falling the last few yards as though it had been thrown down from the sky, and smacko! it hit the seats four rows behind the Harts, bounced high but sort of crooked, and dropped again to the row directly behind Mr. Hart and Booker.

Where the hell's the ball? Where's the ball? Men and kids were yelling and cursing, pushing and kicking each other, but nobody could find the ball. Two boys began to fight because one accused the other of pushing him when he almost had his hand on the ball. The fuss lasted until the end of the inning. Mr. Hart was nervous. He didn't want any trouble, so he concentrated on the game again. Booker had the right idea. He was concentrating on the game. They both concentrated like hell. All they could hear was a mystified murmur among the men and kids. "Well, somebody must of got the god-damn thing." In two minutes the Yanks retired the side and the ball game was over.

"Let's wait till the crowd gets started going, Pop," said Booker.

"O.K.," said Mr. Hart. He was in no hurry to get home, with the things he had on his mind and how sore Lolly would be. He'd give her what was left of the ten bucks, but she'd be sore anyhow. He lit a cigarette and let it hang on his lip. He didn't feel so good sitting there with his elbow on his knee, his chin on his fist.

"Hey, Pop," said Booker.

"Huh?"

"Here," said Booker.

"What?" said Mr. Hart. He looked at his son. His son reached inside his shirt, looked back of him, and then from the inside of the shirt he brought out the ball. "Present for you," said Booker.

Mr. Hart looked down at it. "Lemme see that!" he said. He did not reach for it. Booker handed it to him.

"Go ahead, take it. It's a present for you," said Booker.

Suddenly Mr. Hart threw back his head and laughed. "I'll be a god-damn holy son of a bitch. You got it? The ball?"

"Sure. It's for you," said Booker.

Mr. Hart threw back his head again and slapped his knees. "I'll be damn—boy, some Booker!" He put his arm around his son's shoulders and hugged him. "Boy, some Booker, huh? You givin' it to me? Some Booker!"

A Table at Ciro's

By BUDD SCHULBERG

AT HALF-PAST five Ciro's looks like a woman sitting before her dressing table just beginning to make up for the evening. The waiters are setting up the tables for the dinner trade, the cigarette and hat-check girls are changing from slacks to the abbreviated cancan costumes which are their work clothes, and an undiscovered Rosemary Clooney making her debut tonight is rehearsing. *Don't let the stars get in your eyes . . .*

A telephone rings and the operator, who is suffering from delusions of looking like Ava Gardner, answers. "Ci-ro's. A table for Mr. Nathan? For six. His usual table?" This was not what she had come to Hollywood for, to take reservations over the telephone, but even the small part she played in A. D. Nathan's plans for the evening brought her a little closer to the Hollywood that was like a mirage, always in sight but never within reach. For, like everyone else in Hollywood, the telephone operator at Ciro's had a dream. Once upon a time, ran this one, there was a Famous Movie Producer (called Goldwyn, Zanuck or A. D. Nathan) and one evening this FMP was in Ciro's placing a million-dollar telephone call when he happened to catch a glimpse of her at the switchboard. "Young lady," he would say, "you are wasting your time at that switchboard. You may not realize it, but you *are* Naomi in my forthcoming farm epic, *Sow the Wild Oat!*"

Reluctantly the operator plugged out her dream and sent word of Nathan's reservation to André. André belonged to that great International Race, head waiters, whose flag is an unreadable menu and whose language is French with an accent. Head waiters are diplomats who happened to be born with silver spoons in their hands instead of their mouths. André would have been a typical head waiter. But he had been in Hollywood too long. Which meant that no matter how good a head waiter he was, he was no longer satisfied to be one. André wanted to be a screen writer. In fact, after working only three years, André had managed to finish a screenplay, entitled, surprisingly enough, *Confessions of a Hollywood Waiter*. He had written it all by himself, in English.

With casual deliberateness (hadn't Jimmy Starr called him the poor man's Adolphe Menjou?) André picked out a table one row removed from the dance floor for Mr. Nathan. The waiter, whose ringside table was A. D. Nathan's "usual," raised a protest not entirely motivated by sentiment. In Waiter's Local 67, A. D. Nathan's fame was based not so much on his pictures as on his tips. "Mr. Nathan will have to be satisfied with this table," André explained. "All the ringside tables are already reserved."

André had to smile at his own cleverness. A. D. Nathan did not know it yet, but from the beginning André had had him in mind as the producer of his scenario. A. D. seemed the logical contact because he remembered André as an ordinary waiter in Henry's back in the days before pictures could talk. But André knew he needed something stronger than nostalgia to bring himself to A. D.'s attention. Every Saturday night Nathan presided at the same table overlooking the floor. Tonight André would make him take a back seat. Nathan would threaten and grumble and André would flash his suave head-waiter smile and be *so sorry, M'sieur Nathan, if there were only something I could do* . . . Then, at the opportune moment, just as the floor show was about to begin, André would discover that something could be done. And when Nathan would try to thank André with a crisp green bill for giving him the table André had been saving for him all evening, André's voice would take on an injured tone. *Merci beaucoup, M'sieur Nathan, thank you just the same, but André is glad to do a favor for an old friend.*

André thought of the scene in terms of a scenario. That was the dialogue, just roughed in, of course. Then the business of Nathan insisting on rewarding André for his efforts. And a close-up of André, shyly dropping his eyes as he tells M'sieur Nathan that if he really wants to reward André he could read *Confessions of a Hollywood Waiter* by André de Selco.

So that was Andre's dream and he dreamed it all the while he was fussing over last-minute details like a nervous hostess getting ready for a big party.

By the time Nathan's party arrived, the big room with the cyclamen drapes and pale-green walls of tufted satin was full of laughter, music, shop talk and an inner-circle intimacy that hung over the place like the smoke that rose from lipsticked cigarettes and expensive cigars. Everyone turned to stare at the newcomers, for Hollywood celebrities have a way of gaping at each other with the same wide-eyed curiosity as their supposedly less sophisticated brothers waiting for autographs outside.

Nathan entered with assurance, conscious of the way "There's A.D." was breathed through the room. His figure was slight but imposing, for he carried himself with the air of a man who was used to commanding authority. There was something ghostly about him, with his white hair and pale, clean, faintly pink skin, but his eyes were intensely alive, dark eyes that never softened, even when he smiled. As he followed André toward the dance floor, actors, agents, directors and fellow-producers were anxious to catch his eye. It was "Hello, A. D. How are you tonight, A. D.?" and he would acknowledge them with a word or a nod, knowing how to strike just the right balance between dignity and cordiality.

At his side was his wife, a tall brunette with sculpture-perfect features, hardened by a willful disposition. Some still remembered her as Lita Lawlor, who seemed on the verge of stardom not so many years ago. But she had sacrificed her screen career for love, or so the fan magazines had put it, though gossipers would have you believe that Lita was just swapping one career for another that promised somewhat more permanent security.

Accompanying the Nathans were a plain, middle-aged couple whom no one in Ciro's could identify, an undiscovered girl of seventeen who was beautiful in an undistinguished way, and Bruce Spencer, a young man whom Nathan was grooming as the next Robert Taylor. And grooming was just the word, for this male ingénue pranced and tossed his curly black mane like a horse on exhibition.

André led the party to the inferior table he had picked out for them.

"Wait a minute. André, this isn't my table," Nathan protested.

He frowned at André's silky explanations. He was in no mood to be crossed this evening. It seemed as if everything was out of sync today. First his three-thousand-dollar-a-week writer had turned in a dime-a-dozen script. Then he had decided that what he needed was an evening alone with something young and new like this Jenny Robbins, and instead here he was with his wife, that young ham of hers, and those Carterets he'd been ducking for months. And to top everything, there was that business in New York.

Impatiently Nathan beckoned the waiter. "A magnum of Cordon Rouge, 1935."

1935, Nathan thought. That was the year he almost lost his job. It was a funny thing. All these people hoping to be tossed a bone never thought of A. D. Nathan as a man with a job to hold. But that year, when the panic struck and the banks moved in, he had had to think fast to hold onto that big office and that long title. He wondered what would have become of him if he had lost out. He thought of some of the magic names of the past, like Colonel Selig and J. C. Blackburn, who could walk into Ciro's now without causing a head to turn. And he thought how frightening it would be to enter Ciro's without the salaaming reception he always complained about but would have felt lost without.

But he mustn't worry. His psychiatrist had told him not to worry. He looked across at Jenny with that incredibly young face, so pretty and soft, like a marmalade kitten, he thought. A little wearily, he raised his glass to her. He wondered what she was like, what she was thinking, whether she would. Then he looked at Mimi Carteret. How old she and Lew had become. He could remember when they were the regulars at the Embassy Club and the Coconut Grove. Now their eyes were shining like tourists' because it had been such a long time since their last evening in Ciro's.

"Is the wine all right, Lew?" Nathan asked.

Lew Carteret looked up, his face flushed. "All right! I haven't had wine like this . . ." He paused to think. "In a long time," he said.

There was a silence, and Nathan felt embarrassed for him. He was glad when Mimi broke in with the anecdote about the time during Prohibition when they were leaving for Europe with their Western star, Tex Bradley, and Tex insisted on bringing his own Scotch along because he was afraid to trust those foreign bootleggers.

Nathan was only half-listening, though he joined in the laughter. When is Carteret going to put the bite on me for that job he wants? he was thinking. And what will I have to give the little marmalade kitten? And though he could not divine André's plans, or guess how he figured in the dreams of the telephone operator who looked like Ava Gardner, he could not help feeling that Ciro's was a solar system in which he was the sun and around which all these satellites revolved.

"André," he beckoned, "will you please tell the operator I'm expecting a very important long-distance call?" An empty feeling of excitement rose inside him, but he fought it down. The dancers were swaying to a tango. Nathan saw Spencer and Lita, whirling like professionals, conscious of how well they looked together. He looked at Jenny, and he thought, with a twinge of weariness, of all the Jennys he had looked at this way. "Would you like to dance, my dear?"

He was an old man to Jenny, an old man she hardly knew, and it seemed to her that everybody in the room must be saying, "There goes A. D. with another one." But she tried to smile, tried to be having a terribly good time, thinking, If I want to be an actress, this is part of the job. And if I can't look as if I'm getting the thrill of my life out of dancing with this old fossil, what kind of an actress am I anyway?

Nathan could have told her what kind of an actress she was. He had expressed himself rather vividly on that subject after seeing her test that afternoon.

"Robbins stinks," he had told his assistants as the lights came on in the projection room. "She has a cute figure and a pretty face, but not unusual enough, and her acting is from Hollywood High School."

That's what he should have told her. But he needed to be surrounded by Jenny Robbinses. Even though the analyst had told him what that was, he went on tossing them just enough crumbs of encouragement to keep their hopes alive.

"Enjoying yourself, Jenny?" he said as he led her back to the table.

"Oh, I'm having an elegant time, Mr. Nathan," she said. She tried to say it with personality, her eyes bright and her smile fixed. She felt as if she were back on the set going through the ordeal of making that test again.

"After dancing a tango together, the least we could do is call each other by our first names," he said.

He tried to remember the first time he had used that line; on Betty Bronson he thought it was. But Jenny laughed as if he had said something terribly witty. She laughed with all her ambition if not with all her heart.

Her heart—or so she thought—had been left behind at 1441½ Orange Grove Avenue. That's where Bill Mason lived. Bill worked as a grip on Nathan's lot. The grip is the guy who does the dirty work on a movie set. Or, as Bill liked to explain it, "I'm the guy who carries the set on his back. I may not be the power behind the throne but I'm sure the power *under* it."

Jenny thought of the way she and Bill had planned to spend this evening, down at the Venice Amusement Pier. They usually had a pretty good time down there together Saturday nights. It was their night. Until A. D. Nathan had telephoned, in person.

"Oh, Mr. Nathan, how lovely of you to call! I do have an appointment, but . . ."

"I wish you could cancel it, dear," Nathan had said. "There's . . . there's something I'd like to talk to you about. I thought, over a drink at Ciro's . . ."

Jenny had never been to Ciro's, but she could describe every corner of it. It was her idea of what heaven must be like, with producers for gods and agents as their angels.

"Sorry to keep you waiting, Mac," Bill had called from the door a little later. "But that Old Bag" (referring to one of the screen's most glamorous personalities) "blew her lines in the big love scene fifteen straight times. I thought one of the juicers was going to drop a lamp on her." He looked at Jenny in the sequin dress, the pin-up model. "Hmmm, not bad. But a little fancy for roller-coasting, isn't it, honey?"

"Bill, I know I'm a monster," she had said, watching his face carefully, "but I've got to see Mr. Nathan tonight. I'd've given anything to get out of it, but, well, I don't want to sound dramatic but . . . my whole career may depend on it."

"Listen, Mac," Bill had said. "You may be kidding yourself, but you can't kid me. I was on the set when you made that test. If I'm ever going to be your husband I might as well begin right by telling you the truth. You were NG."

"I suppose you know more about acting than Mr. Nathan," she said, hating Bill, hating the Venice Pier, hating being nobody. "Mr. Nathan told me himself he wanted to keep my test to look at again."

"Are you sure it's the test he wants to keep?" Bill said.

Here in Ciro's the waiter was filling her glass again, and she was laughing at something funny and off-color that Bruce Spencer had just said. But she couldn't forget what she had done to Bill, how she had slapped him and handed back the ring, and how, like a scene from a bad B picture, they had parted forever.

For almost fifteen minutes Jenny had cried because Bill was a wonderful fellow and she was going to miss him. And then she had stopped crying and started making up her face for A. D. Nathan because she had read too many movie magazines. This is what makes a great actress, she thought, sorrow and sacrifice of your personal happiness, and she saw herself years later as a great star, running into Bill in Ciro's after he had become a famous cameraman. "Bill," she would say, "perhaps it is not too late. Each of us had to follow our own path until they crossed again."

"Oh, by the way, Lita," A. D. had told his wife when she came into his dressing room to find out if he had any plans for the evening, "there's a little actress I'd like to take along to Ciro's tonight. Trying to build her up. So we'll need an extra man."

"We might still be able to get hold of Bruce," Lita said. "He said something about being free when we left the club this afternoon."

Nathan knew they could get hold of Bruce. Lita and Bruce were giving the Hollywood wives something to talk about over their canasta these afternoons. Sometimes he dreamt of putting an end to it. But that meant killing two birds with bad publicity. And they were both his birds, his wife and his leading man.

"All right," he said, "I'll give Spence a ring. Might not be a bad idea for the Robbins girl to be seen with him."

Lita pecked him on the cheek. Bruce was dying to get that star-making part in *Wagons Westward*. This might be the evening to talk A. D. into it.

And then, since the four of them might look too obvious, Nathan had wanted an extra couple. He tried several, but it was too late to get anybody in demand, and that's how, at the last minute, he had happened to think of the Carterets.

When you talked about old-time directors you had to mention Lew Carteret in the same breath with D. W. Griffith and Mickey Neilan. Carteret and Nathan had been a famous combination until sound pictures and the jug had knocked Carteret out of the running. The last job he had had was a quickie Western more than a year ago. And a year in Hollywood is at least a decade anywhere else. A. D. had forgotten all about Carteret until he received a letter from him a few months ago, just a friendly letter, suggesting dinner some evening to cut up touches about old times. But A. D. knew those friendly dinners, knew he owed Carteret a debt he was reluctant to repay, and so, somehow, the letter had gone unanswered. But in spite of himself, his conscience had filed it away for further reference.

"I know who we'll get. The Lew Carterets. Been meaning to take them to dinner for months."

"Oh, God," Lita said, as she drew on a pair of long white gloves that set off her firm tanned arms, "why don't we get John Bunny and Flora Finch?"

"It might not be so bad," Nathan said, giving way to the sentimentality that thrives in his profession. "Mimi Carteret used to be a lot of fun."

"I can just imagine," said Lita. "I'll bet she does a mean Turkey Trot."

"Lew, do you think this means he's going to give you a chance again?" Mimi Carteret whispered as they walked off the dance floor together. "Easy on the wine, darling. We just can't let anything go wrong tonight."

"Don't worry, sweetheart," he answered. "I'm watching. I'm waiting for the right moment to talk to him."

Lita and Bruce were dancing again and Jenny was alone with A. D. at the table when the Carterets returned. It was the moment Jenny had been working toward. She could hardly wait to know what he thought of the test.

"I don't think it does you justice," Nathan was saying. "The cameraman didn't know how to light you at all. I think you have great possibilities."

Jenny smiled happily, the wine and encouragement going to her head, and Nathan reached over and patted her hand in what was meant to seem a fatherly gesture, though he lingered a moment too long. But Jenny hardly noticed, swept along in the dream.

Lew Carteret looked at his watch nervously. It was almost time for the floor show. There wouldn't be much chance to talk during the acts, and after that, the party would be over. He looked across at Mimi, trying to find the courage to put it up to A. D. If only A. D. would give him an opening. Lita and Bruce were watching too, wondering when to bring up *Wagons Westward*. And André, behind the head waiter's mask, was thinking, Only ten more minutes and I will be speaking to A. D. about my scenario.

"André," Nathan called, and the head waiter snapped to attention. "Are you sure there hasn't been a call for me?"

"No, m'sieur. I would call you right away, m'sieur."

Nathan frowned. "Well, make sure. It should have been here by now." He felt angry with himself for losing his patience. There was no reason to be so upset. This was just another long-distance call. He had talked to New York a thousand times before—about matters just as serious.

But when André came running with the message that New York was on the wire, he could not keep the old fear from knotting his stomach and he jostled the table in his anxiety to rise.

"You may take it in the second booth on the left, Mr. Nathan," said Ava Gardner, as she looked up from her switchboard with a prefabricated smile. But he merely brushed by her and slammed the door of the booth behind him. The telephone girl looked after him with the dream in her eyes. *When he comes out I'll hafta think of something arresting to sayta him,* she decided. *God, wouldn't it be funny if he did notice me!*

Five minutes later she heard the door of the booth sliding open and she looked up and smiled. "Was the connection clear, Mr. Nathan?"

That might do for a starter, she thought. But he didn't even look up. "Yes. I heard very well. Thank you," he said. He put half a dollar down and walked on. He felt heavy, heavy all over, his body too heavy for his legs to support and his eyes too heavy for the sockets to hold. He walked back to the table without seeing the people who tried to catch his glance.

"Everything all right?" his wife asked.

"Yes. Yes," he said. "Everything."

Was that his voice? It didn't sound like his voice. It sounded more like Lew Carteret's voice. Poor old Lew. Those were great old times when we ran World-Wide together. And that time I lost my shirt in the market and Lew loaned me fifty G's. Wonder what ever happened to Lew.

Then he realized this *was* Lew Carteret, and that he was listening to Lew's voice. "A. D., this has sure been a tonic for Mimi and me. I know we didn't come here to talk shop, but—well, you always used to have faith in me, and . . ."

"Sure, sure, Lew," A. D. said. "Here, you're one behind. Let me pour it. For old times."

He could feel an imperceptible trembling in his hand as he poured the wine.

Under the table a small, slender leg moved slowly, with a surreptitious life of its own, until it pressed meaningfully against his. *Jenny had never slept with anybody except Bill. She was frightened, but not as frightened as she was of living the rest of her life in Hollywood as the wife of a grip in a bungalow court.*

Bruce flipped open his cigarette case—the silver one that Lita had given him for his birthday—and lit a cigarette confidently. "By the way, A. D., Lita let me read the scrip on *Wagons.* That's a terrific part, that bank clerk who has to go west for his health and falls in with a gang of rustlers. Wonderfully written. Who's going to play it?"

"Any leading man in Hollywood except you," Nathan said.

Bruce looked undressed without his assurance. The silence was terrible. Lita said, "But, A. D., that part was written for Bruce."

All the rest of his face seemed to be sagging, but Nathan's hard black eyes watched them with bitter amusement. "There isn't a part in the studio that's written for Bruce. The only thing that kept Bruce from being fired months ago was me. And now there's no longer me."

Lita looked up, really frightened now. "A. D. What do you mean?"

"I mean I'm out," he said. "Finished. Washed up. Through. Hudson called to say the Board voted to ask for my resignation."

"What are you going to do now?" she said.

He thought of the thing he had promised himself to do when his time came, drop out of sight, break it off clean. Hollywood had no use for anticlimaxes on or off the screen. But as he sat there he knew what would really happen. Move over, Colonel Selig and J. C. Blackburn, he thought. Make room for another ghost.

The floor show was just starting. The undiscovered Rosemary Clooney was putting everything she had into her number, and playing right to A. D.'s table. *Don't let the stars get in your eyes* . . .

And as she sang, André smiled in anticipation. So far everything had gone just as he had planned. And now the time had come to move A. D. up to that ringside table.

Race at Morning

By WILLIAM FAULKNER

I was in the boat when I seen him. It was jest dust-dark; I had jest fed
the horses and clumb back down the bank to the boat and shoved off to
cross back to camp when I seen him, about half a quarter up the river,
swimming; jest his head above the water, and it no more than a dot in
that light. But I could see that rocking chair he toted on it and I knowed
it was him, going right back to that canebrake in the fork of the bayou
where he lived all year until the day before the season opened, like the
game wardens had give him a calendar, when he would clear out and
disappear, nobody knowed where, until the day after the season closed.
But here he was, coming back a day ahead of time, like maybe he had got
mixed up and was using last year's calendar by mistake. Which was jest
too bad for him, because me and Mister Ernest would be setting on the
horse right over him when the sun rose tomorrow morning.

So I told Mister Ernest and we et supper and fed the dogs, and then I
holp Mister Ernest in the poker game, standing behind his chair until
about ten o'clock, when Roth Edmonds said, "Why don't you go to bed,
boy?"

"Or if you're going to set up," Willy Legate said, "why don't you take
a spelling book to set up over? He knows every cuss word in the dic-
tionary, every poker hand in the deck and every whiskey label in the dis-
tillery, but he can't even write his name. Can you?" he says to me.

"I don't need to write my name down," I said. "I can remember in my
mind who I am."

"You're twelve years old," Walter Ewell said. "Man to man now, how
many days in your life did you ever spend in school?"

"He ain't got time to go to school," Willy Legate said. "What's the use
in going to school from September to middle of November, when he'll
have to quit then to come in here and do Ernest's hearing for him? And
what's the use in going back to school in January, when in jest eleven
months it will be November fifteenth again and he'll have to start all over
telling Ernest which way the dogs went?"

"Well, stop looking into my hand, anyway," Roth Edmonds said.

"What's that? What's that?" Mister Ernest said. He wore his listening button in his ear all the time, but he never brought the battery to camp with him because the cord would bound to get snagged ever time we run through a thicket.

"Willy says for me to go to bed!" I hollered.

"Don't you never call nobody 'mister'?" Willy said.

"I call Mister Ernest 'mister,'" I said.

"All right," Mister Ernest said. "Go to bed then. I don't need you."

"That ain't no lie," Willy said. "Deaf or no deaf, he can hear a fifty-dollar raise if you don't even move your lips."

So I went to bed, and after a while Mister Ernest come in and I wanted to tell him again how big them horns looked even half a quarter away in the river. Only I would 'a' had to holler, and the only time Mister Ernest agreed he couldn't hear was when we would be setting on Dan, waiting for me to point which way the dogs was going. So we jest laid down, and it wasn't no time Simon was beating the bottom of the dishpan with the spoon, hollering, "Raise up and get your four-o'clock coffee!" and I crossed the river in the dark this time, with the lantern, and fed Dan and Roth Edmondziz horse. It was going to be a fine day, cold and bright; even in the dark I could see the white frost on the leaves and bushes—jest exactly the kind of day that big old son of a gun laying up there in that brake would like to run.

Then we et, and set the stand-holder across for Uncle Ike McCaslin to put them on the stands where he thought they ought to be, because he was the oldest one in camp. He had been hunting deer in these woods for about a hundred years, I reckon, and if anybody would know where a buck would pass, it would be him. Maybe with a big old buck like this one, that had been running the woods for what would amount to a hundred years in a deer's life, too, him and Uncle Ike would sholy manage to be at the same place at the same time this morning—provided, of course, he managed to git away from me and Mister Ernest on the jump. Because me and Mister Ernest was going to git him.

Then me and Mister Ernest and Roth Edmonds sent the dogs over, with Simon holding Eagle and the other old dogs on leash because the young ones, the puppies, wasn't going nowhere until Eagle let them, nohow. Then me and Mister Ernest and Roth saddled up, and Mister Ernest got up and I handed him up his pump gun and let Dan's bridle go for him to git rid of the spell of bucking he had to git shut of ever morning until Mister Ernest hit him between the ears with the gun barrel. Then Mister Ernest loaded the gun and give me the stirrup, and I got up behind him and we taken the fire road up toward the bayou, the four big dogs dragging Simon along in front with his single-barrel britch-loader slung on a piece of plow line across his back, and the puppies moiling along in ever'body's way. It was light now and it was going to be jest fine; the east already yellow for the sun and our breaths smoking in the cold still bright air until the sun would come up and warm it, and a little skim of ice in the ruts, and ever leaf and twig and switch and even the frozen clods frosted over, waiting to sparkle like a rainbow when the sun finally come up and hit them. Until all my insides felt light and strong as a balloon, full of that light cold strong air, so that it seemed to me like I couldn't even feel the horse's back I was straddle of—jest the hot strong muscles moving under the hot strong skin, setting up there without no weight atall, so that when old Eagle struck and jumped, me and Dan and Mister Ernest would go jest like a bird, not even touching the ground. It was jest fine. When that big old buck got killed today, I knowed that even if he had put it off another ten years, he couldn't 'a' picked a better one.

And sho enough, as soon as we come to the bayou we seen his foot in the mud where he had come up out of the river last night spread in the soft mud like a cow's foot, big as a cow's, big as a mule's, with Eagle and the other dogs laying into the leash rope now until Mister Ernest told me to jump down and help Simon hold them. Because me and Mister Ernest knowed exactly where he would be—a little canebrake island in the middle of the bayou, where he could lay up until whatever doe or little deer the dogs had happened to jump could go up or down the bayou in either direction and take the dogs on away, so he could steal out and creep back down the bayou to the river and swim it, and leave the country like he always done the day the season opened.

Which is jest what we never aimed for him to do this time. So we left Roth on his horse to cut him off and turn him over Uncle Ike's standers if he tried to slip back down the bayou, and me and Simon, with the leashed dogs, walked on up the bayou until Mister Ernest on the horse said it was fur enough; then turned up into the woods about half a quarter above the brake because the wind was going to be south this morn- ing when it riz, and turned down toward the brake, and Mister Ernest give the word to cast them, and we slipped the leash and Mister Ernest give me the stirrup again and I got up.

Old Eagle had done already took off because he knowed where that old son of a gun would be laying as good as we did, not making no racket atall yet, but jest boring on through the buck vines with the other dogs trailing along behind him, and even Dan seemed to know about that buck, too, beginning to souple up and jump a little through the vines, so that I taken my holt on Mister Ernest's belt already before the time had come for Mister Ernest to touch him. Because when we got strung out, going fast behind a deer, I wasn't on Dan's back much of the time no- how, but mostly jest strung out from my holt on Mister Ernest's belt, so that Willy Legate said that when we was going through the woods fast, it looked like Mister Ernest had a boy-size pair of empty overalls blowing out of his hind pocket.

So it wasn't even a strike, it was a jump. Eagle must 'a' walked right up behind him or maybe even stepped on him while he was laying there still thinking it was day after tomorrow. Eagle jest throwed his head back and up and said, "There he goes," and we even heard the buck crashing through the first of the cane. Then all the other dogs was hollering behind him, and Dan give a squat to jump, but it was against the curb this time, not jest the snaffle, and Mister Ernest let him down into the bayou and swung him around the brake and up the other bank. Only he never had to say, "Which way?" because I was already pointing past his shoulder, freshening my holt on the belt jest as Mister Ernest touched Dan with that big old rusty spur on his nigh heel, because when Dan felt it he would go off jest like a stick of dynamite, straight through whatever he could bust and over or under what he couldn't, over it like a bird or under it crawling on his knees like a mole or a big coon, with Mister Ernest still on him because he had the saddle to hold on to, and me still there because I had Mister Ernest to hold on to; me and Mister Ernest not riding him, but jest going along with him, provided we held on. Because when the jump come, Dan never cared who else was there neither; I believe to my soul he could 'a' cast and run them dogs by hisself, without me or Mister Ernest or Simon or nobody.

That's what he done. He had to; the dogs was already almost out of hearing. Eagle must 'a' been looking right up that big son of a gun's tail until he finally decided he better git on out of there. And now they must 'a' been getting pretty close to Uncle Ike's standers, and Mister Ernest reined Dan back and held him, squatting and bouncing and trembling like a mule having his tail roached, while we listened for the shots. But never none come, and I hollered to Mister Ernest we better go on while I could still hear the dogs, and he let Dan off, but still there wasn't no shots, and now we knowed the race had done already passed the standers, like that old son of a gun actually was a hant, like Simon and the other field hands said he was, and we busted out of a thicket, and sho enough there was Uncle Ike and Willy standing beside his foot in a soft patch.

"He got through us all," Uncle Ike said. "I don't know how he done it. I just had a glimpse of him. He looked big as a elephant, with a rack on his head you could cradle a yellin' calf in. He went right on down the ridge. You better get on, too; that Hog Bayou camp might not miss him."

So I freshened my holt and Mister Ernest touched Dan again. The ridge run due south; it was clear of vines and bushes so we could go fast, into the wind, too, because it had riz now, and now the sun was up, too; though I hadn't had time to notice it, bright and strong and level through the woods, shining and sparkling like a rainbow on the frosted leaves. So we would hear the dogs again any time now as the wind got up; we could make time now, but still holding Dan back to a canter, because it was either going to be quick, when he got down to the standers from that Hog Bayou camp eight miles below ourn, or a long time, in case he got by them, too. And sho enough, after a while we heard the dogs; we was walking Dan now to let him blow a while, and we heard them, the sound coming faint up the wind, not running now, but trailing because the big son of a gun had decided a good piece back, probably, to put a end to this foolishness, and picked up and soupled out and put about a mile between hisself and the dogs—until he run up on them other standers from that camp below. I could almost see him stopped behind a bush, peeping out and saying, "What's this? What's this? Is this whole durn country full of folks this morning?" Then looking back over his shoulder at where old Eagle and the others was hollering along after him while he decided how much time he had to decide what to do next.

Except he almost shaved it too fine. We heard the shots; it sounded like a war. Old Eagle must 'a' been looking right up his tail again and he had to bust on through the best way he could. "Pow, pow, pow, pow" and then "Pow, pow, pow, pow," like it must 'a' been three or four ganged right up on him before he had time even to swerve, and me hollering, "No! No! No! No!" because he was ourn. It was our beans and oats he et and our brake he laid in; we had been watching him every year, and it was like we had raised him, to be killed at last on our jump, in front of our dogs, by some strangers that would probably try to beat the dogs off and drag him away before we could even git a piece of the meat.

"Shut up and listen," Mister Ernest said. So I done it and we could hear the dogs; not just the others, but Eagle, too, not trailing no scent now and not baying no downed meat neither, but running hot on sight long after the shooting was over. I jest had time to freshen my holt. Yes, sir, they was running on sight. Like Willy Legate would say, if Eagle jest had a drink of whiskey he would ketch that deer; going on, done already gone when we broke out of the thicket and seen the fellers that had done the shooting, five or six of them, squatting and crawling around, looking at the ground and the bushes, like maybe if they looked hard enough, spots of blood would bloom out on the stalks and leaves like frogstools or haw-berries, with old Eagle still in hearing and still telling them that what blood they found wasn't coming out of nothing in front of him.

"Have any luck, boys?" Mister Ernest said.

"I think I hit him," one of them said. "I know I did. We're hunting blood now."

"Well, when you find him, blow your horn and I'll come back and tote him in to camp for you," Mister Ernest said.

So we went on, going fast now because the race was almost out of hearing again, going fast, too, like not jest the buck, but the dogs, too, had took a new leash on life from all the excitement and shooting.

We was in strange country now because we never had to run this fur before, we had always killed before now; now we had come to Hog Bayou that runs into the river a good fifteen miles below our camp. It had water in it, not to mention a mess of down trees and logs and such, and Mister Ernest checked Dan again, saying, "Which way?" I could just barely hear them, off to the east a little, like the old son of a gun had give up the idea of Vicksburg or New Orleans, like he first seemed to have, and had decided to have a look at Alabama, maybe, since he was already up and moving; so I pointed and we turned up the bayou hunting for a crossing, and maybe we could 'a' found one, except that I reckon Mister Ernest decided we never had time to wait.

We come to a place where the bayou had narrowed down to about twelve or fifteen feet, and Mister Ernest said, "Look out, I'm going to touch him" and done it; I didn't even have time to freshen my holt when we was already in the air, and then I seen the vine—it was a loop of grape-vine nigh as big as my wrist, looping down right across the middle of the bayou—and I thought he seen it, too, and was jest waiting to grab it and fling it up over our heads to go under it, and I know Dan seen it because he even ducked his head to jump under it. But Mister Ernest never seen it atall until it skun back along Dan's neck and hooked under the head of the saddle horn, us flying on through the air, the loop of the vine gitting tighter and tighter until something somewhere was going to have to give. It was the saddle girth. It broke, and Dan going on and scrabbling up the other bank bare nekkid except for the bridle, and me and Mister Ernest and the saddle, Mister Ernest still setting in the saddle holding the gun, and me still holding onto Mister Ernest's belt, hanging in the air over the bayou in the tightened loop of that vine like in the drawed-back loop of a big rubber-banded slingshot, until it snapped back and shot us back across the bayou and flang us clear, me still holding onto Mister Ernest's belt and on the bottom now, so that when we lit I would 'a' had Mister Ernest and the saddle both on top of me if I hadn't clumb fast around the saddle and up Mister Ernest's side, so that when we landed, it was the saddle first, then Mister Ernest, and me on top, until I jumped up, and Mister Ernest still laying there with jest the white rim of his eyes showing.

"Mister Ernest!" I hollered, and then clumb down to the bayou and scooped my cap full of water and clumb back and throwed it in his face, and he opened his eyes and laid there on the saddle cussing me.

"God dawg it," he said, "why didn't you stay behind where you started out?"

"You was the biggest!" I said. "You would 'a' mashed me flat!"

"What do you think you done to me?" Mister Ernest said. "Next time, if you can't stay where you start out, jump clear. Don't climb up on top of me no more. You hear?"

"Yes, sir," I said.

So he got up then, still cussing and holding his back, and clumb down to the water and dipped some in his hand onto his face and neck and dipped some more up and drunk it, and I drunk some, too, and clumb back and got the saddle and the gun, and we crossed the bayou on the down logs. If we could jest ketch Dan; not that he would have went them fifteen miles back to camp, because, if anything, he would have went on by hisself to try to help Eagle ketch that buck. But he was about fifty yards away, eating buck vines, so I brought him back, and we taken Mister Ernest's galluses and my belt and the whang leather loop off Mister Ernest's horn and tied the saddle back on Dan. It didn't look like much, but maybe it would hold.

"Provided you don't let me jump him through no more grapevines without hollering first," Mister Ernest said.

"Yes, sir," I said. "I'll holler first next time—provided you'll holler a little quicker when you touch him next time, too." But it was all right; we jest had to be a little easy getting up. "Now which-a-way?" I said. Because we couldn't hear nothing now, after wasting all this time. And this was new country, sho enough. It had been cut over and growed up in thickets we couldn't 'a' seen over even standing up on Dan.

But Mister Ernest never even answered. He jest turned Dan along the bank of the bayou where it was a little more open and we could move faster again, soon as Dan and us got used to that homemade cinch strop and got a little confidence in it. Which jest happened to be east, or so I thought then, because I never paid no particular attention to east then because the sun—I don't know where the morning had went, but it was gone, the morning and the frost, too—was up high now, even if my insides had told me it was past dinnertime.

And then we heard him. No, that's wrong; what we heard was shots. And that was when we realized how fur we had come, because the only camp we knowed about in that direction was the Hollyknowe camp, and Hollyknowe was exactly twenty-eight miles from Van Dorn, where me and Mister Ernest lived—jest the shots, no dogs nor nothing. If old Eagle was still behind him and the buck was still alive, he was too wore out now to even say, "Here he comes."

"Don't touch him!" I hollered. But Mister Ernest remembered that cinch strop, too, and he jest let Dan off the snaffle. And Dan heard them shots, too, picking his way through the thickets, hopping the vines and logs when he could and going under them when he couldn't. And sho enough, it was jest like before—two or three men squatting and creeping among the bushes, looking for blood that Eagle had done already told them wasn't there. But we never stopped this time, jest trotting on by with Dan hopping and dodging among the brush and vines dainty as a dancer. Then Mister Ernest swung Dan until we was going due north.

"Wait!" I hollered. "Not this way."

But Mister Ernest jest turned his face back over his shoulder. It looked tired, too, and there was a smear of mud on it where that ere grapevine had snatched him off the horse.

"Don't you know where he's heading?" he said. "He's done done his part, give everybody a fair open shot at him, and now he's going home, back to that brake in our bayou. He ought to make it exactly at dark."

And that's what he was doing. We went on. It didn't matter to hurry now. There wasn't no sound nowhere; it was that time in the early afternoon in November when don't nothing move or cry, not even birds, the peckerwoods and yellowhammers and jays, and it seemed to me like I could see all three of us—me and Mister Ernest and Dan—and Eagle, and the other dogs, and that big old buck, moving through the quiet woods in the same direction, headed for the same place, not running now but walking, that had all run the fine race the best we knowed how, and all three of us now turned like on a agreement to walk back home, not together in a bunch because we didn't want to worry or tempt one another, because what we had all three spent this morning doing was no play-acting jest for fun, but was serious, and all three of us was still what we was—that old buck that had to run, not because he was skeered, but because running was what he done the best and was proudest at; and Eagle and the dogs chased him, not because they hated or feared him, but because that was the thing they done the best and was proudest at; and me and Mister Ernest and Dan, that run him not because we wanted his meat, which would be too tough to eat anyhow, or his head to hang on a wall, but because now we could go back and work hard for eleven months making a crop, so we would have the right to come back here next November—all three of us going back home now, peaceful and separate, but still side by side, until next year, next time.

Then we seen him for the first time. We was out of the cut-over now; we could even 'a' cantered, except that all three of us was long past that, and now you could tell where west was because the sun was already half-way down it. So we was walking, too, when we come on the dogs—the puppies and one of the old ones—played out, laying in a little wet swag, panting, jest looking up at us when we passed, but not moving when we went on. Then we come to a long open glade, you could see about half a quarter, and we seen the three other old dogs and about a hundred yards ahead of them Eagle, all walking, not making no sound; and then suddenly, at the fur end of the glade, the buck hisself getting up from where he had been resting for the dogs to come up, getting up without no hurry, big, big as a mule, tall as a mule, and turned without no hurry still, and the white underside of his tail for a second or two more before the thicket taken him.

It might 'a' been a signal, a good-by, a farewell. Still walking, we passed the other three old dogs in the middle of the glade, laying down, too, now jest where they was when the buck vanished, and not trying to get up neither when we passed; and still that hundred yards ahead of them, Eagle, too, not laying down, because he was still on his feet, but his legs was spraddled and his head was down; maybe just waiting until we was out of sight of his shame, his eyes saying plain as talk when we passed, "I'm sorry, boys, but this here is all."

Mister Ernest stopped Dan. "Jump down and look at his feet," he said.

"Ain't nothing wrong with his feet," I said. "It's his wind has done give out."

"Jump down and look at his feet," Mister Ernest said.

So I done it, and while I was stooping over Eagle I could hear the pump gun go, "Snick-cluck. Snick-cluck. Snick-cluck" three times, except that I never thought nothing then. Maybe he was jest running the shells through to be sho it would work when we seen him again or maybe to make sho they was all buckshot. Then I got up again, and we went on, still walking; a little west of north now, because when we seen his white flag that second or two before the thicket hid it, it was on a beeline for that notch in the bayou. And it was evening, too, now. The wind had done dropped and there was a edge to the air and the sun jest touched the tops of the trees now, except jest now and then, when it found a hole to come almost level through onto the ground. And he was taking the easiest way, too, now, going straight as he could. When we seen his foot in the soft places he was running for a while at first after his rest. But soon he was walking, too, like he knowed, too, where Eagle and the dogs was.

And then we seen him again. It was the last time—a thicket, with the sun coming through a hole onto it like a searchlight. He crashed jest once; then he was standing there broadside to us, not twenty yards away, big as a statue and red as gold in the sun, and the sun sparking on the tips of his horns—they was twelve of them—so that he looked like he had twelve lighted candles branched around his head, standing there looking at us while Mister Ernest raised the gun and aimed at his neck, and the gun went, "Click. Snick-cluck. Click. Snick-cluck. Click. Snick-cluck" three times, and Mister Ernest still holding the gun aimed while the buck turned and give one long bound, the white underside of his tail like a blaze of fire, too, until the thicket and the shadows put it out; and Mister Ernest laid the gun slow and gentle back across the saddle in front of him, saying quiet and peaceful, and not much louder than jest breathing, "God dawg. God dawg."

Then he jogged me with his elbow and we got down, easy and careful because of that ere cinch strop, and he reached into his vest and taken out one of the cigars. It was busted where I had fell on it, I reckon, when we hit the ground. He throwed it away and taken out the other one. It was busted, too, so he bit off a hunk of it to chew and throwed the rest away. And now the sun was gone even from the tops of the trees and there wasn't nothing left but a big red glare in the west.

"Don't worry," I said. "I ain't going to tell them you forgot to load your gun. For that matter, they don't need to know we ever seed him."

"Much oblige," Mister Ernest said. There wasn't going to be no moon tonight neither, so he taken the compass off the whang leather loop in his buttonhole and handed me the gun and set the compass on a stump and stepped back and looked at it. "Jest about the way we're headed now," he said, and taken the gun from me and opened it and put one shell in the britch and taken up the compass, and I taken Dan's reins and we started, with him in front with the compass in his hand.

And after a while it was full dark; Mister Ernest would have to strike a match ever now and then to read the compass, until the stars come out good and we could pick out one to follow, because I said, "How fur do you reckon it is?" and he said, "A little more than one box of matches." So we used a star when we could, only we couldn't see it all the time be- cause the woods was too dense and we would git a little off until he would have to spend another match. And now it was good and late, and he stopped and said, "Get on the horse."

"I ain't tired," I said.

"Get on the horse," he said. "We don't want to spoil him."

Because he had been a good feller ever since I had knowed him, which was even before that day two years ago when maw went off with the Vicksburg roadhouse feller and the next day pap didn't come home neither, and on the third one Mister Ernest rid Dan up to the door of the cabin on the river he let us live in, so pap could work his piece of land and run his fish line, too, and said, "Put that gun down and come on here and climb up behind."

So I got in the saddle even if I couldn't reach the stirrups, and Mister Ernest taken the reins and I must 'a' went to sleep, because the next thing I knowed a buttonhole of my lumberjack was tied to the saddle horn with that ere whang cord off the compass, and it was good and late now and we wasn't fur, because Dan was already smelling water, the river. Or maybe it was the feed lot itself he smelled, because we struck the fire road not a quarter below it, and soon I could see the river, too, with the white mist laying on it soft and still as cotton. Then the lot, home; and up yonder in the dark, not no piece akchully, close enough to hear us unsaddling and shucking corn prob'ly, and sholy close enough to hear Mister Ernest blowing his horn at the dark camp for Simon to come in the boat and git us, that old buck in his brake in the bayou; home, too, resting, too, after the hard run, waking hisself now and then, dreaming of dogs behind him or maybe it was the racket we was making would wake him, but not neither of them for more than jest a little while before sleeping again.

Then Mister Ernest stood on the bank blowing until Simon's lantern went bobbing down into the mist; then we clumb down to the landing and Mister Ernest blowed again now and then to guide Simon, until we seen the lantern in the mist, and then Simon and the boat; only it looked like ever time I set down and got still, I went back to sleep, because Mister Ernest was shaking me again to git out and climb the bank into the dark camp, until I felt a bed against my knees and tumbled into it.

Then it was morning, tomorrow; it was all over now until next November, next year, and we could come back. Uncle Ike and Willy and Walter and Roth and the rest of them had come in yestiddy, soon as Eagle taken the buck out of hearing and they knowed that deer was gone, to pack up and be ready to leave this morning for Yoknapatawpha, where they lived, until it would be November again and they could come back again.

So, as soon as we et breakfast, Simon run them back up the river in the big boat to where they left their cars and pickups, and now it wasn't nobody but jest me and Mister Ernest setting on the bench against the kitchen wall in the sun; Mister Ernest smoking a cigar—a whole one this time that Dan hadn't had no chance to jump him through a grapevine and bust. He hadn't washed his face neither where that vine had throwed him into the mud. But that was all right, too; his face usually did have a smudge of mud or tractor grease or beard stubble on it, because he wasn't jest a planter; he was a farmer, he worked as hard as ara one of his hands and tenants—which is why I knowed from the very first that we would git along, that I wouldn't have no trouble with him and he wouldn't have no trouble with me, from that very first day when I woke up and maw had done gone off with that Vicksburg roadhouse feller without even waiting to cook breakfast, and the next morning pap was gone, too, and it was almost night the next day when I heard a horse coming up and I taken the gun that I had already throwed a shell into the britch when pap never come home last night, and stood in the door while Mister Ernest rid up and said, "Come on. Your paw ain't coming back neither."

"You mean he give me to you?" I said.

"Who cares?" he said. "Come on. I brought a lock for the door. We'll send the pickup back tomorrow for whatever you want."

So I come home with him and it was all right, it was jest fine—his wife had died about three years ago—without no women to worry us or take off in the middle of the night with a durn Vicksburg roadhouse jake without even waiting to cook breakfast. And we would go home this afternoon, too, but not jest yet; we always stayed one more day after the others left because Uncle Ike always left what grub they hadn't et, and the rest of the homemade corn whisky he drunk and that town whiskey of Roth

Edmondziz he called Scotch that smelled like it come out of a old bucket of roof paint; setting in the sun for one more day before we went back home to git ready to put in next year's crop of cotton and oats and beans and hay; and across the river yonder, behind the wall of trees where the big woods started, that old buck laying up today in the sun, too—resting today, too, without nobody to bother him until next November.

So at least one of us was glad it would be eleven months and two weeks before he would have to run that fur that fast again. So he was glad of the very same thing we was sorry of, and so all of a sudden I thought about how maybe planting and working and then harvesting oats and cotton and beans and hay wasn't jest something me and Mister Ernest done three hundred and fifty-one days to fill in the time until we could come back hunting again, but it was something we had to do, and do honest and good during the three hundred and fifty-one days, to have the right to come back into the big woods and hunt for the other fourteen; and the fourteen days that old buck run in front of dogs wasn't jest something to fill his time until the three hundred and fifty-one when he didn't have to, but the running and the risking in front of guns and dogs was something he had to do for fourteen days to have the right not to be bothered for the other three hundred and fifty-one. And so the hunting and the farming wasn't two different things atall—they was jest the other side of each other.

"Yes," I said. "All we got to do now is put in that next year's crop. Then November won't be no time away atall."

"You ain't going to put in the crop next year," Mister Ernest said. "You're going to school."

So at first I didn't even believe I had heard him. "What?" I said. "Me? Go to school?"

"Yes," Mister Ernest said. "You must make something out of yourself."

"I am," I said. "I'm doing it now. I'm going to be a hunter and a farmer like you."

"No," Mister Ernest said. "That ain't enough any more. Time was when all a man had to do was just farm eleven and a half months, and hunt the other half. But not now. Now just to belong to the farming business and the hunting business ain't enough. You got to belong to the business of mankind."

"Mankind?" I said.

"Yes," Mister Ernest said. "So you're going to school. Because you got to know why. You can belong to the farming and hunting business and you can learn the difference between what's right and what's wrong, and do right. And that used to be enough—just to do right. But not now. You got to know why it's right and why it's wrong, and be able to tell the folks that never had no chance to learn it; teach them how to do what's right, not just because they know it's right, but because they know now why it's right because you just showed them, told them, taught them why. So you're going to school."

"It's because you been listening to that durn Will Legate and Walter Ewell!" I said.

"No," Mister Ernest said.

"Yes!" I said. "No wonder you missed that buck yestiday, taking ideas from the very fellers that let him git away, after me and you had run Dan and the dogs durn nigh clean to death! Because you never even missed him! You never forgot to load that gun! You had done already unloaded it a purpose! I heard you!"

"All right, all right," Mister Ernest said. "Which would you rather have? His bloody head and hide on the kitchen floor yonder and half his meat in a pickup truck on the way to Yoknapatawpha County, or him with his head and hide and meat still together over yonder in that brake, waiting for next November for us to run him again?"

"And git him, too," I said. "We won't even fool with no Willy Legate and Walter Ewell next time."

"Maybe," Mister Ernest said.

"Yes," I said.

"Maybe," Mister Ernest said. "The best word in our language, the best of all. That's what mankind keeps going on: Maybe. The best days of his life ain't the ones when he said 'Yes' beforehand: they're the ones when all he knew to say was 'Maybe.' He can't say 'Yes' until afterward because he not only don't know it until then, he don't want to know 'Yes' until then. . . . Step in the kitchen and make me a toddy. Then we'll see about dinner."

"All right," I said. I got up. "You want some of Uncle Ike's corn or that town whisky of Roth Edmondziz?"

"Can't you say Mister Roth or Mister Edmonds?" Mister Ernest said.

"Yes, sir," I said. "Well, which do you want? Uncle Ike's corn or that ere stuff of Roth Edmondziz?"

V

Love Stories

New Year's Day

By EDITH WHARTON

I

"SHE WAS *bad* . . . always. They used to meet at the Fifth Avenue Hotel," said my mother, as if the scene of the offense added to the guilt of the couple whose past she was revealing. Her spectacles slanted on her knitting, she dropped the words in a hiss that might have singed the snowy baby blanket which engaged her indefatigable fingers. (It was typical of my mother to be always employed in benevolent actions while she uttered uncharitable words.)

"*They used to meet at the Fifth Avenue Hotel*"; how the precision of the phrase characterized my old New York! A generation later, people would have said, in reporting an affair such as Lizzie Hazeldean's with Henry Prest: "They met in hotels"—and today who but a few superannuated spinsters, still feeding on the venom secreted in their youth, would take any interest in the tracing of such topographies?

Life has become too telegraphic for curiosity to linger on any given point in a sentimental relation; as old Sillerton Jackson, in response to my mother, grumbled through his perfect "china set": "Fifth Avenue Hotel? They might meet in the middle of Fifth Avenue nowadays, for all that anybody cares."

But what a flood of light my mother's tart phrase had suddenly focused on an unremarked incident of my boyhood!

The Fifth Avenue Hotel . . . Mrs. Hazeldean and Henry Prest . . . the conjunction of these names had arrested her darting talk on a single point of my memory, as a searchlight, suddenly checked in its gyrations, is held motionless while one notes each of the unnaturally sharp and lustrous images it picks out.

At the time I was a boy of twelve, at home from school for the holidays. My mother's mother, Grandmamma Parrett, still lived in the house in West Twenty-third Street which Grandpapa had built in his pioneering youth, in days when people shuddered at the perils of living north of Union Square—days that Grandmamma and my parents looked back to with a joking incredulity as the years passed and the new houses advanced

New Year's Day by Edith Wharton. Copyright 1924 by D. Appleton and Company. Reprinted by permission of Appleton-Century-Crofts, Inc.

steadily Parkward, outstripping the Thirtieth Streets, taking the Reservoir at a bound, and leaving us in what, in my school days, was already a dullish backwater between Aristocracy to the south and Money to the north.

Even then fashion moved quickly in New York, and my infantile memory barely reached back to the time when Grandmamma, in lace lappets and creaking moiré, used to receive on New Year's Day, supported by her handsome married daughters. As for old Sillerton Jackson, who, once a social custom had dropped into disuse, always affected never to have observed it, he stoutly maintained that the New Year's Day ceremonial had never been taken seriously except among families of Dutch descent, and that that was why Mrs. Henry van der Luyden had clung to it, in a reluctant half-apologetic way, long after her friends had closed their doors on the first of January, and the date had been chosen for those out-of-town parties which are so often used as a pretext for absence when the unfashionable are celebrating their rites.

Grandmamma, of course, no longer received. But it would have seemed to her an exceedingly odd thing to go out of town in winter, especially now that the New York houses were luxuriously warmed by the new hot-air furnaces, and searchingly illuminated by gas chandeliers. No, thank you—no country winters for the chilblained generation of prunella sandals and low-necked sarcenet, the generation brought up in unwarmed and unlit houses, and shipped off to die in Italy when they proved unequal to the struggle of living in New York! Therefore Grandmamma, like most of her contemporaries, remained in town on the first of January, and marked the day by a family reunion, a kind of supplementary Christmas —though to us juniors the absence of presents and plum pudding made it but a pale and moonlike reflection of the Feast.

Still, the day was welcome as a lawful pretext for overeating, dawdling, and looking out of the window: a Dutch habit still extensively practiced in the best New York circles. On the day in question, however, we had not yet placed ourselves behind the plate-glass whence it would presently be so amusing to observe the funny gentlemen who trotted about, their evening ties hardly concealed behind their overcoat collars, darting in and out of chocolate-colored house fronts on their sacramental round of calls. We were still engaged in placidly digesting around the ravaged luncheon table when a servant dashed in to say that the Fifth Avenue Hotel was on fire.

Oh, then the fun began—and what fun it was! For Grandmamma's house was just opposite the noble edifice of white marble which I associated with such deep-piled carpets, and such a rich sultry smell of anthracite and coffee, whenever I was bidden to "step across" for a messenger boy, or to buy the evening paper for my elders.

The hotel, for all its sober state, was no longer fashionable. No one, in my memory, had ever known anyone who went there; it was frequented by "politicians" and "Westerners," two classes of citizens whom my mother's intonation always seemed to deprive of their vote by ranking them with illiterates and criminals.

But for that very reason there was all the more fun to be expected from the calamity in question; for had we not, with infinite amusement, watched the arrival, that morning, of monumental "floral pieces" and towering frosted cakes for the New Year's Day reception across the way? The event was a communal one. All the ladies who were the hotel's "guests" were to receive together in the densely lace-curtained and heavily chandeliered public parlors, and gentlemen with long hair, imperials and white gloves had been hastening since two o'clock to the scene of revelry. And now, thanks to the opportune conflagration, we were going to have the excitement not only of seeing the Fire Brigade in action (supreme joy of the New York youngster), but of witnessing the flight of the ladies and their visitors, staggering out through the smoke in gala array. The idea that the fire might be dangerous did not mar these pleasing expectations. The house was solidly built; New York's invincible Brigade was already at the door, in a glare of polished brass, coruscating helmets and horses shining like table silver; and my tall cousin Hubert Wesson, dashing across at the first alarm, had promptly returned to say that all risk was over, though the two lower floors were so full of smoke and water that the lodgers, in some confusion, were being transported to other hotels. How then could a small boy see in the event anything but an unlimited lark?

Our elders, once reassured, were of the same mind. As they stood behind us in the windows, looking over our heads, we heard chuckles of amusement mingled with ironic comment.

"Oh, my dear, look—here they all come! The New Year ladies! Low neck and short sleeves in broad daylight, every one of them! Oh, and the fat one with the paper roses in her hair . . . they *are* paper, my dear . . . off the frosted cake, probably! Oh! Oh! Oh! *Oh!*"

Aunt Sabina Wesson was obliged to stuff her lace handkerchief between her lips, while her firm poplin-cased figure rocked with delight.

"Well, my dear," Grandmamma gently reminded her, "in my youth we wore low-necked dresses all day long and all the year round."

No one listened. My cousin Kate, who always imitated Aunt Sabina, was pinching my arm in an agony of mirth. "Look at them scuttling! The parlors must be full of smoke. Oh, but this one is still funnier; the one with the tall feather in her hair! Granny, did you wear feathers in your hair in the daytime? Oh, don't ask me to believe it! And the one with the diamond necklace! And all the gentlemen in white ties! Did Grandpapa wear a white tie at two o'clock in the afternoon?" Nothing was

sacred to Kate, and she feigned not to notice Grandmamma's mild frown
of reproval.

"Well, they do in Paris, to this day, at weddings—wear evening clothes
and white ties," said Sillerton Jackson with authority. "When Minnie
Transome of Charleston was married at the Madeleine to the Duc de . . ."

But no one listened even to Sillerton Jackson. One of the party had
abruptly exclaimed: "Oh, there's a lady running out of the hotel who's
not in evening dress!"

The exclamation caused all our eyes to turn toward the person indicated, who had just reached the threshold; and someone added, in an odd
voice: "Why, her figure looks like Lizzie Hazeldean's—"

A dead silence followed. The lady who was not in evening dress paused.
Standing on the doorstep with lifted veil, she faced our window. Her dress
was dark and plain—almost conspicuously plain—and in less time than it
takes to tell she had put her hand to her closely patterned veil and pulled
it down over her face. But my young eyes were keen and farsighted; and
in that hardly perceptible interval I had seen a vision. Was she beautiful
—or was she only someone apart? I felt the shock of a small pale oval,
dark eyebrows curved with one sure stroke, lips made for warmth, and
now drawn up in a grimace of terror; and it seemed as if the mysterious
something, rich, secret and insistent, that broods and murmurs behind a
boy's conscious thoughts, had suddenly peered out at me. . . . As the dart
reached me her veil dropped.

"But it *is* Lizzie Hazeldean!" Aunt Sabina gasped. She had stopped
laughing, and her crumpled handkerchief fell to the carpet.

"Lizzie—*Lizzie?*" The name was echoed over my head with varying
intonations of reprobation, dismay and half-veiled malice.

Lizzie Hazeldean? Running out of the Fifth Avenue Hotel on New
Year's Day with all those dressed-up women? But what on earth could
she have been doing there? No; nonsense! It was impossible. . . .

"There's Henry Prest with her," continued Aunt Sabina in a precipitate
whisper.

"With her?" someone gasped; and *"Oh—"* my mother cried with a
shudder.

The men of the family said nothing, but I saw Hubert Wesson's face
crimson with surprise. Henry Prest! Hubert was forever boring us youngsters with his Henry Prest! That was the kind of chap Hubert meant to
be at thirty: in his eyes Henry Prest embodied all the manly graces. Married? No, thank you! That kind of man wasn't made for the domestic
yoke. Too fond of ladies' society, Hubert hinted with his undergraduate
smirk; and handsome, rich, independent—an all-round sportsman, good
horseman, good shot, crack yachtsman (had his pilot's certificate, and
always sailed his own sloop, whose cabin was full of racing trophies);
gave the most delightful little dinners, never more than six, with cigars

that beat old Beaufort's; was awfully decent to the younger men, chaps of Hubert's age included—and combined, in short, all the qualities, mental and physical, which make up, in such eyes as Hubert's, that oracular and irresistible figure, the man of the world. "Just the fellow," Hubert always solemnly concluded, "that I should go straight to if ever I got into any kind of row that I didn't want the family to know about"; and our blood ran pleasantly cold at the idea of our old Hubert's ever being in such an unthinkable predicament.

I felt sorry to have missed a glimpse of this legendary figure; but my gaze had been enthralled by the lady, and now the couple had vanished in the crowd.

The group in our window continued to keep an embarrassed silence. They looked almost frightened; but what struck me even more deeply was that not one of them looked surprised. Even to my boyish sense it was clear that what they had just seen was only the confirmation of something they had long been prepared for. At length one of my uncles emitted a whistle, was checked by a severe glance from his wife, and muttered: "I'll be damned"; another uncle began an unheeded narrative of a fire at which he had been present in his youth, and my mother said to me severely: "You ought to be at home preparing your lessons—a big boy like you!"—a remark so obviously unfair that it served only to give the measure of her agitation.

"I don't believe it," said Grandmamma, in a low voice of warning, protest and appeal. I saw Hubert steal a grateful look at her.

But nobody else listened: every eye still strained through the window. Livery-stable "hacks," of the old blue-curtained variety, were driving up to carry off the fair fugitives; for the day was bitterly cold, and lit by one of those harsh New York suns of which every ray seems an icicle. Into these ancient vehicles the ladies, now regaining their composure, were being piled with their removable possessions, while their kid-gloved callers ("So like the White Rabbit!" Kate exulted) appeared and reappeared in the doorway, gallantly staggering after them under bags, reticules, bird-cages, pet dogs and heaped-up finery. But to all this—as even I, a little boy, was aware—nobody in Grandmamma's window paid the slightest attention. The thoughts of one and all, with a mute and guarded eagerness, were still following the movements of those two who were so obviously unrelated to the rest. The whole business—discovery, comment, silent visual pursuit—could hardly, all told, have filled a minute, perhaps not as much; before the sixty seconds were over, Mrs. Hazeldean and Henry Prest had been lost in the crowd, and, while the hotel continued to empty itself into the street, had gone their joint or separate ways. But in my grandmother's window the silence continued unbroken.

"Well, it's over: here are the firemen coming out again," someone said at length.

We youngsters were all alert at that; yet I felt that the grown-ups lent but a halfhearted attention to the splendid sight which was New York's only pageant: the piling of scarlet ladders on scarlet carts, the leaping up on the engine of the helmeted flame fighters, and the disciplined plunge forward of each pair of broad-chested black steeds, as one after another the chariots of fire rattled off.

Silently, almost morosely, we withdrew to the drawing-room hearth; where, after an interval of languid monosyllables, my mother, rising first, slipped her knitting into its bag, and turning on me with renewed severity, said: "This racing after fire engines is what makes you too sleepy to prepare your lessons"—a comment so wide of the mark that once again I perceived, without understanding, the extent of the havoc wrought in her mind by the sight of Mrs. Hazeldean and Henry Prest coming out of the Fifth Avenue Hotel together.

It was not until many years later that chance enabled me to relate this fugitive impression to what had preceded and what came after it.

II

Mrs. Hazeldean paused at the corner of Fifth Avenue and Madison Square. The crowd attracted by the fire still enveloped her; it was safe to halt and take breath.

Her companion, she knew, had gone in the opposite direction. Their movements, on such occasions, were as well ordered and as promptly executed as those of the New York Fire Brigade; and after their precipitate descent to the hall, the discovery that the police had barred their usual exit, and the quick: "You're all right?" to which her imperceptible nod had responded, she was sure he had turned down Twenty-third Street toward Sixth Avenue.

"The Parretts' windows were full of people," was her first thought.

She dwelt on it a moment, and then reflected: "Yes, but in all that crowd and excitement nobody would have been thinking of *me!*"

Instinctively she put her hand to her veil, as though recalling that her features had been exposed when she ran out, and unable to remember whether she had covered them in time or not.

"What a fool I am! It can't have been off my face for more than a second—" but immediately afterward another disquieting possibility assailed her. "I'm almost sure I saw Sillerton Jackson's head in one of the windows, just behind Sabina Wesson's. No one else has that particularly silvery gray hair." She shivered, for everyone in New York knew that Sillerton Jackson saw everything, and could piece together seemingly unrelated fragments of fact with the art of a skilled china mender.

Meanwhile, after sending through her veil the circular glance which she always shot about her at that particular corner, she had begun to walk up Broadway. She walked well—fast, but not too fast; easily, assuredly, with the air of a woman who knows that she has a good figure, and expects rather than fears to be identified by it. But under this external appearance of ease she was covered with cold beads of sweat.

Broadway, as usual at that hour, and on a holiday, was nearly deserted; the promenading public still slowly poured up and down Fifth Avenue.

"Luckily there was such a crowd when we came out of the hotel that no one could possibly have noticed me," she murmured over again, reassured by the sense of having the long thoroughfare to herself. Composure and presence of mind were so necessary to a woman in her situation that they had become almost a second nature to her, and in a few minutes her thick uneven heartbeats began to subside and to grow steadier. As if to test their regularity, she paused before a florist's window, and looked appreciatively at the jars of roses and forced lilac, the compact bunches of lilies-of-the-valley and violets, the first pots of close-budded azaleas. Finally she opened the shop door, and after examining the Jacqueminots and Marshal Niels, selected with care two perfect specimens of a new silvery-pink rose, waited for the florist to wrap them in cotton wool, and slipped their long stems into her muff for more complete protection.

"It's so simple, after all," she said to herself as she walked on. "I'll tell him that as I was coming up Fifth Avenue from Cousin Cecilia's I heard the fire-engines turning into Twenty-third Street, and ran after them. Just what *he* would have done . . . once . . ." she ended on a sigh.

At Thirty-first Street she turned the corner with a quicker step. The house she was approaching was low and narrow; but the Christmas holly glistening between frilled curtains, the well-scrubbed steps, the shining bell and door-knob, gave it a welcoming look. From garret to basement it beamed like the abode of a happy couple.

As Lizzie Hazeldean reached the door a curious change came over her. She was conscious of it at once—she had so often said to herself, when her little house rose before her: "It makes me feel younger as soon as I turn the corner." And it was true even today. In spite of her agitation she was aware that the lines between her eyebrows were smoothing themselves out, and that a kind of inner lightness was replacing the heavy tumult of her breast. The lightness revealed itself in her movements, which grew as quick as a girl's as she ran up the steps. She rang twice—it was her signal—and turned an unclouded smile on her elderly parlormaid.

"Is Mr. Hazeldean in the library, Susan? I hope you've kept up the fire for him."

"Oh, yes, ma'am. But Mr. Hazeldean's not in," said Susan, returning the smile respectfully.

"Not in? With his cold—and in this weather?"

"That's what I told him, ma'am. But he just laughed—"

"Just laughed? What do you mean, Susan?" Lizzie Hazeldean felt herself turning pale. She rested her hand quickly on the hall table.

"Well, ma'am, the minute he heard the fire engine, off he rushed like a boy. It seems the Fifth Avenue Hotel's on fire: there's where he's gone."

The blood left Mrs. Hazeldean's lips; she felt it shuddering back to her heart. But a second later she spoke in a tone of natural and good-humored impatience.

"What madness! How long ago—can you remember?" Instantly, she felt the possible imprudence of the question, and added: "The doctor said he ought not to be out more than a quarter of an hour, and only at the sunniest time of the day."

"I know that, ma'am, and so I reminded him. But he's been gone nearly an hour, I should say."

A sense of deep fatigue overwhelmed Mrs. Hazeldean. She felt as if she had walked for miles against an icy gale: her breath came laboriously.

"How could you let him go?" she wailed; then, as the parlormaid again smiled respectfully, she added: "Oh, I know—sometimes one can't stop him. He gets so restless, being shut up with these long colds."

"That's what I *do* feel, ma'am."

Mistress and maid exchanged a glance of sympathy, and Susan felt herself emboldened to suggest: "Perhaps the outing will do him good," with the tendency of her class to encourage favored invalids in disobedience.

Mrs. Hazeldean's look grew severe. "Susan! I've often warned you against talking to him in that way—"

Susan reddened, and assumed a pained expression. "How can you think it, ma'am?—me that never say anything to anybody, as all in the house will bear witness."

Her mistress made an impatient movement. "Oh, well, I daresay he won't be long. The fire's over."

"Ah—you knew of it too, then, ma'am?"

"Of the fire? Why, of course. I *saw* it, even—" Mrs. Hazeldean smiled. "I was walking home from Washington Square—from Miss Cecilia Winter's—and at the corner of Twenty-third Street there was a huge crowd, and clouds of smoke. . . . It's very odd that I shouldn't have run across Mr. Hazeldean." She looked limpidly at the parlormaid. "But, then, of course, in all that crowd and confusion . . ."

Halfway up the stairs she turned to call back: "Make up a good fire in the library, please, and bring the tea up. It's too cold in the drawing room."

The library was on the upper landing. She went in, drew the two roses from her muff, tenderly unswathed them, and put them in a slim glass on her husband's writing table. In the doorway she paused to smile at this touch of summer in the firelit wintry room; but a moment later her frown of anxiety reappeared. She stood listening intently for the sound of a latchkey; then, hearing nothing, passed on to her bedroom.

It was a rosy room, hung with one of the new English chintzes, which also covered the deep sofa, and the bed with its rose-lined pillow covers.

The carpet was cherry red, the toilet table ruffled and looped like a ball dress. Ah, how she and Susan had ripped and sewn and hammered, and pieced together old scraps of lace and ribbon and muslin, in the making of that airy monument! For weeks after she had done over the room her husband never came into it without saying: "I can't think how you managed to squeeze all this loveliness out of that last check of your stepmother's."

On the dressing table Lizzie Hazeldean noticed a long florist's box, one end of which had been cut open to give space to the still longer stems of a bunch of roses. She snipped the string, and extracted from the box an envelope which she flung into the fire without so much as a glance at its contents. Then she pushed the flowers aside, and after rearranging her dark hair before the mirror, carefully dressed herself in a loose garment of velvet and lace which lay awaiting her on the sofa, beside her high-heeled slippers and stockings of openwork silk.

She had been one of the first women in New York to have tea every afternoon at five, and to put off her walking dress for a tea gown.

III

She returned to the library, where the fire was beginning to send a bright blaze through the twilight. It flashed on the bindings of Hazeldean's many books, and she smiled absently at the welcome it held out. A latchkey rattled, and she heard her husband's step, and the sound of his cough below in the hall.

"What madness—what madness!" she murmured.

Slowly—how slowly for a young man!—he mounted the stairs, and still coughing came into the library. She ran to him and took him in her arms.

"Charlie! How could you? In this weather? It's nearly dark!"

His long thin face lit up with a deprecating smile. "I suppose Susan's betrayed me, eh? Don't be cross. You've missed such a show! The Fifth Avenue Hotel's been on fire."

"Yes; I know." She paused, just perceptibly. "I *didn't* miss it, though—I rushed across Madison Square for a look at it myself."

"You did? You were there too? What fun!" The idea appeared to fill him with boyish amusement.

"Naturally I was! On my way home from Cousin Cecilia's. . . ."

"Ah, of course. I'd forgotten you were going there. But how odd, then, that we didn't meet!"

"If we *had* I should have dragged you home long ago. I've been in at least half an hour, and the fire was already over when I got there. What a baby you are to have stayed out so long, staring at smoke and a fire engine!"

He smiled, still holding her, and passing his gaunt hand softly and wistfully over her head. "Oh, don't worry. I've been indoors, safely sheltered, and drinking old Mrs. Parrett's punch. The old lady saw me from her window, and sent one of the Wesson boys across the street to fetch me in. They had just finished a family luncheon. And Sillerton Jackson, who was there, drove me home. So you see—"

He released her, and moved toward the fire, and she stood motionless, staring blindly ahead, while the thoughts spun through her mind like a millrace.

"Sillerton Jackson—" she echoed, without in the least knowing what she said.

"Yes; he has the gout again—luckily for me!—and his sister's brougham came to the Parretts' to fetch him."

She collected herself. "You're coughing more than you did yesterday," she accused him.

"Oh, well—the air's sharpish. But I shall be all right presently. . . . Oh, those roses!" He paused in admiration before his writing table.

Her face glowed with a reflected pleasure, though all the while the names he had pronounced—"The Parretts, the Wessons, Sillerton Jackson"—were clanging through her brain like a death knell.

"They *are* lovely, aren't they?" she beamed.

"Much too lovely for me. You must take them down to the drawing room."

"No; we're going to have tea up here."

"That's jolly—it means there'll be no visitors, I hope?"

She nodded, smiling.

"Good! But the roses—no, they mustn't be wasted on this desert air. You'll wear them in your dress this evening?"

She started perceptibly, and moved slowly back toward the hearth.

"This evening? . . . Oh, I'm not going to Mrs. Struthers'," she said, remembering.

"Yes, you are. Dearest—I want you to!"

"But what shall you do alone all the evening? With that cough, you won't go to sleep till late."

"Well, if I don't, I've a lot of new books to keep me busy."

"Oh, your books—!" She made a little gesture, half teasing, half impatient, in the direction of the freshly cut volumes stacked up beside his student lamp. It was an old joke between them that she had never been able to believe anyone could really "care for reading." Long as she and her husband had lived together, this passion of his remained for her as much of a mystery as on the day when she had first surprised him, mute and absorbed, over what the people she had always lived with would have called "a deep book." It was her first encounter with a born reader; or at least, the few she had known had been, like her stepmother, the retired opera singer, feverish devourers of circulating library fiction: she had never before lived in a house with books in it. Gradually she had learned to take a pride in Hazeldean's reading, as if it had been some rare accomplishment; she had perceived that it reflected credit on him, and was even conscious of its adding to the charm of his talk, a charm she had always felt without being able to define it. But still, in her heart of hearts she regarded books as a mere expedient, and felt sure that they were only an aid to patience, like jackstraws or a game of patience, with the disadvantage of requiring a greater mental effort.

"Shan't you be too tired to read tonight?" she questioned wistfully.

"Too tired? Why, you goose, reading is the greatest rest in the world! —I want you to go to Mrs. Struthers', dear; I want to see you again in that black velvet dress," he added with his coaxing smile.

The parlormaid brought in the tray, and Mrs. Hazeldean busied herself with the tea caddy. Her husband had stretched himself out in the deep armchair which was his habitual seat. He crossed his arms behind his neck, leaning his head back wearily against them, so that, as she glanced at him across the hearth, she saw the salient muscles in his long neck, and the premature wrinkles about his ears and chin. The lower part of his face was singularly ravaged; only the eyes, those quiet ironic gray eyes, and the white forehead above them, reminded her of what he had been seven years before. Only seven years!

She felt a rush of tears: no, there were times when fate was too cruel, the future too horrible to contemplate, and the past—the past, oh, how much worse! And there he sat, coughing, coughing—and thinking God knows what, behind those quiet half-closed lids. At such times he grew so mysteriously remote that she felt lonelier than when he was not in the room.

"Charlie!"

He roused himself. "Yes?"

"Here's your tea."

He took it from her in silence, and she began, nervously, to wonder why he was not talking. Was it because he was afraid it might make him cough again, afraid she would be worried, and scold him? Or was it because he was thinking—thinking of things he had heard at old Mrs. Parrett's, or on the drive home with Sillerton Jackson . . . hints they might have dropped . . . insinuations . . . she didn't know what . . . or of something he had *seen*, perhaps, from old Mrs. Parrett's window? She looked across at his white forehead, so smooth and impenetrable in the lamplight, and thought: "Oh, God, it's like a locked door. I shall dash my brains out against it some day!"

For, after all, it was not impossible that he had actually seen her, seen her from Mrs. Parrett's window, or even from the crowd around the door of the hotel. For all she knew, he might have been near enough, in that crowd, to put out his hand and touch her. And he might have held back, benumbed, aghast, not believing his own eyes. . . . She couldn't tell. She

had never yet made up her mind how he would look, how he would behave, what he would say, if ever he *did* see or hear anything . . .

No! That was the worst of it. They had lived together for nearly nine
years—and how closely!—and nothing that she knew of him, or had observed in him, enabled her to forecast exactly what, in that particular case,
his state of mind and his attitude would be. In his profession, she knew,
he was celebrated for his shrewdness and insight; in personal matters he
often seemed, to her alert mind, oddly absent-minded and indifferent. Yet
that might be merely his instinctive way of saving his strength for things
he considered more important. There were times when she was sure he
was quite deliberate and self-controlled enough to feel in one way and
behave in another: perhaps even to have thought out a course in advance
—just as, at the first bad symptoms of illness, he had calmly made his
will, and planned everything about her future, the house and the servants.
. . . No, she couldn't tell; there always hung over her the thin glittering
menace of a danger she could neither define nor localize—like that aveng-
ing lightning which groped for the lovers in the horrible poem he had
once read aloud to her (what a choice!) on a lazy afternoon of their wedding journey, as they lay stretched under Italian stone pines.

The maid came in to draw the curtains and light the lamps. The fire
glowed, the scent of the roses drifted on the warm air, and the clock ticked
out the minutes, and softly struck a half hour, while Mrs. Hazeldean continued to ask herself, as she so often had before: "Now, what would be
the *natural* thing for me to say?"

And suddenly the words escaped from her, she didn't know how: "I
wonder you didn't see me coming out of the hotel—for I actually squeezed
my way in."

Her husband made no answer. Her heart jumped convulsively; then she
lifted her eyes and saw that he was asleep. How placid his face looked—
years younger than when he was awake! The immensity of her relief
rushed over her in a warm glow, the counterpart of the icy sweat which
had sent her chattering homeward from the fire. After all, if he could fall
asleep, fall into such a peaceful sleep as that—tired, no doubt, by his im-
prudent walk, and the exposure to the cold—it meant, beyond all doubt,
beyond all conceivable dread, that he knew nothing, had seen nothing,
suspected nothing: that she was safe, safe, safe!

The violence of the reaction made her long to spring to her feet and
move about the room. She saw a crooked picture that she wanted to
straighten, she would have liked to give the roses another tilt in their
glass. But there he sat, quietly sleeping, and the long habit of vigilance
made her respect his rest, watching over it as patiently as if it had been
a sick child's.

She drew a contented breath. Now she could afford to think of his outing only as it might affect his health; and she knew that this sudden

drowsiness, even if it were a sign of extreme fatigue, was also the natural restorative for that fatigue. She continued to sit behind the tea tray, her hands folded, her eyes on his face, while the peace of the scene entered into her, and held her under brooding wings.

IV

At Mrs. Struthers', at eleven o'clock that evening, the long overlit drawing rooms were already thronged with people.

Lizzie Hazeldean paused on the threshold and looked about her. The habit of pausing to get her bearings, of sending a circular glance around any assemblage of people, any drawing room, concert hall or theater that she entered, had become so instinctive that she would have been surprised had anyone pointed out to her the unobservant expression and careless movements of the young women of her acquaintance, who also looked about them, it is true, but with the vague unseeing stare of youth, and of beauty conscious only of itself.

Lizzie Hazeldean had long since come to regard most women of her age as children in the art of life. Some savage instinct of self-defense, fostered by experience, had always made her more alert and perceiving than the charming creatures who passed from the nursery to marriage as if lifted from one rose-lined cradle into another. "Rocked to sleep—that's what they've always been," she used to think sometimes, listening to their innocuous talk during the long after-dinners in hot drawing rooms, while their husbands, in the smoking rooms below, exchanged ideas which, if no more striking, were at least based on more direct experiences.

But then, as all the old ladies said, Lizzie Hazeldean had always preferred the society of men.

The man she now sought was not visible, and she gave a little sigh of ease. "If only he has had the sense to stay away!" she thought.

She would have preferred to stay away herself; but it had been her husband's whim that she should come. "You know you always enjoy yourself at Mrs. Struthers's—everybody does. The old girl somehow manages to have the most amusing house in New York. Who is it who's going to sing tonight? . . . If you don't go, I shall know it's because I've coughed two or three times oftener than usual, and you're worrying about me. My dear girl, it will take more than the Fifth Avenue Hotel fire to kill *me*. . . . My heart's feeling unusually steady. . . . Put on your black velvet, will you?—with these two roses. . . ."

So she had gone. And here she was, in her black velvet, under the glitter of Mrs. Struthers' chandeliers, amid all the youth and good looks and gaiety of New York; for, as Hazeldean said, Mrs. Struthers' house was more amusing than anybody else's, and whenever she opened her doors the world flocked through them.

As Mrs. Hazeldean reached the inner drawing room the last notes of a rich tenor were falling on the attentive silence. She saw Campanini's low-necked throat subside into silence above the piano, and the clapping of many tightly fitting gloves was succeeded by a general movement, and the usual irrepressible outburst of talk.

In the breaking up of groups she caught a glimpse of Sillerton Jackson's silvery crown. Their eyes met across bare shoulders, he bowed profoundly, and she fancied that a dry smile lifted his mustache. "He doesn't usually bow to me as low as that," she thought apprehensively.

But as she advanced into the room her self-possession returned. Among all these stupid pretty women she had such a sense of power, of knowing almost everything better than they did, from the way of doing her hair to the art of keeping a secret! She felt a thrill of pride in the slope of her white shoulders above the black velvet, in the one curl escaping from her thick chignon, and the slant of the gold arrow tipped with diamonds which she had thrust in to retain it. And she had done it all without a maid, with no one cleverer than Susan to help her! Ah, as a woman she knew her business. . . .

Mrs. Struthers, plumed and ponderous, with diamond stars studding her black wig like a pincushion, had worked her resolute way back to the outer room. More people were coming in; and with her customary rough skill she was receiving, distributing, introducing them. Suddenly her smile deepened; she was evidently greeting an old friend. The group about her scattered, and Mrs. Hazeldean saw that, in her cordial absent-minded way, and while her wandering hostess eye swept the rooms, she was saying a confidential word to a tall man whose hand she detained. They smiled at each other; then Mrs. Struthers' glance turned toward the inner room, and her smile seemed to say: "You'll find her there."

The tall man nodded. He looked about him composedly, and began to move toward the center of the throng, speaking to everyone, appearing to have no object beyond that of greeting the next person in his path, yet quietly, steadily pursuing that path, which led straight to the inner room.

Mrs. Hazeldean had found a seat near the piano. A good-looking youth, seated beside her, was telling her at considerable length what he was going to wear at the Beauforts' fancy ball. She listened, approved, suggested; but her glance never left the advancing figure of the tall man.

Handsome? Yes, she said to herself; she had to admit that he was handsome. A trifle too broad and florid, perhaps; though his air and his attitude so plainly denied it that, on second thoughts, one agreed that a man of his height had, after all, to carry some ballast. Yes; his assurance made him, as a rule, appear to people exactly as he chose to appear; that is, as a man over forty, but carrying his years carelessly, an active muscular man, whose blue eyes were still clear, whose fair hair waved ever so little less thickly than it used to on a low sunburnt forehead, over eyebrows almost silvery in their blondness, and blue eyes the bluer for their thatch. Stupid-looking? By no means. His smile denied that. Just self-sufficient enough to escape fatuity, yet so cool that one felt the fundamental cold-ness, he steered his way through life as easily and resolutely as he was now working his way through Mrs. Struthers' drawing rooms.

Halfway, he was detained by a tap of Mrs. Wesson's red fan. Mrs. Wesson—surely, Mrs. Hazeldean reflected, Charles had spoken of Mrs. Sabina Wesson's being with her mother, old Mrs. Parrett, while they watched the fire? Sabina Wesson was a redoubtable woman, one of the few of her generation and her clan who had broken with tradition, and gone to Mrs. Struthers' almost as soon as the Shoe Polish Queen had bought her house in Fifth Avenue, and issued her first challenge to so-ciety. Lizzie Hazeldean shut her eyes for an instant; then, rising from her seat, she joined the group about the singer. From there she wandered on to another knot of acquaintances.

"Look here: the fellow's going to sing again. Let's get into that corner over there."

She felt ever so slight a touch on her arm, and met Henry Prest's com-posed glance.

A red-lit and palm-shaded recess divided the drawing rooms from the dining room, which ran across the width of the house at the back. Mrs. Hazeldean hesitated; then she caught Mrs. Wesson's watchful glance, lifted her head with a smile and followed her companion.

They sat down on a small sofa under the palms, and a couple, who had been in search of the same retreat, paused on the threshold, and with an interchange of glances passed on. Mrs. Hazeldean smiled more vividly.

"Where are my roses? Didn't you get them?" Prest asked. He had a way of looking her over from beneath lowered lids, while he affected to be examining a glove button or contemplating the tip of his shining boot.

"Yes, I got them," she answered.

"You're not wearing them. I didn't order those."

"No."

"Whose are they, then?"

She unfolded her mother-of-pearl fan, and bent above its complicated traceries.

"Mine," she pronounced.

"Yours? Well, obviously. But I suppose someone sent them to you?"

"*I* did." She hesitated a second. "I sent them to myself."

He raised his eyebrows a little. "Well, they don't suit you—that washy pink! May I ask why you didn't wear mine?"

"I've already told you. . . . I've often asked you never to send flowers . . . on the day. . . ."

"Nonsense. That's the very day. . . . What's the matter? Are you still nervous?"

She was silent for a moment; then she lowered her voice to say: "You ought not to have come here tonight."

"My dear girl, how unlike you! You *are* nervous."

"Didn't you see all those people in the Parretts' window?"

"What, opposite? Lord, no; I just took to my heels! It was the deuce, the back way being barred. But what of it? In all that crowd, do you suppose for a moment—"

"My husband was in the window with them," she said, still lower.

His confident face fell for a moment, and then almost at once regained its look of easy arrogance.

"Well—?"

"Oh, nothing—as yet. Only I ask you . . . to go away now."

"Just as you asked me not to come! Yet *you* came, because you had the sense to see that if you didn't . . . and I came for the same reason. Look here, my dear, for God's sake don't lose your head!"

The challenge seemed to rouse her. She lifted her chin, glanced about the thronged room which they commanded from their corner, and nodded and smiled invitingly at several acquaintances, with the hope that some one of them might come up to her. But though they all returned her greetings with a somewhat elaborate cordiality, not one advanced toward her secluded seat.

She turned her head slightly toward her companion. "I ask you again to go," she repeated.

"Well, I will then, after the fellow's sung. But I'm bound to say you're a good deal pleasanter—"

The first bars of *"Salve, Dimora"* silenced him, and they sat side by side in the meditative rigidity of fashionable persons listening to expensive music. She had thrown herself into a corner of the sofa, and Henry Prest, about whom everything was discreet but his eyes, sat apart from her, one leg crossed over the other, one hand holding his folded opera hat on his knee, while the other hand rested beside him on the sofa. But an end of her tulle scarf lay in the space between them; and without looking in his direction, without turning her glance from the singer, she was conscious that Prest's hand had reached and drawn the scarf toward him. She shivered a little, made an involuntary motion as though to gather it about her—and then desisted. As the song ended, he bent toward her slightly, said: "Darling" so low that it seemed no more than a breath on her cheek, and then, rising, bowed, and strolled into the other room.

She sighed faintly, and, settling herself once more in her corner, lifted her brilliant eyes to Sillerton Jackson, who was approaching. "It *was* good of you to bring Charlie home from the Parretts' this afternoon." She held out her hand, making way for him at her side.

"Good of me?" he laughed. "Why, I was glad of the chance of getting him safely home; it was rather naughty of *him* to be where he was, I suspect." She fancied a slight pause, as if he waited to see the effect of this, and her lashes beat her cheeks. But already he was going on: "Do you encourage him, with that cough, to run about town after fire engines?"

She gave back the laugh.

"I don't discourage him—ever—if I can help it. But it *was* foolish of him to go out today," she agreed; and all the while she kept on asking herself, as she had that afternoon, in her talk with her husband: "Now, what would be the *natural* thing for me to say?"

Should she speak of having been at the fire herself—or should she not? The question dinned in her brain so loudly that she could hardly hear what her companion was saying; yet she had, at the same time, a queer feeling of his never having been so close to her, or rather so closely intent on her, as now. In her strange state of nervous lucidity, her eyes seemed to absorb with a new precision every facial detail of whoever approached her; and old Sillerton Jackson's narrow mask, his withered pink cheeks, the veins in the hollow of his temples, under the carefully tended silvery hair, and the tiny blood specks in the white of his eyes as he turned their cautious blue gaze on her, appeared as if presented under some powerful lens. With his eyeglasses dangling over one white-gloved hand, the other supporting his opera hat on his knee, he suggested, behind that assumed carelessness of pose, the patient fixity of a naturalist holding his breath near the crack from which some tiny animal might suddenly issue—if one watched long enough, or gave it, completely enough, the impression of not looking for it, or dreaming it was anywhere near. The sense of that tireless attention made Mrs. Hazeldean's temples ache as if she sat under a glare of light even brighter than that of the Struthers' chandeliers—a glare in which each quiver of a half-formed thought might be as visible behind her forehead as the faint lines wrinkling its surface into an uncontrollable frown of anxiety. Yes, Prest was right; she was losing her head—losing it for the first time in the dangerous year during which she had had such continual need to keep it steady.

"What is it? What has happened to me?" she wondered.

There had been alarms before—how could it be otherwise? But they had only stimulated her, made her more alert and prompt; whereas tonight she felt herself quivering away into she knew not what abyss of weakness. What was different, then? Oh, she knew well enough! It was Charles . . . that haggard look in his eyes, and the lines of his throat as he had leaned back sleeping. She had never before admitted to herself how ill she thought him; and now, to have to admit it, and at the same time not to have the complete certainty that the look in his eyes was caused by illness only, made the strain unbearable.

She glanced about her with a sudden sense of despair. Of all the people in those brilliant animated groups—of all the women who called her

Lizzie, and the men who were familiars at her house—she knew that not one, at that moment, guessed, or could have understood, what she was feeling. . . . Her eyes fell on Henry Prest, who had come to the surface a little way off, bending over the chair of the handsome Mrs. Lyman. "And *you* least of all!" she thought. "Yet God knows," she added with a shiver, "they all have their theories about me!"

"My dear Mrs. Hazeldean, you look a little pale. Are you cold? Shall I get you some champagne?" Sillerton Jackson was officiously suggesting.

"If you think the other women look blooming! My dear man, it's this hideous vulgar overhead lighting. . . ." She rose impatiently. It had occurred to her that the thing to do—the "natural" thing—would be to stroll up to Jinny Lyman, over whom Prest was still attentively bending. *Then* people would see if she was nervous, or ill—or afraid!

But halfway she stopped and thought: "Suppose the Parretts and Wessons *did* see me? Then my joining Jinny while he's talking to her will look—how will it look?" She began to regret not having had it out on the spot with Sillerton Jackson, who could be trusted to hold his tongue on occasion, especially if a pretty woman threw herself on his mercy. She glanced over her shoulder as if to call him back; but he had turned away, been absorbed into another group, and she found herself, instead, abruptly face to face with Sabina Wesson. Well, perhaps that was better still. After all, it all depended on how much Mrs. Wesson had seen, and what line she meant to take, supposing she *had* seen anything. She was not likely to be as inscrutable as old Sillerton. Lizzie wished now that she had not forgotten to go to Mrs. Wesson's last party.

"Dear Mrs. Wesson, it was so kind of you—"

But Mrs. Wesson was not there. By the exercise of that mysterious protective power which enables a woman desirous of not being waylaid to make herself invisible, or to transport herself, by means imperceptible, to another part of the earth's surface, Mrs. Wesson, who, two seconds earlier, appeared in all her hard handsomeness to be bearing straight down on Mrs. Hazeldean, with a scant yard of clear parquet between them— Mrs. Wesson, as her animated back and her active red fan now called on all the company to notice, had never been there at all, had never seen Mrs. Hazeldean ("*Was* she at Mrs. Struthers' last Sunday? How odd! I must have left before she got there—"), but was busily engaged, on the farther side of the piano, in examining a picture to which her attention appeared to have been called by the persons nearest her.

"Ah, how *lifelike!* That's what I always feel when I see a Meissonier," she was heard to exclaim, with her well-known instinct for the fitting epithet.

Lizzie Hazeldean stood motionless. Her eyes dazzled as if she had received a blow on the forehead. "So *that's* what it feels like!" she thought. She lifted her head very high, looked about her again, tried to signal to

Henry Prest, but saw him still engaged with the lovely Mrs. Lyman, and at the same moment caught the glance of young Hubert Wesson, Sabina's eldest, who was standing in disengaged expectancy near the supper-room door.

Hubert Wesson, as his eyes met Mrs. Hazeldean's, crimsoned to the forehead, hung back a moment, and then came forward, bowing low— again that too low bow! "So *he* saw me too," she thought. She put her hand on his arm with a laugh. "Dear me, how ceremonious you are! Really, I'm not as old as that bow of yours implies. My dear boy, I hope you want to take me in to supper at once. I was out in the cold all the afternoon, gazing at the Fifth Avenue Hotel fire, and I'm simply dying of hunger and fatigue."

There, the die was cast—she had said it loud enough for all the people nearest her to hear! And she was sure now that it was the right, the "natural" thing to do.

Her spirits rose, and she sailed into the supper room like a goddess, steering Hubert to an unoccupied table in a flowery corner.

"No—I think we're very well by ourselves, don't you? Do you want that fat old bore of a Lucy Vanderlow to join us? If you *do,* of course . . . I can see she's dying to . . . but then, I warn you, I shall ask a young man! Let me see—shall I ask Henry Prest? You see he's hovering! No, it *is* jollier with just you and me, isn't it?" She leaned forward a little, resting her chin on her clasped hands, her elbows on the table, in an attitude which the older women thought shockingly free, but the younger ones were beginning to imitate.

"And now, some champagne, please—and *hot* terrapin! . . . But I suppose you were at the fire yourself, weren't you?" she leaned still a little nearer to say.

The blush again swept over young Wesson's face, rose to his forehead, and turned the lobes of his large ears to balls of fire. ("It looks," she thought, "as if he had on huge coral earrings.") But she forced him to look at her, laughed straight into his eyes, and went on: "Did you ever see a funnier sight than all those dressed-up absurdities rushing out into the cold? It looked like the end of an Inauguration Ball! I was so fascinated that I actually pushed my way into the hall. The firemen were furious, but they couldn't stop me—nobody can stop me at a fire! You should have seen the ladies scuttling downstairs—the fat ones! Oh, but I beg your pardon: I'd forgotten that you admire . . . avoirdupois. No? But . . . Mrs. Van . . . so stupid of me! Why, you're actually blushing! I assure you, you're as red as your mother's fan—and visible from as great a distance! Yes, please; a little more champagne. . . ."

And then the inevitable began. She forgot the fire, forgot her anxieties, forgot Mrs. Wesson's affront, forgot everything but the amusement, the passing childish amusement, of twirling around her little finger this shy clumsy boy, as she had twirled so many others, old and young, not caring afterward if she ever saw them again, but so absorbed in the sport, and in her sense of knowing how to do it better than the other women—more quietly, more insidiously, without ogling, bridling or grimacing—that sometimes she used to ask herself with a shiver: "What was the gift given to me for?" Yes; it always amused her at first: the gradual dawn of attraction in eyes that had regarded her with indifference, the blood rising to the face, the way she could turn and twist the talk as though she had her victim on a leash, spinning him after her down winding paths of sentimentality, irony, caprice . . . and leaving him, with beating heart and dazzled eyes, to visions of an all-promising morrow. . . . "My only accomplishment!" she murmured to herself as she rose from the table followed by young Wesson's fascinated gaze, while already, on her own lips, she felt the taste of cinders.

"But at any rate," she thought, "he'll hold his tongue about having seen me at the fire."

V

She let herself in with her latchkey, glanced at the notes and letters on the hall table (the old habit of allowing nothing to escape her), and stole up through the darkness to her room.

A fire still glowed in the chimney, and its light fell on two vases of crimson roses. The room was full of their scent.

Mrs. Hazeldean frowned, and then shrugged her shoulders. It had been a mistake, after all, to let it appear that she was indifferent to the flowers; she must remember to thank Susan for rescuing them. She began to undress, hastily yet clumsily, as if her deft fingers were all thumbs; but first, detaching the two faded pink roses from her bosom, she put them with a reverent touch into a glass on the toilet table. Then, slipping on her dressing gown, she stole to her husband's door. It was shut, and she leaned her ear to the keyhole. After a moment she caught his breathing, heavy, as it always was when he had a cold, but regular, untroubled. . . . With a sigh of relief she tiptoed back. Her uncovered bed, with its fresh pillows and satin coverlet, sent her a rosy invitation; but she cowered down by the fire, hugging her knees and staring into the coals.

"So *that's* what it feels like!" she repeated.

It was the first time in her life that she had ever been deliberately "cut"; and the cut was a deadly injury in old New York. For Sabina Wesson to have used it, consciously, deliberately—for there was no doubt that she had purposely advanced toward her victim—she must have done so with intent to kill. And to risk that, she must have been sure of her facts, sure of corroborating witnesses, sure of being backed up by all her clan.

Lizzie Hazeldean had her clan too—but it was a small and weak one, and she hung on its outer fringe by a thread of little-regarded cousinship. As for the Hazeldean tribe, which was larger and stronger (though nothing like the great organized Wesson-Parrett gens, with half New York and all Albany at its back)—well, the Hazeldeans were not much to be counted on, and would even, perhaps, in a furtive negative way, be not too sorry ("if it were not for poor Charlie") that poor Charlie's wife should at last be made to pay for her good looks, her popularity, above all for being, in spite of her origin, treated by poor Charlie as if she were one of them!

Her origin was, of course, respectable enough. Everybody knew all about the Winters—she had been Lizzie Winter. But the Winters were very small people, and her father, the Reverend Arcadius Winter, the sentimental overpopular rector of a fashionable New York church, after a few seasons of too great success as preacher and director of female consciences, had suddenly had to resign and go to Bermuda for his health— or was it France?—to some obscure watering place, it was rumored. At any rate, Lizzie, who went with him (with a crushed bedridden mother), was ultimately, after the mother's death, fished out of a girls' school in Brussels—they seemed to have been in so many countries at once!—and brought back to New York by a former parishioner of poor Arcadius', who had always "believed in him," in spite of the Bishop, and who took pity on his lonely daughter.

The parishioner, Mrs. Mant, was "one of the Hazeldeans." She was a rich widow, given to generous gestures which she was often at a loss how to complete; and when she had brought Lizzie Winter home, and sufficiently celebrated her own courage in doing so, she did not quite know what step to take next. She had fancied it would be pleasant to have a clever handsome girl about the house; but her housekeeper was not of the same mind. The spare-room sheets had not been out of lavender for twenty years—and Miss Winter always left the blinds up in her room, and the carpet and curtains, unused to such exposure, suffered accordingly. Then young men began to call—they called in numbers. Mrs. Mant had not supposed that the daughter of a clergyman—and a clergyman "under a cloud"—would expect visitors. She had imagined herself taking Lizzie Winter to Church Fairs, and having the stitches of her knitting picked up by the young girl, whose "eyes were better" than her benefactress's. But Lizzie did not know how to knit—she possessed no useful accomplishments—and she was visibly bored by Church Fairs, where her presence was of little use, since she had no money to spend. Mrs. Mant began to see her mistake; and the discovery made her dislike her protégée, whom she secretly regarded as having intentionally misled her.

In Mrs. Mant's life, the transition from one enthusiasm to another was always marked by an interval of disillusionment, during which, Providence having failed to fulfill her requirements, its existence was openly called into question. But in this flux of moods there was one fixed point: Mrs. Mant was a woman whose life revolved about a bunch of keys. What treasures they gave access to, what disasters would have ensued had they been forever lost, was not quite clear; but whenever they were missed the household was in an uproar, and as Mrs. Mant would trust them to no one but herself, these occasions were frequent. One of them arose at the very moment when Mrs. Mant was recovering from her enthusiasm for Miss Winter. A minute before, the keys had been there, in a pocket of her work table; she had actually touched them in hunting for her buttonhole scissors. She had been called away to speak to the plumber about the bathroom leak, and when she left the room there was no one in it but Miss Winter. When she returned, the keys were gone. The house had been turned inside out; everyone had been, if not accused, at least suspected; and in a rash moment Mrs. Mant had spoken of the police. The housemaid had thereupon given warning, and her own maid threatened to follow; when suddenly the Bishop's hints recurred to Mrs. Mant. The Bishop had always implied that there had been something irregular in Dr. Winter's accounts, besides the other unfortunate business. . . .

Very mildly, she had asked Miss Winter if she might not have seen the keys, and "picked them up without thinking." Miss Winter permitted herself to smile in denying the suggestion; the smile irritated Mrs. Mant; and in a moment the floodgates were opened. She saw nothing to smile at in her question—unless it was of a kind that Miss Winter was already used to, prepared for . . . with that sort of background . . . her unfortunate father. . . .

"Stop!" Lizzie Winter cried. She remembered now, as if it had happened yesterday, the abyss suddenly opening at her feet. It was her first direct contact with human cruelty. Suffering, weakness, frailties other than Mrs. Mant's restricted fancy could have pictured, the girl had known, or at least suspected; but she had found as much kindness as folly in her path, and no one had ever before attempted to visit upon her the dimly guessed shortcomings of her poor old father. She shook with horror as much as with indignation, and her "Stop!" blazed out so violently that Mrs. Mant, turning white, feebly groped for the bell.

And it was then, at that very moment, that Charles Hazeldean came in—Charles Hazeldean, the favorite nephew, the pride of the tribe. Lizzie had seen him only once or twice, for he had been absent since her return to New York. She had thought him distinguished-looking, but rather serious and sarcastic; and he had apparently taken little notice of her—which perhaps accounted for her opinion.

"Oh, Charles, dearest Charles—that you should be here to hear such things said to me!" his aunt gasped, her hand on her outraged heart.

"What things? Said by whom? I see no one here to say them but Miss Winter," Charles had laughed, taking the girl's icy hand.

"Don't shake hands with her! She has insulted me! She has ordered me to keep silence—in my own house. 'Stop!' she said, when I was trying, in the kindness of my heart, to get her to admit privately . . . Well, if she prefers to have the police. . . ."

"I do! I ask you to send for them!" Lizzie cried.

How vividly she remembered all that followed: the finding of the keys, Mrs. Mant's reluctant apologies, her own cold acceptance of them, and the sense on both sides of the impossibility of continuing their life together! She had been wounded to the soul, and her own plight first revealed to her in all its destitution. Before that, despite the ups and downs of a wandering life, her youth, her good looks, the sense of a certain bright power over people and events, had hurried her along on a spring tide of confidence; she had never thought of herself as the dependent, the beneficiary, of the persons who were kind to her. Now she saw herself, at twenty, a penniless girl, with a feeble discredited father carrying his snowy head, his unctuous voice, his edifying manner from one cheap watering place to another, through an endless succession of sentimental and pecuniary entanglements. To him she could be of no more help than he to her; and save for him she was alone. The Winter cousins, as much humiliated by his disgrace as they had been puffed up by his triumphs, let it be understood, when the breach with Mrs. Mant became known, that they were not in a position to interfere; and among Dr. Winter's former parishioners none was left to champion him. Almost at the same time, Lizzie heard that he was about to marry a Portuguese opera singer and be received into the Church of Rome; and this crowning scandal too promptly justified his family.

The situation was a grave one, and called for energetic measures. Lizzie understood it—and a week later she was engaged to Charles Hazeldean.

She always said afterward that but for the keys he would never have thought of marrying her; while he laughingly affirmed that, on the contrary, but for the keys she would never have looked at *him*.

But what did it all matter, in the complete and blessed understanding which was to follow on their hasty union? If all the advantages on both sides had been weighed and found equal by judicious advisers, harmony more complete could hardly have been predicted. As a matter of fact, the advisers, had they been judicious, would probably have found only elements of discord in the characters concerned. Charles Hazeldean was by nature an observer and a student, brooding and curious of mind: Lizzie Winter (as she looked back at herself)—what was she, what would she ever be, but a quick, ephemeral creature, in whom a perpetual and adaptable activity simulated mind, as her grace, her swiftness, her expressiveness simulated beauty? So others would have judged her; so, now, she judged herself. And she knew that in fundamental things she was still the same. And yet she had satisfied him: satisfied him, to all appearances, as completely in the quiet later years as in the first flushed hours. As completely, or perhaps even more so. In the early months, dazzled gratitude made her the humbler, fonder worshiper; but as her powers expanded in the warm air of comprehension, as she felt herself grow handsomer, cleverer, more competent and more companionable than he had hoped, or she had dreamed herself capable of becoming, the balance was imperceptibly reversed, and the triumph in his eyes when they rested on her.

The Hazeldeans were conquered; they had to admit it. Such a brilliant recruit to the clan was not to be disowned. Mrs. Mant was left to nurse her grievance in solitude, till she too fell into line, carelessly but handsomely forgiven.

Ah, those first years of triumph! They frightened Lizzie now as she looked back. One day, the friendless defenseless daughter of a discredited man; the next, almost, the wife of Charlie Hazeldean, the popular successful young lawyer, with a good practice already assured, and the best of professional and private prospects. His own parents were dead, and had died poor; but two or three childless relatives were understood to be letting their capital accumulate for his benefit, and meanwhile in Lizzie's thrifty hands his earnings were largely sufficient.

Ah, those first years! There had been barely six; but even now there were moments when their sweetness drenched her to the soul. . . . Barely six; and then the sharp reawakening of an inherited weakness of the heart that Hazeldean and his doctors had imagined to be completely cured. Once before, for the same cause, he had been sent off, suddenly, for a year of travel in mild climates and distant scenes; and his first return had coincided with the close of Lizzie's sojourn at Mrs. Mant's. The young man felt sure enough of the future to marry and take up his professional duties again, and for the following six years he had led, without interruption, the busy life of a successful lawyer; then had come a second breakdown, more unexpectedly, and with more alarming symptoms. The "Hazeldean heart" was a proverbial boast in the family; the Hazeldeans privately considered it more distinguished than the Sillerton gout, and far more refined than the Wesson liver; and it had permitted most of them to survive, in valetudinarian ease, to a ripe old age, when they died of some quite other disorder. But Charles Hazeldean had defied it, and it took its revenge, and took it savagely.

One by one, hopes and plans faded. The Hazeldeans went south for a winter; he lay on a deck chair in a Florida garden, and read and dreamed, and was happy with Lizzie beside him. So the months passed; and by the following autumn he was better, returned to New York, and took up his profession. Intermittently but obstinately, he had continued the struggle for two more years; but before they were over husband and wife understood that the good days were done.

He could be at his office only at lengthening intervals; he sank gradually into invalidism without submitting to it. His income dwindled; and, indifferent for himself, he fretted ceaselessly at the thought of depriving Lizzie of the least of her luxuries.

At heart she was indifferent to them too; but she could not convince him of it. He had been brought up in the old New York tradition, which decreed that a man, at whatever cost, must provide his wife with what she had always "been accustomed to"; and he had gloried too much in her prettiness, her elegance, her easy way of wearing her expensive dresses, and his friends' enjoyment of the good dinners she knew how to order, not to accustom her to everything which could enhance such graces. Mrs. Mant's secret satisfaction rankled in him. She sent him Baltimore terrapin, and her famous clam broth, and a dozen of the old Hazeldean port, and said "I told you so" to her confidants when Lizzie was mentioned; and Charles Hazeldean knew it, and swore at it.

"I won't be pauperized by her!" he declared; but Lizzie smiled away his anger, and persuaded him to taste the terrapin and sip the port.

She was smiling faintly at the memory of the last passage between him and Mrs. Mant when the turning of the bedroom door handle startled her. She jumped up, and he stood there. The blood rushed to her forehead; his expression frightened her; for an instant she stared at him as if he had been an enemy. Then she saw that the look in his face was only the remote lost look of excessive physical pain.

She was at his side at once, supporting him, guiding him to the nearest armchair. He sank into it, and she flung a shawl over him, and knelt at his side while his inscrutable eyes continued to repel her.

"Charles . . . Charles," she pleaded.

For a while he could not speak; and she said to herself that she would perhaps never know whether he had sought her because he was ill, or whether illness had seized him as he entered her room to question, accuse, or reveal what he had seen or heard that afternoon.

Suddenly he lifted his hand and pressed back her forehead, so that her face lay bare under his eyes.

"Love, love—you've been happy?"

"Happy?" The word choked her. She clung to him, burying her anguish against his knees. His hand stirred weakly in her hair, and gathering her whole strength into the gesture, she raised her head again, looked into his eyes, and breathed back: "And you?"

He gave her one full look; all their life together was in it, from the first day to the last. His hand brushed her once more, like a blessing, and then dropped. The moment of their communion was over; the next she was preparing remedies, ringing for the servants, ordering the doctor to be called. Her husband was once more the harmless helpless captive that sickness makes of the most dreaded and the most loved.

VI

It was in Mrs. Mant's drawing room that, some half-year later, Mrs. Charles Hazeldean, after a moment's hesitation, said to the servant that, yes, he might show in Mr. Prest.

Mrs. Mant was away. She had been leaving for Washington to visit a new protégée when Mrs. Hazeldean arrived from Europe, and after a rapid consultation with the clan had decided that it would not be "decent" to let poor Charles's widow go to an hotel. Lizzie had therefore the strange sensation of returning, after nearly nine years, to the house from which her husband had triumphantly rescued her; of returning there, to be sure, in comparative independence, and without danger of falling into her former bondage, yet with every nerve shrinking from all that the scene revived.

Mrs. Mant, the next day, had left for Washington; but before starting she had tossed a note across the breakfast table to her visitor.

"Very proper—he was one of Charlie's oldest friends, I believe?" she said, with her mild frosty smile. Mrs. Hazeldean glanced at the note, turned it over as if to examine the signature, and restored it to her hostess.

"Yes. But I don't think I care to see anyone just yet."

There was a pause, during which the butler brought in fresh griddle cakes, replenished the hot milk, and withdrew. As the door closed on him, Mrs. Mant said, with a dangerous cordiality: "No one would misunderstand your receiving an old friend of your husband's . . . like Mr. Prest."

Lizzie Hazeldean cast a sharp glance at the large empty mysterious face across the table. They *wanted* her to receive Henry Prest, then? Ah, well . . . perhaps she understood. . . .

"Shall I answer this for you, my dear? Or will you?" Mrs. Mant pursued.

"Oh, as you like. But don't fix a day, please. Later—"

Mrs. Mant's face again became vacuous. She murmured: "You must not shut yourself up too much. It will not do to be morbid. I'm sorry to have to leave you here alone—"

Lizzie's eyes filled: Mrs. Mant's sympathy seemed more cruel than her cruelty. Every word that she used had a veiled taunt for its counterpart.

"Oh, you mustn't think of giving up your visit—"

"My dear, how can I? It's a *duty*. I'll send a line to Henry Prest, then. . . . If you would sip a little port at luncheon and dinner we should have you looking less like a ghost. . . ."

Mrs. Mant departed; and two days later—the interval was "decent"— Mr. Henry Prest was announced. Mrs. Hazeldean had not seen him since the previous New Year's Day. Their last words had been exchanged in

Mrs. Struthers' crimson boudoir, and since then half a year had elapsed. Charles Hazeldean had lingered for a fortnight; but though there had been ups and downs, and intervals of hope when none could have criticized his wife for seeing her friends, her door had been barred against everyone. She had not excluded Henry Prest more rigorously than the others; he had simply been one of the many who received, day by day, the same answer: "Mrs. Hazeldean sees no one but the family."

Almost immediately after her husband's death she had sailed for Europe on a long-deferred visit to her father, who was now settled at Nice; but from this expedition she had presumably brought back little comfort, for when she arrived in New York her relations were struck by her air of ill-health and depression. It spoke in her favor, however; they were agreed that she was behaving with propriety.

She looked at Henry Prest as if he were a stranger: so difficult was it, at the first moment, to fit his robust and splendid person into the region of twilight shades which, for the last months, she had inhabited. She was beginning to find that everyone had an air of remoteness; she seemed to see people and life through the confusing blur of the long crape veil in which it was a widow's duty to shroud her affliction. But she gave him her hand without perceptible reluctance.

He lifted it toward his lips, in an obvious attempt to combine gallantry with condolence, and then, halfway up, seemed to feel that the occasion required him to release it.

"Well—you'll admit that I've been patient!" he exclaimed.

"Patient? Yes. What else was there to be?" she rejoined with a faint smile, as he seated himself beside her, a little too near.

"Oh, well . . . of course! I understood all that, I hope you'll believe. But mightn't you at least have answered my letters—one or two of them?"

She shook her head. "I couldn't write."

"Not to anyone? Or not to me?" he queried, with ironic emphasis.

"I wrote only the letters I had to—no others."

"Ah, I see." He laughed slightly. "And you didn't consider that letters to *me* were among them?"

She was silent, and he stood up and took a turn across the room. His face was redder than usual, and now and then a twitch passed over it. She saw that he felt the barrier of her crape, and that it left him baffled and resentful. A struggle was still perceptibly going on in him between his traditional standard of behavior at such a meeting, and primitive impulses renewed by the memory of their last hours together. When he turned back and paused before her his ruddy flush had paled, and he stood there, frowning, uncertain, and visibly resenting the fact that she made him so.

"You sit there like a stone!" he said.

"I feel like a stone."

"Oh, come—!"

She knew well enough what he was thinking: that the only way to bridge over such a bad beginning was to get the woman into your arms—and talk afterward. It was the classic move. He had done it dozens of times, no doubt, and was evidently asking himself why the deuce he couldn't do it now. . . . But something in her look must have benumbed him. He sat down again beside her.

"What you must have been through, dearest!" He waited and coughed. "I can understand your being—all broken up. But I know nothing; remember, I know nothing as to what actually happened. . . ."

"Nothing happened."

"As to—what we feared? No hint—?"

She shook her head.

He cleared his throat before the next question. "And you don't think that in your absence he may have spoken—to anyone?"

"Never!"

"Then, my dear, we seem to have had the most unbelievable good luck; and I can't see—"

He had edged slowly nearer, and now laid a large ringed hand on her sleeve. How well she knew those rings—the two dull gold snakes with malevolent jeweled eyes! She sat as motionless as if their coils were about her, till slowly his tentative grasp relaxed.

"Lizzie, you know"—his tone was discouraged—"this is morbid. . . ."

"Morbid?"

"When you're safe out of the worst scrape . . . and free, my darling, *free!* Don't you realize it? I suppose the strain's been too much for you; but I want you to feel that now—"

She stood up suddenly, and put half the length of the room between them.

"Stop! Stop! Stop!" she almost screamed, as she had screamed long ago at Mrs. Mant.

He stood up also, darkly red under his rich sunburn, and forced a smile. "Really," he protested, "all things considered—and after a separation of six months!" She was silent. "My dear," he continued mildly, "will you tell me what you expect me to think?"

"Oh, don't take that tone," she murmured.

"What tone?"

"As if—as if—you still imagined we could go back—"

She saw his face fall. Had he ever before, she wondered, stumbled upon an obstacle in that smooth walk of his? It flashed over her that this was the danger besetting men who had a "way with women"—the day came when they might follow it too blindly.

The reflection evidently occurred to him almost as soon as it did to her. He summoned another propitiatory smile, and drawing near, took her hand gently. "But I don't want to go back . . . I want to go forward, dearest. . . . Now that at last you're free."

She seized on the word as if she had been waiting for her cue. "Free! Oh, that's it—*free!* Can't you see, can't you understand, that I mean to stay free?"

Again a shadow of distrust crossed his face, and the smile he had begun for her reassurance seemed to remain on his lips for his own.

"But of course! Can you imagine that I want to put you in chains? I want you to be as free as you please—free to love me as much as you choose!" He was visibly pleased with the last phrase.

She drew away her hand, but not unkindly. "I'm sorry—I *am* sorry, Henry. But you don't understand."

"What don't I understand?"

"That what you ask is quite impossible—ever. I can't go on . . . in the old way. . . ."

She saw his face working nervously. "In the old way? You mean—?" Before she could explain he hurried on with an increasing majesty of manner: "Don't answer! I see—I understand. When you spoke of freedom just now I was misled for a moment—I frankly own I was—into thinking that, after your wretched marriage, you might prefer discreeter ties . . . an apparent independence which would leave us both . . . I say *apparent,* for on my side there has never been the least wish to conceal. . . . But if I was mistaken, if on the contrary what you wish is . . . is to take advantage of your freedom to regularize our . . . our attachment . . ."

She said nothing, not because she had any desire to have him complete the phrase, but because she found nothing to say. To all that concerned their common past she was aware of offering a numbed soul. But her silence evidently perplexed him, and in his perplexity he began to lose his footing, and to flounder in a sea of words.

"Lizzie! Do you hear me? If I was mistaken, I say—and I hope I'm not above owning that at times I *may* be mistaken; if I was—why, by God, my dear, no woman ever heard me speak the words before; but here I am to have and to hold, as the Book says! Why, hadn't you realized it? Lizzie, look up—! *I'm asking you to marry me.*"

Still, for a moment, she made no reply, but stood gazing about her as if she had the sudden sense of unseen presences between them. At length she gave a faint laugh. It visibly ruffled her visitor.

"I'm not conscious," he began again, "of having said anything particularly laughable—" He stopped and scrutinized her narrowly, as though checked by the thought that there might be something not quite normal. . . . Then, apparently reassured, he half-murmured his only French phrase: *"La joie fait peur . . .* eh?"

She did not seem to hear. "I wasn't laughing at you," she said, "but only at the coincidences of life. It was in this room that my husband asked me to marry him."

"Ah?" Her suitor appeared politely doubtful of the good taste, or the opportunity, of producing this reminiscence. But he made another call on his magnanimity. "Really? But, I say, my dear, I couldn't be expected to know it, could I? If I'd guessed that such a painful association—"

"Painful?" She turned upon him. "A painful association? Do you think that was what I meant?" Her voice sank. "This room is sacred to me."

She had her eyes on his face, which, perhaps because of its architectural completeness, seemed to lack the mobility necessary to follow such a leap of thought. It was so ostensibly a solid building, and not a nomad's tent. He struggled with a ruffled pride, rose again to playful magnanimity, and murmured: "Compassionate angel!"

"Oh, compassionate? To whom? Do you imagine—did I ever say anything to make you doubt the truth of what I'm telling you?"

His brows fretted: his temper was up. "*Say* anything? No," he insinuated ironically; then, in a hasty plunge after his lost forbearance, added with exquisite mildness: "Your tact was perfect . . . always. I've invariably done you that justice. No one could have been more thoroughly the . . . the lady. I never failed to admire your good breeding in avoiding any reference to your . . . your other life."

She faced him steadily. "Well, that other life *was* my life—my only life! Now you know."

There was a silence. Henry Prest drew out a monogrammed handkerchief and passed it over his dry lips. As he did so, a whiff of his eau de Cologne reached her, and she winced a little. It was evident that he was seeking what to say next; wondering, rather helplessly, how to get back his lost command of the situation. He finally induced his features to break again into a persuasive smile.

"Not your *only* life, dearest," he reproached her.

She met it instantly. "Yes; so you thought—because I chose you should."

"You chose—?" The smile became incredulous.

"Oh, deliberately. But I suppose I've no excuse that you would not dislike to hear. . . . Why shouldn't we break off now?"

"Break off . . . this conversation?" His tone was aggrieved. "Of course I've no wish to force myself—"

She interrupted him with a raised hand. "Break off for good, Henry."

"For good?" He stared, and gave a quick swallow, as though the dose were choking him. "For good? Are you really—? You and I? Is this serious, Lizzie?"

"Perfectly. But if you prefer to hear . . . what can only be painful. . . ."

He straightened himself, threw back his shoulders, and said in an uncertain voice: "I hope you don't take me for a coward."

She made no direct reply, but continued: "Well, then, you thought I loved you, I suppose—"

He smiled again, revived his mustache with a slight twist, and gave a hardly perceptible shrug. "You . . . ah . . . managed to produce the illusion. . . ."

"Oh, well, yes: a woman *can*—so easily! That's what men often forget. You thought I was a lovelorn mistress; and I was only an expensive prostitute."

"Elizabeth!" he gasped, pale now to the ruddy eyelids. She saw that the word had wounded more than his pride, and that, before realizing the insult to his love, he was shuddering at the offense to his taste. Mistress! Prostitute! Such words were banned. No one reproved coarseness of language in women more than Henry Prest; one of Mrs. Hazeldean's greatest charms (as he had just told her) had been her way of remaining, "through it all," so ineffably "the lady." He looked at her as if a fresh doubt of her sanity had assailed him.

"Shall I go on?" she smiled.

He bent his head stiffly. "I am still at a loss to imagine for what purpose you made a fool of me."

"Well, then, it was as I say. I wanted money—money for my husband."

He moistened his lips. "For your husband?"

"Yes; when he began to be so ill; when he needed comforts, luxury, the opportunity to get away. He saved me, when I was a girl, from untold humiliation and wretchedness. No one else lifted a finger to help me—not one of my own family. I hadn't a penny or a friend. Mrs. Mant had grown sick of me, and was trying to find an excuse to throw me over. Oh, you don't know what a girl has to put up with—a girl alone in the world—who depends for her clothes, and her food, and the roof over her head, on the whims of a vain capricious old woman! It was because *he* knew, because he understood, that he married me. . . . He took me out of misery into blessedness. He put me up above them all . . . he put me beside himself. I didn't care for anything but that; I didn't care for the money or the freedom; I cared only for him. I would have followed him into the desert—I would have gone barefoot to be with him. I would have starved, begged, done anything for him—*anything*." She broke off, her voice lost in a sob. She was no longer aware of Prest's presence—all her consciousness was absorbed in the vision she had evoked. "It was *he* who cared—who wanted me to be rich and independent and admired! He wanted to heap everything on me—during the first years I could hardly persuade him to keep enough money for himself. . . . And then he was taken ill; and as he got worse, and gradually dropped out of affairs, his income grew smaller, and then stopped altogether; and all the while there were new expenses piling up—nurses, doctors, travel; and he grew frightened; frightened not for himself but for me. . . . And what was I to do?

I had to pay for things somehow. For the first year I managed to put off paying—then I borrowed small sums here and there. But that couldn't last. And all the while I had to keep on looking pretty and prosperous, or else he began to worry, and think we were ruined, and wonder what would become of me if he didn't get well. By the time you came I was desperate—I would have done anything, anything! He thought the money came from my Portuguese stepmother. She really was rich, as it happens. Unluckily my poor father tried to invest her money, and lost it all; but when they were first married she sent a thousand dollars—and all the rest, all you gave me, I built on that."

She paused pantingly, as if her tale were at an end. Gradually her consciousness of present things returned, and she saw Henry Prest, as if far off, a small indistinct figure looming through the mist of her blurred eyes. She thought to herself: "He doesn't believe me," and the thought exasperated her.

"You wonder, I suppose," she began again, "that a woman should dare confess such things about herself—"

He cleared his throat. "About herself? No; perhaps not. But about her husband."

The blood rushed to her forehead. "About her husband? But you don't dare to imagine—?"

"You leave me," he rejoined icily, "no other inference that I can see." She stood dumbfounded, and he added: "At any rate, it certainly explains your extraordinary coolness—pluck, I used to think it. I perceive that I needn't have taken such precautions."

She considered this. "You think, then, that he knew? You think, perhaps, that I knew he did?" She pondered again painfully, and then her face lit up. "He never knew—never! That's enough for me—and for you it doesn't matter. Think what you please. He was happy to the end—that's all I care for."

"There can be no doubt about your frankness," he said with pinched lips.

"There's no longer any reason for not being frank."

He picked up his hat, and studiously considered its lining; then he took the gloves he had laid in it, and drew them thoughtfully through his hands. She thought: "Thank God, he's going!"

But he set the hat and gloves down on a table, and moved a little nearer to her. His face looked as ravaged as a reveler's at daybreak.

"You—leave positively nothing to the imagination!" he murmured.

"I told you it was useless—" she began; but he interrupted her: "Nothing, that is—if I believed you." He moistened his lips again, and tapped them with his handkerchief. Again she had a whiff of the eau de Cologne. "But I don't!" he proclaimed. "Too many memories . . . too many . . .

proofs, my dearest. . . ." He stopped, smiling somewhat convulsively. She saw that he imagined the smile would soothe her.

She remained silent, and he began once more, as if appealing to her against her own verdict: "I know better, Lizzie. In spite of everything, *I know you're not that kind of woman."*

"I took your money—"

"As a favor. I knew the difficulties of your position. . . . I understood completely. I beg of you never again to allude to—all that." It dawned on her that anything would be more endurable to him than to think he had been a dupe—and one of two dupes! The part was not one that he could conceive of having played. His pride was up in arms to defend her, not so much for her sake as for his own. The discovery gave her a baffling sense of helplessness; against that impenetrable self-sufficiency all her affirmations might spend themselves in vain.

"No man who has had the privilege of being loved by you could ever for a moment . . ."

She raised her head and looked at him. "You have never had that privilege," she interrupted.

His jaw fell. She saw his eyes pass from uneasy supplication to a cold anger. He gave a little inarticulate grunt before his voice came back to him.

"You spare no pains in degrading yourself in my eyes."

"I am not degrading myself. I am telling you the truth. I needed money. I knew no way of earning it. You were willing to give it . . . for what you call the privilege . . ."

"Lizzie," he interrupted solemnly, "don't go on! I believe I enter into all your feelings—I believe I always have. In so sensitive, so hypersensitive a nature, there are moments when every other feeling is swept away by scruples. . . . For those scruples I only honor you the more. But I won't hear another word now. If I allowed you to go on in your present state of . . . nervous exaltation . . . you might be the first to deplore . . . I wish to forget everything you have said . . . I wish to look forward, not back. . . ." He squared his shoulders, took a deep breath, and fixed her with a glance of recovered confidence. "How little you know me if you believe that I could fail you *now!"*

She returned his look with a weary steadiness. "You are kind—you mean to be generous, I'm sure. But don't you see that I *can't* marry you?"

"I only see that, in the natural rush of your remorse—"

"Remorse? Remorse?" She broke in with a laugh. "Do you imagine I feel any remorse? I'd do it all over again tomorrow—for the same object! I got what I wanted—I gave him that last year, that last good year. It was the relief from anxiety that kept him alive, that kept him happy. Oh, he *was* happy—I know that!" She turned to Prest with a strange smile. "I do thank you for that—I'm not ungrateful."

"You . . . you . . . *ungrateful?* This . . . is really . . . indecent. . . ."
He took up his hat again, and stood in the middle of the room as if waiting to be waked from a bad dream.

"You are—rejecting an opportunity—" he began.

She made a faint motion of assent.

"You do realize it? I'm still prepared to—to help you, if you should
. . ." She made no answer, and he continued: "How do you expect to
live—since you have chosen to drag in such considerations?"

"I don't care how I live. I never wanted the money for myself."

He raised a deprecating hand. "Oh, don't—*again!* The woman I had
meant to . . ." Suddenly, to her surprise, she saw a glitter of moisture on
his lower lids. He applied his handkerchief to them, and the waft of scent
checked her momentary impulse of compunction. That Cologne water!
It called up picture after picture with a hideous precision. "Well, it was
worth it," she murmured doggedly.

Henry Prest restored his handkerchief to his pocket. He waited, glanced
about the room, turned back to her.

"If your decision is final—"

"Oh, final!"

He bowed. "There is one thing more—which I should have mentioned
if you had ever given me the opportunity of seeing you after—after last
New Year's Day. Something I preferred not to commit to writing—"

"Yes?" she questioned indifferently.

"Your husband, you are positively convinced, had no idea . . . that
day . . .?"

"None."

"Well, others, it appears, had." He paused. "Mrs. Wesson saw us."

"So I supposed. I remember now that she went out of her way to cut
me that evening at Mrs. Struthers'."

"Exactly. And she was not the only person who saw us. If people had
not been disarmed by your husband's falling ill that very day you would
have found yourself—ostracized."

She made no comment, and he pursued, with a last effort: "In your
grief, your solitude, you haven't yet realized what your future will be—
how difficult. It is what I wished to guard you against—it was my purpose in asking you to marry me." He drew himself up and smiled as if
he were looking at his own reflection in a mirror, and thought favorably
of it. "A man who has had the misfortune to compromise a woman is
bound in honor— Even if my own inclination were not what it is, I should
consider . . ."

She turned to him with a softened smile. Yes, he had really brought
himself to think that he was proposing to marry her to save her reputation. At this glimpse of the old hackneyed axioms on which he actually

believed that his conduct was based, she felt anew her remoteness from the life he would have drawn her back to.

"My poor Henry, don't you see how far I've got beyond the Mrs. Wessons? If all New York wants to ostracize me, let it! I've had my day . . . no woman has more than one. Why shouldn't I have to pay for it? I'm ready."

"Good heavens!" he murmured.

She was aware that he had put forth his last effort. The wound she had inflicted had gone to the most vital spot; she had prevented his being magnanimous, and the injury was unforgivable. He was glad, yes, actually glad now, to have her know that New York meant to cut her; but, strive as she might, she could not bring herself to care either for the fact, or for his secret pleasure in it. Her own secret pleasures were beyond New York's reach and his.

"I'm sorry," she reiterated gently. He bowed, without trying to take her hand, and left the room.

As the door closed she looked after him with a dazed stare. "He's right, I suppose; I don't realize yet—" She heard the shutting of the outer door, and dropped to the sofa, pressing her hands against her aching eyes. At that moment, for the first time, she asked herself what the next day, and the next, would be like. . . .

"If only I cared more about reading," she moaned, remembering how vainly she had tried to acquire her husband's tastes, and how gently and humorously he had smiled at her efforts. "Well—there are always cards; and when I get older, knitting and patience, I suppose. And if everybody cuts me I shan't need any evening dresses. That will be an economy, at any rate," she concluded with a little shiver.

VII

· · · · · · ·

"She was *bad* . . . always. They used to meet at the Fifth Avenue Hotel."

I must go back now to this phrase of my mother's—the phrase from which, at the opening of my narrative, I broke away for a time in order to project more vividly on the scene that anxious moving vision of Lizzie Hazeldean: a vision in which memories of my one boyish glimpse of her were pieced together with hints collected afterward.

When my mother uttered her condemnatory judgment I was a young man of twenty-one, newly graduated from Harvard, and at home again under the family roof in New York. It was long since I had heard Mrs. Hazeldean spoken of. I had been away, at school and at Harvard, for the greater part of the interval, and in the holidays she was probably not

considered a fitting subject of conversation, especially now that my sisters
came to the table.

At any rate, I had forgotten everything I might ever have picked up
about her when, on the evening after my return, my cousin Hubert Wesson—now towering above me as a pillar of the Knickerbocker Club, and
a final authority on the ways of the world—suggested our joining her at
the opera.

"Mrs. Hazeldean? But I don't know her. What will she think?"

"That it's all right. Come along. She's the jolliest woman I know. We'll
go back afterward and have supper with her—jolliest house I know."
Hubert twirled a self-conscious mustache.

We were dining at the Knickerbocker, to which I had just been elected,
and the bottle of Pommery we were finishing disposed me to think that
nothing could be more fitting for two men of the world than to end their
evening in the box of the jolliest woman Hubert knew. I groped for my
own mustache, gave a twirl in the void, and followed him, after meticu-
lously sliding my overcoat sleeve around my silk hat as I had seen him do.

But once in Mrs. Hazeldean's box I was only an overgrown boy again,
bathed in such blushes as used, at the same age, to visit Hubert, forgetting
that I had a mustache to twirl, and knocking my hat from the peg on
which I had just hung it, in my zeal to pick up a program she had not
dropped.

For she was really too lovely—too formidably lovely. I was used by
now to mere unadjectived loveliness, the kind that youth and spirits hang
like a rosy veil over commonplace features, an average outline and a pointless merriment. But this was something calculated, accomplished, finished
—and just a little worn. It frightened me with my first glimpse of the
infinity of beauty and the multiplicity of her pitfalls. What! There were
women who need not fear crow's-feet, were more beautiful for being pale,
could let a silver hair or two show among the dark, and their eyes brood
inwardly while they smiled and chatted? But then no young man was
safe for a moment! But then the world I had hitherto known had been
only a warm pink nursery, while this new one was a place of darkness,
perils and enchantments. . . .

It was the next day that one of my sisters asked me where I had been
the evening before, and that I puffed out my chest to answer: "With Mrs.
Hazeldean—at the opera." My mother looked up, but did not speak till
the governess had swept the girls off; then she said with pinched lips:
"Hubert Wesson took you to Mrs. Hazeldean's box?"

"Yes."

"Well, a young man may go where he pleases. I hear Hubert is still
infatuated; it serves Sabina right for not letting him marry the youngest
Lyman girl. But don't mention Mrs. Hazeldean again before your sisters.
. . . They say her husband never knew—I suppose if he *had* she would

never have got old Miss Cecilia Winter's money." And it was then that my mother pronounced the name of Henry Prest, and added that phrase about the Fifth Avenue Hotel which suddenly woke my boyish memories. . . .

In a flash I saw again, under its quickly lowered veil, the face with the exposed eyes and the frozen smile, and felt through my grown-up waistcoat the stab to my boy's heart and the loosened murmur of my soul; felt all this, and at the same moment tried to relate that former face, so fresh and clear despite its anguish, to the smiling guarded countenance of Hubert's "jolliest woman I know."

I was familiar with Hubert's indiscriminate use of his one adjective, and had not expected to find Mrs. Hazeldean "jolly" in the literal sense: in the case of the lady he happened to be in love with the epithet simply meant that she justified his choice. Nevertheless, as I compared Mrs. Hazeldean's earlier face to this one, I had my first sense of what may befall in the long years between youth and maturity, and of how short a distance I had traveled on that mysterious journey. If only she would take me by the hand!

I was not wholly unprepared for my mother's comment. There was no other lady in Mrs. Hazeldean's box when we entered; none joined her during the evening, and our hostess offered no apology for her isolation. In the New York of my youth everyone knew what to think of a woman who was seen "alone at the opera"; if Mrs. Hazeldean was not openly classed with Fanny Ring, our one conspicuous "professional," it was because, out of respect for her social origin, New York preferred to avoid such juxtapositions. Young as I was, I knew this social law, and had guessed, before the evening was over, that Mrs. Hazeldean was not a lady on whom other ladies called, though she was not, on the other hand, a lady whom it was forbidden to mention to other ladies. So I did mention her, with bravado.

No ladies showed themselves at the opera with Mrs. Hazeldean; but one or two dropped in to the jolly supper announced by Hubert, an entertainment whose jollity consisted in a good deal of harmless banter over broiled canvasbacks and celery, with the best of champagne. These same ladies I sometimes met at her house afterward. They were mostly younger than their hostess, and still, though precariously, within the social pale: pretty trivial creatures, bored with a monotonous prosperity, and yearning for such unlawful joys as cigarettes, plain speaking, and a drive home in the small hours with the young man of the moment. But such daring spirits were few in old New York, their appearances infrequent and somewhat furtive. Mrs. Hazeldean's society consisted mainly of men, men of all ages, from her bald or gray-headed contemporaries to youths of Hubert's accomplished years and raw novices of mine.

A great dignity and decency prevailed in her little circle. It was not the oppressive respectability which weighs on the reformed *déclassée,* but the air of ease imparted by a woman of distinction who has wearied of society and closed her doors to all save her intimates. One always felt, at Lizzie Hazeldean's, that the next moment one's grandmother and aunts might be announced; and yet so pleasantly certain that they wouldn't be.

What is there in the atmosphere of such houses that makes them so enchanting to a fastidious and imaginative youth? Why is it that "those women" (as the others call them) alone know how to put the awkward at ease, check the familiar, smile a little at the overknowing, and yet encourage naturalness in all? The difference of atmosphere is felt on the very threshold. The flowers grow differently in their vases, the lamps and easy chairs have found a cleverer way of coming together, the books on the table are the very ones that one is longing to get hold of. The most perilous coquetry may not be in a woman's way of arranging her dress but in her way of arranging her drawing room; and in this art Mrs. Hazeldean excelled.

I have spoken of books; even then they were usually the first objects to attract me in a room, whatever else of beauty it contained; and I remember, on the evening of that first "jolly supper," coming to an astonished pause before the crowded shelves that took up one wall of the drawing room. What! The goddess read, then? She could accompany one on those flights too? Lead one, no doubt? My heart beat high. . . .

But I soon learned that Lizzie Hazeldean did not read. She turned but languidly even the pages of the last Ouida novel; and I remember seeing Mallock's *New Republic* uncut on her table for weeks. It took me no long time to make the discovery: at my very next visit she caught my glance of surprise in the direction of the rich shelves, smiled, colored a little, and met it with the confession: "No, I can't read them. I've tried— I *have* tried—but print makes me sleepy. Even novels do. . . ." "They" were the accumulated treasures of English poetry, and a rich and varied selection of history, criticism, letters, in English, French and Italian—she spoke these languages, I knew—books evidently assembled by a sensitive and widely ranging reader. We were alone at the time, and Mrs. Hazeldean went on in a lower tone: "I kept just the few he liked best—my husband, you know." It was the first time that Charles Hazeldean's name had been spoken between us, and my surprise was so great that my candid cheek must have reflected the blush on hers. I had fancied that women in her situation avoided alluding to their husbands. But she continued to look at me, wistfully, humbly almost, as if there were something more that she wanted to say, and was inwardly entreating me to understand.

"He was a great reader: a student. And he tried so hard to make me read too—he wanted to share everything with me. And I *did* like poetry —some poetry—when he read it aloud to me. After his death I thought: 'There'll be his books. I can go back to them—I shall find him there.' And

I tried—oh, so hard—but it's no use. They've lost their meaning . . . as most things have." She stood up, lit a cigarette, pushed back a log on the hearth. I felt that she was waiting for me to speak. If life had but taught me how to answer her, what was there of her story I might not have learned? But I was too inexperienced; I could not shake off my bewilderment. What! This woman whom I had been pitying for matrimonial miseries which seemed to justify her seeking solace elsewhere—this woman could speak of her husband in such a tone! I had instantly perceived that the tone was not feigned; and a confused sense of the complexity—or the chaos—of human relations held me as tongue-tied as a schoolboy to whom a problem beyond his grasp is suddenly propounded.

Before the thought took shape she had read it, and with the smile which drew such sad lines about her mouth, had continued gaily: "What are you up to this evening, by the way? What do you say to going to the *Black Crook* with your cousin Hubert and one or two others? I have a box."

It was inevitable that, not long after this candid confession, I should have persuaded myself that a taste for reading was boring in a woman, and that one of Mrs. Hazeldean's chief charms lay in her freedom from literary pretensions. The truth was, of course, that it lay in her sincerity; in her humble yet fearless estimate of her own qualities and shortcomings. I had never met its like in a woman of any age, and coming to me in such early days, and clothed in such looks and intonations, it saved me, in after years, from all peril of meaner beauties.

But before I had come to understand that, or to guess what falling in love with Lizzie Hazeldean was to do for me, I had quite unwittingly and fatuously done the falling. The affair turned out, in the perspective of the years, to be but an incident of our long friendship; and if I touch on it here it is only to illustrate another of my poor friend's gifts. If she could not read books she could read hearts; and she bent a playful yet compassionate gaze on mine while it still floundered in unawareness.

I remember it all as if it were yesterday. We were sitting alone in her drawing room, in the winter twilight, over the fire. We had reached—in her company it was not difficult—the degree of fellowship when friendly talk lapses naturally into a friendlier silence, and she had taken up the evening paper while I glowered dumbly at the embers. One little foot, just emerging below her dress, swung, I remember, between me and the fire, and seemed to hold her all in the spring of its instep. . . .

"Oh," she exclaimed, "poor Henry Prest—" She dropped the paper. "His wife is dead—poor fellow," she said simply.

The blood rushed to my forehead: my heart was in my throat. She had named him—named him at last, the recreant lover, the man who had "dishonored" her! My hands were clenched: if he had entered the room they would have been at his throat. . . .

And then, after a quick interval, I had again the humiliating disheartening sense of not understanding: of being too young, too inexperienced, to know. This woman, who spoke of her deceived husband with tenderness, spoke compassionately of her faithless lover! And she did the one as naturally as the other, not as if this impartial charity were an attitude she had determined to assume, but as if it were part of the lesson life had taught her.

"I didn't know he was married," I growled between my teeth.

She meditated absently. "Married? Oh, yes; when was it? The year after"— her voice dropped again—"after my husband died. He married a quiet cousin, who had always been in love with him, I believe. They had two boys. . . . You knew him?" she abruptly questioned.

I nodded grimly.

"People always thought he would never marry—he used to say so himself," she went on, still absently.

I burst out: "The—hound!"

"*Oh!*" she exclaimed. I started up, our eyes met, and hers filled with tears of reproach and understanding. We sat looking at each other in silence. Two of the tears overflowed, hung on her lashes, melted down her cheeks. I continued to stare at her shamefacedly; then I got to my feet, drew out my handkerchief, and tremblingly, reverently, as if I had touched a sacred image, I wiped them away.

My love-making went no farther. In another moment she had contrived to put a safe distance between us. She did not want to turn a boy's head; long since (she told me afterward) such amusements had ceased to excite her. But she did want my sympathy, wanted it overwhelmingly: amid the various feelings she was aware of arousing, she let me see that sympathy, in the sense of a moved understanding, had always been lacking. "But then," she added ingenuously, "I've never really been sure, because I've never told anyone my story. Only I take it for granted that, if I haven't, it's *their* fault rather than mine. . . ." She smiled half-deprecatingly, and my bosom swelled, acknowledging the distinction. "And now I want to tell *you*—" she began.

I have said that my love for Mrs. Hazeldean was a brief episode in our long relation. At my age, it was inevitable that it should be so. The "fresher face" soon came, and in its light I saw my old friend as a middle-aged woman, turning gray, with a mechanical smile and haunted eyes. But it was in the first glow of my feeling that she had told me her story; and when the glow subsided, and in the afternoon light of a long intimacy I judged and tested her statements, I found that each detail fitted into the earlier picture.

My opportunities were many; for once she had told the tale she always wanted to be retelling it. A perpetual longing to relive the past, a perpetual need to explain and justify herself—the satisfaction of these two cravings, once she had permitted herself to indulge them, became the luxury of her empty life. She had kept it empty—emotionally, sentimentally empty—from the day of her husband's death, as the guardian of an abandoned temple might go on forever sweeping and tending what had once been the god's abode. But this duty performed, she had no other. She had done one great—or abominable—thing; rank it as you please, it had been done heroically. But there was nothing in her to keep her at that height. Her tastes, her interests, her conceivable occupations, were all on the level of a middling domesticity; she did not know how to create for herself any inner life in keeping with that one unprecedented impulse.

Soon after her husband's death, one of her cousins, the Miss Cecilia Winter of Washington Square to whom my mother had referred, had died also, and left Mrs. Hazeldean a handsome legacy. And a year or two later Charles Hazeldean's small estate had undergone the favorable change that befell New York realty in the eighties. The property he had bequeathed to his wife had doubled, then tripled, in value; and she found herself, after a few years of widowhood, in possession of an income large enough to supply her with all the luxuries which her husband had struggled so hard to provide. It was the peculiar irony of her lot to be secured from temptation when all danger of temptation was over; for she would never, I am certain, have held out the tip of her finger to any man to obtain such luxuries for her own enjoyment. But if she did not value her money for itself, she owed to it—and the service was perhaps greater than she was aware—the power of mitigating her solitude, and filling it with the trivial distractions without which she was less and less able to live.

She had been put into the world, apparently, to amuse men and enchant them; yet, her husband dead, her sacrifice accomplished, she would have preferred, I am sure, to shut herself up in a lonely monumental attitude, with thoughts and pursuits on a scale with her one great hour. But what was she to do? She had known of no way of earning money except by her graces; and now she knew no way of filling her days except with cards and chatter and theater-going. Not one of the men who approached her passed beyond the friendly barrier she had opposed to me. Of that I was sure. She had not shut out Henry Prest in order to replace him—her face grew white at the suggestion. But what else was there to do, she asked me; what? The days had to be spent somehow; and she was incurably, disconsolately sociable.

So she lived, in a cold celibacy that passed for I don't know what license; so she lived, withdrawn from us all, yet needing us so desperately, inwardly faithful to her one high impulse, yet so incapable of attuning her daily behavior to it! And so, at the very moment when she ceased to deserve the blame of society, she found herself cut off from it, and reduced to the status of the "fast" widow noted for her jolly suppers.

I bent bewildered over the depths of her plight. What else, at any stage

of her career, could she have done, I often wondered? Among the young
women now growing up about me I find none with enough imagination
to picture the helpless incapacity of the pretty girl of the seventies, the
girl without money or vocation, seemingly put into the world only to
please, and unlearned in any way of maintaining herself there by her
own efforts. Marriage alone could save such a girl from starvation, unless
she happened to run across an old lady who wanted her dogs exercised
and her *Churchman* read aloud to her. Even the day of painting wild
roses on fans, of coloring photographs to "look like" miniatures, of manu-
facturing lampshades and trimming hats for more fortunate friends—even
this precarious beginning of feminine independence had not dawned. It
was inconceivable to my mother's generation that a portionless girl should
not be provided for by her relations until she found a husband; and that,
having found him, she should have to help him to earn a living, was
more inconceivable still. The self-sufficing little society of that vanished
New York attached no great importance to wealth, but regarded poverty
as so distasteful that it simply took no account of it.

These things pleaded in favor of poor Lizzie Hazeldean, though to
superficial observers her daily life seemed to belie the plea. She had known
no way of smoothing her husband's last years but by being false to him;
but once he was dead, she expiated her betrayal by a rigidity of conduct
for which she asked no reward but her own inner satisfaction. As she
grew older, and her friends scattered, married, or were kept away from
one cause or another, she filled her depleted circle with a less fastidious
hand. One met in her drawing room dull men, common men, men who
too obviously came there because they were not invited elsewhere, and
hoped to use her as a social steppingstone. She was aware of the difference
—her eyes said so whenever I found one of these newcomers installed in
my armchair—but never, by word or sign, did she admit it. She said to
me once: "You find it duller here than it used to be. It's my fault, perhaps; I think I knew better how to draw out my old friends." And another day: "Remember, the people you meet here now come out of kindness. I'm an old woman, and I consider nothing else." That was all.

She went more assiduously than ever to the theater and the opera; she
performed for her friends a hundred trivial services; in her eagerness to
be always busy she invented superfluous attentions, oppressed people by
offering assistance they did not need, verged at times—for all her tact—
on the officiousness of the desperately lonely. At her little suppers she
surprised us with exquisite flowers and novel delicacies. The champagne
and cigars grew better and better as the quality of the guests declined;
and sometimes, as the last of her dull company dispersed, I used to see
her, among the scattered ashtrays and liqueur decanters, turn a stealthy
glance at her reflection in the mirror, with haggard eyes which seemed
to ask: "Will even *these* come back tomorrow?"

I should be loth to leave the picture at this point; my last vision of her is more satisfying. I had been away, traveling for a year at the other end of the world; the day I came back I ran across Hubert Wesson at my club. Hubert had grown pompous and heavy. He drew me into a corner, and said, turning red, and glancing cautiously over his shoulder: "Have you seen our old friend Mrs. Hazeldean? She's very ill, I hear."

I was about to take up the "I hear"; then I remembered that in my absence Hubert had married, and that his caution was probably a tribute to his new state. I hurried at once to Mrs. Hazeldean's; and on her doorstep, to my surprise, I ran against a Catholic priest, who looked gravely at me, bowed and passed out.

I was unprepared for such an encounter, for my old friend had never spoken to me of religious matters. The spectacle of her father's career had presumably shaken whatever incipient faith was in her; though in her little-girlhood, as she often told me, she had been as deeply impressed by Dr. Winter's eloquence as any grown-up member of his flock. But now, as soon as I laid eyes on her, I understood. She was very ill, she was visibly dying; and in her extremity, fate, not always kind, had sent her the solace which she needed. Had some obscure inheritance of religious feeling awaked in her? Had she remembered that her poor father, after his long life of mental and moral vagabondage, had finally found rest in the ancient fold? I never knew the explanation—she probably never knew it herself.

But she knew that she had found what she wanted. At last she could talk of Charles, she could confess her sin, she could be absolved of it. Since cards and suppers and chatter were over, what more blessed barrier could she find against solitude? All her life, henceforth, was a long preparation for that daily hour of expansion and consolation. And then this merciful visitor, who understood her so well, could also tell her things about Charles: knew where he was, how he felt, what exquisite daily attentions could still be paid to him, and how, with all unworthiness washed away, she might at last hope to reach him. Heaven could never seem strange, so interpreted; each time that I saw her, during the weeks of her slow fading, she was more and more like a traveler with her face turned homeward, yet smilingly resigned to await her summons. The house no longer seemed lonely, nor the hours tedious; there had even been found for her, among the books she had so often tried to read, those books which had long looked at her with such hostile faces, two or three (they were always on her bed) containing messages from the world where Charles was waiting.

Thus provided and led, one day she went to him.

The Old Chevalier

By ISAK DINESEN

My FATHER had a friend, old Baron von Brackel, who had in his day traveled much and known many cities and men. Otherwise he was not at all like Odysseus, and could least of all be called ingenious, for he had shown very little skill in managing his own affairs. Probably from a sense of failure in this respect he carefully kept from discussing practical matters with an efficient younger generation, keen on their careers and success in life. But on theology, the opera, moral right and wrong, and other unprofitable pursuits he was a pleasant talker.

He had been a singularly good-looking young man, a sort of ideally handsome youth, and although no trace of this past beauty could be found in his face, the history of it could be traced in a certain lighthearted dignity and self-reliance which are the product of a career of good looks, and which will be found, unaccountably, in the carriage of those shaking ruins who used to look into the mirrors of the last century with delight. In this way one should be able to point out, at a *danse macabre,* the skeletons of the real great beauties of their time.

One night he and I came to discuss an old theme, which has done its duty in the literature of the past: namely, whether one is ever likely to get any real benefit, any lasting moral satisfaction, out of forsaking an inclination for the sake of principle, and in the course of our talk he told me the following story:

On a rainy night in the winter of 1874, on an avenue in Paris, a drunken young girl came up and spoke to me. I was then, as you will understand, quite a young man. I was very upset and unhappy, and was sitting bareheaded in the rain on a seat along the avenue because I had just parted from a lady whom, as we said then, I did adore, and who had within this last hour tried to poison me.

This, though it has nothing to do with what I was going to tell you, was in itself a curious story. I had not thought of it for many years until, when I was last in Paris, I saw the lady in her box at the opera, now a very old woman, with two charming little girls in pink who were, I was told, her great-granddaughters. She was lovely no more, but I had never, in the time that I have known her, seen her look so contented. I was sorry afterward that I had not gone up and called on her in her box, for though there had been but little happiness for either of us in that old love affair of ours, I think that she would have been as pleased to be reminded of the beautiful young woman, who made men unhappy, as I had been to remember, vaguely as it was, the young man who had been so unhappy that long time ago.

Her great beauty, unless some rare artist has been able to preserve it in color or clay, now probably exists only within a few very old brains like mine. It was in its day something very wonderful. She was a blonde, the fairest, I think, that I have ever seen, but not one of your pink-and-white beauties. She was pale, colorless, all through, like an old pastel or the image of a woman in a dim mirror. Within that cool and frail form there was an unrivaled energy, and a distinction such as women have no more, or no more care to have.

I had met her and had fallen in love with her in the autumn, at the château of a friend where we were both staying together with a large party of other gay young people who are now, if they are alive, faded and crooked and deaf. We were there to hunt, and I think that I shall be able to remember to the last of my days how she used to look on a big bay horse that she had, and that autumn air, just touched with frost, when we came home in the evenings, warm in cold clothes, tired, riding side by side over an old stone bridge. My love was both humble and audacious, like that of a page for his lady, for she was so much admired, and her beauty had in itself a sort of disdain which might well give sad dreams to a boy of twenty, poor and a stranger in her set. So that every hour of our rides, dances and *tableaux vivants* was exuberant with ecstasy and pain, the sort of thing you will know yourself: a whole orchestra in the heart. When she made me happy, as one says, I thought that I was happy indeed. I remembered smoking a cigar on the terrace one morning, looking out over the large view of low, wood-covered blue hills, and giving the Lord a sort of receipt for all the happiness that I should ever have any claim to in my life. Whatever would happen to me now, I had had my due, and declared myself satisfied.

Love, with very young people, is a heartless business. We drink at that age from thirst, or to get drunk; it is only later in life that we occupy ourselves with the individuality of our wine. A young man in love is essentially enraptured by the forces within himself. You may come back to that view again, in a second adolescence. I knew a very old Russian in Paris, enormously rich, who used to keep the most charming young dancers, and who, when once asked whether he had, or needed to have, any illusions as to their feelings for him, thought the question over and said: "I do not think, if my chef succeeds in making me a good omelette, that I bother much whether he loves me or not." A young man could not have put his answer into those words, but he might say that he did not care whether his wine merchant was of his own religion or not, and imagine that he had got close to the truth of things. In middle age, though, you arrive at a deeper humility, and you come to consider it of importance that the person who sells or grows your wine shall be of the same religion as you yourself. In this case of my own, of which I am telling you, my youthful vanity, if I had too much of it, was to be taught a lesson very soon. For during the months of that winter, while we were both living in Paris, where her house was the meeting place of many *bel-esprits,* and she herself the admired dilettante in music and arts, I began to think that she was making use of me, or of her own love for me, if such can be said, to make her husband jealous. This has happened, I suppose, to many young men down through the ages, without the total sum of their experience being much use to the young man who finds himself in the same position today. I began to wonder what the relations between those two were really like, and what strange forces there might be in her or in him, to toss me about between them in this way, and I think that I began to be afraid. She was jealous of me, too, and would scold me with a sort of moral indignation, as if I had been a groom failing in his duties. I thought that I could not live without her, and also that she did not want to live without me, but exactly what she wanted me for I did not know. Her contact hurt me as one is hurt by touching iron on a winter day: you do not know whether the pain comes from heat or from cold.

Before I had ever met her I had read about her family, whose name ran down for centuries through the history of France, and learned that there used to be werewolves amongst them, and I sometimes thought that I should have been happier to see her really go down on all fours and snarl at me, for then I should have known where I was. And even up to the end we had hours together of a particular charm, for which I shall always be thankful to her. During my first year in Paris, before I knew any people there, I had taken up studying the history of the old hotels of the town, and this hobby of mine appealed to her, so that we used to dive into old quarters and ages of Paris, and dwell together in the age of Abélard or of Molière, and while we were playing in this way she was serious and gentle with me, like a little girl. But at other times I thought that I could stand it no longer, and would try to get away from her, and any suspicion of this was enough, I imagine, to make her lie awake at night thinking out new methods of punishing me. It was between us the old game of the cat and the mouse—probably the original model of all the games of the world. But because the cat has more passion in it, and the mouse only the plain interest of existence, the mouse is bound to become tired first. Toward the end I thought that she wished us to be found out, she was so careless in this *liaison* of ours; and in those days a love affair had to be managed with prudence.

I remember during this period coming to her hotel on the night of a ball to which she was going, while I had not been asked, disguised as a hairdresser. In the seventies ladies had large chignons and the work of a *coiffeur* took time. And through everything the thought of her husband would follow me, like, I thought, the gigantic shadow, upon the white back curtain, of an absurd little punchinello. I began to feel so tired—not exactly of her, but really exhausted in myself—that I was making up my mind to have a scene and an explanation from her, even if I should lose her by it, when suddenly, on the night of which I am telling you, she herself produced both the scene and the explanation, such a hurricane as I have never again been out in; and all with exactly the same weapons as I had myself had ready: with the accusation that I thought more of her husband than I did of her. And when she said this to me, in that pale blue boudoir of hers that I knew so well—the silk-lined, upholstered and scented box, such as the ladies of that time liked to keep themselves in, with, I remember, some paintings of flowers on the walls, and very soft silk cushions everywhere, and a lot of lilacs in the corner behind me, with the lamp subdued by a large red shade—I had no reply, for I knew that she was right.

You would know his name if I told you, for he is still talked about, though he has been dead for many years. Or you would find it in any of the memoirs of that period, for he was the idol of our generation. Later on, great unhappiness came upon him, but at that moment—I believe that he was then thirty-three years old—he was walking quietly in the full splendor of his strange power. I once, about that time, heard two old men talk about his mother, who had been one of the beauties of the Restoration, and one of them said of her that she carried all her famous jewels as lightly and gracefully as other young ladies would wear garlands of field flowers. "Yes," the other said after he had thought it over for a moment, "and she scattered them about her, in the end, like flowers, *à la* Ophelia." Therefore I think that this rare lightness of his must have been, together with the weakness, a family trait. Even in his wildest whims, and in a sort of mannerism which we then named *fin de siècle* and were rather proud of, he had something of *le grand siècle* about him: a straight nobility that belonged to the old France.

I have looked since at those great buildings of the seventeenth century which seem altogether inexpedient as dwellings for human beings, and have thought that they must have been built for him—and his mother, I suppose—to live in. He had a confidence in life, independent of the successes which we envied him, as if he knew that he could draw upon greater forces, unknown to us, if he wanted to. It gave me much to think about, on the fate of man, when many years later I was told how this young man had, toward the end of his tragic destiny, answered the friends who implored him in the name of God, in the words of Sophocles' Ajax: "You worry me too much, woman. Do you not know that I am no longer a debtor of the gods?"

I see that I ought not to have started talking about him, even after all these years; but an ideal of one's youth will always be a landmark amongst happenings and feelings long gone. He himself has nothing to do with this story.

I told you that I myself felt it to be true that my feelings for the lovely young woman, whom I adored, were really light of weight compared to my feelings for the young man. If he had been with her when we first met, or if I had known him before I met her, I do not think that I should ever have dreamed of falling in love with his wife.

But his wife's love for him, and her jealousy, were indeed of a strange nature. For that she was in love with him I knew from the moment that she began to speak of him. Probably I had known it a long time before. And she was jealous. She suffered, she cried—she was, as I have told you, ready to kill if nothing else would help her—and all the time that fight, which was very likely the only reality in her life, was not a struggle for possession, but a competition. She was jealous of him as if he had been another young woman of fashion, her rival, or as if she herself had been a young man who envied him his triumphs. I think that she was, in herself, always alone with him in a world that she despised. When she rode so madly, when she surrounded herself with admirers, she had her eye on him, as a competitor in a chariot race would have his eyes only on the driver just beside him. As for the rest of us, we only existed for her in so far as we were to belong to her or to him, and she took her lovers as she took her fences, to pile up more conquests than the man with whom she was in love.

I cannot, of course, know how this had begun between them. Afterward I tried to believe that it must have arisen from a desire for revenge, on her side, for something that he had done to her in the past. But I had the feeling that it was this barren passion which had burned all the color out of her.

Now you will know that all this happened in the early days of what we called then the "emancipation of woman." Many strange things took place then. I do not think that at the time the movement went very deep down in the social world, but here were the young women of the highest intelligence, and the most daring and ingenious of them, coming out of the chiaroscuro of a thousand years, blinking at the sun and wild with desire to try their wings. I believe that some of them put on the armor and the halo of St. Joan of Arc, who was herself an emancipated virgin, and became like white-hot angels. But most women, when they feel free to experiment with life, will go straight to the witches' Sabbath. I myself respect them for it, and do not think that I could ever really love a woman who had not, at some time or other, been up on a broomstick.

I have always thought it unfair to woman that she has never been alone in the world. Adam had a time, whether long or short, when he could wander about on a fresh and peaceful earth, among the beasts, in full possession of his soul, and most men are born with a memory of that period. But poor Eve found him there, with all his claims upon her, the moment she looked into the world. That is a grudge that woman has always had against the Creator: she feels that she is entitled to have that epoch of paradise back for herself. Only, worse luck, when chasing a time that has gone, one is bound to get hold of it by the tail, the wrong way around. Thus these young witches got everything they wanted as in a catoptric image.

Old ladies of those days, patronesses of the church and of home, said that emancipation was turning the heads of the young women. Probably there were more young ladies than my mistress galloping high up above the ground, with their fair faces at the backs of their necks, after the manner of the wild huntsman in the tale. And in the air there was a theory, which caught hold of them there, that the jealousy of lovers was an ignoble affair, and that no woman should allow herself to be possessed by any male but the devil. On their way to him they were proud of being, according to Dr. Faust, always a hundred steps ahead of man. But the jealousy of competition was, as between Adam and Lilith, a noble striving. So there you would find, not only the old witches of Macbeth, of whom one might have expected it, but even young ladies with faces smooth as flowers, wild and mad with jealousy of their lovers' mustachios. All this they got from reading—in the orthodox witches' manner—the book of Genesis backwards. Left to themselves, they might have got a lot out of it. It was the poor, tame, male preachers of emancipation, cutting, as warlocks always will, a miserable figure at the Sabbath, who spoiled the style and flight of the whole thing by bringing it down to earth and under laws of earthly reason. I believe, though, that things have changed by now, and that at the present day, when males have likewise emancipated themselves, you may find the young lover on the hearth, following the track of the witch's shadow along the ground, and, with infinitely less imagination, blending the deadly brew for his mistress, out of envy of her breasts.

The part which had been granted to me, in the story of my emancipated young witch, was not in itself flattering. Still I believe that she was desperately fond of me, probably with the kind of passion which a little girl has for her favorite doll. And as far as that goes I was really the central figure of our drama. If she would be Othello, it was I, and not her husband, who must take the part of Desdemona, and I can well imagine her sighing, "Oh, the pity of it, the pity of it, Iago," over this unfortunate business, even wanting to give me a kiss and yet another before finishing it altogether. Only she did not want to kill me out of a feeling of justice or revenge. She wished to destroy me so that she should not have to lose me and to see a very dear possession belong to her rival, in the manner of a determined general, who will blow up a fortress which he can no longer hold, rather than see it in the hands of the enemy.

It was toward the end of our interview that she tried to poison me. I believe that this was really against her program, and that she had meant to tell me what she thought of me when I already had the poison in me, but had been unable to control herself for so long. There was, as you will understand, something unnatural in drinking coffee at that stage of our dialogue. The way in which she insisted upon it, and her sudden deadly silence as I raised the cup to my mouth, gave her away. I can still, although I only just touched it, recall the mortal, insipid taste of the opium, and had I emptied the cup, it could not have made my stomach rise and the marrow in my bones turn to water more than did the abrupt and fatal conviction that she wanted me to die. I let the cup drop, faint as a drowning man, and stood and stared at her, and she made one wild movement, as if she meant to throw herself at me still. Then we stood quite immovable for a minute, both knowing that all was lost. And after a little while she began to rock and whimper, with her hands at her mouth, suddenly changed into a very old woman. For my own part, I was not able to utter a sound, and I think that I just ran from the house as soon as I had strength enough to move. The air, the rain, and the street itself met me like old forgotten friends, faithful still in the hour of need.

And there I sat on a seat of the Avenue Montaigne, with the entire building of my pride and happiness lying around me in ruins, sick to death with horror and humiliation, when this girl, of whom I was telling you, came up to me.

I think that I must have been sitting there for some time, and that she must have stood and watched me before she could summon up her courage to approach. She probably felt herself in sympathy with me, thinking that I was drunk too, as sensible people do not sit without a hat in the rain, perhaps also because I was so near her own age. I did not hear what she said, neither the first nor the second time. I was not in a mood to enter into talk with a little girl of the streets. I think that it must have been from sheer instinct of self-preservation that I did in the end come to look at her and to listen. I had to get away from my own thoughts, and any human being was welcome to assist me. But there was at the same time something extraordinarily graceful and expressive about the girl, which may have attracted my attention. She stood there in the rain, highly rouged, with radiant eyes like stars, very erect though only just steady on her legs. When I kept on staring at her, she laughed at me, a low, clear laughter. She was very young. She was holding up her dress with one hand—in those days ladies wore long trains in the streets. On her head she had a black hat with ostrich feathers drooping sadly in the rain and overshadowing her forehead and eyes. The firm gentle curve of her chin, and her round young neck shone in the light of the gas lamp. Thus I can see her still, though I have another picture of her as well.

What impressed me about her was that she seemed altogether so strangely moved, intoxicated by the situation. Hers was not the conventional advance. She looked like a person out on a great adventure, or someone keeping a secret. I think that on looking at her I began to smile, some sort of bitter and wild smile, known only to young people, and that this encouraged her. She came nearer. I fumbled in my pocket for some money to give her, but I had no money on me. I got up and started to walk, and she came on, walking beside me. There was, I remember, a certain comfort in having her near me, for I did not want to be alone. In this way it happened that I let her come with me.

I asked her what her name was. She told me that it was Nathalie.

At this time I had a job at the Legation, and I was living in an apartment on the Place François I, so we had not far to go. I was prepared to come back late, and in those days, when I would come home at all sorts of hours, I used to keep a fire and a cold supper waiting for me. When we came into the room it was lighted and warm, and the table was laid for me in front of the fire. There was a bottle of champagne on ice. I used to keep a bottle of champagne to drink when I returned from my shepherd's hours.

The young girl looked around the room with a contented face. Here in the light of my lamp I could see how she really looked. She had soft brown curls and blue eyes. Her face was round, with a broad forehead. She was wonderfully pretty and graceful. I think that I just wondered at her, as one would wonder at finding a fresh bunch of roses in a gutter, no more. If I had been normally balanced I suppose I should have tried to get from her some explanation of the sort of mystery that she seemed to be, but now I do not think that this occurred to me at all.

The truth was that we must both have been in quite a peculiar sort of mood, such as will hardly ever have repeated itself for either of us. I knew as little of what moved her as she could have known about my state of mind, but, highly excited and strained, we met in a special sort of sympathy. I, partly stunned and partly abnormally wide awake and sensitive, took her quite selfishly, without any thought of where she came from or where she would disappear to again, as if she were a gift to me, and her presence a kind and friendly act of fate at this moment when I could not be alone. She seemed to me to have come as a little wild spirit from the great town outside—Paris—which may at any moment bestow unexpected favors on one, and which had in the right moment sent her to me. What she thought of me or what she felt about me, of that I can say nothing. At the moment I did not think about it, but on looking back now I should say that I must also have symbolized something to her, and that I hardly existed for her as an individual.

I felt it as a great happiness, a warmth all through me, that she was so young and lovely. It made me laugh again after those weird and dismal hours. I pulled off her hat, lifted her face up, and kissed her. Then I felt how wet she was. She must have walked for a long time on the streets in the rain, for her clothes were like the feathers of a wet hen. I went over and opened the bottle on the table, poured her out a glass, and handed it to her. She took it, standing in front of the fire, her tumbled wet curls falling down over her forehead. With her red cheeks and shining eyes she looked like a child that was just awakened from sleep, or like a doll. She drank half the glass of wine quite slowly, with her eyes on my face, and, as if this half-glass of champagne had brought her to a point where she could no longer be silent, she started to sing, in a low, gentle voice, hardly moving her lips, the first lines of a song, a waltz, which was then sung in all the music halls. She broke it off, emptied her glass, and handed it back to me. *À votre santé,* she said.

Her voice was so merry, so pure, like the song of a bird in a bush, and of all things music at that time went most directly to my heart. Her song increased the feeling I had, that something special and more than natural had been sent to me. I filled her glass again, put my hand on her round white neck, and brushed the damp ringlets back from her face. "How on earth have you come to be so wet, Nathalie?" I said, as if I had been her grandmother. "You must take off your clothes and get warm." As I spoke my voice changed. I began to laugh again. She fixed her starlike eyes on me. Her face quivered for a moment. Then she started to unbutton her cloak, and let it fall onto the floor. Underneath this cloak of black lace, badly suited for the season and faded at the edges into a rusty brown, she had a black silk frock, tightly fitted over the bust, waist and hips, and pleated and draped below, with flounces and ruffles such as ladies wore at that time, in the early days of the bustle. Its folds shone in the light of my fire. I began to undress her, as I might have undressed a doll, very slowly and clumsily, and she stood up straight and let me do it. Her fresh face had a grave and childlike expression. Once or twice she colored under my hands, but as I undid her tight bodice and my hands touched her cool shoulders and bosom, her face broke into a gentle and wide smile, and she lifted up her hand and touched my fingers.

The old Baron von Brackel made a long pause. "I think that I must explain to you," he said, "so that you may be able to understand this tale aright, that to undress a woman was then a very different thing from what it must be now. What are the clothes that your ladies of these days are wearing? In themselves as little as possible—a few perpendicular lines, cut off again before they have had time to develop any sense. There is no plan about them. They exist for the sake of the body, and have no career of their own, or, if they have any mission at all, it is to reveal.

"But in those days a woman's body was a secret which her clothes did their utmost to keep. We would walk about in the streets in bad weather in order to catch a glimpse of an ankle, the sight of which must be as familiar to you young men of the present day as the stems of these wineglasses of ours. Clothes then had a being, an idea of their own. With a serenity that it was not easy to look through, they made it their object to transform the body which they encircled, and to create a silhouette so far from its real form as to make it a mystery which it was a divine privilege to solve. The long tight stays, the whalebones, skirts and petticoats, bustle and draperies, all that mass of material under which the women of my day were buried where they were not laced together as tightly as they could possibly stand it—all aimed at one thing: to disguise.

"Out of a tremendous froth of trains, pleatings, lace, and flounces which waved and undulated, *secundum artem,* at every movement of the bearer, the waist would shoot up like the chalice of a flower, carrying the bust, high and rounded as a rose, but imprisoned in whalebone up to the shoulder. Imagine now how different life must have appeared and felt to creatures living in those tight corsets within which they could just manage to breathe, and in those fathoms of clothes which they dragged along with them wherever they walked or sat, and who never dreamed that it could be otherwise, compared to the existence of your young women, whose clothes hardly touch them and take up no room. A woman was then a work of art, the product of centuries of civilization, and you talked of her figure as you talked of her salon, with the admiration which one gives to the achievement of a skilled and untiring artist.

"And underneath all this Eve herself breathed and moved, to be indeed a revelation to us every time she stepped out of her disguise, with her waist still delicately marked by the stays, as with a girdle of rose petals.

"To you young people who laugh at the ideas, as at the bustles, of the seventies, and who will tell me that in spite of all our artificiality there can have been but little mystery left to any of us, may I be allowed to say that you do not, perhaps, quite understand the meaning of the word? Nothing is mysterious until it symbolizes something. The bread and wine of the church itself has to be baked and bottled, I suppose. The women of those days were more than a collection of individuals. They symbolized, or represented, Woman. I understand that the word itself, in that sense, has gone out of the language. Where we talked of woman—pretty cynically, we liked to think—you talk of women, and all the difference lies there.

"Do you remember the scholars of the Middle Ages who discussed the question of which had been created first: the idea of a dog, or the individual dogs? To you, who are taught statistics in your kindergartens, there is no doubt, I suppose. And it is but justice to say that your world does in reality look as if it had been made experimentally. But to us even the ideas of old Mr. Darwin were new and strange. We had our ideas from such undertakings as symphonies and ceremonials of court, and had been brought up with strong feelings about the distinction between legitimate and illegitimate birth. We had faith in purpose. The idea of Woman—of *das ewig weibliche,* about which you yourself will not deny that there is some mystery—had to us been created in the beginning, and our women made it their mission to represent it worthily, as I suppose the mission of the individual dog must have been worthily to represent the Creator's idea of a dog.

"You could follow, then, the development of this idea in a little girl, as she was growing up and was gradually, no doubt in accordance with very ancient rules, inaugurated into the rites of the cult, and finally ordained. Slowly the center of gravity of her being would be shifted from individuality to symbol, and you would be met with that particular pride and modesty characteristic of the representative of the great powers—such as you may find again in a really great artist. Indeed, the haughtiness of the pretty young girl, or the old ladies' majesty, existed no more on account of personal vanity, or on any personal account whatever, than did the pride of Michelangelo himself, or the Spanish Ambassador to France. However much greeted at the banks of the Styx by the indignation of his individual victims with flowing hair and naked breasts, Don Giovanni would have been acquitted by a board of women of my day, sitting in judgment on him, for the sake of his great faith in the idea of Woman. But they would have agreed with the masters of Oxford in condemning Shelley as an atheist; and they managed to master Christ himself only by representing him forever as an infant in arms, dependent upon the Virgin.

"The multitude outside the temple of mystery is not very interesting. The real interest lies with the priest inside. The crowd waiting at the porch for the fulfillment of the miracle of the boiling blood of St. Pantaleone—that I have seen many times and in many places. But very rarely have I had admittance to the cool vaults behind, or the chance of seeing the priests, old and young, down to the choirboys, who feel themselves to be the most important persons at the ceremony, and are both scared and impudent, occupying themselves, in a measure of their own, with the preparations, guardians of a mystery that they know all about. What was the cynicism of Lord Byron, or of Baudelaire, whom we were just reading then with the *frisson nouveau,* to the cynicism of these little priestesses, augurs all of them, performing with the utmost conscientiousness all the rites of a religion which they knew all about and did not believe in, upholding, I feel sure, the doctrine of their mystery even amongst themselves. Our poets of those days would tell us how a party of young beauties, behind the curtain of the bathing machine, would blush and giggle as they 'put lilies in water.'

"I do not know if you remember the tale of the girl who saves the ship under mutiny by sitting on the powder barrel with her lighted torch, threatening to put fire to it, and all the time knowing herself that it is empty? This has seemed to me a charming image of the woman of my time. There they were, keeping the world in order, and preserving the balance and rhythm of it, by sitting upon the mystery of life, and knowing themselves that there was no mystery. I have heard you young people saying that the women of old days had no sense of humor. Thinking of the face of my young girl upon the barrel, with severely downcast eyes, I have wondered if our famous male humor be not a little insipid compared to theirs. If we were more thankful to them for existing than you are to your women of the present day, I think that we had good reason for it.

"I trust that you will not mind," he said, "an old man lingering over these pictures of an age gone by. It will be, I suppose, like being detained a little in a museum, before a *montre* showing its fashions. You may laugh at them, if you like."

The old chevalier then resumed his story:

As I then undressed this young girl, and the layers of clothes which so severely dominated and concealed her fell one by one there in front of my fire, in the light of my large lamp, itself swathed in layers of silk— all, my dear, was thus draped in those days, and my large chairs had, I remember, long silk fringes all around them and on the tops of those little velvet pompons, otherwise they would not have been thought really pretty—until she stood naked, I had before me the greatest masterpiece of nature that my eyes have ever been privileged to rest upon, a sight to take away your breath. I know that there may be something very lovable in the little imperfections of the female form, and I have myself worshiped a knock-kneed Venus, but this young figure was pathetic, was heart-piercing, by reason of its pure faultlessness. She was so young that you felt, in the midst of your deep admiration, the anticipation of a still higher perfection, and that was all there was to be said.

All her body shone in the light, delicately rounded and smooth as marble. One straight line ran through it from neck to ankle, as though the heaven-aspiring column of a young tree. The same character was expressed in the high instep of the foot, as she pushed off her old shoes, as in the curve of the chin, as in the straight gentle glance of her eyes, and the delicate and strong lines of her shoulder and wrist.

The comfort of the warmth of the fire on her skin, after the clinging of her wet and tumbled clothes, made her sigh with pleasure and turn a little, like a cat. She laughed softly, like a child who quits the doorstep of school for a holiday. She stood up erect before the fire; her wet curls fell down over her forehead and she did not try to push them back; her bright painted cheeks looked even more like a doll's above her fair naked body.

I think that all my soul was in my eyes. Reality had met me, such a short time ago, in such an ugly shape, that I had no wish to come into contact with it again. Somewhere in me a dark fear was still crouching, and I took refuge within the fantastic like a distressed child in his book of fairy tales. I did not want to look ahead, and not at all to look back. I felt the moment close over me, like a wave. I drank a large glass of wine to catch up with her, looking at her.

I was so young then that I could no more than other young people give up the deep faith in my own star, in a power that loved me and looked after me in preference to all other human beings. No miracle was incredible to me as long as it happened to myself. It is when this faith begins to wear out, and when you conceive the possibility of being in the same position as other people, that youth is really over. I was not surprised or suspicious of this act of favor on the part of the gods, but I think that my heart was filled with a very sweet gratitude toward them. I thought it after all only reasonable, only to be expected, that the great friendly power of the universe should manifest itself again, and send me, out of the night, as a help and consolation, this naked and drunk young girl, a miracle of gracefulness.

We sat down to supper, Nathalie and I, high up there in my warm and quiet room, with the great town below us and my heavy silk curtains drawn upon the wet night, like two owls in a ruined tower within the depth of the forest, and nobody in the world knew about us. She leaned one arm on the table and rested her head on it. I think that she was very hungry, under the influence of the drink. We had some caviar, I remember, and a cold bird. She began to beam on me, to laugh, to talk to me, and to listen to what I said to her.

I do not remember what we talked about. I think we were very open-hearted, and that I told her, what I could not have mentioned to anybody else, of how I had come near to being poisoned just before I met her. I also think that I must have told her about my country, for I know that at a time afterwards the idea came to me that she would write to me there, or even come to look for me. I remember that she told me, rather sadly to begin with, a story of a very old monkey which could do tricks, and had belonged to an Armenian organ grinder. Its master had died, and now it wanted to do its tricks and was always waiting for the catchword, but nobody knew it. In the course of this tale she imitated the monkey in the funniest and most gracefully inspired manner that one can imagine. But I remember most of her movements. Sometimes I have thought that the understanding of some pieces of music for violin and piano has come to me through the contemplation of the contrast, or the harmony, between her long slim hand and her short rounded chin as she held the glass to her mouth.

I have never in any other love affair—if this can be called a love affair—had the same feeling of freedom and security. In my last adventure I had all the time been worrying to find out what my mistress really thought of me, and what part I was playing in the eyes of the world. But no such doubts or fears could possibly penetrate into our little room here. I believe that this feeling of safety and perfect freedom must be what happily married people mean when they talk about the two being one. I wonder if that understanding can possibly, in marriage, be as harmonious as when you meet as strangers; but this, I suppose, is a matter of taste.

One thing did play in to both of us, though we were not conscious of it. The world outside was bad, was dreadful. Life had made a very nasty face at me, and must have made a worse at her. But this room and this night were ours, and were faithful to us. Although we did not think about it, ours was in reality a supper of the Girondists.

The wine helped us. I had not drunk much, but my head was fairly light before I began. Champagne is a very kind and friendly thing on a rainy night. I remember an old Danish bishop's saying to me that there are many ways to the recognition of truth, and that Burgundy is one of them. This is, I know, very well for an old man within his paneled study. But young people, who have seen the devil face to face, need a stronger helping hand. Over our softly hissing glasses we were brought back to seeing ourselves and this night of ours as a great artist might have seen us and it, worthy of the genius of a god.

I had a guitar lying on my sofa, for I was to serenade, in a *tableau vivant,* a romantic beauty—in real life an American woman from the Embassy who could not have given you an echo back from whatever angle you would have cried to her. Nathalie reached out for it, a little later in our supper. She shuddered slightly at the first sound, for I had not had time or thought for playing it, and crossing her knees, in my large low chair, she began to tune it. Then she sang two little songs to me. In my quiet room her low voice, a little hoarse, was clear as a bell, faintly giddy with happiness, like a bee's in a flower. She sang first a song from the music halls, a gay tune with a striking rhythm. Then she thought for a moment and changed over into a strange plaintive little song in a language that I did not understand. She had a great sense of music. That strong and delicate personality which showed itself in all her body came out again in her voice. The light metallic timbre, the straightness and ease of it, corresponded with her eyes, knees, and fingers. Only it was a little richer and fuller, as if it had grown up faster or had stolen a march somehow upon her body. Her voice knew more than she did herself, as did the bow of Mischa Elman when he played as a *Wunderkind.*

All my balance, which I had kept somehow while looking at her, suddenly left me at the sound of her voice. These words that I did not understand seemed to me more directly meaningful than any I had ever understood. I sat in another low chair, opposite her. I remember the silence when her song was finished, and that I pushed the table away, and how I came slowly down on one knee before her. She looked at me with such a clear, severe, wild look as I think that a hawk's eyes must have when they lift off his hood. I went down on my other knee and put my arms around her legs. I do not know what there was in my face to convince her, but her own face changed and lighted up with a kind of heroic gentleness. Altogether there had been from the beginning something heroic about her. That was, I think, what had made her put up with the young fool that I was. For *du ridicule jusqu'au sublime,* surely, *il n'y a qu'un pas.*

My friend, she was as innocent as she looked. She was the first young girl who had been mine. There is a theory that a very young man should not make love to a virgin, but ought to have a more experienced partner. That is not true; it is the only natural thing.

It must have been an hour or two later in the night that I woke up to the feeling that something was wrong, or dangerous. We say when we turn suddenly cold that someone is walking over our grave—the future brings itself into memory. And as *l'on meurt en plein bonheur de ses malheurs passés,* so do we let go our hold of our present happiness on account of coming misfortune. It was not the *omne animal* affair only; it was a distrust of the future as if I had heard myself asking it: "I am to pay for this; what am I to pay?" But at the time I may have believed that what I felt was only fear of her going away.

Once before she had sat up and moved as if to leave me, and I had dragged her back. Now she said: "I must go back," and got up. The lamp was still burning, the fire was smoldering. It seemed to me natural that she should be taken away by the same mysterious forces which had brought her, like Cinderella, or a little spirit out of the *Arabian Nights.* I was waiting for her to come up and let me know when she would come back to me, and what I was to do. All the same I was more silent now.

She dressed and got back into her black shabby disguise. She put on her hat and stood there just as I had seen her first in the rain on the avenue. Then she came up to me where I was sitting on the arm of my chair, and said: "And you will give me twenty francs, will you not?" As I did not answer, she repeated her question and said: "Marie said that— she said that I should get twenty francs."

I did not speak. I sat there looking at her. Her clear and light eyes met mine.

A great clearness came upon me then, as if all the illusions and arts with which we try to transform our world, coloring and music and dreams, had been drawn aside, and reality was shown to me, waste as a burnt house. This was the end of the play. There was no room for any superfluous word.

This was the first moment, I think, since I had met her those few hours ago, in which I saw her as a human being, within an existence of her own, and not as a gift to me. I believe that all thoughts of myself left me at the sight, but now it was too late.

We two had played. A rare jest had been offered me and I had accepted it; now it was up to me to keep the spirit of our game until the end. Her own demand was well within the spirit of the night. For the palace which he builds, for four hundred white and four hundred black slaves all loaded with jewels, the djinn asks for an old copper lamp; and the forest witch who moves three towns and creates for the woodcutter's son an army of horse soldiers demands for herself the heart of a hare. The girl asked me for her pay in the voice and manner of the djinn and the forest witch, and if I were to give her twenty francs she might still be safe within the magic circle of her free and graceful and defiant spirit. It was I who was out of character, as I sat there in silence with all the weight of the cold and real world upon me, knowing well that I should have to answer her or I might, even within these few seconds, pass it on to her.

Later on I reflected that I might have had it in me to invent something which would have kept her safe, and still have allowed me to keep her. I thought then that I should only have had to give her twenty francs and to have said: "And if you want another twenty, come back tomorrow night." If she had been less lovely to me, if she had not been so young and so innocent, I might perhaps have done it. But this young girl had called, during our few hours, on all the chivalrousness that I had in my nature. And chivalrousness, I think, means this: to love, or cherish, the pride of your partner, or of your adversary, as you will define it, as highly, or higher than, your own. Or if I had been as innocent of heart as she was, I might perhaps have thought of it, but I had kept company with this deadly world of reality. I was practiced in its laws and had the mortal bacilli of its ways in my blood. Now it did not enter my head any more than it ever has to alter my answers in church. When the priest says: "O God, make clean our hearts within us," I have never thought of telling him that it is not needed, or to answer anything whatever but, "And take not your holy spirit from us."

So, as if it were the only natural and reasonable thing to do, I took out twenty francs and gave them to her.

Before she went she did a thing that I have never forgotten. With my note in her left hand she stood close to me. She did not kiss me or take my hand to say good-by, but with the three fingers of her right hand she lifted my chin up a little and looked at me, gave me an encouraging, consoling glance, such as a sister might give her brother in farewell. Then she went away.

In the days that followed—not the first days, but later—I tried to con-
struct for myself some theory and explanation of my adventure.

This happened only a short time after the fall of the Second Empire,
that strange sham millennium, and the Commune of Paris. The atmosphere had been filled with catastrophe. A world had fallen. The Empress
herself, whom, on a visit to Paris as a child, I had envisaged as a female
deity resting upon clouds, smilingly conducting the ways of humanity,
had flown in the night, in a carriage with her American dentist, miserable
for the lack of a handkerchief. The members of her court were crowded
into lodgings in Brussels and London while their country houses served
as stables for the Prussians' horses. The Commune had followed, and the
massacres in Paris by the Versailles army. A whole world must have tumbled down within these months of disaster.

This was also the time of Nihilism in Russia, when the revolutionaries
had lost all and were fleeing into exile. I thought of them because of the
little song that Nathalie had sung to me, of which I had not understood
the words.

Whatever it was that had happened to her, it must have been a catastrophe of an extraordinary violent nature. She must have gone down with
a unique swiftness, or she would have known something of the resignation, the dreadful reconciliation to fate which life works upon us when
it gets time to impress us drop by drop.

Also, I thought, she must have been tied to, and dragged down with,
somebody else, for if she had been alone it could not have happened. It
would have been, I reflected, somebody who held her, and yet was unable
to help her, someone either very old, helpless from shock and ruin, or very
young, children or a child, a little brother or sister. Left to herself she
would have floated, or she would have been picked up near the surface
by someone who would have valued her rare beauty, grace, and charm
and have congratulated himself upon acquiring them; or, lower down, by
somebody who might not have understood them, but whom they would
still have impressed. Or, near the bottom, by people who would have
thought of turning them to their own advantage. But she must have gone
straight down from the world of beauty and harmony in which she had
learned that confidence and radiance of hers, where they had taught her
to sing, and to move and laugh as she did, where they had loved her, to
a world where beauty and grace are of no account, and where the facts of
life look you in the face, quite straight to ruin, desolation and starvation.
And there, on the last step of the ladder, had been Marie, whoever she
was, a friend who out of her narrow and dark knowledge of the world
had given her advice, and lent her the miserable clothes, and poured some
sort of spirit into her, to give her courage.

About all this I thought much, and for a long time; but of course I
could not know.

As soon as she had gone and I was alone—so strange are the automatic movements which we make within the hands of fate—I had no thought but to go after her and get her back. I think that I went, in those minutes, through the exact experience, even to the sensation of suffocation, of a person who has been buried alive. But I had no clothes on. When I got into some clothes and came down to the street it was empty. I walked about in the streets for a long time. I came back, in the course of the early morning, to the seat on which I had been sitting when she first spoke to me, and to the hotel of my former mistress. I thought what a strange thing is a young man who runs about, within the selfsame night, driven by the mad passion and loss of two women. Mercutio's words to Romeo about it came into my mind, and, as if I had been shown a brilliant caricature of myself or of all young men, I laughed. When the day began to spring I walked back to my room, and there was the lamp, still burning, and the supper table.

This state of mine lasted for some time. During the first days it was not so bad, for I lived then in the thought of going down, at the same hour, to the same place where I had met her first. I thought that she might come there again. I attached much hope to this idea, which only slowly died away.

I tried many things to make it possible to live. One night I went to the opera, because I had heard other people talk about going there. It was clear that it was done, and there might be something in it. It happened to be a performance of *Orpheus*. Do you remember the music where he implores the shadows in Hades, and where Euridice is for such a short time given back to him? There I sat, in the brilliant light of the *entr'actes,* a young man in a white tie and lavender gloves, with bright people who smiled and talked all around, some of them nodding to me, closely covered and wrapped up in the huge black wings of the Eumenides.

At this time I developed also another theory. I thought of the goddess Nemesis, and I believed that had I not had the moment of doubt and fear in the night, I might have felt, in the morning, the strength in me, and the right, to move her destiny and mine. It is said about the highwaymen who in the old days haunted the forests of Denmark that they used to have a wire stretched across the road with a bell attached. The coaches in passing would touch the wire and the bell would ring within their den and call out the robbers. I had touched the wire and a bell had rung somewhere. The girl had not been afraid, but I had been afraid. I had asked: "What am I to pay for this?" and the goddess herself had answered: "Twenty francs," and with her you cannot bargain. You think of many things, when you are young.

All this is now a long time ago. The Eumenides, if they will excuse me for saying so, are like fleas, by which I was also much worried as a child. They like young blood, and leave us alone later in life. I have had, however, the honor of having them on me once more, not very many years ago. I had sold a piece of my land to a neighbor, and when I saw it again, he had cut down the forest that had been on it. Where were now the green shades, the glades and the hidden footpaths? And when I then heard again the whistle of their wings in the air, it gave me, with the pain, also a strange feeling of hope and strength—it was, after all, music of my youth.

"And did you never see her again?" I asked him.

"No," he said, and then, after a little while, "but I had a fantasy about her, a *fantaisie macabre,* if you like.

"Fifteen years later, in 1889, I passed through Paris on my way to Rome, and stayed there for a few days to see the exhibition and the Eiffel Tower which they had just built. One afternoon I went to see a friend, a painter. He had been rather wild as a young artist, but later had turned about completely, and was at the time studying anatomy with great zeal, after the example of Leonardo. I stayed there over the evening, and after we had discussed his pictures, and art in general, he said that he would show me the prettiest thing that he had in his studio. It was a skull from which he was drawing. He was keen to explain its rare beauty to me. 'It is really,' he said, 'the skull of a young woman, but the skull of Antinoüs must have looked like that, if one had been able to get hold of it.'

"I had it in my hand, and as I was looking at the broad, low brow, the clear and noble line of the chin, and the clean deep sockets of the eyes, it seemed suddenly familiar to me. The white polished bone shone in the light of the lamp, so pure. And safe. In those few seconds I was taken back to my room in the Place François I, with the silk fringes and the heavy curtains, on a rainy night of fifteen years before."

"Did you ask your friend anything about it?" I said.

"No," said the old man, "what would have been the use? He would not have known."

The Coming of Pan

By JAMES STEPHENS

MEEHAWL MACMURRACHU had good reason to be perplexed. He was the father of one child only, and she was the most beautiful girl in the whole world. The pity of it was that no one at all knew she was beautiful, and she did not even know it herself. At times when she bathed in the eddy of a mountain stream and saw her reflection looking up from the placid water she thought that she looked very nice, and then a great sadness would come upon her, for what is the use of looking nice if there is nobody to see one's beauty? Beauty, also, is usefulness. The arts as well as the crafts, the graces equally with the utilities must stand up in the market place and be judged by the gombeen men.

The only house near to her father's was that occupied by Bessie Hannigan. The other few houses were scattered widely with long, quiet miles of hill and bog between them, so that she had hardly seen more than a couple of men beside her father since she was born. She helped her father and mother in all the small businesses of their house, and every day also she drove their three cows and two goats to pasture on the mountain slopes. Here through the sunny days the years had passed in a slow, warm thoughtlessness wherein, without thinking, many thoughts had entered into her mind and many pictures hung for a moment like birds in the thin air. At first, and for a long time, she had been happy enough; there were many things in which a child might be interested: the spacious heavens which never wore the same beauty on any day; the innumerable little creatures living among the grasses or in the heather; the steep swing of a bird down from the mountain to the infinite plains below; the little flowers which were so contented each in its peaceful place; the bees gathering food for their houses, and the stout beetles who are always losing their way in the dusk. These things, and many others, interested her. The three cows after they had grazed for a long time would come and lie by her side and look at her as they chewed their cud and the goats would prance from the bracken to push their heads against her breast because they loved her.

Indeed, everything in her quiet world loved this girl: but very slowly there was growing in her consciousness an unrest, a disquietude to which she had hitherto been a stranger. Sometimes an infinite weariness oppressed her to the earth. A thought was born in her mind and it had no name. It was growing and could not be expressed. She had no words wherewith to meet it, to exorcise or greet this stranger who, more and more insistently and pleadingly, tapped upon her doors and begged to be spoken to, admitted and caressed and nourished. A thought is a real thing and words are only its raiment, but a thought is as shy as a virgin; unless it is fittingly appareled we may not look on its shadowy nakedness: it will fly from us and only return again in the darkness crying in a thin, childish voice which we may not comprehend until, with aching mind, listening and divining, we at last fashion for it those symbols which are its protection and its banner. So she could not understand the touch that came to her from afar and yet how intimately, the whisper so aloof and yet so thrillingly personal. The standard of either language or experience was not hers; she could listen but not think, she could feel but not know, her eyes looked forward and did not see, her hands groped in the sunlight and felt nothing. It was like the edge of a little wind which stirred her tresses but could not lift them, or the first white peep of the dawn which is neither light nor darkness. But she listened, not with her ears, but with her blood. The fingers of her soul stretched out to clasp a stranger's hand, and her disquietude was quickened through with an eagerness which was neither physical nor mental, for neither her body nor her mind was definitely interested. Some dim region between these grew alarmed and watched and waited and did not sleep or grow weary at all.

One morning she lay among the long, warm grasses. She watched a bird who soared and sang for a little time, and then it sped swiftly away down the steep air and out of sight in the blue distance. Even when it was gone the song seemed to ring in her ears. It seemed to linger with her as a faint, sweet echo, coming fitfully, with little pauses as though a wind disturbed it, and careless, distant eddies. After a few moments she knew it was not a bird. No bird's song had that consecutive melody, for their themes are as careless as their wings. She sat up and looked about her, but there was nothing in sight: the mountains sloped gently above her and away to the clear sky; around her the scattered clumps of heather were drowsing in the sunlight; far below she could see her father's house, a little, gray patch near some trees—and then the music stopped and left her wondering.

She could not find her goats anywhere, although for a long time she searched. They came to her at last of their own accord from behind a fold in the hills and they were more wildly excited than she had ever seen them before. Even the cows forsook their solemnity and broke into awkward gambols around her. As she walked home that evening a strange elation taught her feet to dance. Hither and thither she flitted in front of the beasts and behind them. Her feet tripped to a wayward measure. There was a tune in her ears and she danced to it, throwing her arms out and above her head and swaying and bending as she went. The full freedom of her body was hers now: the lightness and poise and certainty of her limbs delighted her, and the strength that did not tire delighted her also. The evening was full of peace and quietude, the mellow, dusky sunlight made a path for her feet, and everywhere through the wide fields birds were flashing and singing, and she sang with them a song that had no words and wanted none.

The following day she heard the music again, faint and thin, wonderfully sweet and as wild as the song of a bird, but it was a melody which no bird would adhere to. A theme was repeated again and again. In the middle of trills, grace notes, runs and catches it recurred with a strange, almost holy, solemnity. A hushing, slender melody full of austerity and aloofness. There was something in it to set her heart beating. She yearned to it with her ears and her lips. Was it joy, menace, carelessness? She did not know, but this she did know, that however terrible it was personal to her. It was her unborn thought strangely audible and felt rather than understood.

On that day she did not see anybody either. She drove her charges home in the evening listlessly and the beasts also were very quiet.

When the music came again she made no effort to discover where it came from. She only listened, and when the tune was ended she saw a figure rise from the fold of a little hill. The sunlight was gleaming from his arms and shoulders, but the rest of his body was hidden by the bracken, and he did not look at her as he went away playing softly on a double pipe.

The next day he did look at her. He stood waist-deep in greenery fronting her squarely. She had never seen so strange a face before. Her eyes almost died on him as she gazed, and he returned her look for a long minute with an intent, expressionless regard. His hair was a cluster of brown curls, his nose was little and straight, and his wide mouth drooped sadly at the corners. His eyes were wide and most mournful and his forehead was very broad and white. His sad eyes and mouth almost made her weep.

When he turned away he smiled at her, and it was as though the sun had shone suddenly in a dark place banishing all sadness and gloom. Then he went mincingly away. As he went he lifted the slender double reed to his lips and blew a few careless notes.

The next day he fronted her as before, looking down to her eyes from a short distance. He played for only a few moments, and fitfully, and then he came to her. When he left the bracken the girl suddenly clapped her hands against her eyes affrighted. There was something different, terrible about him. The upper part of his body was beautiful, but the lower part. . . . She dared not look at him again. She would have risen and fled away, but she feared he might pursue her, and the thought of such a chase and the inevitable capture froze her blood. The thought of anything behind us is always terrible. The sound of pursuing feet is worse than the murder from which we fly.—So she sat still and waited, but nothing happened. At last, desperately, she dropped her hands. He was sitting on the ground a few paces from her. He was not looking at her, but far away sidewards across the spreading hill. His legs were crossed; they were shaggy and hoofed like the legs of a goat: but she would not look at these because of his wonderful, sad, grotesque face. Gaiety is good to look upon and an innocent face is delightful to our souls, but no woman can resist sadness or weakness, and ugliness she dare not resist. Her nature leaps to be the comforter. It is her reason. It exalts her to an ecstasy wherein nothing but the sacrifice of herself has any proportion. Men are not fathers by instinct but by chance, but women are mothers beyond thought, beyond instinct which is the father of thought. Motherliness, pity, self-sacrifice—these are the charges of her primal cell, and not even the discovery that men are comedians, liars, and egotists will wean her from this. As she looked at the pathos of his face she repudiated the hideousness of his body. The beast which is in all men is glossed by women; it is his childishness, the destructive energy inseparable from youth and high spirits, and it is always forgiven by women, often forgotten, sometimes, and not rarely, cherished and fostered.

After a few moments of this silence he placed the reed to his lips and played a plaintive little air, and then he spoke to her in a strange voice, coming like a wind from distant places.

"What is your name, shepherd girl?" said he.

"Caitilin, Ingin Ni Murrachu," she whispered.

"Daughter of Murrachu," said he, "I have come from a far place where there are high hills. The men and maidens who follow their flocks in that place know me and love me, for I am the Master of the Shepherds. They sing and dance and are glad when I come to them in the sunlight; but in this country no people have done any reverence to me. The shepherds fly away when they hear my pipes in the pastures; the maidens scream in fear when I dance to them in the meadows. I am very lonely in this strange country. You also, although you danced to the music of my pipes, have covered your face against me and made no reverence."

"I will do whatever you say if it is right," said she.

"You must not do anything because it is right, but because it is your wish. Right is a word and Wrong is a word, but the sun shines in the morning and the dew falls in the dusk without thinking of these words which have no meaning. The bee flies to the flower and the seed goes abroad and is happy. Is that right, shepherd girl?—it is wrong also. I come to you because the bee goes to the flower—it is wrong! If I did not come to you to whom would I go? There is no right and no wrong, but only the will of the gods."

"I am afraid of you," said the girl.

"You fear me because my legs are shaggy like the legs of a goat. Look at them well, O Maiden, and know that they are indeed the legs of a beast and then you will not be afraid any more. Do you not love beasts? Surely you should love them for they yearn to you humbly or fiercely, craving your hand upon their heads as I do. If I were not fashioned thus I would not come to you because I would not need you. Man is a god and a brute. He aspires to the stars with his head, but his feet are contented in the grasses of the field, and when he forsakes the brute upon which he stands then there will be no more men and no more women and the immortal gods will blow this world away like smoke."

"I don't know what you want me to do," said the girl.

"I want you to want me. I want you to forget right and wrong; to be as happy as the beasts, as careless as the flowers and the birds. To live to the depths of your nature as well as to the heights. Truly there are stars in the heights and they will be a garland for your forehead. But the depths are equal to the heights. Wondrous deep are the depths, very fertile is the lowest deep. There are stars there also, brighter than the stars on high. The name of the heights is Wisdom and the name of the depths is Love. How shall they come together and be fruitful if you do not plunge deeply and fearlessly? Wisdom is the spirit and the wings of the spirit, Love is the shaggy beast that goes down. Gallantly he dives, below thought, beyond Wisdom, to rise again as high above these as he had first descended. Wisdom is righteous and clean, but Love is unclean and holy. I sing of the beast and the descent: the great unclean purging itself in fire: the thought that is not born in the measure or the ice or the head, but in the feet and the hot blood and the pulse of fury. The Crown of Life is not lodged in the sun: the wise gods have buried it deeply where the thoughtful will not find it, nor the good: but the Gay Ones, the Adventurous Ones, the Careless Plungers, they will bring it to the wise and astonish them. All things are seen in the light— How shall we value that which is easy to see? But the precious things which are hidden, they will be more precious for our search: they will be beautiful with our sorrow: they will be noble because of our desire for them. Come away with me, shepherd girl, through the fields and we will be careless and happy, and we will leave thought to find us when it can, for that is the duty of thought and it is more anxious to discover us than we are to be found."

So Caitilin Ni Murrachu arose and went with him through the fields, and she did not go with him because of love, nor because his words had been understood by her, but only because he was naked and unashamed.

The Sea Change

By ERNEST HEMINGWAY

"ALL RIGHT," said the man. "What about it?"

"No," said the girl, "I can't."

"You mean you won't."

"I can't," said the girl. "That's all that I mean."

"You mean that you won't."

"All right," said the girl. "You have it your own way."

"I don't have it my own way. I wish to God I did."

"You did for a long time," the girl said.

It was early, and there was no one in the café except the barman and these two who sat together at a table in the corner. It was the end of the summer and they were both tanned, so that they looked out of place in Paris. The girl wore a tweed suit, her skin was a smooth golden brown, her blond hair was cut short and grew beautifully away from her forehead. The man looked at her.

"I'll kill her," he said.

"Please don't," the girl said. She had very fine hands and the man looked at them. They were slim and brown and very beautiful.

"I will. I swear to God I will."

"It won't make you happy."

"Couldn't you have gotten into something else? Couldn't you have gotten into some other jam?"

"It seems not," the girl said. "What are you going to do about it?"

"I told you."

"No; I mean really."

"I don't know," he said. She looked at him and put out her hand. "Poor old Phil," she said. He looked at her hands, but he did not touch her hand with his.

"No, thanks," he said.

"It doesn't do any good to say I'm sorry?"

"No."

"Nor to tell you how it is?"

"I'd rather not hear."

"I love you very much."

"Yes, this proves it."

"I'm sorry," she said, "if you don't understand."

"I understand. That's the trouble. I understand."

"You do," she said. "That makes it worse, of course."

"Sure," he said, looking at her. "I'll understand all the time. All day and all night. Especially all night. I'll understand. You don't have to worry about that."

"I'm sorry," she said.

"If it was a man—"

"Don't say that. It wouldn't be a man. You know that. Don't you trust me?"

"That's funny," he said. "Trust you. That's really funny."

"I'm sorry," she said. "That's all I seem to say. But when we do understand each other there's no use to pretend we don't."

"No," he said. "I suppose not."

"I'll come back if you want me."

"No. I don't want you."

Then they did not say anything for a while.

"You don't believe I love you, do you?" the girl asked.

"Let's not talk rot," the man said.

"Don't you really believe I love you?"

"Why don't you prove it?"

"You didn't use to be that way. You never asked me to prove anything. That isn't polite."

"You're a funny girl."

"You're not. You're a fine man and it breaks my heart to go off and leave you—"

"You have to, of course."

"Yes," she said. "I have to and you know it."

He did not say anything and she looked at him and put her hand out again. The barman was at the far end of the bar. His face was white and so was his jacket. He knew these two and thought them a handsome young couple. He had seen many handsome young couples break up and new couples form that were never so handsome long. He was not thinking about this, but about a horse. In half an hour he could send across the street to find if the horse had won.

"Couldn't you just be good to me and let me go?" the girl asked.

"What do you think I'm going to do?"

Two people came in the door and went up to the bar.

"Yes, sir," the barman took the orders.

"You can't forgive me? When you know about it?" the girl asked.

"No."

"You don't think things we've had and done should make any differ-ence in understanding?"

" 'Vice is a monster of such fearful mien,' " the young man said bitterly, "that to be something or other needs but to be seen. Then we something, something, then embrace." He could not remember the words. "I can't quote," he said.

"Let's not say vice," she said. "That's not very polite."

"Perversion," he said.

"James," one of the clients addressed the barman, "you're looking very well."

"You're looking very well yourself," the barman said.

"Old James," the other client said. "You're fatter, James."

"It's terrible," the barman said, "the way I put it on."

"Don't neglect to insert the brandy, James," the first client said.

"No, sir," said the barman. "Trust me."

The two at the bar looked over at the two at the table, then looked back at the barman again. Toward the barman was the comfortable direction.

"I'd like it better if you didn't use words like that," the girl said. "There's no necessity to use a word like that."

"What do you want me to call it?"

"You don't have to call it. You don't have to put any name to it."

"That's the name for it."

"No," she said. "We're made up of all sorts of things. You've known that. You've used it well enough."

"You don't have to say that again."

"Because that explains it to you."

"All right," he said. "All right."

"You mean all wrong. I know. It's all wrong. But I'll come back. I told you I'd come back. I'll come back right away."

"No, you won't."

"I'll come back."

"No, you won't. Not to me."

"You'll see."

"Yes," he said. "That's the hell of it. You probably will."

"Of course I will."

"Go on, then."

"Really?" She could not believe him, but her voice was happy.

"Go on," his voice sounded strange to him. He was looking at her, at the way her mouth went and the curve of her cheekbones, at her eyes and at the way her hair grew on her forehead and at the edge of her ear and at her neck.

"Not really. Oh, you're too sweet," she said. "You're too good to me."

"And when you come back tell me all about it." His voice sounded very strange. He did not recognize it. She looked at him quickly. He was settled into something.

"You want me to go?" she asked seriously.

"Yes," he said seriously. "Right away." His voice was not the same, and his mouth was very dry. "Now," he said.

She stood up and went out quickly. She did not look back at him. He watched her go. He was not the same-looking man as he had been before he had told her to go. He got up from the table, picked up the two checks and went over to the bar with them.

"I'm a different man, James," he said to the barman. "You see in me quite a different man."

"Yes, sir?" said James.

"Vice," said the brown young man, "is a very strange thing, James." He looked out the door. He saw her going down the street. As he looked in the glass, he saw he was really quite a different-looking man. The other two at the bar moved down to make room for him.

"You're right there, sir," James said.

The other two moved down a little more, so that he would be quite comfortable. The young man saw himself in the mirror behind the bar. "I said I was a different man, James," he said. Looking into the mirror he saw that this was quite true.

"You look very well, sir," James said. "You must have had a very good summer."

Sense of Humour

By V. S. PRITCHETT

IT STARTED one Saturday. I was working new ground and I decided I'd stay at the hotel the week end and put in an appearance at church.

"All alone?" asked the girl at the cash desk.

It had been raining since ten o'clock.

"Mr. Good has gone," she said. "And Mr. Straker. He usually stays with us. But he's gone."

"That's where they make their mistake," I said. "They think they know everything because they've been on the road all their lives."

"You're a stranger here, aren't you?" she said.

"I am," I said. "And so are you."

"How do you know that?"

"Obvious," I said. "Way you speak."

"Let's have a light," she said.

"So's I can see you," I said.

That was how it started. The rain was pouring down on the glass roof of the office.

She'd a cup of tea steaming on the register. I said I'd have one, too. What's it going to be and I'll tell them, she said, but I said just a cup of tea.

"I'm T.T.," I said. "Too many soakers on the road as it is."

I was staying there the week end so as to be sharp on the job on Monday morning. What's more it pays in these small towns to turn up at church on Sundays, Presbyterians in the morning, Methodists in the evening. Say "Good morning" and "Good evening" to them. "Ah!" they say. "Churchgoer! Pleased to see that! T.T., too." Makes them have a second look at your lines in the morning. "Did you like our service, Mr.—er—er?" "Humphrey's my name." "Mr. Humphrey." See? It pays.

"Come into the office, Mr. Humphrey," she said, bringing me a cup. "Listen to that rain."

I went inside.

"Sugar?" she said.

"Three," I said. We settled to a very pleasant chat. She told me all about herself, and we got on next to families.

"My father was on the railway," she said.

"'The engine gave a squeal,'" I said. "'The driver took out his pocket-knife and scraped him off the wheel.'"

"That's it," she said. "And what is your father's business? You said he had a business."

"Undertaker," I said.

"Undertaker?" she said.

"Why not?" I said. "Good business. Seasonable like everything else. High-class undertaker," I said.

She was looking at me all the time wondering what to say, and suddenly she went into fits of laughter.

"Undertaker," she said, covering her face with her hands and went on laughing.

"Here," I said, "what's up?"

"Undertaker!" She laughed and laughed. Struck me as being a pretty thin joke.

"Don't mind me," she said. "I'm Irish."

"Oh, I see," I said. "That's it, is it? Got a sense of humour."

Then the bell rang and a woman called out "Muriel! Muriel!" and there was a motor bike making a row at the front door.

"All right," the girl called out. "Excuse me a moment, Mr. Humphrey," she said. "Don't think me rude. That's my boy friend. He wants the bird turning up like this."

She went out, but there was her boy friend looking over the window ledge into the office. He had come in. He had a cape on, soaked with rain, and the rain was in beads in his hair. It was fair hair. It stood up on end. He'd been economizing on the brilliantine. He didn't wear a hat. He gave me a look and I gave him a look. I didn't like the look of him. And he didn't like the look of me. A smell of oil and petrol and rain and mackintosh came off him. He had a big mouth with thick lips. They were very red. I recognized him at once as the son of the man who ran the Kounty Garage. I saw this chap when I put my car away. The firm's car. Locked up, because of the samples. Took me ten minutes to ram the idea into his head. He looked as though he'd never heard of samples. Slow— you know the way they are in the provinces. Slow on the job.

"Oh, Colin," says she. "What do you want?"

"Nothing," the chap said. "I came in to see you."

"To see me?"

"Just to see you."

"You came in this morning."

"That's right," he said. He went red. "You was busy," he said.

"Well, I'm busy now," she said.

He bit his tongue and licked his big lips over and took a look at me. Then he started grinning.

"I got the new bike, Muriel," he said. "I've got it outside. It's just come down from the works," he said.

"The laddie wants you to look at his bike," I said. So she went out and had a look at it.

When she came back she had got rid of him.

"Listen to that rain," she said. "Lord, I'm fed up with this line," she said.

"What line?" I said. "The hotel line?"

"Yes," she said. "I'm fed right up to the back teeth with it."

"And you've got good teeth," I said.

"There's not the class of person there used to be in it," she said. "All our family have got good teeth."

"Not the class?"

"I've been in it five years and there's not the same class at all. You never meet any fellows."

"Well," said I, "if they're like that half-wit at the garage, they're nothing to be stuck on. And you've met me."

I said it to her like that.

"Oh," says she. "It isn't as bad as that yet."

It was cold in the office. She used to sit all day in her overcoat. She was a smart girl with a big friendly chin and a second one coming, and her forehead and nose were covered with freckles. She had copper-coloured hair too. She got her shoes through the trade from Duke's traveller and her clothes, too, off the Hollenborough mantle man. I told her I could do her better stockings than the ones she'd got on. She got a good reduction on everything. Twenty-five or thirty-three and a third. She had her expenses cut right back. I took her to the pictures that night in the car. I made Colin get the car out for me.

"That boy wanted me to go on the back of his bike. On a night like this," she said.

"Oh," she said, when we got to the pictures. "Two shilling's too much. Let's go into the one-and-sixes at the side and we can nip across into the two-shillings when the lights go down."

"Fancy your father being an undertaker," she said in the middle of the show. And she started laughing as she had laughed before.

She had her head screwed on all right. She said:

"Some girls have no pride once the lights go down."

Every time I went to that town I took a box of something. Samples, mostly, they didn't cost me anything.

"Don't thank me," I said. "Thank the firm."

Every time I took her out I pulled the blinds in the back seat of the car to hide the samples. That chap Colin used to give us oil and petrol.

He used to give me a funny look. Fishy sort of small eyes he'd got. Always looking miserable. Then we would go off. Sunday was her free day. Not that driving's any holiday for me. And, of course, the firm paid. She used to take me down to see her family for the day. Start in the morning, and taking it you had dinner and tea there, a day's outing cost us nothing. Her father was something on the railway, retired. He had a long stocking, somewhere, but her sister, the one that was married, had had her share already.

He had a tumour after his wife died and they just played upon the old man's feelings. It wasn't right. She wouldn't go near her sister and I don't blame her, taking the money like that. Just played upon the old man's feelings.

Every time I was up there Colin used to come in looking for her.

"Oh, Colin," I used to say. "Done my car yet?" He knew where he got off with me.

"No, now, I can't, Colin. I tell you I'm going out with Mr. Humphrey," she used to say to him. I heard her.

"He keeps on badgering me," she said to me.

"You leave him to me," I said.

"No, he's all right," she said.

"You let me know if there's any trouble with Colin," I said. "Seems to be a harum-scarum sort of half-wit to me," I said.

"And he spends every penny he makes," she said.

Well, we know that sort of thing is all right while it lasts, I told her, but the trouble is that it doesn't last.

We were always meeting Colin on the road. I took no notice of it first of all and then I grew suspicious and awkward at always meeting him. He had a new motor bicycle. It was an Indian, a scarlet thing that he used to fly over the moor with, flat out. Muriel and I used to go out over the moor to Ingley Wood in the firm's Morris—I had a customer out that way.

"May as well do a bit of business while you're about it," I said.

"About what?" she said.

"Ah ha!" I said. "That's what Colin wants to know," I said.

Sure enough, coming back we'd hear him popping and backfiring close behind us, and I put out my hand to stop him and keep him following us, biting our dirt.

"I see his little game," I said. "Following us."

So I saw to it that he did follow. We could hear him banging away behind us, and the traffic is thick on the Ingley road in the afternoon.

"Oh, let him pass," Muriel said. "I can't stand those dirty things banging in my ears."

I waved him on and past he flew with his scarf flying out, blazing red into the traffic. "We're doing fifty-eight ourselves," she said, leaning across to look.

"Powerful buses those," I said. "Any fool can do it if he's got the power. Watch me step on it."

But we did not catch Colin. Half an hour later he passed us coming back. Cut right in between us and a lorry—I had to brake hard. I damn nearly killed him. His ears were red with the wind. He didn't wear a hat. I got after him as soon as I could, but I couldn't touch him.

Nearly every week end I was in that town seeing my girl, that fellow was hanging around. He came into the bar on Saturday nights, he poked his head into the office on Sunday mornings. It was a sure bet that if we went out in the car he would pass us on the road. Every time we would hear that scarlet thing roar by like a horse-stinger. It didn't matter where we were. He passed us on the main road, he met us down the side roads. There was a little cliff under oak trees at May Ponds, she said, where the view was pretty. And there, soon after we got there, was Colin on the other side of the water, watching us. Once we found him sitting on his bike, just as though he were waiting for us.

"You been here in a car?" I said.

"No, motor bike," she said, and blushed. "Cars can't follow in these tracks."

She knew a lot of places in that country. Some of the roads weren't roads at all and were bad for tires and I didn't want the firm's car scratched by bushes, but you would have thought Colin could read what was in her mind. For nine times out of ten he was there. It got on my nerves. It was a red, roaring, powerful thing and he opened it full out.

"I'm going to speak to Colin," I said. "I won't have him annoying you."

"He's not annoying me," she said. "I've got a sense of humour."

"Here, Colin," I said one evening when I put the car away. "What's the idea?"

He was taking off his overalls. He pretended he did not know what I was talking about. He had a way of rolling his eyeballs, as if they had got wet and loose in his head, while he was speaking to me, and you never knew if it was sweat or oil on his face. It was always pale, with high colour on his cheeks and very red lips.

"Miss MacFarlane doesn't like being followed," I said.

He dropped his jaw and gaped at me. I could not tell whether he was being very surprised or very sly. I used to call him "Marbles" because when he spoke he seemed to have a lot of marbles in his mouth.

Then he said he never went to the places we went to, except by accident. He wasn't following us, he said, but we were following him. We never let him alone, he said. Everywhere he went, he said, we were there. Take last Saturday, he said, we were following him for miles down the bypass, he said. "But you passed us first and then sat down in front," I said. "I went to Ingley Wood," he said. "And you followed me there." No, we didn't, I said, Miss MacFarlane decided to go there.

He said he did not want to complain, but fair was fair. "I suppose you know," he said, "that you have taken my girl off me. Well, you can leave *me* alone, can't you?"

"Here," I said. "One minute! Not so fast! You said I've taken Miss MacFarlane from you. Well, she was never your girl. She only knew you in a friendly way."

"She was my girl," was all he said.

He was pouring oil into my engine. He had some cotton wool in one hand and the can in the other. He wiped up the green oil that had over-flowed, screwed on the cap, pulled down the bonnet, and whistled to himself.

I went back to Muriel and told her what Colin had said.

"I don't like trouble," I said.

"Don't you worry," she said. "I had to have someone to go to all these places with before you came. Couldn't stick in here all day Sunday."

"Ah," I said. "That's it, is it? You've been to all these places with him?"

"Yes," she said. "And he keeps on going to them. He's sloppy about me."

"Good God," I said. "Sentimental memories."

I felt sorry for that fellow. He knew it was hopeless, but he loved her. I suppose he couldn't help himself. Well, it takes all sorts to make a world, as my old mother used to say. If we were all alike it wouldn't do. Some men can't save money. It just runs through their fingers. He couldn't save money, so he lost her. I suppose all he thought of was love.

I could have been friends with that fellow. As it was, I put a lot of business his way. I didn't want him to get the wrong idea about me. We're all human after all.

We didn't have any more trouble with Colin after this until bank holi-day. I was going to take her down to see my family. The old man's get-ting a bit past it now and has given up living over the shop. He's living out on the Barnum Road, beyond the tram stop. We were going down in the firm's car, as per usual, but something went wrong with the mag and Colin had not got it right for the holiday. I was wild about this. What's the use of a garage who can't do a rush job for the holidays! What's the use of being an old customer if they're going to let you down! I went for Colin bald-headed.

"You knew I wanted it," I said. "It's no use trying to put me off with a tale about the stuff not coming down from the works. I've heard that one before."

I told him he'd got to let me have another car, because he'd let me down. I told him I wouldn't pay his account. I said I'd take my business away from him. But there wasn't a car to be had in the town because of the holiday. I could have knocked the fellow down. After the way I'd sent business to him.

Then I saw through his little game. He knew Muriel and I were going to my people and he had done this to stop it. The moment I saw this I let him know that it would take more than him to stop me doing what I wanted.

I said: "Right. I shall take the amount of Miss MacFarlane's train fare and my own from the account at the end of the month."

I said: "You may run a garage, but you don't run the railway service."

I was damned angry going by train. I felt quite lost on the railway after having a car. It was crowded with trippers too. It was slow—stopping at all the stations. The people come in, they tread all over your feet, they make you squeeze up till you're crammed against the window, and the women stick out their elbows and fidget. And then the expense! a return for two runs you into just over a couple of quid. I could have murdered Colin.

We got there at last. We walked up from the tram stop. Mother was at the window and let us in.

"This is Miss MacFarlane," I said.

And mother said: "Oh, pleased to meet you. We've heard a lot about you.

"Oh," Mother said to me, giving me a kiss, "are you tired? You haven't had your tea, have you? Sit down. Have this chair, dear. It's more comfortable."

"Well, my boy," my father said.

"Want a wash," my father said. "We've got a washbasin downstairs," he said. "I used not to mind about washing upstairs before. Now I couldn't do without it. Funny how your ideas change as you get older."

"How's business?" he said.

"Mustn't grumble," I said. "How's yours?"

"You knew," he said, "we took off the horses: except for one or two of the older families we have got motors now."

But he'd told me that the last time I was there. I'd been at him for years about motor hearses.

"You've forgotten I used to drive them," I said.

"Bless me, so you did," he said.

He took me up to my room. He showed me everything he had done to the house. "Your mother likes it," he said. "The traffic's company for her. You know what your mother is for company."

Then he gives me a funny look.

"Who's the girl?" he says.

My mother came in then and said: "She's pretty, Arthur."

"Of course she's pretty," I said. "She's Irish."

"Oh," said the old man. "Irish! Got a sense of humour, eh?"

"She wouldn't be marrying me if she hadn't," I said. And then I gave *them* a look.

"Marrying her, did you say?" exclaimed my father.

"Any objection?" I said.

"Now, Ernest dear," said my mother. "Leave the boy alone. Come down while I pop the kettle on."

She was terribly excited.

"Miss MacFarlane," the old man said.

"No sugar, thank you, Mrs. Humphrey. I beg your pardon, Mr. Humphrey?"

"The Glen Hotel at Swansea, I don't suppose you know that?" my father said. "I wondered if you did, being in the catering line."

"It doesn't follow she knows every hotel," my mother said.

"Forty years ago," the old man said. "I was staying at the Glen in Swansea and the head waiter—"

"Oh no, not that one. I'm sure Miss MacFarlane doesn't want to hear that one," my mother said.

"How's business with you, Mr. Humphrey?" said Muriel. "We passed a large cemetery near the station."

"Dad's Ledger," I said.

"The whole business has changed so that you wouldn't know it, in my lifetime," said my father. "Silver fittings have gone clean out. Everyone wants simplicity nowadays. Restraint. Dignity," my father said.

"Prices did it," my father said.

"The war," he said.

"You couldn't get the wood," he said.

"Take ordinary mahogany, just an ordinary piece of mahogany. Or teak," he said. "Take teak. Or walnut."

"You can certainly see the world go by in this room," I said to my mother.

"It never stops," she said.

Now it was all bicycles over the new concrete road from the gun factory. Then traction engines and cars. They came up over the hill where the A.A. man stands and choked up round the tram stop. It was mostly holiday traffic. Everything with a wheel on it was out.

"On this stretch," my father told me, "they get three accidents a week." There was an ambulance station at the crossroads.

We had hardly finished talking about this—in fact, the old man was still saying that something ought to be done—when the telephone rang.

"Name of MacFarlane?" the voice said on the wire.

"No. Humphrey," my father said. "There is a Miss MacFarlane here."

"There's a man named Colin Mitchell lying seriously injured in an accident at the Cottage Hospital, gave me the name of MacFarlane as his nearest relative."

That was the Police. On to it at once. That fellow Colin had followed us down by road.

Cry, I never heard a girl cry as Muriel cried when we came back from the hospital. He had died in the ambulance. Cutting in, the old game he used to play on me. Clean off the saddle and under the Birmingham bus. The blood was everywhere, they said. People were still looking at it when we went by. Head on. What a mess! Don't let's talk about it.

She wanted to see him, but they said "No." There wasn't anything recognizable to see. She put her arms round my neck and cried: "Colin, Colin," as if I were Colin, and clung to me. I was feeling sick myself. I held her tight and I kissed her and I thought: "Holiday ruined.

"Damn fool man," I thought. "Poor devil," I thought.

"I knew he'd do something like this."

"There, there," I said to her. "Don't think about Colin."

Didn't she love me, I said, and not Colin? Hadn't she got me? She said, yes, she had. And she loved me. But, "Oh, Colin! Oh, Colin!" she cried. "And Colin's mother," she cried. "Oh, it's terrible." She cried and cried.

We put her to bed and I sat with her, and my mother kept coming in. "Leave her to me," I said. "I understand her."

Before they went to bed they both came in and looked at her. She lay sobbing with her head in the pillow.

I could quite understand her being upset. Colin was a decent fellow. He was always doing things for her. He mended her electric lamp and he riveted the stem of a wineglass so that you couldn't see the break. He used to make things for her. He was very good with his hands.

She lay on her side with her face burning and feverish with misery and crying, scalded by the salt, and her lips shriveled up. I put my arm under her neck and I stroked her forehead. She groaned. Sometimes she shivered and sometimes she clung to me, crying: "Oh, Colin! Colin!"

My arm ached with the cramp and I had a crick in my back, sitting in the awkward way I was on the bed. It was late. There was nothing to do but to ache and sit watching her and thinking. It is funny the way your mind drifts. When I was kissing her and watching her I was thinking out who I'd show our new autumn range to first. Her hand held my wrist tight, and when I kissed her I got her tears on my lips. They burned and stung. Her neck and shoulders were soft and I could feel her breath hot out of her nostrils on the back of my hand. Ever noticed how hot a woman's breath gets when she's crying? I drew out my hand and lay down beside her and "Oh, Colin, Colin," she sobbed, turning over and clinging to me. And so I lay there, listening to the traffic, staring at the ceiling, and shivering whenever the picture of Colin shooting right off that damned red thing into the bus came into my mind—until I did not hear the traffic any more, or see the ceiling any more, or think any more, but a change happened—I don't know when. This Colin thing seemed to have knocked the bottom out of everything and I had a funny feeling we were going down and down and down in a lift. And the further we went, the hotter and softer she got. Perhaps it was when I found with my hands that she had very big breasts. But it was like being on the mail steamer and feeling engines start under your feet, thumping louder and louder. You can feel it in every vein of your body. Her mouth opened and her tears dried. Her breath came through her open mouth and her voice was blind and husky. Colin, Colin, Colin, she said, and her fingers were hooked into me. I got out and turned the key in the door.

In the morning I left her sleeping. It did not matter to me what my father might have heard in the night, but still I wondered. She would hardly let me touch her before that. I told her I was sorry, but she shut me up. I was afraid of her. I was afraid of mentioning Colin. I wanted to go out of the house there and then and tell someone everything. Did she love Colin all the time? Did she think I was Colin? And every time I thought of that poor devil covered over with a white sheet in the hospital mortuary, a kind of picture of her and me under the sheets with love came into my mind. I couldn't separate the two things. Just as though it had all come from Colin.

I'd rather not talk any more about that. I never talked to Muriel about it. I waited for her to say something, but she didn't. She didn't say a word.

The next day was a bad day. It was grey and hot and the air smelled of oil fumes from the road. There's always a mess to clear up when things like this happen. I had to see to it. I had the job of ringing up the boy's mother. But I got round that, thank God, by ringing up the garage and getting them to go round and see the old lady. My father is useless when things are like this. I was the whole morning on the phone: to the hospital, the police, the coroner—and he stood fussing beside me, jerking up and down like a fat india-rubber ball.

I found my mother washing up at the sink and she said: "That poor boy's mother! I can't stop thinking of her."

Then my father comes in and says—just as though I was a customer: "Of course if Mrs. Mitchell desires it we can have the remains of the deceased conveyed to his house by one of our new specially sprung motor hearses and can, if necessary, make all the funeral arrangements."

I could have hit him because Muriel came into the room when he was saying this. But she stood there as if nothing had happened.

"It's the least we can do for poor Mrs. Mitchell," she said. There were small creases of shadow under her eyes, which shone with a soft strong light I had never seen before. She walked as if she were really still in that room with me, asleep. God, I loved that girl! God, I wanted to get all this over, this damned Colin business that had come right into the middle of everything like this, and I wanted to get married right away. I wanted to be alone with her. That's what Colin did for me.

"Yes," I said. "We must do the right thing by Colin."

"We are sometimes asked for long-distance estimates," my father said.

"It will be a little something," my mother said.

"Dad and I will talk it over," I said.

"Come into the office," my father said. "It occurred to me that it would be nice to do the right thing by this friend of yours."

We talked it over. We went into the cost of it. There was the return journey to reckon. We worked it out that it would come no dearer to old Mrs. Mitchell than if she took the train and buried the boy here. That is to say, my father said, if I drove it.

"It would look nice," my father said. "Saves money and it would look a bit friendly," my father said. "You've done it before."

"Well," I said. "I suppose I can get a refund on my return ticket from the railway."

But it was not as simple as it looked, because Muriel wanted to come. She wanted to drive back with me and the hearse. My mother was very worried about this. It might upset Muriel, she thought. Father thought it might not look nice to see a young girl sitting by the coffin of a grown man.

"It must be dignified," my father said. "You see, if she was there, it might look as though she were just doing it for the ride—like these young women on bakers' vans."

My father took me out into the hall to tell me this because he did not want her to hear. But she would not have it. She wanted to come back with Colin.

"Colin loved me. It is my duty to him," she said. "Besides," she said, suddenly, in her full open voice—it had seemed to be closed and carved and broken and small—"I've never been in a hearse before."

"And it will save her fare too," I said to my father.

That night I went again to her room. She was awake. I said I was sorry to disturb her, but I would go at once only I wanted to see if she was all right. She said, in the closed voice again, that she was all right.

"Are you sure?" I said.

She did not answer. I was worried. I went over to the bed.

"What is the matter? Tell me what is the matter," I said.

For a long time she was silent. I held her hand, I stroked her head. She was lying stiff in the bed. She would not answer. I dropped my hand to her small white shoulder. She stirred and drew up her legs and half turned and said, "I was thinking of Colin. Where is he?" she asked.

"They've brought him round. He's lying downstairs."

"In the front room?"

"Yes, ready for the morning. Now be a sensible girl and go back by train."

"No, no," she said. "I want to go with Colin. Poor Colin. He loved me and I didn't love him." And she drew my hands down to her breasts.

"Colin loved me," she whispered.

"Not like this," I whispered.

It was a warm grey morning like all the others when we took Colin
back. They had fixed the coffin in before Muriel came out. She came
down wearing the bright blue hat she had got off Dormer's millinery
man and she kissed my mother and father good-bye. They were very sorry
for her. "Look after her, Arthur," my mother said. Muriel got in beside
me without a glance behind her at the coffin. I started the engine. They
smiled at us. My father raised his hat, but whether it was to Muriel and
me or to Colin, or to the three of us, I do not know. He was not, you
see, wearing his top hat. I'll say this for the old boy, thirty years in the
trade have taught him tact.

After leaving my father's house you have to go down to the tram ter-
minus before you get on the bypass. There was always one or two drivers,
conductors, or inspectors there, doing up their tickets, or changing over
the trolley arms. When we passed I saw two of them drop their jaws,
stick their pencils in their ears, and raise their hats. I was so surprised by
this that I nearly raised mine in acknowledgment, forgetting that we had
the coffin behind. I had not driven one of my father's hearses for years.

Hearses are funny things to drive. They are well-sprung, smooth-run-
ning cars, with quiet engines, and, if you are used to driving a smaller
car, before you know where you are, you are speeding. You know you
ought to go slow, say twenty-five to thirty maximum, and it's hard to
keep it down. You can return empty at seventy if you like. It's like driving
a fire engine. Go fast out and come back slow—only the other way round.
Open out in the country, but slow down past houses. That's what it means.
My father was very particular about this.

Muriel and I didn't speak very much at first. We sat listening to the
engine and the occasional jerk of the coffin behind when we went over
a pot hole. We passed the place where poor Colin—but I didn't say anything to Muriel, and she, if she noticed—which I doubt—did not say
anything to me. We went through Cox Hill, Wammering, and Yodley
Mount, flat country, don't care for it myself. "There's a wonderful lot of
building going on," Muriel said at last.

"You won't know these places in five years," I said.

But my mind kept drifting away from the road and the green fields
and the dullness, and back to Colin—five days before, he had come down
this way. I expected to see that Indian coming flying straight out of every
corner. But it was all bent and bust up properly now. I saw the damned
thing.

He had been up to his old game, following us, and that had put the
end to following. But not quite; he was following us now, behind us in
the coffin. Then my mind drifted off that and I thought of those nights
at my parents' house, and Muriel. You never know what a woman is
going to be like. I thought, too, that it had put my calculations out. I

mean, supposing she had a baby. You see I had reckoned on waiting eighteen months or so. I would have eight hundred then. But if we had to get married at once, we should have to cut right down. Then I kept thinking it was funny her saying "Colin!" like that in the night; it was funny it made her feel that way with me, and how it made me feel when she called me Colin. I'd never thought of her in that way, in what you might call the "Colin" way.

I looked at her and she looked at me and she smiled but still we did not say very much, but the smiles kept coming to both of us. The light railway bridge at Dootheby took me by surprise and I thought the coffin gave a jump as we took it.

"Colin's still watching us," I nearly said.

There were tears in her eyes.

"What was the matter with Colin?" I said. "Nice chap, I thought. Why didn't you marry him?"

"Yes," she said. "He was a nice boy. But he'd no sense of humour."

"And I wanted to get out of that town," she said.

"I'm not going to stay there, at that hotel," she said.

"I want to get away," she said. "I've had enough."

She had a way of getting angry with the air, like that. "You've got to take me away," she said. We were passing slowly into Muster, there was a tram ahead and people thick on the narrow pavements, dodging out into the road. But when we got into the Market Square, where they were standing around, they saw the coffin. They began to raise their hats. Suddenly she laughed. "It's like being the King and Queen," she said.

"They're raising their hats," she said.

"Not all of them," I said.

She squeezed my hand and I had to keep her from jumping about like a child on the seat as we went through.

"There they go."

"Boys always do," I said.

"And another.

"Let's see what the policeman does."

She started to laugh, but I shut her up. "Keep your sense of humour to yourself," I said.

Through all those towns that run into one another as you might say, we caught it. We went through, as she said, like royalty. So many years since I drove a hearse, I'd forgotten what it was like.

I was proud of her, I was proud of Colin, and I was proud of myself. And after what had happened, I mean on the last two nights, it was like a wedding. And although we knew it was for Colin, it was for us too, because Colin was with both of us. It was like this all the way.

"Look at that man there. Why doesn't he raise his hat? People ought to show respect for the dead," she said.

Barrow Street

By RICHARD SHERMAN

IT WAS a warm evening in late spring, and the apartment windows were open to the many sounds of the city's roar; but the girl, standing in the center of the living room and nervously twisting a plain gold band around her third finger, heard only two sounds. One was the convulsive throb of the automatic elevator in the corridor outside, and the other was the single chime struck by the mantel clock as its hands marked seven-thirty. For an instant the girl remained motionless, her eyes directed toward the clock's dial. It was a very pretty clock, all gold and ivory. It was, in fact, a very pretty room, spacious and high-ceilinged. The colors were "decorators' colors," the furniture was graceful in design and had the patina of age on it, and wherever one looked there was a combination of comfort and taste. The books lining one wall had the appearance of having been read, and the fireplace, though at present unlighted, was obviously functional. It was a room made warm by much living and much love.

There was a large, silver-framed photograph on the piano between the two windows, and now the girl went slowly toward it and stood gazing meditatively at the handsome and grave face of a dark-mustached young man wearing the uniform of a Navy lieutenant. Her hand went out and touched the photograph, then lifted it. For a moment she glanced around the room, as if seeking a place of concealment. But the somber, appealing eyes below the visored cap seemed to summon her back, and as she looked at them again, she hesitated, and in the end returned the photograph to its original position. Absently and almost as if unconsciously, her hand drifted down to the piano keys and formed a chord, softly. She waited until the last ripple of the chord, washing through the room, had died away, and after that, sighing, she turned toward the hall. But the sigh was not one of sadness. It spoke, rather, of a certain definitiveness, of a chapter closed and a story done. Or another story beginning.

In the hall she moved briskly and with assurance. To her left was a small dining room, and she went through it and the swinging door beyond, to the kitchen. She groped for the switch, flicked it, and was confronted by gleaming white walls and stainless steel. In order. Yes, per-

fectly in order, even to the starched frills of the gay red gingham at the
window and to the graduated knives poised bright and pendulous in their
wall holder. A dream kitchen, surely, with not even the telltale aroma of
tonight's dinner to spoil the dream. But the plate of cookies that stood invitingly on the white-enameled table was no dream. The girl picked one
up and munched it. As she ate, she noticed a sheet of paper sticking from
the refrigerator door, and bending closer, she read the laboriously pen-
ciled scrawl: "Mrs. Ryder. Pls deefrost tonite. Olive." She opened the refrigerator and stood gazing speculatively at its crowded shelves. She
pulled out an ice tray, shoved it back. Then, after the customary moment
of examination and self-doubt, she turned the knob to "Defrost" and
closed the door.

"Okay, Olive," she said aloud. "You're defrosted."

From the kitchen she went into the hall and from there to the nursery.
She had left the door partially open, and now she entered the room softly.
A small, rose-shaded night light burned in one corner, atop the ivory chest
of drawers, and the crib stood in the opposite corner, against the wall.
Moving toward the crib, the girl paused by it, looking downward and
smiling. A dark fuzz of hair lay against the white satin pillows, and below
it was a profiled roundness of cream and pink, bounded by blue blankets.
He slept. Mr. Timothy Ryder, Jr., slept.

"Hello, Tim," whispered the girl, leaning over the rail of the crib.
"Hello, Timmy. My baby, my baby, my baby."

The door leading to the adjoining room was open also, and from beyond it now sounded the muffled burr of a telephone ringing. With a
final glance at the crib, the girl went toward the sound. The telephone
stood on a night table beside the oversize bed, and the girl's hand rested
on it for an instant before she picked it up. Then she lifted the instrument. "Hello?" she said.

"Mrs. Ryder, please," said a voice, a once-familiar voice.

"George?" said the girl, and her tone was suddenly light and filled with
a thousand secret excitements and enchantments. "Is that you, George?
Are you really in town? Are you really here?"

"Oh," he said, with a trace of embarrassment, "I guess I didn't recognize you, did I? Yes, I'm here. I'm at the hotel. Just got in."

"Well, come right on down. I've been waiting and waiting."

There was a small silence at the other end of the line. "Look, Dorothy,"
said the voice, "when I wired you I was coming, I had no idea you were
married. I mean, I wouldn't have bothered you if I'd known that."

"Wouldn't have bothered me?" The girl's tone was a mingling of
tender reproof and indignation. "Why, George Hargrave, I'd never have
forgiven you if you'd passed through town without looking me up. Never
in the world. Now, you stop being silly and get in a taxi and come right
down here this very minute. Quick like a rabbit."

"But are you sure it'll be—all right?"

"All right? What on earth do you mean?"

"I mean, how about—your husband?"

"Tim? Oh, George, don't be so difficult. As it happens, Tim isn't here, unfortunately—if that's what's worrying you. He had to go to Boston. But even if he were here, I'd want you to come down anyway. I want to see you. I told you when I wired you back that I wanted to see you. And you've simply got to see the baby."

"Well—"

There was spirit in the girl's voice now, spirit and light sarcasm. "Unless, of course, it would be too dull for a gay young blade like you to sit around and reminisce with an old married woman. Unless it would be too boring. After all, I certainly wouldn't want to bore you."

"Now, Dorothy, please. You know that I—"

She spoke persuasively, and as if to end the discussion. "Enough of this nonsense, George—you ought to be too grown-up for it. Now, you just get on your horse. It's seventeen West Twelfth, the third floor, and all you have to do is get into the elevator and push the button, and I'll be at the door to meet you."

"Okay," he said finally, though with no great enthusiasm. "Okay, I'll be there."

"That's better."

Replacing the phone, the girl regarded it for a moment. She had been sitting on the bed, and now, rising, she smoothed the place where she had sat. She glanced around the room. It was a large room, white, light, and airy. Only one small light was burning, and now she turned on two others, pink-shaded lamps which flanked the dressing table. The girl looked at herself in the dressing-table mirror. Then she went to a mirrored door and looked at herself full length. She was wearing a black dress that could have been called serviceable, though not much more. She frowned. Then she opened the door. A row of dresses met her eyes—a rainbow wall. She tentatively fingered a blue one, a sequined one, and finally settled on one of a chartreuse color. Lifting it from its hanger, she held it up against herself and, looking into the mirror, nodded approvingly. It was a housecoat, long and faintly formal and definitely expensive.

"You'll do," she murmured, and her words might have had reference either to the housecoat or to herself or to both together.

Within the next hour several things happened. Many things, in fact, all of them minor yet all important. The girl was transformed and so, in a sense, was the apartment, which before had had an air of loneliness and desertion about it and which now took on a nervous expectancy. Both the girl and the apartment became illumined, and gayer. Except for the nursery, which remained a shadowy pink, lights went on everywhere. Wearing the chartreuse housecoat, and with her lips freshly rouged, the girl moved busily and efficiently about the kitchen, getting a bottle of Coke from the refrigerator, dumping ice cubes into a silver vacuum bucket, running water into a silver pitcher. Then she placed bottle, bucket, pitcher, and two tall glasses on a tray and carried them to the living room, depositing the tray on a low table in front of the sofa. Her next move was to go to the entrance hall, where she opened the door of the coat closet and, reaching up to the hat shelf, took down an oblong package wrapped in brown paper and tied with string. This she took to the living room, undoing the string and removing the paper as she walked. From a corrugated-cardboard box she lifted out a full and as yet unopened bottle of whisky and, after ripping off the lead foil around its top, put it on the tray on the low table. The string she wound around her finger, the paper she folded and refolded and then pressed flat, and then she dropped both of them, along with the shreds of foil, into a wastebasket. The corrugated-cardboard box she tossed into the wastebasket also.

Her chores completed, she looked at the results—the lamplit room, the laden tray—and moved her head up and down in satisfaction, as if finding them good. Then she lifted the cover of a crystal box on the low table and from it took a cigarette and lighted it. After that she seated herself on the sofa; but almost immediately she rose, to sit in first one and then the other of the two matching modern chairs that stood beside another small table. Then she left those chairs, also, and began to pace up and down the room. Once in her pacing she paused by the radio-phonograph and, lifting its lid, studied the record on the turntable. But she made no effort to play it. Instead, she closed the lid and resumed her pacing.

The gold-and-ivory clock on the mantel struck nine.

Then, at last, she heard the elevator door opening and, an instant later, the sound of the buzzer. She waited a moment, a full moment, and then took a deep breath and went to the door.

The man standing in the corridor was young, blond, handsome, and her first gesture was to extend both hands welcomingly toward his and to cry, "George, how wonderful to see you! How perfectly, perfectly wonderful!"

His reply was somewhat more guarded. He was a highly personable young man, well groomed and well tailored, but at the moment he seemed to be distinctly ill at ease. "Hello, Dorothy," he said. "Well, it's—ah—it's good to see you, too."

She took his hat, and as she placed it on the foyer table and then led him toward the living room, she kept talking. He was looking so well. He really was looking so very, very well, wasn't he? And hadn't he taken on just a little bit of weight? Hadn't he? Just the littlest, littlest bit? Not that it wasn't becoming, because it most definitely was becoming. Anyway, it showed that he was eating well and that the Chicago climate, God forbid, must be agreeing with him.

She had seated herself on the sofa, while he, more cautious and more wary, had chosen one of the matching chairs. Her hands were busy over the tray, and now she interrupted her soliloquy on the fascinating subject of his weight and general condition of health in order to look at him fondly and say, "Why, do you know, George, it just this minute occurred to me. This is actually the first time I've ever seen you in civilian clothes."

"That's right. It is, isn't it?" said the young man. His eyes had been roaming the room. "Nice place," he said appreciatively and with respect and with possibly just a faint note of surprise. "Very nice."

She ignored the tribute, her mind apparently wandering back in gentle nostalgia. "Three years ago," she said, and sighed. "My, it seems a lifetime, doesn't it? And so much has happened since." She held a glass toward him, and he rose to accept it. "Well, here you are. Bourbon and water. See? I remember." She lifted her own glass. "Cheers, darling. And happy days and all that."

He drank. "What's that you've got there? Just a Coke?"

She nodded. "Isn't it ridiculous? Imagine—me, of all people. But I used to get so drunk, and I was such a bad drunk. All that quarreling and those scenes and those awful, awful—" She broke off, and then looked at him with great seriousness. "Tell me, George, how did you ever manage to stand me? I mean, even for as long as you did manage to stand me?"

A sudden flush appeared in the young man's cheeks. "I—ah—" But the rest of his words were lost in the glass, which he again raised to his lips.

"Of course," she said, "I know now why I drank so much. It was because I was so miserable. And now that I'm not miserable—in fact, just the opposite—I don't feel the need of a drink at all."

"Um," said the young man. He cleared his throat. "How long you been married, Dorothy?"

"Two and a half years. It was—let's see—it was just about six months after you went out to Chicago." Her tone seemed to assume a special significance. "You know, when your mother was so sick. Remember?"

"Yeah," said the young man, somewhat uncomfortably. "Yeah, I remember."

"Did your mother ever get well, George?" she asked solicitously.

"Oh, sure. Sure, she got well. She's fine."

She nodded. "I thought she would be," she said. "I was practically certain of it." Smiling, she cradled her glass between her palms, gazed down into it, and then spoke reflectively, though not bitterly. "You know, George, I probably might as well tell you that I really hated you for a while there. I wished you were dead—and I wished I was, too. Just think. There wasn't even a letter. Not one single letter. Not even a post card."

He was silent, and he shifted uneasily in his chair. "I guess it was kind of a lousy trick, wasn't it?" he said then. "But we weren't hitting it off, you know we weren't. And things were getting so—" He stopped, and seemed to grope for the proper word and not find it.

"Complicated, maybe? Messy? Involved?"

"All right. Involved."

"For you, you mean. Not for me. I knew what I wanted. Or at least I thought I did."

He became slightly self-defensive. "I admitted it was a lousy trick, didn't I? I apologized. I—"

She looked at him, and she shook her head. Her manner was friendly, even generous. "Darling, you needn't apologize. I suppose in a way it wasn't the most chivalrous conduct in the world, but for me it turned out to be—well, the most wonderful thing that ever happened, though I didn't realize it at the time. Because it was shortly after that I met Tim. And maybe if you'd still been around, I wouldn't have."

He had got up from his chair and had gone to the two tall windows. Now he stood looking out. From the street below came the cracked treble of a hurdy-gurdy playing one of its many songs of spring. "You're pretty happy, aren't you, Dorothy?" he said.

Her answer came to him like a sigh. "Oh, George, you'll never know." There was a pause, and then she added, "And somehow I have the feeling that you never will know. But—" she shrugged—"you're you, and that's that, and nothing can be done about it."

He had turned, and now he was standing in front of the silver-framed photograph. He indicated it with a gesture. "Is this Tim?"

"Yes," she said. "That's Tim."

"Nice-looking. Quite a guy."

She had risen and was starting toward the hall. "It doesn't half do him justice. He's handsomer than that—much." Turning, she beckoned to the young man. "But if you want to see something really handsome, you just follow me."

He did follow her, and she led him into the nursery, entering stealthily and with a warning finger at her lips. He stood looking down at the sleeping infant. "Fine," he said at last. "Mighty fine."

"Oh, now, George, surely you can do better than that. He's more than just fine." She was engaged in several small maternal operations—the adjustment of a blanket, the straightening of a pillow, the hand held up to detect a possible draft.

"Well, you know I—well, I never can think of anything to say about a baby." And then, inspirationally, he did think of something to say, something brilliant. "How old is he?"

"Ten months." Carelessly, yet with affectionate pressure, she placed her hand on the young man's sleeve. "George, honey, you really ought to get married. You really, really should."

"Um-hum. I suppose so. I suppose I should, at that."

From the nursery the girl led the young man on a conducted tour of the entire apartment, because, she said it was such a funny old apartment and they had been so lucky to discover it, and she wanted him to see what could be accomplished with these remodeled apartments in old brownstones if you had patience and went at the job properly. Each room called for its own special footnote; but although she displayed a natural pride of ownership, there was no evidence of boastfulness in her manner. Flaws, when there were flaws, were recognized and even emphasized as such. Of the large master bedroom she said, "See—a fireplace. I always wanted a fireplace in my bedroom, and now I've got one. Smoke and all." Of the small room which was mostly filled with a drawing board and scattered blueprints and architect's equipment, she said, "This was intended as a maid's room, but our Olive prefers to sleep out, so Tim decided to fix it up as a place where he could work at home when he wanted to." Of the kitchen she said, "Tim keeps calling it the galley. It's the Navy in him." And of the bath she said, "Isn't it huge? Tim's always saying we ought to give a party in it. But just try to keep it warm. Not all the heaters in Arabia—"

The tour took time, and during it the young man appeared gradually to lose his uneasiness and to become more relaxed. Several times he laughed at the girl's remarks, even though the remarks were not particularly witty. And as she preceded him into this room and into that, he kept his eyes on her slim, chartreuse waistline. The housecoat rustled pleasantly and sibilantly when she moved. The young man's face, which had shown signs of strain, softened and grew thoughtful. It became more than thoughtful. It became admiring. The charms of domesticity had never been revealed more sweetly.

They were back in the living room now, and he had started on his second drink. That is, it was only the second drink he had had since his arrival, but the suddenly accelerated effect it was having on him seemed to indicate that it might have been preceded by others, perhaps by a number of others.

This time he was sitting on the sofa beside the girl, and when she reached for a cigarette from the crystal box, he struck a match for her and cupped the flame as she bent her head toward it. There was a liquid brightness in his eyes, and when he spoke, his voice had a new and almost caressing warmth in it. "Your hair," he said. "I like it that new way. Looks very good."

"Thank you, George," she said. She became the conscientious hostess. "But all we've done ever since you got here is talk about me. Now let's talk about you, for a change. I want to hear all about Chicago. What are you doing out there? Did you go back into advertising again, the way you said you were going to?"

He nooded. "Yup. I'm with an advertising agency."

"Copy?"

Again he nodded. "Mostly. Now and then I do a little selling. Or try to. It hasn't been going too well."

Immediately sympathy welled from her. "Oh, I'm so sorry." She tapped the ash from her cigarette onto a tray and glanced at him with a kind, though detached, benevolence. "And have you got a girl out there, George?"

He hesitated. "Mm, well—yes. Matter of fact, I have."

"That's nice. And is she gay? Is she fun?"

He seemed to consider the question. "Yes, I guess so." Then he set his glass on the low table. His voice was earnest, serious, even moodily philosophical. "But you know, Dorothy, sooner or later the time comes when a man wants more than just fun. You know?"

Her eyes widened in surprise. "But surely not you, George."

"Why not me?"

"No reason, except—well, for instance, when you wired me that you were coming, it was because you wanted just fun, wasn't it?" She was gently reminding. "Wasn't it?" she repeated.

"Well—"

"Of course it was." Leaning back against the sofa pillows, she clasped her hands behind her head, her breasts rounded beneath the chartreuse housecoat. She quoted as if from memory, and ran all the words together without a stop. " 'Lonely and forlorn stranger arriving Thursday evening en route to Washington would appreciate companionship for light wines and dancing please wire reply to University Club love George.' " Turning, she smiled at him, dazzlingly. "Now, if that didn't mean 'just fun,' what did it mean?"

"I wanted to see you," he said stubbornly. "I wanted—old times."

"Undoubtedly." Her arms came down, and her hands folded themselves placidly in her lap. "And probably it would have been like old times, too. Could have been, anyway. We'd have gone to a bar, and then we'd have gone on to another bar, and then we'd have had dinner—or perhaps we'd even have skipped dinner—and then you'd have picked up a bottle of something, and we'd have gone down to my place on Barrow Street." For the first time there was an edge in her voice, a trace of bite. "And in the morning I'd have got up and gone to the office and you'd have gone to Washington. Exactly as you'll be going to Washington tomorrow." She paused, and added, "Only not quite exactly."

The young man had reached for his glass and was helping himself to more whisky. The portion was generous. "All right," he said. "So I was a heel."

"No, not a heel, George dear. Not a heel at all. Just on the loose. And on the town. And the victim, I think, of certain misconceptions."

He drank. "All right, maybe that was my original plan. I don't say definitely that it was, but it might have been." He looked at her. "But now that I've seen you again, you're—well, you're different. You've changed."

The girl's fingers became less placid. They interlocked. "Changed how?"

He passed a puzzled hand over his brow. "I don't know what it is, exactly. I can't explain it." He gestured at the room. "But look at this place. You never used to have any talent for making a room look like this. You never even had any desire to. Barrow Street always used to be a mess, you know it did. And the baby. I watched you when you were looking at the baby. You were—you were downright beautiful."

"Thank you, George," said the girl. "That's the first time you've ever said that. You used to say I was attractive, sometimes—but never beautiful."

He moved closer to her and leaned forward intently, curiously. "How did you develop it, Dorothy? All this—this serenity you've got. Where did it come from?"

At first she appeared not to understand him, and then she smiled. She spoke as to a child. "But it was there all the time, George. You say I've changed, but I haven't. Really I haven't. It's just that I'm happy, that's all. Basically I'm the same person I always was."

"You're not," he contradicted her. "You don't look the same. You don't act the same."

"Oh," she granted, "I probably needed someone to bring me out, yes. Someone who had faith in me and who loved me. But that was easy. Tim did that."

"The hell with Tim." He placed his hand on her wrist. "Dot. Dot, honey."

"Yes, George?"

"We made a mistake, didn't we?"

"I didn't."

"Well, then I did. And I admit it." His arm had gone round her, but for the moment he made no attempt to draw her close. "But it's not too late, is it?" Then his arm tightened. "Is it?"

For just a fraction of an instant the girl's arms seemed about to creep up to return his embrace, and then, as he bent his head down and was about to place his lips on hers, her eyes, which had been cast downward, looked up at him. There was no affection in them now, and no warmth. It was a cold, level, contemptuous gaze, and it froze him.

" 'Were' a heel, did you say, George?" she said. And after that, with one swift and agile movement, she had risen from the sofa and was standing looking down at him.

The clock on the mantel struck eleven-thirty.

"I think you'd better go," said the girl. "I think you'd better go right now."

The young man's tie was awry, his coat was mussed, and his face was flushed. "Now, look, Dot," he began. "There's no need to be—"

"I said you'd better go."

He shrugged, and after a moment got up from the sofa. "Okay," he said. "If that's the way you want it."

There was no pretense of a conventionally polite farewell or even of a civil exchange of good nights. She watched him as he walked into the hall, watched him as he picked up his hat. With his hand on the door-knob, he looked back at her. He presented the figure of a very sad, very discomfited, and rather pathetic young man.

"I could have 'brought you out,' too," he said, "just as much as your wonderful Tim did."

"Maybe you could have," she said. "But you didn't. You didn't even want to try."

He opened his mouth as if to speak, and then closed it. Then he went out. Still standing by the sofa, she heard the whine of the elevator ascending, heard the door clang open and clang shut, heard the drone of the car as it started down again. Then and only then did she move. Her first act was to exhale deeply, her shoulders and her whole body slumping. After that she bent to the table and, placing the whisky bottle aside, picked up the tray with the ice bucket and the pitcher and the glasses and the smaller bottle. Methodically she carried the tray to the kitchen and set it on the sink. She put the Coke bottle with other empty bottles in a wooden container under the stove. Then, being careful not to splash the housecoat, she washed and dried the bucket, the pitcher, the glasses. She wiped the sink with the damp dishcloth, hung the dishcloth on the rack. After that, she turned out the light in the kitchen.

She turned out all the other lights, too, all those she previously had turned on. But before turning out the dressing-table lights in the bedroom, she opened the closet door and lifted out the black dress. She took off the chartreuse housecoat and returned it to its hanger, putting it back carefully and adjusting its folds so that they hung straight. Then she got into the black dress again and, after a final look in the full-length mirror, closed the closet door.

From the bedroom she went into the nursery, and for a time she stood looking down at the sleeping child. But she did not look at him long, for from there she went into the living room, emptied the ashtrays, and rubbed her handkerchief over the table to remove the circles left by the glasses. That done, she picked up the whisky bottle and held it to the light, noting that the level of the liquid in it had gone down some three inches. But there was plenty left. Plenty. Stooping to the wastebasket, she retrieved the string, the brown paper, the cardboard box, and the foil. She wadded the foil into a ball and thrust it into one of the pockets in the black dress. She placed the bottle back in the box and skillfully rewrapped and tied it. Then she went to the closet in the hall and put it back on the shelf.

Back in the living room, her final gesture was to remove the plain gold band from her finger and drop it into her pocket. Then she selected a magazine and sat down by the fireplace. But although she opened the magazine, she did not read it. Instead, she looked into the black and empty grate.

She was still seated by the empty grate when there was the sound of a key in the lock, laughter, and voices in the entrance hall. Almost immediately two people entered the room, a man and a woman, and with them there seemed to come a fresh breeze cooling the sluggish night air. Both were young and both were handsome. The man had a dark mustache, and around her head the woman was wearing a silk chartreuse scarf.

"Well," said the man, as the mantel clock chimed once more, "that's timing it. We told you twelve-thirty, and we just made it, right on the button."

"Did everything go all right?" said the young woman pleasantly.

"Everything went fine," said the girl, who had risen from her chair and was placing the magazine on the table. "Just fine."

"No fuss?"

"Not a bit. It was just the way it should be."

"That's good," said the young woman. She turned toward the hall. "Well, I think I'll just go in and have a look at him. Tim, you'd better—ah—"

"Sure," said the young man with the dark mustache. "Sure."

The girl had stepped to the hall and was returning with the paper-wrapped package and a light jacket, which she was draping around her shoulders.

Now the man took out a wallet. "Let's see," he said. "Five hours at ninety cents an hour. That makes it—four-fifty, doesn't it?"

"That's right," she said.

He held out four bills and a coin. "There you are, exactly. And thank you."

"Thank you, Mr. Ryder," she said. The "you" was stressed, but only naturally so.

She moved toward the hall, and as she did so, she met the young woman returning from the nursery. The young woman was smiling. "He's sleeping like a lamb," she said to the girl. "Not a peep."

"He's a very good baby," said the girl. "He's a wonderful baby. I felt as if he were mine. Really mine."

"Did you find the cookies?"

"Yes, thank you. And I took a Coke from the refrigerator. I didn't think you'd mind. There was a note from the maid on the refrigerator door, asking you to defrost. So I did that, too."

"Oh, I'm glad you did," said the young woman. "I might have forgotten." She had taken the scarf from her head and was looping it into loose folds. "Well, I guess that's all, then. Would you be available again if we should need you? What do we do? Call the agency and request Miss—Prescott, is it?"

"That's right," said the girl. "Miss Dorothy Prescott." She hesitated. "But you see, I don't do this regularly. It was—an unusual occasion, a favor. The woman who runs the agency happens to be a friend of mine."

"Oh," said the young woman disappointedly. "I'm sorry. Well, in any case, it was very nice of you to help us out."

"I didn't mind," said the girl. "I loved it. Thank you. Thank you so much."

"Look," said the young man with the dark mustache. "It's late. Do you have far to go?"

"Not far," said the girl, hugging the package more closely and opening the door. "Barrow Street."

VI

✹ ✹ ✹

Children's Hour

Charlotte's Web

(CHAPTERS 1–5)

By E. B. WHITE

CHAPTER I

BEFORE BREAKFAST

"WHERE's Papa going with that ax?" said Fern to her mother as they were setting the table for breakfast.

"Out to the hoghouse," replied Mrs. Arable. "Some pigs were born last night."

"I don't see why he needs an ax," continued Fern, who was only eight.

"Well," said her mother, "one of the pigs is a runt. It's very small and weak, and it will never amount to anything. So your father has decided to do away with it."

"Do *away* with it?" shrieked Fern. "You mean *kill* it? Just because it's smaller than the others?"

Mrs. Arable put a pitcher of cream on the table.

"Don't yell, Fern!" she said. "Your father is right. The pig would probably die anyway."

Fern pushed a chair out of the way and ran outdoors. The grass was wet and the earth smelled of springtime. Fern's sneakers were sopping by the time she caught up with her father.

"Please don't kill it!" she sobbed. "It's unfair."

Mr. Arable stopped walking.

"Fern," he said gently, "you will have to learn to control yourself."

"Control myself?" yelled Fern. "This is a matter of life and death, and talk about *controlling* myself." Tears ran down her cheeks and she took hold of the ax and tried to pull it out of her father's hand.

"Fern," said Mr. Arable, "I know more about raising a litter of pigs than you do. A weakling makes trouble. Now run along!"

"But it's unfair," cried Fern. "The pig couldn't help being born small, could it? If *I* had been very small at birth, would you have killed *me?*"

Mr. Arable smiled. "Certainly not," he said, looking down at his daughter with love. "But this is different. A little girl is one thing, a little runty pig is another."

"I see no difference," replied Fern, still hanging on to the ax. "This is the most terrible case of injustice I ever heard of."

A queer look came over John Arable's face. He seemed almost ready to cry himself.

"All right," he said. "You go back to the house and I will bring the runt when I come in. I'll let you start it on a bottle, like a baby. Then you'll see what trouble a pig can be."

When Mr. Arable returned to the house half an hour later, he carried a carton under his arm. Fern was upstairs changing her sneakers. The kitchen table was set for breakfast, and the room smelled of coffee, bacon, damp plaster, and wood smoke from the stove.

"Put it on her chair!" said Mrs. Arable. Mr. Arable set the carton down at Fern's place. Then he walked to the sink and washed his hands and dried them on the roller towel.

Fern came slowly down the stairs. Her eyes were red from crying. As she approached her chair, the carton wobbled, and there was a scratching noise. Fern looked at her father. Then she lifted the lid of the carton. There, inside, looking up at her, was the newborn pig. It was a white one. The morning light shone through its ears, turning them pink.

"He's yours," said Mr. Arable. "Saved from an untimely death. And may the good Lord forgive me for this foolishness."

Fern couldn't take her eyes off the tiny pig. "Oh," she whispered. "Oh, *look* at him! He's absolutely perfect."

She closed the carton carefully. First she kissed her father, then she kissed her mother. Then she opened the lid again, lifted the pig out, and held it against her cheek. At this moment her brother Avery came into the room. Avery was ten. He was heavily armed—an air rifle in one hand, a wooden dagger in the other.

"What's that?" he demanded. "What's Fern got?"

"She's got a guest for breakfast," said Mrs. Arable. "Wash your hands and face, Avery!"

"Let's see it!" said Avery, setting his gun down. "You call that miserable thing a pig? That's a *fine* specimen of a pig—it's no bigger than a white rat."

"Wash up and eat your breakfast, Avery!" said his mother. "The school bus will be along in half an hour."

"Can I have a pig, too, Pop?" asked Avery.

"No, I only distribute pigs to early risers," said Mr. Arable. "Fern was up at daylight, trying to rid the world of injustice. As a result, she now has a pig. A small one, to be sure, but nevertheless a pig. It just shows what can happen if a person gets out of bed promptly. Let's eat!"

But Fern couldn't eat until her pig had had a drink of milk. Mrs. Arable found a baby's nursing bottle and a rubber nipple. She poured warm milk into the bottle, fitted the nipple over the top, and handed it to Fern. "Give him his breakfast!" she said.

A minute later, Fern was seated on the floor in the corner of the kitchen with her infant between her knees, teaching it to suck from the bottle. The pig, although tiny, had a good appetite and caught on quickly.

The school bus honked from the road.

"Run!" commanded Mrs. Arable, taking the pig from Fern and slipping a doughnut into her hand. Avery grabbed his gun and another doughnut.

The children ran out to the road and climbed into the bus. Fern took no notice of the others in the bus. She just sat and stared out of the window, thinking what a blissful world it was and how lucky she was to have entire charge of a pig. By the time the bus reached school, Fern had named her pet, selecting the most beautiful name she could think of.

"Its name is Wilbur," she whispered to herself.

She was still thinking about the pig when the teacher said: "Fern, what is the capital of Pennsylvania?"

"Wilbur," replied Fern, dreamily. The pupils giggled. Fern blushed.

CHAPTER II

WILBUR

Fern loved Wilbur more than anything. She loved to stroke him, to feed him, to put him to bed. Every morning, as soon as she got up, she warmed his milk, tied his bib on, and held the bottle for him. Every afternoon, when the school bus stopped in front of her house, she jumped out and ran to the kitchen to fix another bottle for him. She fed him again at suppertime, and again just before going to bed. Mrs. Arable gave him a feeding around noontime each day, when Fern was away in school. Wilbur loved his milk, and he was never happier than when Fern was warming up a bottle for him. He would stand and gaze up at her with adoring eyes.

For the first few days of his life, Wilbur was allowed to live in a box near the stove in the kitchen. Then, when Mrs. Arable complained, he was moved to a bigger box in the woodshed. At two weeks of age, he was moved outdoors. It was apple-blossom time, and the days were getting warmer. Mr. Arable fixed a small yard specially for Wilbur under an apple tree, and gave him a large wooden box full of straw, with a doorway cut in it so he could walk in and out as he pleased.

"Won't he be cold at night?" asked Fern.

"No," said her father. "You watch and see what he does."

Carrying a bottle of milk, Fern sat down under the apple tree inside the yard. Wilbur ran to her and she held the bottle for him while he sucked. When he had finished the last drop, he grunted and walked sleepily into the box. Fern peered through the door. Wilbur was poking the straw with his snout. In a short time he had dug a tunnel in the straw. He crawled into the tunnel and disappeared from sight, completely covered with straw. Fern was enchanted. It relieved her mind to know that her baby would sleep covered up, and would stay warm.

Every morning after breakfast, Wilbur walked out to the road with Fern and waited with her till the bus came. She would wave good-by to him, and he would stand and watch the bus until it vanished around a turn. While Fern was in school, Wilbur was shut up inside his yard. But as soon as she got home in the afternoon, she would take him out and he would follow her around the place. If she went into the house, Wilbur went, too. If she went upstairs, Wilbur would wait at the bottom step until she came down again. If she took her doll for a walk in the doll carriage, Wilbur followed along. Sometimes, on these journeys, Wilbur would get tired, and Fern would pick him up and put him in the carriage alongside the doll. He liked this. And if he was *very* tired, he would close his eyes and go to sleep under the doll's blanket. He looked cute when his eyes were closed, because his lashes were so long. The doll would close her eyes, too, and Fern would wheel the carriage very slowly and smoothly so as not to wake her infants.

One warm afternoon, Fern and Avery put on bathing suits and went down to the brook for a swim. Wilbur tagged along at Fern's heels. When she waded into the brook, Wilbur waded in with her. He found the water quite cold—too cold for his liking. So while the children swam and played and splashed water at each other, Wilbur amused himself in the mud along the edge of the brook, where it was warm and moist and delightfully sticky and oozy.

Every day was a happy day, and every night was peaceful.

Wilbur was what farmers call a spring pig, which simply means that he was born in springtime. When he was five weeks old, Mr. Arable said he was now big enough to sell, and would have to be sold. Fern broke down and wept. But her father was firm about it. Wilbur's appetite had increased; he was beginning to eat scraps of food in addition to milk. Mr. Arable was not willing to provide for him any longer. He had already sold Wilbur's ten brothers and sisters.

"He's got to go, Fern," he said. "You have had your fun raising a baby pig, but Wilbur is not a baby any longer and he has got to be sold."

"Call up the Zuckermans," suggested Mrs. Arable to Fern. "Your Uncle Homer sometimes raises a pig. And if Wilbur goes there to live, you can walk down the road and visit him as often as you like."

"How much money should I ask for him?" Fern wanted to know.

"Well," said her father, "he's a runt. Tell your Uncle Homer you've got a pig you'll sell for six dollars, and see what he says."

It was soon arranged. Fern phoned and got her Aunt Edith, and her

Aunt Edith hollered for Uncle Homer, and Uncle Homer came in from the barn and talked to Fern. When he heard that the price was only six dollars, he said he would buy the pig. Next day Wilbur was taken from his home under the apple tree and went to live in a manure pile in the cellar of Zuckerman's barn.

Chapter III

Escape

The barn was very large. It was very old. It smelled of hay and it smelled of manure. It smelled of the perspiration of tired horses and the wonderful sweet breath of patient cows. It often had a sort of peaceful smell—as though nothing bad could happen ever again in the world. It smelled of grain and of harness dressing and of axle grease and of rubber boots and of new rope. And whenever the cat was given a fish head to eat, the barn would smell of fish. But mostly it smelled of hay, for there was always hay in the great loft up overhead. And there was always hay being pitched down to the cows and the horses and the sheep.

The barn was pleasantly warm in winter when the animals spent most of their time indoors, and it was pleasantly cool in summer when the big doors stood wide open to the breeze. The barn had stalls on the main floor for the work horses, tie-ups on the main floor for the cows, a sheepfold down below for the sheep, a pigpen down below for Wilbur, and it was full of all sorts of things that you find in barns: ladders, grindstones, pitchforks, monkey wrenches, scythes, lawn mowers, snow shovels, ax handles, milk pails, water buckets, empty grain sacks, and rusty rat traps. It was the kind of barn that swallows like to build their nests in. It was the kind of barn that children like to play in. And the whole thing was owned by Fern's uncle, Mr. Homer L. Zuckerman.

Wilbur's new home was in the lower part of the barn, directly underneath the cows. Mr. Zuckerman knew that a manure pile is a good place to keep a young pig. Pigs need warmth, and it was warm and comfortable down there in the barn cellar on the south side.

Fern came almost every day to visit him. She found an old milking stool that had been discarded, and she placed the stool in the sheepfold next to Wilbur's pen. Here she sat quietly during the long afternoons, thinking and listening and watching Wilbur. The sheep soon got to know her and trust her. So did the geese, who lived with the sheep. All the animals trusted her, she was so quiet and friendly. Mr. Zuckerman did not allow her to take Wilbur out, and he did not allow her to get into the pigpen. But he told Fern that she could sit on the stool and watch Wilbur as long as she wanted to. It made her happy just to be near the pig, and it made Wilbur happy to know that she was sitting there, right outside his pen. But he never had any fun—no walks, no rides, no swims.

One afternoon in June, when Wilbur was almost two months old, he wandered out into his small yard outside the barn. Fern had not arrived for her usual visit. Wilbur stood in the sun feeling lonely and bored.

"There's never anything to do around here," he thought. He walked slowly to his food trough and sniffed to see if anything had been over-looked at lunch. He found a small strip of potato skin and ate it. His back itched, so he leaned against the fence and rubbed against the boards. When he tired of this, he walked indoors, climbed to the top of the manure pile, and sat down. He didn't feel like going to sleep, he didn't feel like digging, he was tired of standing still, tired of lying down. "I'm less than two months old and I'm tired of living," he said. He walked out to the yard again.

"When I'm out here," he said, "there's no place to go but in. When I'm indoors, there's no place to go but out in the yard."

"That's where you're wrong, my friend, my friend," said a voice.

Wilbur looked through the fence and saw the goose standing there.

"You don't have to stay in that dirty-little dirty-little dirty-little yard," said the goose, who talked rather fast. "One of the boards is loose. Push on it, push-push-push on it, and come on out!"

"What?" said Wilbur. "Say it slower!"

"At-at-at, at the risk of repeating myself," said the goose. "I suggest that you come on out. It's wonderful out here."

"Did you say a board was loose?"

"That I did, that I did," said the goose.

Wilbur walked up to the fence and saw that the goose was right—one board was loose. He put his head down, shut his eyes, and pushed. The board gave way. In a minute he had squeezed through the fence and was standing in the long grass outside his yard. The goose chuckled.

"How does it feel to be free?" she asked.

"I like it," said Wilbur. "That is, I *guess* I like it." Actually, Wilbur felt queer to be outside his fence, with nothing between him and the big world.

"Where do you think I'd better go?"

"Anywhere you like, anywhere you like," said the goose. "Go down through the orchard, root up the sod! Go down through the garden, dig up the radishes! Root up everything! Eat grass! Look for corn! Look for oats! Run all over! Skip and dance, jump and prance! Go down through the orchard and stroll in the woods! The world is a wonderful place when you're young."

"I can see that," replied Wilbur. He gave a jump in the air, twirled, ran a few steps, stopped, looked all around, sniffed the smells of after-noon, and then set off walking down through the orchard. Pausing in the shade of an apple tree, he put his strong snout into the ground and began pushing, digging, and rooting. He felt very happy. He had plowed up quite a piece of ground before anyone noticed him. Mrs. Zuckerman was the first to see him. She saw him from the kitchen window, and she immediately shouted for the men.

"Ho-*mer!*" she cried. "Pig's out! Lurvy! Pig's out! Homer! Lurvy! Pig's out. He's down there under that apple tree."

"Now the trouble starts," thought Wilbur. "Now I'll catch it."

The goose heard the racket and she, too, started hollering. "Run-run-run downhill, make for the woods, the woods!" she shouted to Wilbur. "They'll never-never-never catch you in the woods."

The cocker spaniel heard the commotion and he ran out from the barn to join the chase. Mr. Zuckerman heard, and he came out of the machine shed where he was mending a tool. Lurvy, the hired man, heard the noise and came up from the asparagus patch where he was pulling weeds. Everybody walked toward Wilbur and Wilbur didn't know what to do. The woods seemed a long way off, and anyway, he had never been down there in the woods and wasn't sure he would like it.

"Get around behind him, Lurvy," said Mr. Zuckerman, "and drive him toward the barn! And take it easy—don't rush him! I'll go and get a bucket of slops."

The news of Wilbur's escape spread rapidly among the animals on the place. Whenever any creature broke loose on Zuckerman's farm, the event was of great interest to the others. The goose shouted to the nearest cow that Wilbur was free, and soon all the cows knew. Then one of the cows told one of the sheep, and soon all the sheep knew. The lambs learned about it from their mothers. The horses, in their stalls in the barn, pricked up their ears when they heard the goose hollering; and soon the horses had caught on to what was happening. "Wilbur's out," they said. Every animal stirred and lifted its head and became excited to know that one of his friends had got free and was no longer penned up or tied fast.

Wilbur didn't know what to do or which way to run. It seemed as though everybody was after him. "If this is what it's like to be free," he thought, "I believe I'd rather be penned up in my own yard."

The cocker spaniel was sneaking up on him from one side, Lurvy the hired man was sneaking up on him from the other side. Mrs. Zuckerman stood ready to head him off if he started for the garden, and now Mr. Zuckerman was coming down toward him carrying a pail. "This is really awful," thought Wilbur. "Why doesn't Fern come?" He began to cry.

The goose took command and began to give orders.

"Don't just stand there, Wilbur! Dodge about, dodge about!" cried the goose. "Skip around, run toward me, slip in and out, in and out, in and out! Make for the woods! Twist and turn!"

The cocker spaniel sprang for Wilbur's hind leg. Wilbur jumped and ran. Lurvy reached out and grabbed. Mrs. Zuckerman screamed at Lurvy. The goose cheered for Wilbur. Wilbur dodged between Lurvy's legs.

Lurvy missed Wilbur and grabbed the spaniel instead. "Nicely done, nicely done!" cried the goose. "Try it again, try it again!"

"Run downhill!" suggested the cows.

"Run toward me!" yelled the gander.

"Run uphill!" cried the sheep.

"Turn and twist!" honked the goose.

"Jump and dance!" said the rooster.

"Look out for Lurvy!" called the cows.

"Look out for Zuckerman!" yelled the gander.

"Watch out for the dog!" cried the sheep.

"Listen to me, listen to me!" screamed the goose.

Poor Wilbur was dazed and frightened by this hullabaloo. He didn't like being the center of all this fuss. He tried to follow the instructions his friends were giving him, but he couldn't run downhill and uphill at the same time, and he couldn't turn and twist when he was jumping and dancing, and he was crying so hard he could barely see anything that was happening. After all, Wilbur was a very young pig—not much more than a baby, really. He wished Fern were there to take him in her arms and comfort him. When he looked up and saw Mr. Zuckerman standing quite close to him, holding a pail of warm slops, he felt relieved. He lifted his nose and sniffed. The smell was delicious—warm milk, potato skins, wheat middlings, Kellogg's Corn Flakes, and a popover left from the Zuckermans' breakfast.

"Come, pig!" said Mr. Zuckerman, tapping the pail. "Come, pig!"

Wilbur took a step toward the pail.

"No-no-no!" said the goose. "It's the old pail trick, Wilbur. Don't fall for it, don't fall for it! He's trying to lure you back into captivity-ivity. He's appealing to your stomach."

Wilbur didn't care. The food smelled appetizing. He took another step toward the pail.

"Pig, pig!" said Mr. Zuckerman in a kind voice, and began walking slowly toward the barnyard, looking all about him innocently, as if he didn't know that a little white pig was following along behind him.

"You'll be sorry-sorry-sorry," called the goose.

Wilbur didn't care. He kept walking toward the pail of slops.

"You'll miss your freedom," honked the goose. "An hour of freedom is worth a barrel of slops."

Wilbur didn't care.

When Mr. Zuckerman reached the pigpen, he climbed over the fence and poured the slops into the trough. Then he pulled the loose board away from the fence, so that there was a wide hole for Wilbur to walk through.

"Reconsider, reconsider!" cried the goose.

Wilbur paid no attention. He stepped through the fence into his yard.

He walked to the trough and took a long drink of slops, sucking in the milk hungrily and chewing the popover. It was good to be home again.

While Wilbur ate, Lurvy fetched a hammer and some 8-penny nails and nailed the board in place. Then he and Mr. Zuckerman leaned lazily on the fence and Mr. Zuckerman scratched Wilbur's back with a stick.

"He's quite a pig," said Lurvy.

"Yes, he'll make a good pig," said Mr. Zuckerman.

Wilbur heard the words of praise. He felt the warm milk inside his stomach. He felt the pleasant rubbing of the stick along his itchy back. He felt peaceful and happy and sleepy. This had been a tiring afternoon. It was still only about four o'clock but Wilbur was ready for bed.

"I'm really too young to go out into the world alone," he thought as he lay down.

CHAPTER IV

LONELINESS

THE NEXT day was rainy and dark. Rain fell on the roof of the barn and dripped steadily from the eaves. Rain fell in the barnyard and ran in crooked courses down into the lane where thistles and pigweed grow. Rain spattered against Mrs. Zuckerman's kitchen windows and came gushing out of the downspouts. Rain fell on the backs of the sheep as they grazed in the meadow. When the sheep tired of standing in the rain, they walked slowly up the lane and into the fold.

Rain upset Wilbur's plans. Wilbur had planned to go out, this day, and dig a new hole in his yard. He had other plans, too. His plans for the day went something like this:

Breakfast at six-thirty. Skim milk, crusts, middlings, bits of doughnuts, wheat cakes with drops of maple syrup sticking to them, potato skins, leftover custard pudding with raisins, and bits of Shredded Wheat.

Breakfast would be finished at seven.

From seven to eight, Wilbur planned to have a talk with Templeton, the rat that lived under his trough. Talking with Templeton was not the most interesting occupation in the world but it was better than nothing.

From eight to nine, Wilbur planned to take a nap outdoors in the sun.

From nine to eleven he planned to dig a hole, or trench, and possibly, find something good to eat buried in the dirt.

From eleven to twelve he planned to stand still and watch flies on the boards, watch bees in the clover, and watch swallows in the air.

Twelve o'clock—lunchtime. Middlings, warm water, apple parings, meat gravy, carrot scrapings, meat scraps, stale hominy, and the wrapper off a package of cheese. Lunch would be over at one.

From one to two, Wilbur planned to sleep.

From two to three, he planned to scratch itchy places by rubbing against the fence.

From three to four, he planned to stand perfectly still and think of what it was like to be alive, and to wait for Fern.

At four would come supper. Skim milk, provender, leftover sandwich from Lurvy's lunchbox, prune skins, a morsel of this, a bit of that, fried potatoes, marmalade drippings, a little more of this, a little more of that, a piece of baked apple, a scrap of upsidedown cake.

Wilbur had gone to sleep thinking about these plans. He awoke at six and saw the rain, and it seemed as though he couldn't bear it.

"I get everything all beautifully planned out and it has to go and rain," he said.

For a while he stood gloomily indoors. Then he walked to the door and looked out. Drops of rain struck his face. His yard was cold and wet. His trough had an inch of rainwater in it. Templeton was nowhere to be seen.

"Are you out there, Templeton?" called Wilbur. There was no answer. Suddenly Wilbur felt lonely and friendless.

"One day just like another," he groaned. "I'm very young, I have no real friend here in the barn, it's going to rain all morning and all afternoon, and Fern won't come in such bad weather. Oh, *honestly!*" And Wilbur was crying again, for the second time in two days.

At six-thirty Wilbur heard the banging of a pail. Lurvy was standing outside in the rain, stirring up breakfast.

"C'mon, pig!" said Lurvy.

Wilbur did not budge. Lurvy dumped the slops, scraped the pail, and walked away. He noticed that something was wrong with the pig.

Wilbur didn't want food, he wanted love. He wanted a friend—someone who would play with him. He mentioned this to the goose, who was sitting quietly in a corner of the sheepfold.

"Will you come over and play with me?" he asked.

"Sorry, sonny, sorry," said the goose. "I'm sitting-sitting on my eggs. Eight of them. Got to keep them toasty-oasty-oasty warm. I have to stay right here, I'm no flibberty-ibberty-gibbet. I do not play when there are eggs to hatch. I'm expecting goslings."

"Well, I didn't think you were expecting woodpeckers," said Wilbur, bitterly.

Wilbur next tried one of the lambs.

"Will you please play with me?" he asked.

"Certainly not," said the lamb. "In the first place, I cannot get into your pen, as I am not old enough to jump over the fence. In the second place, I am not interested in pigs. Pigs mean less than nothing to me."

"What do you mean, *less* than nothing?" replied Wilbur. "I don't think there is any such thing as *less* than nothing. Nothing is absolutely the limit of nothingness. It's the lowest you can go. It's the end of the line.

How can something be less than nothing? If there were something that was less than nothing, then nothing would not be nothing, it would be something—even though it's just a very little bit of something. But if nothing is *nothing,* then nothing has nothing that is less than *it* is."

"Oh, be quiet!" said the lamb. "Go play by yourself! I don't play with pigs."

Sadly, Wilbur lay down and listened to the rain. Soon he saw the rat climbing down a slanting board that he used as a stairway.

"Will you play with me, Templeton?" asked Wilbur.

"Play?" said Templeton, twirling his whiskers. "Play? I hardly know the meaning of the word."

"Well," said Wilbur, "it means to have fun, to frolic, to run and skip and make merry."

"I never do those things if I can avoid them," replied the rat, sourly. "I prefer to spend my time eating, gnawing, spying, and hiding. I am a glutton but not a merrymaker. Right now I am on my way to your trough to eat your breakfast, since you haven't got sense enough to eat it yourself." And Templeton, the rat, crept stealthily along the wall and disappeared into a private tunnel that he had dug between the door and the trough in Wilbur's yard. Templeton was a crafty rat, and he had things pretty much his own way. The tunnel was an example of his skill and cunning. The tunnel enabled him to get from the barn to his hiding place under the pig trough without coming out into the open. He had tunnels and runways all over Mr. Zuckerman's farm and could get from one place to another without being seen. Usually he slept during the daytime and was abroad only after dark.

Wilbur watched him disappear into his tunnel. In a moment he saw the rat's sharp nose poke out from underneath the wooden trough. Cautiously Templeton pulled himself up over the edge of the trough. This was almost more than Wilbur could stand: on this dreary, rainy day to see his breakfast being eaten by somebody else. He knew Templeton was getting soaked, out there in the pouring rain, but even that didn't comfort him. Friendless, dejected, and hungry, he threw himself down in the manure and sobbed.

Late that afternoon, Lurvey went to Mr. Zuckerman, "I think there's something wrong with that pig of yours. He hasn't touched his food."

"Give him two spoonfuls of sulphur and a little molasses," said Mr. Zuckerman.

Wilbur couldn't believe what was happening to him when Lurvy caught him and forced the medicine down his throat. This was certainly the worst day of his life. He didn't know whether he could endure the awful loneliness any more.

Darkness settled over everything. Soon there were only shadows and the noises of the sheep chewing their cuds, and occasionally the rattle of a cow-chain up overhead. You can imagine Wilbur's surprise when, out of the darkness, came a small voice he had never heard before. It sounded rather thin, but pleasant. "Do you want a friend, Wilbur?" it said. "I'll be a friend to you. I've watched you all day and I like you."

"But I can't see you," said Wilbur, jumping to his feet. "Where are you? And *who* are you?"

"I'm right up here," said the voice. "Go to sleep. You'll see me in the morning."

CHAPTER V

CHARLOTTE

THE NIGHT seemed long. Wilbur's stomach was empty and his mind was full. And when your stomach is empty and your mind is full, it's always hard to sleep.

A dozen times during the night Wilbur woke and stared into the blackness, listening to the sounds and trying to figure out what time it was. A barn is never perfectly quiet. Even at midnight there is usually something stirring.

The first time he woke, he heard Templeton gnawing a hole in the grain bin. Templeton's teeth scraped loudly against the wood and made quite a racket. "That crazy rat!" thought Wilbur. "Why does he have to stay up all night, grinding his clashers and destroying people's property? Why can't he go to sleep, like any decent animal?"

The second time Wilbur woke, he heard the goose turning on her nest and chuckling to herself.

"What time is it?" whispered Wilbur to the goose.

"Probably-obably-obably about half-past eleven," said the goose. "Why aren't you asleep, Wilbur?"

"Too many things on my mind," said Wilbur.

"Well," said the goose, "that's not *my* trouble. I have nothing at all on my mind, but I've too many things under my behind. Have you ever tried to sleep while sitting on eight eggs?"

"No," replied Wilbur. "I suppose it *is* uncomfortable. How long does it take a goose egg to hatch?"

"Approximately-oximately thirty days, all told," answered the goose. "But I cheat a little. On warm afternoons, I just pull a little straw over the eggs and go out for a walk."

Wilbur yawned and went back to sleep. In his dreams he heard again the voice saying, "I'll be a friend to you. Go to sleep—you'll see me in the morning."

About half an hour before dawn, Wilbur woke and listened. The barn was still dark. The sheep lay motionless. Even the goose was quiet. Overhead, on the main floor, nothing stirred: the cows were resting, the horses dozed. Templeton had quit work and gone off somewhere on an errand. The only sound was a slight scraping noise from the rooftop, where the weather vane swung back and forth. Wilbur loved the barn when it was like this—calm and quiet, waiting for light.

"Day is almost here," he thought.

Through a small window, a faint gleam appeared. One by one the stars went out. Wilbur could see the goose a few feet away. She sat with head tucked under a wing. Then he could see the sheep and the lambs. The sky lightened.

"Oh, beautiful day, it is here at last! Today I shall find my friend."

Wilbur looked everywhere. He searched his pen thoroughly. He examined the window ledge, stared up at the ceiling. But he saw nothing new. Finally he decided he would have to speak up. He hated to break the lovely stillness of dawn by using his voice, but he couldn't think of any other way to locate the mysterious new friend who was nowhere to be seen. So, Wilbur cleared his throat.

"Attention, please!" he said in a loud, firm voice. "Will the party who addressed me at bedtime last night kindly make himself or herself known by giving an appropriate sign or signal!"

Wilbur paused and listened. All the other animals lifted their heads and stared at him. Wilbur blushed. But he was determined to get in touch with his unknown friend.

"Attention, please!" he said. "I will repeat the message. Will the party who addressed me at bedtime last night kindly speak up. Please tell me where you are, if you are my friend!"

The sheep looked at each other in disgust.

"Stop your nonsense, Wilbur!" said the oldest sheep. "If you have a new friend here, you are probably disturbing his rest; and the quickest way to spoil a friendship is to wake somebody up in the morning before he is ready. How can you be sure your friend is an early riser?"

"I beg everyone's pardon," whispered Wilbur. "I didn't mean to be objectionable."

He lay down meekly in the manure, facing the door. He did not know it, but his friend was very near. And the old sheep was right—the friend was still asleep.

Soon Lurvy appeared with slops for breakfast. Wilbur rushed out, ate everything in a hurry, and licked the trough. The sheep moved off down the lane, the gander waddled along behind them, pulling grass. And then, just as Wilbur was settling down for his morning nap, he heard again the thin voice that had addressed him the night before.

"Salutations!" said the voice.

Wilbur jumped to his feet. "Salu-what?" he cried.

"Salutations!" repeated the voice.

"What are *they,* and *where* are *you?*" screamed Wilbur. "Please, *please,* tell me where you are. And what are salutations?"

"Salutations are greetings," said the voice. "When I say 'salutations,' it's just my fancy way of saying hello or good morning. Actually, it's a silly expression, and I am surprised that I used it at all. As for my where-abouts, that's easy. Look up here in the corner of the doorway! Here I am. Look, I'm waving!"

At last Wilbur saw the creature that had spoken to him in such a kindly way. Stretched across the upper part of the doorway was a big spiderweb, and hanging from the top of the web, head down, was a large gray spider. She was about the size of a gumdrop. She had eight legs, and she was waving one of them at Wilbur in friendly greeting. "See me now?" she asked.

"Oh, yes indeed," said Wilbur. "Yes indeed! How are you? Good morning! Salutations! Very pleased to meet you. What is your name, please? May I have your name?"

"My name," said the spider, "is Charlotte."

"Charlotte what?" asked Wilbur eagerly.

"Charlotte A. Cavatica. But just call me Charlotte."

"I think you're beautiful," said Wilbur.

"Well, I *am* pretty," replied Charlotte. "There's no denying that. Almost all spiders are rather nice-looking. I'm not as flashy as some, but I'll do. I wish I could see you, Wilbur, as clearly as you can see me."

"Why can't you?" asked the pig. "I'm right here."

"Yes, but I'm nearsighted," replied Charlotte. "I've always been dread-fully nearsighted. It's good in some ways, not so good in others. Watch me wrap up this fly."

A fly that had been crawling along Wilbur's trough had flown up and blundered into the lower part of Charlotte's web and was tangled in the sticky threads. The fly was beating its wings furiously, trying to break loose and free itself.

"First," said Charlotte, "I dive at him." She plunged headfirst toward the fly. As she dropped, a tiny silken thread unwound from her rear end.

"Next, I wrap him up." She grabbed the fly, threw a few jets of silk around it, and rolled it over and over, wrapping it so that it couldn't move. Wilbur watched in horror. He could hardly believe what he was seeing, and although he detested flies, he was sorry for this one.

"There!" said Charlotte. "Now I knock him out, so he'll be more com-fortable." She bit the fly. "He can't feel a thing now," she remarked. "He'll make a perfect breakfast for me."

"You mean you *eat* flies?" gasped Wilbur.

"Certainly. Flies, bugs, grasshoppers, choice beetles, moths, butterflies, tasty cockroaches, gnats, midges, daddy longlegs, centipedes, mosquitoes, crickets—anything that is careless enough to get caught in my web. I have to live, don't I?"

"Why, yes, of course," said Wilbur. "Do they taste good?"

"Delicious. Of course, I don't really eat them. I drink them—drink their blood. I love blood," said Charlotte, and her pleasant, thin voice grew even thinner and more pleasant.

"Don't say that!" groaned Wilbur. "Please don't say things like that!"

"Why not? It's true, and I have to say what is true. I am not entirely happy about my diet of flies and bugs, but it's the way I'm made. A spider has to pick up a living somehow or other, and I happen to be a trapper. I just naturally build a web and trap flies and other insects. My mother was a trapper before me. Her mother was a trapper before her. All our family have been trappers. Way back for thousands and thousands of years we spiders have been laying for flies and bugs."

"It's a miserable inheritance," said Wilbur, gloomily. He was sad because his new friend was so bloodthirsty.

"Yes, it is," agreed Charlotte. "But I can't help it. I don't know how the first spider in the early days of the world happened to think up this fancy idea of spinning a web, but she did, and it was clever of her, too. And since then, all of us spiders have had to work the same trick. It's not a bad pitch, on the whole."

"It's cruel," replied Wilbur, who did not intend to be argued out of his position.

"Well, *you* can't talk," said Charlotte. "*You* have your meals brought to you in a pail. Nobody feeds me. I have to get my own living. I live by my wits. I have to be sharp and clever, lest I go hungry. I have to think things out, catch what I can, take what comes. And it just so happens, my friend, that what comes is flies and insects and bugs. And *further*more," said Charlotte, shaking one of her legs, "do you realize that if I didn't catch bugs and eat them, bugs would increase and multiply and get so numerous that they'd destroy the earth, wipe out everything?"

"Really?" said Wilbur. "I wouldn't want *that* to happen. Perhaps your web is a good thing after all."

The goose had been listening to this conversation and chuckling to herself. "There are a lot of things Wilbur doesn't know about life," she thought. "He's really a very innocent little pig. He doesn't even know what's going to happen to him around Christmastime; he has no idea that Mr. Zuckerman and Lurvy are plotting to kill him." And the goose raised herself a bit and poked her eggs a little further under her so that they would receive the full heat from her warm body and soft feathers.

Charlotte stood quietly over the fly, preparing to eat it. Wilbur lay down and closed his eyes. He was tired from his wakeful night and from the excitement of meeting someone for the first time. A breeze brought him the smell of clover—the sweet-smelling world beyond his fence.

"Well," he thought, "I've got a new friend, all right. But what a gamble friendship is! Charlotte is fierce, brutal, scheming, bloodthirsty—everything I don't like. How can I learn to like her, even though she is pretty and, of course, clever?"

Wilbur was merely suffering the doubts and fears that often go with finding a new friend. In good time he was to discover that he was mistaken about Charlotte. Underneath her rather bold and cruel exterior, she had a kind heart, and she was to prove loyal and true to the very end.

Adam and Eve and Pinch Me

By A. E. COPPARD

AND IN the whole of his days, vividly at the end of the afternoon—he repeated it again and again to himself—the kind country spaces had *never* absorbed *quite* so rich a glamour of light, so miraculous a bloom of clarity. He could feel streaming in his own mind, in his bones, the same crystalline brightness that lay upon the land. Thoughts and images went flowing through him as easily and amiably as fish swim in their pools; and as idly, too, for one of his speculations took up the theme of his family name. There was such an agreeable oddness about it, just as there was about all the luminous sky today, that it touched him as just a little remarkable. What *did* such a name connote, signify, or symbolize? It was a rann of a name, but it had euphony! Then again, like the fish, his ambulating fancy flashed into other shallows, and he giggled as he paused, peering at the buds in the brake. Turning back towards his house again he could see, beyond its roofs, the spire of the Church tinctured richly as the vane: all round him was a new grandeur upon the grass of the fields, and the spare trees had shadows below that seemed to support them in the manner of a plinth, more real than themselves, and the dikes and any chance heave of the level fields were underlined, as if for special emphasis, with long shades of mysterious blackness.

With a little drift of emotion that had at other times assailed him in the wonder and ecstasy of pure light, Jaffa Codling pushed through the slit in the back hedge and stood within his own garden. The gardener was at work. He could hear the voices of the children about the lawn at the other side of the house. He was very happy, and the place was beautiful, a fine white many-windowed house rising from a lawn bowered with plots of mold, turreted with shrubs, and overset with a vast walnut tree. This house had deep clean eaves, a roof of faint colored slates that, after rain, glowed dully, like onyx or jade, under the red chimneys, and halfway up at one end was a balcony set with black balusters. He went to a French window that stood open and stepped into the dining room. There was no one within, and, on that lonely instant, a strange feeling of emptiness dropped upon him. The clock ticked almost as if it had been caught in some indecent act; the air was dim and troubled after that glory outside. Well, now, he would go up at once to the study and write down for his new book the ideas and images he had accumulated—beautiful rich thoughts they were—during that wonderful afternoon. He went to mount the stairs and he was passed by one of the maids; humming a silly song she brushed past him rudely, but he was an easygoing man—maids were unteachably tiresome—and reaching the landing he sauntered towards his room. The door stood slightly open and he could hear voices within. He put his hand upon the door . . . it would not open any further. What the devil . . . he pushed—like the bear in the tale—and he pushed, and he pushed—was there something against it on the other side? He put his shoulder to it . . . some wedge must be there, and *that* was extraordinary. Then his whole apprehension was swept up and whirled as by an avalanche—Mildred, his wife, was in there; he could hear her speaking to a man in fair soft tones and the rich phrases that could be used only by a woman yielding a deep affection for him. Codling kept still. Her words burned on his mind and thrilled him as if spoken to himself. There was a movement in the room, then utter silence. He again thrust savagely at the partly open door, but he could not stir it. The silence within continued. He beat upon the door with his fists, crying: "Mildred, Mildred!" There was no response, but he could hear the rocking armchair commence to swing to and fro. Pushing his hand round the edge of the door he tried to thrust his head between the opening. There was not space for this, but he could just peer into the corner of a mirror hung near, and this is what he saw: the chair at one end of its swing, a man sitting in it, and upon one arm of it Mildred, the beloved woman, with her lips upon the man's face, caressing him with her hands. Codling made another effort to get into the room—as vain as it was violent. "Do you hear me, Mildred?" he shouted. Apparently neither of them heard him; they rocked to and fro while he gazed stupefied. What, in the name of God, . . . What this . . . was she bewitched . . . were there such things after all as magic, devilry!

He drew back and held himself quite steadily. The chair stopped swaying, and the room grew awfully still. The sharp ticking of the clock in the hall rose upon the house like the tongue of some perfunctory mocker. Couldn't they hear the clock? . . . Couldn't they hear his heart? He had to put his hand upon his heart, for, surely, in that great silence inside there, they would hear its beat, growing so loud now that it seemed almost to stun him! Then in a queer way he found himself reflecting, observing, analyzing his own actions and intentions. He found some of them to be just a little spurious, counterfeit. He felt it would be easy, so perfectly easy to flash in one blast of anger and annihilate the two. He would do nothing of the kind. There was no occasion for it. People didn't really do that sort of thing, or, at least, not with a genuine passion. There was no need for anger. His curiosity was satisfied, quite satisfied, he was certain, he had not the remotest interest in the man. A welter of unexpected thoughts swept upon his mind as he stood there. As a writer of books he was often stimulated by the emotions and impulses of other people, and now his own surprise was beginning to intrigue him, leaving him, oh, quite un-stirred emotionlly, but interesting him profoundly.

He heard the maid come stepping up the stairway again, humming her silly song. He did not want a scene, or to be caught eavesdropping, and so turned quickly to another door. It was locked. He sprang to one beyond it; the handle would not turn. "Bah! what's *up* with 'em?" But the girl was now upon him, carrying a tray of coffee things. "Oh, Mary!" he ex-claimed casually, "I . . ." To his astonishment the girl stepped past him as if she did not hear or see him, tapped open the door of his study, entered, and closed the door behind her. Jaffa Codling then got really angry. "Hell! were the blasted servants in it!" He dashed to the door again and tore at the handle. It would not even turn, and, though he wrenched with fury at it, the room was utterly sealed against him. He went away for a chair with which to smash the effrontery of that door. No, he wasn't angry, either with his wife or this fellow—Gilbert, she had called him—who had a strangely familiar aspect as far as he had been able to take it in; but when one's servants . . . faugh!

The door opened and Mary came forth smiling demurely. He was a few yards further along the corridor at that moment. "Mary!" he shouted, "leave the door open!" Mary carefully closed it and turned her back on him. He sprang after her with bad words bursting from him as she went towards the stairs and flitted lightly down, humming all the way as if in derision. He leaped downwards after her three steps at a time, but she trotted with amazing swiftness into the kitchen and slammed the door in his face. Codling stood, but kept his hands carefully away from the door, kept them behind him. "No, no," he whispered cunningly, "there's some-thing fiendish about door handles today; I'll go and get a bar, or a butt of timber," and, jumping out into the garden for some such thing, the miracle happened to him. For it was nothing else than a miracle, the un-believable, the impossible, simple and laughable if you will, but having as much validity as any miracle can ever invoke. It was simple and laugh-able because by all the known physical laws he should have collided with his gardener, who happened to pass the window with his wheelbarrow as Codling jumped out onto the path. And it was unbelievable that they should not, and impossible that they *did* not collide; and it was miracu-lous, because Codling stood for a brief moment in the garden path and the wheelbarrow of Bond, its contents, and Bond himself passed ap-parently through the figure of Codling as if he were so much air, as if he were not a living breathing man but just a common ghost. There was no impact, just a momentary breathlessness. Codling stood and looked at the retreating figure going on utterly unaware of him. It is interesting to record that Codling's first feelings were mirthful. He giggled. He was jocular. He ran along in front of the gardener, and let him pass through him once more; then after him again; he scrambled into the man's barrow, and was wheeled about by this incomprehensible thickheaded gardener who was dead to all his master's efforts to engage his attention. Presently he dropped the wheelbarrow and went away, leaving Codling to cogitate upon the occurrence. There was no room for doubt, some essential part of him had become detached from the obviously not less vital part. He felt he was essential because he was responding to the experience, he was reacting in the normal way to normal stimuli, although he happened for the time being to be invisible to his fellows and unable to communicate with them. How had it come about—this queer thing? How could he discover what part of him had cut loose, as it were? There was no question of this being death; death wasn't funny, it wasn't a joke; he had still all his human instincts. You didn't get angry with a faithless wife or joke with a fool of a gardener if you were dead, certainly not! He had realized enough of himself to know he was the usual man of instincts, desires, and prohibitions, complex and contradictory; his family history for a million or two years would have denoted that, not explicitly—obviously impossible—but suggestively. He had found himself doing things he had no desire to do, doing things he had a desire *not* to do, thinking thoughts that had no contiguous meaning, no meaning that could be related to his general experience. At odd times he had been chilled—aye, and even agreeably surprised—at the immense potential evil in himself. But still, this was no mere Jekyll and Hyde affair, that a man and his own ghost should separately inhabit the same world was a horse of quite another color. The other part of him was alive and active somewhere . . . as alive . . . as alive . . . yes, as *he* was, but dashed if he knew where! What a lark when they got back to each other and compared notes! In his tales he had brooded over so many imagined personalities, followed in the track of so many psychological enigmas that he *had* felt at times a stranger to himself. What if, after all, that brooding had given him the faculty of projecting this figment of himself into the world of men. Or was he some unrealized latent element of being without its natural integument, doomed now to drift over the ridge of the world forever? Was it his personality, his spirit? Then how was the dashed thing working? Here was he with the most wonderful happening in human experience, and he couldn't differentiate or disinter things. He was like a new Adam flung into some old Eden.

There was Bond tinkering about with some plants a dozen yards in front of him. Suddenly his three children came round from the other side of the house, the youngest boy leading them, carrying in his hand a small sword which was made, not of steel, but of some more brightly shining material; indeed it seemed at one moment to be of gold, and then again of flame, transmuting everything in its neighborhood into the likeness of flame, the hair of the little girl Eve, a part of Adam's tunic; and the fingers of the boy Gabriel as he held the sword were like pale tongues of fire. Gabriel, the youngest boy, went up to the gardener and gave the sword into his hands, saying: "Bond, is this sword any good?" Codling saw the gardener take the weapon and examine it with a careful sort of smile; his great gnarled hands became immediately transparent, the blood could be seen moving diligently about the veins. Codling was so interested in the sight that he did not gather in the gardener's reply. The little boy was dissatisfied and repeated his question, "No, but, Bond, *is* this sword any good?" Codling rose, and stood by invisible. The three beautiful children were grouped about the great angular figure of the gardener in his soiled clothes, looking up now into his face, and now at the sword, with anxiety in all their puckered eyes. "Well, Marse Gabriel," Codling could hear him reply, "as far as a sword goes, it may be a good un, or it may be a bad un, but, good as it is, it can never be anything but a bad thing." He then gave it back to them; the boy Adam held the haft of it, and the girl Eve rubbed the blade with curious fingers. The younger boy stood looking up at the gardener with unsatisfied gaze. "But, Bond, *can't* you say if this sword's any *good?*" Bond turned to his spade and trowels. "Mebbe the shape of it's wrong, Marse Gabriel, though it seems a pretty handy size." Saying this he moved off across the lawn. Gabriel turned to his brother and sister and took the sword from them; they all followed after the gardener and once more Gabriel made inquiry: "Bond, is this sword any *good?*" The gardener again took it and made a few passes in the air like a valiant soldier at exercise. Turning then, he lifted a bright curl from the head of Eve and cut it off with a sweep of the weapon. He held it up to look at it critically and then let it fall to the ground. Codling sneaked behind him and, picking it up, stood stupidly looking at it. "Mebbe, Marse Gabriel," the gardener was saying, "it ud be better made of steel, but it has a smartish edge on it." He went to pick up the barrow but Gabriel seized it with a spasm of anger, and cried out: "No, no, Bond, will you say, just yes or no, Bond, is this sword any *good?*" The gardener stood still, and looked down at the little boy, who repeated his question—"just yes or no, Bond!" "No, Marse Gabriel!" "Thank you, Bond!" replied the child with dignity. "That's all we wanted to know," and calling to his mates to follow him, he ran away to the other side of the house.

Codling stared again at the beautiful lock of hair in his hand, and felt himself grow so angry that he picked up a strange-looking flower pot at his feet and hurled it at the retreating gardener. It struck Bond in the middle of the back and, passing clean through him, broke on the wheel of his barrow, but Bond seemed to be quite unaware of this catastrophe.

Codling rushed after, and, taking the gardener by the throat, he yelled, "Damn you, will you tell me what all this means?" But Bond proceeded calmly about his work unnoticing, carrying his master about as if he were a clinging vapor, or a scarf hung upon his neck. In a few moments, Codling dropped exhausted to the ground. "What . . . oh, Hell . . . what, what am I to do?" he groaned. "What has happened to me? What shall I *do*? What *can* I do?" He looked at the broken flower pot. "Did I invent that?" He pulled out his watch. "That's a real watch, I hear it ticking, and it's six o'clock." Was he dead or disembodied or mad? What was this infernal lapse of identity? And who the devil, yes, who was it upstairs with Mildred? He jumped to his feet and hurried to the window; it was shut; to the door, it was fastened; he was powerless to open either. Well! well! this was experimental psychology with a vengeance, and he began to chuckle again. He'd have to write to McDougall about it. Then he turned and saw Bond wheeling across the lawn towards him again. *"Why* is that fellow always shoving that infernal green barrow around?" he asked, and, the fit of fury seizing him again, he rushed towards Bond, but, before he reached him, the three children danced into the garden again, crying, with great excitement, "Bond, oh, Bond!" The gardener stopped and set down the terrifying barrow; the children crowded about him, and Gabriel held out another shining thing, asking: "Bond, is this box any good?" The gardener took the box and at once his eyes lit up with interest and delight. "Oh, Marse Gabriel, where'd ye get it? Where'd ye get it?" "Bond," said the boy impatiently, "is the box any *good?*" "Any good?" echoed the man, "Why, Marse Gabriel, Marse Adam, Miss Eve, look yere!" Holding it down in front of them, he lifted the lid from the box and a bright-colored bird flashed out and flew round and round above their heads. "Oh," screamed Gabriel with delight, "it's a kingfisher!" "That's what it is," said Bond, "a kingfisher!" "Where?" asked Adam. "Where?" asked Eve. "There it flies—round the fountain—see it? see it!" "No," said Adam. "No," said Eve.

"Oh, do, do see it," cried Gabriel, "here it comes, it's coming!" and, holding his hands on high, and standing on his toes, the child cried out as happy as the bird which Codling saw flying above them.

"I can't see it," said Adam.

"Where is it, Gaby?" asked Eve.

"Oh, you stupids," cried the boy. *"There* it goes. There it goes . . . there . . . it's gone!"

He stood looking brightly at Bond, who replaced the lid.

"What shall we do now?" he exclaimed eagerly. For reply, the gardener gave the box into his hand, and walked off with the barrow. Gabriel took the box over to the fountain. Codling, unseen, went after him, almost as excited as the boy; Eve and her brother followed. They sat upon the stone tank that held the falling water. It was difficult for the child to unfasten the lid; Codling attempted to help him, but he was powerless. Gabriel looked up into his father's face and smiled. Then he stood up and said to the others:

"Now, *do* watch it this time."

They all knelt carefully beside the water. He lifted the lid and, behold, a fish like a gold carp, but made wholly of fire, leaped from the box into the fountain. The man saw it dart down into the water, he saw the water bubble up behind it, he heard the hiss that the junction of fire and water produced, and saw a little track of steam follow the bubbles about the tank until the figure of the fish was consumed and disappeared. Gabriel, in ecstasies, turned to his sister with blazing happy eyes, exclaiming:

"There! Evey!"

"What was it?" asked Eve, nonchalantly. "I didn't see anything."

"More didn't I," said Adam.

"Didn't you see that lovely fish?"

"No," said Adam.

"No," said Eve.

"Oh, stupids," cried Gabriel, "it went right past the bottom of the water."

"Let's get a fishin' hook," said Adam.

"No, no, no," said Gabriel, replacing the lid of the box. "Oh, no."

Jaffa Codling had remained on his knees staring at the water so long that, when he looked around him again, the children had gone away. He got up and went to the door, and that was closed; the windows, fastened. He went moodily to a garden bench and sat on it with folded arms. Dusk had begun to fall into the shrubs and trees, the grass to grow dull, the air chill, the sky to muster its gloom. Bond had overturned his barrow, stalled his tools in the lodge, and gone to his home in the village. A curious cat came round the house and surveyed the man who sat chained to his seven-horned dilemma. It grew dark and fearfully silent. Was the world empty now? Some small thing, a snail, perhaps, crept among the dead leaves in the hedge, with a sharp, irritating noise. A strange flood of mixed thoughts poured through his mind until at last one idea disentangled itself, and he began thinking with tremendous fixity of little Gabriel. He wondered if he could brood or meditate, or "will" with sufficient power to bring him into the garden again. The child had just vaguely recognized him for a moment at the waterside. He'd try that dodge, telepathy was a mild kind of a trick after so much of the miraculous. If he'd lost his blessed body, at least the part that ate and smoked and talked to Mildred . . . He stopped as his mind stumbled on a strange recognition. . . . What a joke, of course . . . idiot . . . not to have seen *that*. He stood up in the garden with joy . . . of course, *he* was upstairs with Mildred, it was himself, the other bit of him, that Mildred had been talking to. What a howling fool he'd been.

He found himself concentrating his mind on the purpose of getting the child Gabriel into the garden once more, but it was with a curious mood that he endeavored to establish this relationship. He could not fix his will into any calm intensity of power, or fixity of purpose, or pleasurable mental ecstasy. The utmost force seemed to come with a malicious threatening splenetic "entreaty." That damned snail in the hedge broke the thread of his meditation; a dog began to bark sturdily from a distant farm; the faculties of his mind became joggled up like a child's picture puzzle, and he brooded unintelligibly upon such things as skating and steam engines, and Elizabethan drama so lapped about with themes like jealousy and chastity. Really now, Shakespeare's Isabella was the most consummate snob in . . . He looked up quickly to his wife's room and saw Gabriel step from the window to the balcony as if he were fearful of being seen. The boy lifted up his hands and placed the bright box on the rail of the balcony. He looked up at the faint stars for a moment or two, and then carefully released the lid of the box. What came out of it and rose into the air appeared to Codling to be just a piece of floating light, but as it soared above the roof he saw it grow to be a little ancient ship, with its hull and fully set sails and its three masts all of faint-primrose flame color. It cleaved through the air, rolling slightly as a ship through the wave, in widening circles above the house, making a curving ascent until it lost the shape of a vessel and became only a moving light hurrying to some sidereal shrine. Codling glanced at the boy on the balcony, but in that brief instant something had happened, the ship had burst like a rocket and released three colored drops of fire which came falling slowly, leaving beautiful gray furrows of smoke in their track. Gabriel leaned over the rail with outstretched palms, and, catching the green star and the blue one as they drifted down to him, he ran with a rill of laughter back into the house. Codling sprang forward just in time to catch the red star; it lay vividly blasting his own palm for a monstrous second, and then, slipping through, was gone. He stared at the ground, at the balcony, the sky, and then heard an exclamation . . . his wife stood at his side.

"Gilbert! How you frightened me!" she cried. "I thought you were in your room; come along in to dinner." She took his arm and they walked up the steps into the dining room together. "Just a moment," said her husband, turning to the door of the room. His hand was upon the handle, which turned easily in his grasp, and he ran upstairs to his own room. He opened the door. The light was on, the fire was burning brightly, a smell of cigarette smoke about, pen and paper upon his desk, the Japanese book knife, the gilt matchbox, everything all right, no one there. He picked up a book from his desk. . . . *Monna Vanna.* His bookplate was in it—*Ex Libris—Gilbert Cannister.* He put it down beside the green dish; two yellow oranges were in the green dish, and two most deliberately green Canadian apples rested by their side. He went to the door and swung it backwards and forwards quite easily. He sat on his desk trying to piece the thing together, glaring at the print and the book knife and the smart matchbox, until his wife came up behind him exclaiming: "Come along, Gilbert!"

"Where are the kids, old man?" he asked her, and, before she replied, he had gone along to the nursery. He saw the two cots, his boy in one, his girl in the other. He turned whimsically to Mildred, saying, "There *are* only two, *are* there?" Such a question did not call for reply, but he confronted her as if expecting some assuring answer. She was staring at him with her bright beautiful eyes.

"Are there?" he repeated.

"How strange you should ask me that now!" she said. . . . "If you're a very good man . . . perhaps. . . ."

"Mildred!"

She nodded brightly.

He sat down in the rocking chair, but got up again saying to her gently—"We'll call him Gabriel."

"But suppose—"

"No, no," he said, stopping her lovely lips, "I know all about him." And he told her a pleasant little tale.

The Fifty-first Dragon

By HEYWOOD BROUN

OF ALL the pupils at the knight school Gawaine le Cœur-Hardy was among the least promising. He was tall and sturdy, but his instructors soon discovered that he lacked spirit. He would hide in the woods when the jousting class was called, although his companions and members of the faculty sought to appeal to his better nature by shouting to him to come out and break his neck like a man. Even when they told him that the lances were padded, the horses no more than ponies and the field unusually soft for late autumn, Gawaine refused to grow enthusiastic. The Headmaster and the Assistant Professor of Pleasaunce were discussing the case one spring afternoon and the Assistant Professor could see no remedy but expulsion.

"No," said the Headmaster, as he looked out at the purple hills which ringed the school, "I think I'll train him to slay dragons."

"He might be killed," objected the Assistant Professor.

"So he might," replied the Headmaster brightly, but he added, more soberly, "We must consider the greater good. We are responsible for the formation of this lad's character."

"Are the dragons particularly bad this year?" interrupted the Assistant Professor. This was characteristic. He always seemed restive when the head of the school began to talk ethics and the ideals of the institution.

"I've never known them worse," replied the Headmaster. "Up in the hills to the south last week they killed a number of peasants, two cows and a prize pig. And if this dry spell holds there's no telling when they may start a forest fire simply by breathing around indiscriminately."

"Would any refund on the tuition fee be necessary in case of an accident to young Cœur-Hardy?"

"No," the principal answered, judicially, "that's all covered in the contract. But as a matter of fact he won't be killed. Before I send him up in the hills I'm going to give him a magic word."

"That's a good idea," said the Professor. "Sometimes they work wonders."

From that day on Gawaine specialized in dragons. His course included both theory and practice. In the morning there were long lectures on the history, anatomy, manners and customs of dragons. Gawaine did not distinguish himself in these studies. He had a marvelously versatile gift for forgetting things. In the afternoon he showed to better advantage, for then he would go down to the South Meadow and practice with a battle ax. In this exercise he was truly impressive, for he had enormous strength as well as speed and grace. He even developed a deceptive display of ferocity. Old alumni say that it was a thrilling sight to see Gawaine charging across the field toward the dummy paper dragon which had been set up for his practice. As he ran he would brandish his ax and shout "A murrain on thee!" or some other vivid bit of campus slang. It never took him more than one stroke to behead the dummy dragon.

Gradually his task was made more difficult. Paper gave way to papier-mâché and finally to wood, but even the toughest of these dummy dragons had no terrors for Gawaine. One sweep of the ax always did the business. There were those who said that when the practice was protracted until dusk and the dragons threw long, fantastic shadows across the meadow Gawaine did not charge so impetuously nor shout so loudly. It is possible there was malice in this charge. At any rate, the Headmaster decided by the end of June that it was time for the test. Only the night before a dragon had come close to the school grounds and had eaten some of the lettuce from the garden. The faculty decided that Gawaine was ready. They gave him a diploma and a new battle ax and the Headmaster summoned him to a private conference.

"Sit down," said the Headmaster. "Have a cigarette."

Gawaine hesitated.

"Oh, I know it's against the rules," said the Headmaster. "But after all, you have received your preliminary degree. You are no longer a boy. You are a man. Tomorrow you will go out into the world, the great world of achievement."

Gawaine took a cigarette. The Headmaster offered him a match, but he produced one of his own and began to puff away with a dexterity which quite amazed the principal.

"Here you have learned the theories of life," continued the Headmaster, resuming the thread of his discourse, "but after all, life is not a matter of theories. Life is a matter of facts. It calls on the young and the old alike to face these facts, even though they are hard and sometimes unpleasant. Your problem, for example, is to slay dragons."

"They say that those dragons down in the south wood are five hundred feet long," ventured Gawaine, timorously.

"Stuff and nonsense!" said the Headmaster. "The curate saw one last week from the top of Arthur's Hill. The dragon was sunning himself down in the valley. The curate didn't have an opportunity to look at him very long because he felt it was his duty to hurry back to make a report to me. He said the monster, or shall I say, the big lizard?—wasn't an inch over two hundred feet. But the size has nothing at all to do with it. You'll find the big ones even easier than the little ones. They're far slower on their feet and less aggressive, I'm told. Besides, before you go I'm going to equip you in such fashion that you need have no fear of all the dragons in the world."

"I'd like an enchanted cap," said Gawaine.

"What's that?" answered the Headmaster, testily.

"A cap to make me disappear," explained Gawaine.

The Headmaster laughed indulgently. "You mustn't believe all those old wives' stories," he said. "There isn't any such thing. A cap to make you disappear, indeed! What would you do with it? You haven't even appeared yet. Why, my boy, you could walk from here to London, and nobody would so much as look at you. You're nobody. You couldn't be more invisible than that."

Gawaine seemed dangerously close to a relapse into his old habit of whimpering. The Headmaster reassured him: "Don't worry; I'll give you something much better than an enchanted cap. I'm going to give you a magic word. All you have to do is to repeat this magic charm once and no dragon can possibly harm a hair of your head. You can cut off his head at your leisure."

He took a heavy book from the shelf behind his desk and began to run through it. "Sometimes," he said, "the charm is a whole phrase or even a sentence. I might, for instance, give you 'To make the'—No, that might not do. I think a single word would be best for dragons."

"A short word," suggested Gawaine.

"It can't be too short or it wouldn't be potent. There isn't so much hurry as all that. Here's a splendid magic word: 'Rumplesnitz.' Do you think you can learn that?"

Gawaine tried and in an hour or so he seemed to have the word well in hand. Again and again he interrupted the lesson to inquire, "And if I say 'Rumplesnitz,'" the dragon can't possibly hurt me?" And always the Headmaster replied, "If you only say 'Rumplesnitz,' you are perfectly safe."

Toward morning Gawaine seemed resigned to his career. At daybreak the Headmaster saw him to the edge of the forest and pointed him to the direction on which he should proceed. About a mile away to the south-west a cloud of steam hovered over an open meadow in the woods and the Headmaster assured Gawaine that under the steam he would find a dragon. Gawaine went forward slowly. He wondered whether it would be best to approach the dragon on the run as he did in his practice in the South Meadow or to walk slowly toward him, shouting "Rumplesnitz" all the way.

The problem was decided for him. No sooner had he come to the fringe of the meadow than the dragon spied him and began to charge. It was a large dragon and yet it seemed decidedly aggressive in spite of the Headmaster's statement to the contrary. As the dragon charged it released huge clouds of hissing steam through its nostrils. It was almost as if a gigantic teapot had gone mad. The dragon came forward so fast and Gawaine was so frightened that he had time to say "Rumplesnitz" only once. As he said it, he swung his battle ax and off popped the head of the dragon. Gawaine had to admit that it was even easier to kill a real dragon than a wooden one if only you said "Rumplesnitz."

Gawaine brought the ears home and a small section of the tail. His school mates and the faculty made much of him, but the Headmaster wisely kept him from being spoiled by insisting that he go on with his work. Every clear day Gawaine rose at dawn and went out to kill dragons. The Headmaster kept him at home when it rained, because he said the woods were damp and unhealthy at such times and that he didn't want the boy to run needless risks. Few good days passed in which Gawaine failed to get a dragon. On one particularly fortunate day he killed three, a husband and wife and a visiting relative. Gradually he developed a technique. Pupils who sometimes watched him from the hilltops a long way off said that he often allowed the dragon to come within a few feet before he said "Rumplesnitz." He came to say it with a mocking sneer. Occasionally he did stunts. Once when an excursion party from London was watching him he went into action with his right hand tied behind his neck. The dragon's head came off just as easily.

As Gawaine's record of killings mounted higher the Headmaster found it impossible to keep him completely in hand. He fell into the habit of stealing out at night and engaging in long drinking bouts at the village tavern. It was after such a debauch that he rose a little before dawn one fine August morning and started out after his fiftieth dragon. His head was heavy and his mind sluggish. He was heavy in other respects as well, for he had adopted the somewhat vulgar practice of wearing his medals, ribbons and all, when he went out dragon hunting. The decorations began on his chest and ran all the way down to his abdomen. They must have weighed at least eight pounds.

Gawaine found a dragon in the same meadow where he had killed the first one. It was a fair-sized dragon, but evidently an old one. Its face was wrinkled and Gawaine thought he had never seen so hideous a countenance. Much to the lad's disgust, the monster refused to charge and Gawaine was obliged to walk toward him. He whistled as he went. The dragon regarded him hopelessly, but craftily. Of course it had heard of Gawaine. Even when the lad raised his battle ax the dragon made no move. It knew that there was no salvation in the quickest thrust of the head, for it had been informed that this hunter was protected by an enchantment. It merely waited, hoping something would turn up. Gawaine raised the battle ax and suddenly lowered it again. He had grown very pale and he trembled violently. The dragon suspected a trick. "What's the matter?" it asked, with false solicitude.

"I've forgotten the magic word," stammered Gawaine.

"What a pity," said the dragon. "So that was the secret. It doesn't seem quite sporting to me, all this magic stuff, you know. Not cricket, as we used to say when I was a little dragon; but after all, that's a matter of opinion."

Gawaine was so helpless with terror that the dragon's confidence rose immeasurably and it could not resist the temptation to show off a bit.

"Could I possibly be of any assistance?" it asked. "What's the first letter of the magic word?"

"It begins with an 'r,'" said Gawaine weakly.

"Let's see," mused the dragon, "that doesn't tell us much, does it? What sort of a word is this? Is it an epithet, do you think?"

Gawaine could do no more than nod.

"Why, of course," exclaimed the dragon, "reactionary Republican."

Gawaine shook his head.

"Well, then," said the dragon, "we'd better get down to business. Will you surrender?"

With the suggestion of a compromise Gawaine mustered up enough courage to speak.

"What will you do if I surrender?" he asked.

"Why, I'll eat you," said the dragon.

"And if I don't surrender?"

"I'll eat you just the same."

"Then it doesn't make any difference, does it?" moaned Gawaine.

"It does to me," said the dragon with a smile. "I'd rather you didn't surrender. You'd taste much better if you didn't."

The dragon waited for a long time for Gawaine to ask "Why?" but the boy was too frightened to speak. At last the dragon had to give the explanation without his cue line. "You see," he said, "if you don't surrender you'll taste better because you'll die game."

This was an old and ancient trick of the dragon's. By means of some such quip he was accustomed to paralyze his victims with laughter and then to destroy them. Gawaine was sufficiently paralyzed as it was, but laughter had no part in his helplessness. With the last word of the joke the dragon drew back his head and struck. In that second there flashed into the mind of Gawaine the magic word "Rumplesnitz," but there was no time to say it. There was time only to strike and, without a word, Gawaine met the onrush of the dragon with a full swing. He put all his back and shoulders into it. The impact was terrific and the head of the dragon flew away almost a hundred yards and landed in a thicket.

Gawaine did not remain frightened very long after the death of the dragon. His mood was one of wonder. He was enormously puzzled. He cut off the ears of the monster almost in a trance. Again and again he thought to himself, "I didn't say 'Rumplesnitz'!" He was sure of that and yet there was no question that he had killed the dragon. In fact, he had never killed one so utterly. Never before had he driven a head for anything like the same distance. Twenty-five yards was perhaps his best previous record. All the way back to the knight school he kept rumbling about in his mind seeking an explanation for what had occurred. He went to the Headmaster immediately and after closing the door told him what had happened. "I didn't say 'Rumplesnitz,'" he explained with great earnestness.

The Headmaster laughed. "I'm glad you've found out," he said. "It makes you ever so much more of a hero. Don't you see that? Now you know that it was you who killed all these dragons and not that foolish little word 'Rumplesnitz.'"

Gawaine frowned. "Then it wasn't a magic word after all?" he asked.

"Of course not," said the Headmaster, "you ought to be too old for such foolishness. There isn't any such thing as a magic word."

"But you told me it was magic," protested Gawaine. "You said it was magic and now you say it isn't."

"It wasn't magic in a literal sense," answered the Headmaster, "but it was much more wonderful than that. The word gave you confidence. It took away fears. If I hadn't told you that you might have been killed the very first time. It was your battle ax did the trick."

Gawaine surprised the Headmaster by his attitude. He was obviously distressed by the explanation. He interrupted a long philosophic and ethical discourse by the Headmaster with, "If I hadn't of hit 'em all mighty hard and fast any one of 'em might have crushed me like a, like a—" He fumbled for a word.

"Egg shell," suggested the Headmaster.

"Like a egg shell," assented Gawaine, and he said it many times. All through the evening meal people who sat near him heard him muttering, "Like a egg shell, like a egg shell."

The next day was clear, but Gawaine did not get up at dawn. Indeed, it was almost noon when the Headmaster found him cowering in bed, with the clothes pulled over his head. The principal called the Assistant Professor of Pleasaunce, and together they dragged the boy toward the forest.

"He'll be all right as soon as he gets a couple more dragons under his belt," explained the Headmaster.

The Assistant Professor of Pleasaunce agreed. "It would be a shame to stop such a fine run," he said. "Why, counting that one yesterday, he's killed fifty dragons."

They pushed the boy into a thicket above which hung a meager cloud of steam. It was obviously quite a small dragon. But Gawaine did not come back that night or the next. In fact, he never came back. Some weeks afterward brave spirits from the school explored the thicket, but they could find nothing to remind them of Gawaine except the metal parts of his medals. Even the ribbons had been devoured.

The Headmaster and the Assistant Professor of Pleasaunce agreed that it would be just as well not to tell the school how Gawaine had achieved his record and still less how he came to die. They held that it might have a bad effect on school spirit. Accordingly, Gawaine has lived in the memory of the school as its greatest hero. No visitor succeeds in leaving the building today without seeing a great shield which hangs on the wall of the dining hall. Fifty pairs of dragons' ears are mounted upon the shield and underneath in gilt letters is "Gawaine le Cœur-Hardy," followed by the simple inscription, "He killed fifty dragons." The record has never been equaled.

A Christmas Memory

By TRUMAN CAPOTE

IMAGINE a morning in late November. A coming of winter morning more than twenty years ago. Consider the kitchen of a spreading old house in a country town. A great black stove is its main feature; but there is also a big round table and a fireplace with two rocking chairs placed in front of it. Just today the fireplace commenced its seasonal roar.

A woman with shorn white hair is standing at the kitchen window. She is wearing tennis shoes and a shapeless gray sweater over a summery calico dress. She is small and sprightly, like a bantam hen; but, due to a long youthful illness, her shoulders are pitifully hunched. Her face is remarkable—not unlike Lincoln's, craggy like that, and tinted by sun and wind; but it is delicate too, finely boned, and her eyes are sherry-colored and timid. "Oh, my," she exclaims, her breath smoking the windowpane, "it's fruitcake weather!"

The person to whom she is speaking is myself. I am seven; she is sixty-something. We are cousins, very distant ones, and we have lived together —well, as long as I can remember. Other people inhabit the house, relatives; and though they have power over us, and frequently make us cry, we are not, on the whole, too much aware of them. We are each other's best friend. She calls me Buddy, in memory of a boy who was formerly her best friend. The other Buddy died in the 1880's, when she was still a child. She is still a child.

"I knew it before I got out of bed," she says, turning away from the window with a purposeful excitement in her eyes. "The courthouse bell sounded so cold and clear. And there were no birds singing; they've gone to warmer country, yes indeed. Oh, Buddy, stop stuffing biscuit and fetch our buggy. Help me find my hat. We've thirty cakes to bake."

It's always the same: a morning arrives in November, and my friend, as though officially inaugurating the Christmas time of year that exhilarates her imagination and fuels the blaze of her heart, announces: "It's fruitcake weather! Fetch our buggy. Help me find my hat."

The hat is found, a straw cartwheel corsaged with velvet roses out-of-

Reprinted from *Mademoiselle;* © 1956 by Street & Smith Publications, Inc. Reprinted by permission of the author.

doors has faded: it once belonged to a more fashionable relative. Together, we guide our buggy, a dilapidated baby carriage, out to the garden and into a grove of pecan trees. The buggy is mine; that is, it was bought for me when I was born. It is made of wicker, rather unraveled, and the wheels wobble like a drunkard's legs. But it is a faithful object; springtimes, we take it to the woods and fill it with flowers, herbs, wild fern for our porch pots; in the summer, we pile it with picnic paraphernalia and sugar-cane fishing poles and roll it down to the edge of a creek; it has its winter uses, too: as a truck for hauling firewood from the yard to the kitchen, as a warm bed for Queenie, our tough little orange and white rat terrier who has survived distemper and two rattlesnake bites. Queenie is trotting beside it now.

Three hours later we are back in the kitchen hulling a heaping buggyload of windfall pecans. Our backs hurt from gathering them: how hard they were to find (the main crop having been shaken off the trees and sold by the orchard's owners, who are not us) among the concealing leaves, the frosted, deceiving grass. Caarackle! A cheery crunch, scraps of miniature thunder sound as the shells collapse and the golden mound of sweet oily ivory meat mounts in a milk glass bowl. Queenie begs to taste, and now and again my friend sneaks her a mite, though insisting we deprive ourselves. "We mustn't, Buddy. If we start, we won't stop. And there's scarcely enough as there is. For thirty cakes." The kitchen is growing dark. Dusk turns the window into a mirror: our reflections mingle with the rising moon as we work by the fireside in the firelight. At last, when the moon is quite high, we toss the final hull into the fire and, with joined sighs, watch it catch flame. The buggy is empty, the bowl is brimful.

We eat our supper (cold biscuits, bacon, blackberry jam) and discuss tomorrow. Tomorrow the kind of work I like best begins: buying. Cherries and citron, ginger and vanilla and canned Hawaiian pineapple, rinds and raisins and walnuts and whiskey and oh, so much flour, butter, so many eggs, spices, flavorings: why, we'll need a pony to pull the buggy home.

But before these purchases can be made, there is the question of money. Neither of us has any. Except for skinflint sums persons in the house occasionally provide (a dime is considered very big money); or what we earn ourselves from various activities: holding rummage sales, selling buckets of hand-picked blackberries, jars of homemade jam and apple jelly and peach preserves, rounding up flowers for funerals and weddings. Once we won seventy-ninth prize, five dollars, in a national football contest. Not that we know a fool thing about football. It's just that we enter any contest we hear about: at the moment our hopes are centered on the fifty-thousand-dollar Grand Prize being offered to name a new brand of coffee (we suggested "A.M."; and, after some hesitation, for my friend thought it perhaps sacrilegious, the slogan "A.M.! Amen!"). To tell the truth, our only *really* profitable enterprise was the Fun and Freak Museum we conducted in a back-yard woodshed two summers ago. The Fun was a stereopticon with slide views of Washington and New York lent us by a relative who had been to those places (she was furious when she discovered why we'd borrowed it); the Freak was a three-legged biddy chicken hatched by one of our own hens. Everybody hereabouts wanted to see that biddy: we charged grownups a nickel, kids two cents. And took in a good twenty dollars before the museum shut down due to the decease of the main attraction.

But one way and another we do each year accumulate Christmas savings, a Fruitcake Fund. These moneys we keep hidden in an ancient bead purse under a loose board under the floor under a chamber pot under my friend's bed. The purse is seldom removed from this safe location except to make a deposit or, as happens every Saturday, a withdrawal; for on Saturdays I am allowed ten cents to go to the picture show. My friend has never been to a picture show, nor does she intend to: "I'd rather hear you tell the story, Buddy. That way I can imagine it more. Besides, a person my age shouldn't squander their eyes. When the Lord comes, let me see him clear." In addition to never having seen a movie, she has never: eaten in a restaurant, traveled more than five miles from home, received or sent a telegram, read anything except funny papers and the Bible, worn cosmetics, cursed, wished someone harm, told a lie on purpose, let a hungry dog go hungry. Here are a few things she has done, does do: killed with a hoe the biggest rattlesnake ever seen in this county (sixteen rattles), dip snuff (secretly), tame hummingbirds (just try it) till they balance on her finger, tell ghost stories (we both believe in ghosts) so tingling they chill you in July, talk to herself, take walks in the rain, grow the prettiest japonicas in town, know the recipe for every sort of old-time Indian cure, including a magical wart-remover.

Now, with supper finished, we retire to the room in a faraway part of the house where my friend sleeps in a scrap-quilt-covered iron bed painted rose pink, her favorite color. Silently, wallowing in the pleasures of conspiracy, we take the bead purse from its secret place and spill its contents on the scrap quilt. Dollar bills, tightly rolled and green as May buds. Somber fifty-cent pieces, heavy enough to weight a dead man's eyes. Lovely dimes, the liveliest coin, the one that really jingles. Nickels and quarters, worn smooth as creek pebbles. But mostly a hateful heap of bitter-odored pennies. Last summer others in the house contracted to pay us a penny for every twenty-five flies we killed. Oh, the carnage of August: the flies that flew to heaven! Yet it was not work in which we took pride. And, as we sit counting pennies, it is as though we were back tabulating dead flies. Neither of us has a head for figures; we count slowly, lose track, start again. According to her calculations, we have $12.73. According to mine, exactly $13. "I do hope you're wrong, Buddy. We can't mess around with thirteen. The cakes will fall. Or put somebody in the cemetery. Why, I wouldn't dream of getting out of bed on the thirteenth." This is true: she always spends thirteenths in bed. So, to be on the safe side, we subtract a penny and toss it out the window.

Of the ingredients that go into our fruitcakes, whiskey is the most expensive, as well as the hardest to obtain: State laws forbid its sale. But everybody knows you can buy a bottle from Mr. Haha Jones. And the next day, having completed our more prosaic shopping, we set out for Mr. Haha's business address, a "sinful" (to quote public opinion) fish-fry and dancing café down by the river. We've been there before, and on the same errand; but in previous years our dealings have been with Haha's wife, an iodine-dark Indian woman with brassy peroxided hair and a dead-tired disposition. Actually, we've never laid eyes on her husband, though we've heard that he's an Indian too. A giant with razor scars across his cheeks. They call him Haha because he's so gloomy, a man who never laughs. As we approach his café (a large log cabin festooned inside and out with chains of garish-gay naked light bulbs and standing by the river's muddy edge under the shade of river trees where moss drifts through the branches like gray mist) our steps slow down. Even Queenie stops prancing and sticks close by. People have been murdered in Haha's café. Cut to pieces. Hit on the head. There's a case coming up in court next month. Naturally these goings-on happen at night when the colored lights cast crazy patterns and the victrola wails. In the daytime Haha's is shabby and deserted. I knock at the door, Queenie barks, my friend calls: "Mrs. Haha, ma'am? Anyone to home?"

Footsteps. The door opens. Our hearts overturn. It's Mr. Haha Jones himself! And he *is* a giant; he *does* have scars; he *doesn't* smile. No, he glowers at us through Satan-tilted eyes and demands to know: "What you want with Haha?"

For a moment we are too paralyzed to tell. Presently my friend half-finds her voice, a whispery voice at best: "If you please, Mr. Haha, we'd like a quart of your finest whiskey."

His eyes tilt more. Would you believe it? Haha is smiling! Laughing, too. "Which one of you is a drinkin' man?"

"It's for making fruitcakes, Mr. Haha. Cooking."

This sobers him. He frowns. "That's no way to waste good whiskey." Nevertheless, he retreats into the shadowed café and seconds later appears carrying a bottle of daisy yellow unlabeled liquor. He demonstrates its sparkle in the sunlight and says: "Two dollars."

We pay him with nickels and dimes and pennies. Suddenly, jangling the coins in his hand like a fistful of dice, his face softens. "Tell you what," he proposes, pouring the money back into our bead purse, "just send me one of them fruitcakes instead."

"Well," my friend remarks on our way home, "there's a lovely man. We'll put an extra cup of raisins in *his* cake."

The black stove, stoked with coal and firewood, glows like a lighted pumpkin. Eggbeaters whirl, spoons spin round in bowls of butter and sugar, vanilla sweetens the air, ginger spices it; melting, nose-tingling odors saturate the kitchen, suffuse the house, drift out to the world on puffs of chimney smoke. In four days our work is done. Thirty-one cakes, dampened with whiskey, bask on window sills and shelves.

Who are they for?

Friends. Not necessarily neighbor friends: indeed, the larger share are intended for persons we've met maybe once, perhaps not at all. People who've struck our fancy. Like President Roosevelt. Like the Reverend and Mrs. J. C. Lucey, Baptist missionaries to Borneo who lectured here last winter. Or the little knife grinder who comes through town twice a year. Or Abner Packer, the driver of the six o'clock bus from Mobile, who exchanges waves with us every day as he passes in a dust-cloud whoosh. Or the young Wistons, a California couple whose car one afternoon broke down outside the house and who spent a pleasant hour chatting with us on the porch (young Mr. Wiston snapped our picture, the only one we've ever had taken). Is it because my friend is shy with everyone *except* strangers that these strangers, and merest acquaintances, seem to us our truest friends? I think yes. Also, the scrapbooks we keep of thank-you's on White House stationery, time to time communications from California and Borneo, the knife grinder's penny post cards, make us feel connected to eventful worlds beyond the kitchen with its view of a sky that stops.

Now a nude December fig branch grates against the window. The kitchen is empty, the cakes are gone; yesterday we carted the last of them to the post office, where the cost of stamps turned our purse inside out. We're broke. That rather depresses me, but my friend insists on celebrating—with two inches of whiskey left in Haha's bottle. Queenie has a spoonful in a bowl of coffee (she likes her coffee chicory-flavored and strong). The rest we divide between a pair of jelly glasses. We're both quite awed at the prospect of drinking straight whiskey; the taste of it brings screwed-up expressions and sour shudders. But by and by we begin to sing, the two of us singing different songs simultaneously. I don't know the words to mine, just: *Come on along, come on along, to the dark-town strutters' ball.* But I can dance: that's what I mean to be, a tap dancer in the movies. My dancing shadow rollicks on the walls; our voices rock the chinaware; we giggle: as if unseen hands were tickling us. Queenie rolls on her back, her paws plow the air, something like a grin stretches her black lips. Inside myself, I feel warm and sparky as those crumbling logs, carefree as the wind in the chimney. My friend waltzes round the stove, the hem of her poor calico skirt pinched between her fingers as though it were a party dress: *Show me the way to go home,* she sings, her tennis shoes squeaking on the floor, *Show me the way to go home.*

Enter: two relatives. Very angry. Potent with eyes that scold, tongues that scald. Listen to what they have to say, the words tumbling together into a wrathful tune: "A child of seven! whiskey on his breath! are you out of your mind? feeding a child of seven! must be loony! road to ruination! remember Cousin Kate? Uncle Charlie? Uncle Charlie's brother-in-law? shame! scandal! humiliation! kneel, pray, beg the Lord!"

Queenie sneaks under the stove. My friend gazes at her shoes, her chin quivers, she lifts her skirt and blows her nose and runs to her room. Long after the town has gone to sleep and the house is silent except for the chimings of clocks and the sputter of fading fires, she is weeping into a pillow already as wet as a widow's handkerchief.

"Don't cry," I say, sitting at the bottom of her bed and shivering despite my flannel nightgown that smells of last winter's cough sirup, "don't cry," I beg, teasing her toes, tickling her feet, "you're too old for that."

"It's because," she hiccups, "I *am* too old. Old and funny."

"Not funny. Fun. More fun than anybody. Listen. If you don't stop crying you'll be so tired tomorrow we can't go cut a tree."

She straightens up. Queenie jumps on the bed (where Queenie is not allowed) to lick her cheeks. "I know where we'll find real pretty trees, Buddy. And holly, too. With berries big as your eyes. It's way off in the woods. Farther than we've ever been. Papa used to bring us Christmas trees from there: carry them on his shoulder. That's fifty years ago. Well, now: I can't wait for morning."

Morning. Frozen rime lusters the grass; the sun, round as an orange and orange as hot-weather moons, balances on the horizon, burnishes the silvered winter woods. A wild turkey calls. A renegade hog grunts in the undergrowth. Soon, by the edge of knee-deep, rapid-running water, we have to abandon the buggy. Queenie wades the stream first, paddles across barking complaints at the swiftness of the current, the pneumonia-making coldness of it. We follow, holding our shoes and equipment (a hatchet, a burlap sack) above our heads. A mile more: of chastising thorns, burrs and briers that catch at our clothes; of rusty pine needles brilliant with gaudy fungus and molted feathers. Here, there, a flash, a flutter, an ecstasy of shrillings remind us that not all the birds have flown south. Always, the path unwinds through lemony sun pools and pitch vine tunnels. Another creek to cross: a disturbed armada of speckled trout froths the water round us, and frogs the size of plates practice belly flops; beaver workmen are building a dam. On the farther shore, Queenie shakes herself and trembles. My friend shivers, too: not with cold but enthusiasm. One of her hat's ragged roses sheds a petal as she lifts her head and inhales the pine-heavy air. "We're almost there; can you smell it, Buddy?" she says, as though we were approaching an ocean.

And, indeed, it is a kind of ocean. Scented acres of holiday trees, prickly-leafed holly. Red berries shiny as Chinese bells: black crows swoop upon them screaming. Having stuffed our burlap sacks with enough greenery and crimson to garland a dozen windows, we set about choosing a tree. "It should be," muses my friend, "twice as tall as a boy. So a boy can't steal the star." The one we pick is twice as tall as me. A brave handsome brute that survives thirty hatchet strokes before it kneels with a creaking rending cry. Lugging it like a kill, we commence the long trek out. Every few yards we abandon the struggle, sit down and pant. But we have the strength of triumphant huntsmen; that and the tree's virile, icy perfume revive us, goad us on. Many compliments accompany our sunset return along the red clay road to town; but my friend is sly and non-committal when passers-by praise the treasure perched in our buggy: what a fine tree and where did it come from? "Yonderways," she murmurs vaguely. Once a car stops and the rich mill owner's lazy wife leans out and whines: "Giveya two-bits cash for that ol tree." Ordinarily my friend is afraid of saying no; but on this occasion she promptly shakes her head: "We wouldn't take a dollar." The mill owner's wife persists. "A dollar, my foot! Fifty cents. That's my last offer. Goodness, woman, you can get another one." In answer, my friend gently reflects: "I doubt it. There's never two of anything."

Home: Queenie slumps by the fire and sleeps till tomorrow, snoring loud as a human.

A trunk in the attic contains: a shoebox of ermine tails (off the opera cape of a curious lady who once rented a room in the house), coils of frazzled tinsel gone gold with age, one silver star, a brief rope of dilapidated, undoubtedly dangerous candy-like light bulbs. Excellent decorations, as far as they go, which isn't far enough: my friend wants our tree to blaze "like a Baptist window," droop with weighty snows of ornament. But we can't afford the made-in-Japan splendors at the five-and-dime. So we do what we've always done: sit for days at the kitchen table with scissors and crayons and stacks of colored paper. I make sketches and my friend cuts them out: lots of cats, fish too (because they're easy to draw), some apples, some watermelons, a few winged angels devised from saved-up sheets of Hershey bar tin foil. We use safety pins to attach these creations to the tree; as a final touch, we sprinkle the branches with shredded cotton (picked in August for this purpose). My friend, surveying the effect, clasps her hands together. "Now honest, Buddy. Doesn't it look good enough to eat?" Queenie tries to eat an angel.

After weaving and ribboning holly wreaths for all the front windows, our next project is the fashioning of family gifts. Tie-dye scarves for the ladies, for the men a home-brewed lemon and licorice and aspirin sirup to be taken "at the first Symptoms of a Cold and after Hunting." But when it comes time for making each other's gift, my friend and I separate to work secretly. I would like to buy her a pearl-handled knife, a radio, a whole pound of chocolate-covered cherries (we tasted some once, and she always swears: "I could live on them, Buddy, Lord yes I could—and that's not taking His name in vain"). Instead, I am building her a kite. She would like to give me a bicycle (she's said so on several million occasions: "If only I could, Buddy. It's bad enough in life to do without something *you* want; but confound it, what gets my goat is not being able to give somebody something you want *them* to have. Only one of these days I will, Buddy. Locate you a bike. Don't ask how. Steal it, maybe"). Instead, I'm fairly certain that she is building me a kite—the same as last year, and the year before: the year before that we exchanged slingshots. All of which is fine by me. For we are champion kite-fliers who study the wind like sailors; my friend, more accomplished than I, can get a kite aloft when there isn't enough breeze to carry clouds.

Christmas Eve afternoon we scrape together a nickel and go to the butcher's to buy Queenie's traditional gift, a good gnawable beef bone. The bone, wrapped in funny paper, is placed high in the tree near the silver star. Queenie knows it's there. She squats at the foot of the tree staring up in a trance of greed: when bedtime arrives she refuses to budge. Her excitement is equaled by my own. I kick the covers and turn my pillow as though it were a scorching summer's night. Somewhere a rooster crows: falsely, for the sun is still on the other side of the world.

"Buddy, are you awake?" It is my friend, calling from her room, which is next to mine; and an instant later she is sitting on my bed holding a candle. "Well, I can't sleep a hoot," she declares. "My mind's jumping like a jack rabbit. Buddy, do you think Mrs. Roosevelt will serve our cake at dinner?" We huddle in the bed, and she squeezes my hand I-love-you. "Seems like your hand used to be so much smaller. I guess I hate to see you grow up. When you're grown up, will we still be friends?" I say always. "But I feel so bad, Buddy. I wanted so bad to give you a bike. I tried to sell my cameo Papa gave me. Buddy," she hesitates, as though embarrassed, "—I made you another kite." Then I confess that I made her one, too; and we laugh. The candle burns too short to hold. Out it goes, exposing the starlight, the stars spinning at the window like a visible caroling that slowly, slowly daybreak silences. Possibly we doze; but the beginnings of dawn splash us like cold water: we're up, wide-eyed and wandering while we wait for others to waken. Quite deliberately my friend drops a kettle on the kitchen floor. I tap-dance in front of closed doors. One by one the household emerges, looking as though they'd like to kill us both; but it's Christmas, so they can't. First, a gorgeous breakfast: just everything you can imagine—from flapjacks and fried squirrel to hominy grits and honey-in-the-comb. Which puts everyone in a good humor except my friend and I. Frankly, we're so impatient to get at the presents we can't eat a mouthful.

Well, I'm disappointed. Who wouldn't be? With socks, a Sunday school shirt, some handkerchiefs, a hand-me-down sweater and a year's subscription to a religious magazine for children. *The Little Shepherd*. It makes me boil. It really does.

My friend has a beter haul. A sack of Satsumas, that's her best present. She is proudest, however, of a white wool shawl knitted by her married sister. But she *says* her favorite gift is the kite I built her. And it *is* very beautiful; though not as beautiful as the one she made me, which is blue and scattered with gold and green Good Conduct stars; moreover, my name is painted on it, "Buddy."

"Buddy, the wind is blowing."

The wind is blowing, and nothing will do till we've run to a pasture below the house where Queenie has scooted to bury her bone (and where, a winter hence, Queenie will be buried, too.) There, plunging through the healthy waist-high grass, we unreel our kites, feel them twitching at the string like sky fish as they swim into the wind. Satisfied, sun-warmed, we sprawl in the grass and peel Satsumas and watch our kites cavort. Soon I forget the socks and hand-me-down sweater. I'm as happy as if we'd already won the fifty-thousand-dollar Grand Prize in that coffee-naming contest.

"My, how foolish I am!" my friend cries, suddenly alert, like a woman remembering too late she has biscuits in the oven. "You know what I've always thought?" she asks in a tone of discovery, and not smiling at me but a point beyond. "I've always thought a body would have to be sick and dying before they saw the Lord. And I imagined that when he came it would be like looking at the Baptist window: pretty as colored glass with the sun pouring through, such a shine you don't know it's getting dark. And it's been a comfort: to think of that shine taking away all the spooky feeling. But I'll wager it never happens. I'll wager at the very end a body realizes the Lord has already shown himself. That things as they are," her hand circles in a gesture that gathers clouds and kites and grass and Queenie pawing earth over her bone, "just what they've always seen, was seeing him. As for me, I could leave the world with today in my eyes."

This is our last Christmas together.

Life separates us. Those who Know Best decide that I belong in a military school. And so follows a miserable succession of bugle-blowing prisons, grim reveille-ridden summer camps. I have a new home too. But it doesn't count. Home is where my friend is, and there I never go.

And there she remains, puttering around the kitchen. Alone with Queenie. Then alone. ("Buddy dear," she writes in her wild hard-to-read script, "yesterday Jim Macy's horse kicked Queenie bad. Be thankful she didn't feel much. I wrapped her in a Fine Linen sheet and rode her in the buggy down to Simpson's pasture where she can be with all her Bones . . ."). For a few Novembers she continues to bake her fruitcakes singlehanded; not as many, but some: and, of course, she always sends me "the best of the batch." Also, in every letter she encloses a dime wadded in toilet paper: "See a picture show and write me the story." But gradually in her letters she tends to confuse me with her other friend, the Buddy who died in the 1880's; more and more thirteenths are not the only days she stays in bed: a morning arrives in November, a leafless birdless coming of winter morning, when she cannot rouse herself to exclaim: "Oh my, it's fruitcake weather!"

And when that happens, I know it. A message saying so merely confirms a piece of news some secret vein had already received, severing from me an irreplaceable part of myself, letting it loose like a kite on a broken string. That is why, walking across a school campus on this particular December morning, I keep searching the sky. As if I expected to see, rather like hearts, a lost pair of kites hurrying toward heaven.

BOYS AND GIRLS TOGETHER

1. Vive la Difference!

By ALAN BECK

If mail response or requests for reprints are any criterion the most successful leaflets ever distributed by a private company in America are a pair of brief essays entitled, respectively, "What Is a Boy?" and "What Is a Girl?" They were written by Alan Beck for the New England Mutual Life Insurance Company, which owns the copyrights.

To date the company itself has distributed over 2,000,000 copies of each of these essays. There have been over a thousand authorized reprints—and some, possibly innocently, just "copied." Figure in republication in the *Saturday Evening Post,* the *Reader's Digest,* the *New York Times,* and other newspapers, and the total circulation becomes almost astronomical.

"Which essay has proven the most popular?" I asked author Alan Beck. "I'd say it was about a standoff," he replied cautiously. "After all, they're both cut from the same pattern. I think the Girl essay is better written because it was done 'on purpose' whereas the Boy essay originally was just an editorial in our company magazine, *The Pilot's Log.* I had no idea anyone would give it more than a casual reading!"

Beck treasures a letter from one lady which concluded, "For a long time my husband refused to have any children, but after hearing 'What Is a Boy?' on the radio he has changed his mind." There also was a request from a distinguished matriarch worded, "I have three great-granddaughters, five granddaughters, and four daughters. Please send me a copy of 'What Is a Girl?' (as if I didn't know!)."

The essays have been translated into more than a dozen languages, put into *The Congressional Record,* transcribed into Braille, used by the State Department in Japan, recorded by Victor, Columbia, and Decca, and beamed behind the Iron Curtain on the Voice of America. Ministers have used them in sermons; prison publications featured them; doctors handed them to prospective fathers. Framed copies hang on every kind of wall—from convents to barrooms.

Is it possible that you may have overlooked one or both of these essays yourself? With that thought in mind they are reprinted here, by permission of Alan Beck and New England Mutual.

Ed. Note

What Is a Boy?

Between the innocence of babyhood and the dignity of manhood we find a delightful creature called a boy. Boys come in assorted sizes, weights, and colors, but all boys have the same creed: To enjoy every second of every minute of every hour of every day and to protest with noise (their only weapon) when their last minute is finished and the adult males pack them off to bed at night.

Boys are found everywhere—on top of, underneath, inside of, climbing on, swinging from, running around, or jumping to. Mothers love them, little girls hate them, older sisters and brothers tolerate them, adults ignore them, and Heaven protects them. A boy is Truth with dirt on its face, Beauty with a cut on its finger, Wisdom with bubble gum in its hair, and the Hope of the future with a frog in its pocket.

When you are busy a boy is an inconsiderate, bothersome, intruding jangle of noise. When you want him to make a good impression his brain turns to jelly or else he becomes a savage, sadistic, jungle creature bent on destroying the world and himself with it.

A boy is a composite—he has the appetite of a horse, the digestion of a sword swallower, the energy of a pocket-size atomic bomb, the curiosity of a cat, the lungs of a dictator, the imagination of a Paul Bunyan, the shyness of a violet, the audacity of a steel trap, the enthusiasm of a fire-cracker, and when he makes something he has five thumbs on each hand.

He likes ice cream, knives, saws, Christmas, comic books, the boy across the street, woods, water (in its natural habitat), large animals, Dad, trains, Saturday mornings, and fire engines. He is not much for Sunday school, company, schools, books without pictures, music lessons, neckties, barbers, girls, overcoats, adults, or bedtime.

Nobody else is so early to rise or so late to supper. Nobody else gets so much fun out of trees, dogs, and breezes. Nobody else can cram into one pocket a rusty knife, a half-eaten apple, three feet of string, an empty Bull Durham sack, two gumdrops, six cents, a slingshot, a chunk of unknown substance, and a genuine supersonic code ring with a secret compartment.

A boy is a magical creature—you can lock him out of your workshop, but you can't lock him out of your heart. You can get him out of your study, but you can't get him out your mind. Might as well give up—he is your captor, your jailer, your boss, and your master—a freckle-faced, pint-sized, cat-chasing bundle of noise. But when you come home at night with only the shattered pieces of your hopes and dreams he can mend them like new with two magic words—"Hi, Dad!"

What Is a Girl?

Little girls are the nicest things that happen to people. They are born with a little bit of angel-shine about them and though it wears thin sometimes there is always enough left to lasso your heart—even when they are sitting in the mud, or crying temperamental tears, or parading up the street in Mother's best clothes.

A little girl can be sweeter (and badder) oftener than anyone else in the world. She can jitter around, and stomp, and make funny noises that frazzle your nerves, yet just when you open your mouth she stands there demure with that special look in her eyes. A girl is Innocence playing in the mud, Beauty standing on its head, and Motherhood dragging a doll by the foot.

Girls are available in five colors—black, white, red, yellow, or brown, yet Mother Nature always manages to select your favorite color when you place your order. They disprove the law of supply and demand—there are millions of little girls, but each is as precious as rubies.

God borrows from many creatures to make a little girl. He uses the song of a bird, the squeal of a pig, the stubbornness of a mule, the antics of a monkey, the spryness of a grasshopper, the curiosity of a cat, the speed of a gazelle, the slyness of a fox, the softness of a kitten, and to top it all off He adds the mysterious mind of a woman.

A little girl likes new shoes, party dresses, small animals, first-grade noisemakers, the girl next door, dolls, make-believe, dancing lessons, ice-cream parlors, coloring books, make-up, cans of water, going visiting, tea parties, and one boy. She doesn't care so much for visitors, boys in general, large dogs, hand-me-downs, straight chairs, vegetables, snow suits, or staying in the front yard. She is loudest when you are thinking, the prettiest when she has provoked you, the busiest at bedtime, the quietest when you want to show her off, and the most flirtatious when she absolutely must not get the best of you again.

Who else can cause you more grief, joy, irritation, satisfaction, embarrassment, and genuine delight than this combination of Eve, Salome, and Florence Nightingale? She can muss up your home, your hair, and your dignity—spend your money, your time, and your temper—then just when your patience is ready to crack, her sunshine peeks through and you've lost again.

Yes, she is a nerve-racking nuisance, just a noisy bundle of mischief. But when your dreams tumble down and the world is a mess—when it seems you are pretty much of a fool after all—she can make you a king when she climbs on your knees and whispers, "I love you best of all!"

2. *The Klobber System*

By MOSS HART

Moss Hart and his wife, the lovely Kitty Carlisle, have two children (a boy, Christopher, and a girl, Cathy) whom they adore and spoil. In other words, they are typical American parents. Occasionally, however, the Hart offspring become obstreperous at the very hour Mr. Hart, in the throes of creation, most desires a deep and impenetrable silence in the house.

It was in such a moment of frustration that Mr. Hart conceived his now famous Klobber System. He didn't mean one word of it, of course, but the first time he so much as mentioned it, my own wife and his reacted so violently, I urged him to write it out for me. This he did, after considerable prodding, adding a few improvisations in the process. When I gleefully printed his piece in my Trade Winds column in the *Saturday Review,* over a hundred outraged mothers took it seriously enough to write indignant letters. Two ladies, in fact, canceled their subscriptions. (There were favorable comments, too. A man in Baltimore sent a one-word telegram: "Hallelujah!")

Mr. Hart was duly gratified, and has, indeed, been advocating the Klobber System (when his wife and children aren't listening) ever since.

ED. NOTE

DEAR BENNETT:

Do you remember, one lovely starlit evening on the desert a few weeks ago, our discussing, at some length and with a good deal of parental acrimony, the proper method of bringing up children? That usually discerning and extremely wise lady, your wife, disagreed violently and somewhat haughtily, I thought, at the method we use in our house, but I thought you showed unusual interest in our experiment and silently longed to apply it yourself, so I pass it on to you and to any other frantic and harassed parents who, like ourselves, were damn near ready for the booby hatch until the Klobber System came into our home.

The Klobber Method was discovered, or rather invented, by Ernest J. Klobber, a Viennese psychiatrist who, at the time of the discovery of the method which was to bear his name, was a staunch believer in the modern and accepted formula for rearing children. Give them a reason for everything—watch out for traumas—plenty of love and security—and never a harsh word. So great an exponent of this formula was Professor Klobber that, at the time of his discovery, the Professor, who has six children of his own, was about to be carted off to a sanitarium in a state of complete nervous collapse; a condition any modern parent will understand at once. As the stretcher was being carried out of the house one of the children aimed a kick at it which, with unerring childlike aim, landed exactly where it was meant to land. The Professor, though thoroughly used to being kicked by his children, was under mild sedation at the time, and it may have been this that caused a curious reflex action on the Professor's part. Bringing his arm up from the stretcher, he brought his hand down with a good sharp crack on the child's head. There was an anguished howl from the child—first time in its life no reason had been given for an action—but the effect on the Professor was startling. He leaped up from the stretcher and gave each of the other five kiddies in turn a good smart crack over the head—a Klobber, as he afterward termed it—and never went near the sanitarium. Instead, in suddenly excellent spirits and health, he began to develop the Klobber Method. No reason was given for anything. "No" meant "no" and "yes" meant "yes," and trauma or no trauma, at the first hint of an argument the children got a Klobber, and life, for the Professor and his good wife, was livable for the first time since the patter of little feet had thundered through the house.

Like all great discoveries, however, the Klobber Method met with furious opposition on the part of educators and progressive parent organizations, and it was not until a refinement of the Method was suggested by an assistant of the Professor's that it began to meet with popular, if secretive, approval. The Professor's assistant, one Heinrich Klonk, suggested that—since a good Klobber usually left a telltale lump—a short side swipe, or a Klonk, in other words, would do the trick just as well, and to hell with PTA's and such. Heinrich Klonk is one of the unsung heroes of our time for, though he gets small credit for the Klobber Method, his little refinement worked like a charm, and the word "Klonk" echoes through thousands of peaceful homes like a balm.

The charm of this method, my dear Bennett, is its utter simplicity. In place of long hours of dreary explanation that Daddy cannot work if Junior bangs on the radiator and if Daddy cannot work and make money, how will we go to the circus; in place of that tortured quiet between husband and wife in the long night hours as to which one warped the childish id by refusing to allow the hot foot to be applied to Uncle Robert; in place of all that—just "Klonk!" and serenity reigns. It is the greatest invention since the wheel, my dear fellow, and as your wife seems to object to it, try it on her first instead of the children and let me know the results. I'll still be out here—three thousand miles away—but I'd like to know what happens.

Ever yours,
Moss HART

3. Apology at Bedtime

By HARLAN MILLER

Harlan Miller's best pieces about the lighter side of family life, written over a period of years for the *Ladies' Home Journal* and the Des Moines *Register*, have been collected in book form under the title of *There's a Man in the House*. One of the pieces in the book that attracted the most attention is "Apology at Bedtime." Miller insists that he didn't write it himself; that although he revamped it several times, he believes the original author was one W. Livingston Larned, "whom he has been unable to locate." Until this mysterious Mr. Larned steps forward to identify himself, I will cling to the belief that Mr. Miller is just playing modest.

ED. NOTE

Listen, son: I am saying this to you as you lie asleep, one little paw crumpled under your cheek, blond curls on your damp forehead.

I have just stolen into your room alone. Just a few minutes ago, as I sat reading my paper in the library, a hot, stifling wave of remorse swept over me. I could not resist it. Guiltily I came to your bedside.

These things I was thinking, son: I had been cross. I scolded you as you were dressing for school because you gave your face just a dab with a towel.

I took you to task for not cleaning your shoes. I called out angrily when I found that you had thrown some of your things on the floor.

At breakfast, too, I found fault. You spilled things. You put your elbows on the table. You spread butter too thick on your bread.

As you started off to play, I made for my car, you turned & waved your your little hand and called, "Good-by, Daddy!" & I frowned and said in reply, "Straighten your shoulders!"

Then it began all over again the late afternoon. As I came up the hill I spied you down on your knees playing marbles. There were holes in your stockings. I humiliated you before your boy friends by making you march ahead of me back to the house.

"Stockings are expensive—and if you had to buy them you would be more careful." Imagine that, son, from a father! Such stupid logic.

Do you remember, later, when I was reading in the library, how you came in, softly, timidly, with a sort of hurt look in your eyes? When I glanced up over my paper, impatient at the interruption, you hesitated at the door. "What is it you want?" I snapped.

You said nothing, but ran across, in one tempestuous plunge, & threw your arms around my neck & kissed me, again & again, & your small arms tightened with an affection that God had set blooming in your heart & which even neglect could not wither. And then you were gone, pattering up the stairs.

Well, son, it was shortly afterward that my paper slipped from my hands & a terrible sickening fear came over me. Suddenly I saw my horrible selfishness, & I felt sick at heart.

What has habit been doing to me? The habit of complaining, of finding fault, of reprimanding, all of these were my reward to you for being only a small boy.

It was not that I did not love you; it was that I expected too much of youth. I was measuring you by the yardstick of my own age. Son, I am sorry . . . I'll try not to let my impatience, my nervousness, my worries, muddle or conceal my love for you.

Let the Bridges Fall Down

By DOROTHY CANFIELD FISHER

TOWN MEETINGS are important events in any Vermont town. Once in a while, there is one which the community never forgets, because in it a crisis was reached and passed. One such came in Arlington as the ending of years of effort to build a graded school.

Till then, we had had district schools scattered all around the township, as was the old way of providing educational opportunities. Children lived then in homes very much more widely separated than now. For instance, up on what is called Southeast Corners, where there isn't now a single house or even a cellar hole left, there was quite a sizable settlement in the early days. More than thirty children learned to read and write and do their sums in the schoolhouse, and a lively community of active young people lived all around them. But little by little, after the building of the railroad, homes became more and more concentrated down in the valley near the three established settlements of Arlington, East Arlington and West Arlington. The schools in the settlements never had been more than big district schools, poorly equipped, nearly always very much over-crowded. The only education they could offer was a primitive and scanty preparation for American life, which grew constantly more complex. The educational requirements for success in the modern world were ever so much higher than in the old days.

It took a long time for Arlington to recognize the need for a new, well-equipped school if its children were to have a fair chance. Everybody was startled by the high cost of such education. Year after year, the proposition was voted down by one of the two kinds of opinion which always exist in every human group. On one side was the feeling that the *status quo,* the old, venerated, community-life pattern must not be touched. "What was good enough for my grandfather is all right for anybody. *He* got along all right." These citizens represented the natural human love for the past. Also the natural human dislike for taxes. Against them were the citizens who hoped that the future would be better than the past. Such voters always struggle to help bring the future to birth, rather than to coast along protecting the way of life of years gone by. Year after year, spirited discussions were held, as these two elements in our community fought—with ballots, the American way—for their idea of what was the best thing to do for our town.

The proposition was to erect a graded school where the primary education would be improved, and which would also provide high school education. Till then, the nearest high school had been in North Bennington. There were few automobiles, the roads were not left open in winter, North Bennington was too far for horse transportation. The only way to reach that nearest high school was by very slow, very inconvenient train service. This meant that of our Arlington children none except those of the relatively well-to-do could get high school training. Would it be possible to give them, here in Arlington, the chance for a preparation for life which other American children had? One group of our voters believed that the town could never raise the money for the building and upkeep of the school. They admitted that, from the long-range point of view, better education was needed; but against that need were listed Arlington's immediate wants. The hill roads should be resurfaced. Care for the sick poor was more costly every year. But above all the bridges.

Our bridges needed reinforcement not only from recurring flash floods and high water but against the increasing tonnage of modern traffic. It would take all the tax money we could raise to keep the bridges in repair; and there were many other absolutely necessary material needs. It would be simply crazy to add to our spending the enormous (so it seemed to us) cost of a new school.

The discussion was hot. The material needs of the body, and the immaterial needs of the mind and spirit, stood up to see which was the stronger. As often happens, the material needs outshouted the need for human development and growth. They sounded much more actual and real.

The little flickering flame of responsibility to protect the future of the town's children grew dimmer. Those who had, year after year, worked for a good school sat silent. The predicted crashing of the bridges sounded loud in their ears. What could be said against *that?*

Then up sprang Patrick Thompson. What education he had—such as it was, was sound—he had received in our meager district schools. And he knew that it was not enough for his children.

We usually saw him in a white apron standing behind the counter in his grocery store selling sugar and tea. We have never forgotten how he looked that day at Town Meeting, his powerful shoulders squared, his hands clenched. I still remember his exact words, intense as the flame of a blowtorch. "We are being told," he said, "that our town cannot afford to keep its bridges safe and also make a decent provision for its children's education. That's what we are being *told*. Not one of us here really believes it. We just can't think of anything to say back. But suppose it were true—then I say, *if we have to choose,* 'Let the bridges fall down!' What kind of a town would we rather have, fifty years from now—a place where nitwit folks go back and forth over good bridges? Or a town which has always given its children a fair chance, and prepares them to hold their own in modern life? If they've had a fair chance, they can build their own bridges. You know which of these two is really wanted by every one of us here. I say, If we have to choose, *let the bridges fall down!*"

He took his seat in silence.

It was the turning point in the life of our town. We knew it was. So we spoke not a word but sat thinking. When the vote was taken, a big majority voted "yes" for the school. Some years later, that school—not very well built—burned and was replaced, almost without an opposing vote, by a better one. The whole town had moved forward by a long step.

Patrick Thompson has been long in his grave. But he walks at the head of every graduating class in our high school.

This story was written just as it happened, and put into *Vermont Tradition*. From that book it has been taken out to be reprinted in ever so many newspapers and magazines and books all across the United States. And it has been translated and published in magazines in France, in Portugal, in Spain, and in Japan.

Think of our Arlington citizen shouting out his cry for better education—in Japanese!

The Great Pancake Record

By OWen JOHNSON

LITTLE SMEED stood apart, in the obscure shelter of the station, waiting to take his place on the stage which would carry him to the great new boarding school. He was frail and undersized, with a long, pointed nose and vacant eyes that stupidly assisted the wide mouth to make up a famished face. The scarred bag in his hand hung from one clasp, the premature trousers were at half-mast, while pink polka dots blazed from the cuffs of his nervous sleeves.

By the wheels of the stage, "Fire Crackers" Glendenning and "Jock" Hasbrouck, veterans of the Kennedy House, sporting the varsity initials on their sweaters and caps, were busily engaged in cross-examining the new boys who clambered timidly to their places on top. Presently, Fire Crackers, perceiving Smeed, hailed him.

"Hello, over there—what's your name?"

"Smeed, sir."

"Smeed what?"

"Johnnie Smeed."

The questioner looked him over with disfavor and said aggressively: "You're not for the Kennedy?"

"No, sir."

"What house?"

"The Dickinson, sir."

"The Dickinson, eh? That's a good one," said Fire Crackers, with a laugh, and, turning to his companion, he added, "Say, Jock, won't Hickey and the old Turkey be wild when they get this one?"

Little Smeed, uncomprehending of the judgment that had been passed, stowed his bag inside and clambered up to a place on the top. Jimmy, at the reins, gave a warning shout. The horses, stirred by the whip, churned obediently through the sideways of Trenton.

Lounging on the stage were half a dozen newcomers, six well-assorted types, from the well-groomed stripling of the city to the aggressive, big-limbed animal from the West, all profoundly under the sway of the two old boys who sat on the box with Jimmy and rattled on with quiet superi-

From *The Prodigious Hickey* by Owen Johnson. Copyright 1910 by Little, Brown & Company, Copyright 1938 by Owen Johnson. Reprinted by permission of Little, Brown & Company.

ority. The coach left the outskirts of the city and rolled into the white highway that leads to Lawrenceville. The known world departed for Smeed. He gazed fearfully ahead, waiting the first glimpse of the new continent.

Suddenly Fire Crackers turned and, scanning the embarrassed group, singled out the strong Westerner with an approving glance.

"You're for the Kennedy?"

The boy, stirring uneasily, blurted out:

"Yes, sir."

"What's your name?"

"Tom Walsh."

"How old are you"

"Eighteen."

"What do you weigh?"

"One hundred and seventy."

"Stripped?"

"What? Oh, no, sir—regular way."

"You've played a good deal of football?"

"Yes, sir."

Hasbrouck took up the questioning with a critical appreciation.

"What position?"

"Guard and tackle."

"You know Bill Stevens?"

"Yes, sir."

"He spoke about you; said you played on the Military Academy. You'll try for the varsity?"

"I guess so."

Hasbrouck turned to Fire Crackers in solemn conclave.

"He ought to stand up against Turkey if he knows anything about the game. If we get a good end we ought to give that Dickinson crowd the fight of their lives."

"There's a fellow came from Montclair they say is pretty good," Fire Crackers said, with solicitous gravity. "The line'll be all right if we can get some good halves. That's where the Dickinson has it on us."

Smeed listened in awe to the two statesmen studying out the chances of the Kennedy eleven for the house championship, realizing suddenly that there were new and sacred purposes about his new life of which he had no conception. Then, absorbed by the fantasy of the trip and the strange unfolding world into which he was jogging, he forgot the lords of the Kennedy, forgot his fellows in ignorance, forgot that he didn't play football and was only a stripling, forgot everything but the fascination of the moment when the great school would rise out of the distance and fix itself indelibly in his memory.

"There's the water tower," said Jimmy, extending the whip; "you'll see the school from the top of the hill."

Little Smeed craned forward with a sudden thumping of his heart. In the distance, a mile away, a cluster of brick and tile sprang out of the green, like a herd of red deer surprised in the forest. Groups of boys began to show on the roadside. Strange greetings were flung back and forth.

"Hello-oo, Fire Crackers!"

"How-de-do, Saphead!"

"Oh, there, Jock Hasbrouck!"

"Oh, you Morning Glory!"

"Oh, you Kennedys, we're going to lick you!"

"Yes you are, Dickinson!"

The coach passed down the shaded vault of the village street, turned into the campus, passed the ivy-clad house of the head master and rolled around a circle of well-trimmed lawn, past the long, low Upper House where the Fourth Form gazed at them in senior superiority; past the great brown masses of Memorial Hall and the pointed chapel, around to where the houses were ranged in red, extended bodies. Little Smeed felt an abject sinking of the heart at this sudden exposure to the thousand eyes fastened upon him from the wide esplanade of the Upper, from the steps of Memorial, from house, windows and stoops, from the shade of apple trees and the glistening road.

All at once the stage stopped and Jimmy cried:

"Dickinson!"

At one end of the red brick building, overrun with cool vines, a group of boys were lolling in flannels and light jerseys. A chorus went up.

"Hello, Fire Crackers!"

"Hello, Jock!"

"Hello, you Hickey boy!"

"Hello, Turkey; see what we've brought you!"

Smeed dropped to the ground amid a sudden hush.

"Fare," said Jimmy aggressively.

Smeed dug into his pocket and tendered the necessary coin. The coach squeaked away, while from the top Fire Crackers' exulting voice returned in insolent exultation:

"Hard luck, Dickinson! Hard luck, you old Hickey!"

Little Smeed, his hat askew, his collar rolled up, his bag at his feet, stood in the road, alone in the world, miserable and thoroughly frightened. One path led to the silent, hostile group on the steps, another went in safety to the master's entrance. He picked up his bag hastily.

"Hello, you—over there!"

Smeed understood it was a command. He turned submissively and approached with embarrassed steps. Face to face with these superior beings, tanned and muscular, stretched in Olympian attitudes, he realized all at once the hopelessness of his ever daring to associate with such demigods. Still he stood, shifting from foot to foot, eying the steps, waiting for the solemn ordeal of examination and classification to be over.

"Well, Hungry—what's your name?"

Smeed comprehended that the future was decided, and that to the grave he would go down as "Hungry" Smeed. With a sigh of relief he answered:

"Smeed—John Smeed."

"Sir!"

"Sir."

"How old?"

"Fifteen."

"Sir!!'

"Sir."

"What do you weigh?"

"One hundred and six—sir!"

A grim silence succeeded this depressing information. Then someone in the back, as a mere matter of form, asked:

"Never played football?"

"No, sir."

"Baseball?"

"No, sir."

"Anything on the track?"

"No, sir."

"Sing?"

"No, sir," said Smeed, humbly.

"Do anything at all?"

Little Smeed glanced at the eaves where the swallows were swaying and then down at the soft couch of green at his feet and answered faintly:

"No, sir—I'm afraid not."

Another silence came, then some one said, in a voice of deepest conviction:

"A dead loss!"

Smeed went sadly into the house.

At the door he lingered long enough to hear the chorus burst out:

"A fine football team we'll have!"

"It's a put-up job!"

"They don't want us to win the championship again—that's it!"

"I say, we ought to kick."

Then, after a little, the same deep voice:

"A dead loss!"

With each succeeding week Hungry Smeed comprehended more fully the enormity of his offense in doing nothing and weighing one hundred and six pounds. He saw the new boys arrive, pass through the fire of christening, give respectable weights and go forth to the gridiron to be whipped into shape by Turkey and the Butcher, who played on the school eleven. Smeed humbly and thankfully went down each afternoon to the practice, carrying the sweaters and shinguards, like the grateful little beast of burden that he was. He watched his juniors, Spider and Red Dog, rolling in the mud or flung gloriously under an avalanche of bodies; but then, they weighed over one hundred and thirty, while he was still at one hundred and six—a dead loss! The fever of house loyalty invaded him; he even came to look with resentment on the faculty and to repeat secretly to himself that they never would have unloaded him on the Dickinson if they hadn't been willing to stoop to any methods to prevent the House again securing the championship.

The fact that the Dickinson, in an extraordinary manner, finally won by the closest of margins, consoled Smeed but a little while. There were no more sweaters to carry, or pails of barley water to fetch, or guard to be mounted on the old rail fence, to make certain that the spies from the Davis and Kennedy did not surprise the sceret plays which Hickey and Slugger Jones had craftily evolved.

With the long winter months he felt more keenly his obscurity and the hopelessness of ever leaving a mark on the great desert of school life that would bring honor to the Dickinson. He resented even the lack of the mild hazing the other boys received—he was too insignificant to be so honored. He was only a "dead loss," good for nothing but to squeeze through his recitations, to sleep enormously, and to eat like a glutton with a hunger that could never be satisfied, little suspecting the future that lay in this famine of his stomach.

For it was written in the inscrutable fates that Hungry Smeed should leave a name that would go down imperishably to decades of schoolboys, when Dibbles' touchdown against Princeton and Kafer's home run should be only tinkling sounds. So it happened, and the agent of this divine destiny was Hickey.

It so happened that examinations being still in the threatening distance, Hickey's fertile brain was unoccupied with methods of facilitating his scholarly progress by homely inventions that allowed formulas and dates to be concealed in the palm and disappear obligingly up the sleeve on the approach of the Natural Enemy. Moreover, Hickey and Hickey's friends were in straitened circumstances, with all credit gone at the jigger shop, and the appetite for jiggers in an acute stage of deprivation.

In this keenly sensitive, famished state of his imagination, Hickey suddenly became aware of a fact fraught with possibilities. Hungry Smeed had an appetite distinguished and remarkable even in that company of aching voids.

No sooner had this pregnant idea become his property than Hickey confided his hopes to Doc Macnooder, his chum and partner in plans that were dark and mysterious. Macnooder saw in a flash the glorious and lucrative possibilities. A very short series of tests sufficed to convince the twain that in little Smeed they had a phenomenon who needed only to be properly developed to pass into history.

Accordingly, on a certain muddy morning in March, Hickey and Doc Macnooder, with Smeed in tow, stole into the jigger shop at an hour in defiance of regulations and fraught with delightful risks of detection.

Al, the watchdog of the jigger, was tilted back, near a farther window, the parted tow hair falling doglike over his eyes, absorbed in the reading of Spenser's *Faerie Queen,* an abnormal taste which made him absolutely incomprehensible to the boyish mind. At the sound of the stolen entrance, Al put down the volume and started mechanically to rise. Then, recognizing his visitors, he returned to his chair, saying wearily:

"Nothing doing, Hickey."

"Guess again," said Hickey, cheerily. "We're not asking you to hang us up this time, Al."

"You haven't got any money," said Al, the recorder of allowances; "not unless you stole it."

"Al, we don't come to take your hard-earned money, but to do you good," put in Macnooder impudently. "We're bringing you a little sporting proposition."

"Have you come to pay up that account of yours?" said Al. "If not, run along, you Macnooder; don't waste my time, with your wildcat schemes."

"Al, this is a sporting proposition," took up Hickey.

"Has *he* any money?" said Al, who suddenly remembered that Smeed was not yet under suspicion.

"See here, Al," said Macnooder, "we'll back Smeed to eat the jiggers against you—for the crowd!"

"Where's your money?"

"Here," said Hickey; "this goes up if we lose." He produced a gold watch of Smeed's, and was about to tender it when he withdrew it with a sudden caution. "On the condition, if we win I get it back and you won't hold it up against my account."

"All right. Let's see it."

The watch was given to Al, who looked it over, grunted in approval, and then looked at little Smeed.

"Now, Al," said Macnooder softly, "give us a gambling chance; he's only a runt."

Al considered, and Al was wise. The proposition came often and he never lost. A jigger is unlike any other ice cream; it is dipped from the creamy tin by a cone-shaped scoop called a jigger, which gives it an unusual and peculiar flavor. Since those days the original jigger has been contaminated and made ridiculous by offensive alliances with upstart syrups, meringues and macaroons with absurd titles; but then the boy went to the simple jigger as the sturdy Roman went to the cold waters of the Tiber. A double jigger fills a large soda glass when ten cents has been laid on the counter, and two such glasses quench all desire in the normal appetite.

"If he can eat twelve double jiggers," Al said slowly, "I'll set them up and the jiggers for youse. Otherwise, I'll hold the watch."

At this there was a protest from the backers of the champion, with the result that the limit was reduced to ten.

"Is it a go?" Al said, turning to Smeed, who had waited modestly in the background.

"Sure," he answered, with calm certainty.

"You've got nerve, you have," said Al, with a scornful smile, scooping up the first jiggers and shoving the glass to him. "Ten doubles is the record in these parts, young fellow!"

Then little Smeed, methodically, and without apparent pain, ate the ten doubles.

Conover's was not in the catalogue that anxious parents study, but then catalogues are like epitaphs in a cemetery. Next to the jigger shop, Conover's was quite the most important institution in the school. In a little white Colonial cottage, Conover, veteran of the late war, and Mrs. Conover, still in active service, supplied pancakes and maple syrup on a cash basis, two dollars credit to second-year boys in good repute. Conover's, too, had its traditions. Twenty-six pancakes, large and thick, in one continuous sitting, was the record, five years old, standing to the credit of Guzzler Wilkins, which succeeding classes had attacked in vain. Wily Conover, to stimulate such profitable tests, had solemnly pledged himself to the delivery of free pancakes to all comers during that day on which any boy, at one continuous sitting, unaided, should succeed in swallowing the awful number of thirty-two. Conover was not considered a prodigal.

This deed of heroic accomplishment and public benefaction was the true goal of Hickey's planning. The test of the jigger shop was but a preliminary trying out. With medical caution, Doc Macnooder refused to permit Smeed to go beyond the ten doubles, holding very wisely that the jigger record could wait for a further day. The amazed Al was sworn to secrecy.

It was Wednesday, and the following Saturday was decided upon for the supreme test at Conover's. Smeed at once was subjected to a graduated system of starvation. Thursday he was hungry, but Friday he was so ravenous that a watch was instituted on all his movements.

The next morning the Dickinson House, let into the secret, accompanied Smeed to Conover's. If there was even a possibility of free pancakes, the House intended to be satisfied before the deluge broke.

Great was the astonishment at Conover's at the arrival of the procession.

"Mr. Conover," said Hickey, in the quality of manager, "we're going after that pancake record."

"Mr. Wilkins' record?" said Conover, seeking vainly the champion in the crowd.

"No—after that record of *yours,*" answered Hickey. "Thirty-two pancakes—we're here to get free pancakes today—that's what we're here for."

"So, boys, so," said Conover, smiling pleasantly; "and you want to begin now?"

"Right off the bat."

"Well, where is he?"

Little Smeed, famished to the point of tears, was thrust forward. Conover, who was expecting something on the lines of a buffalo, smiled confidently.

"So, boys, so," he said, leading the way with alacrity. "I guess we're ready, too."

"Thirty-two pancakes, Conover—and we get 'em free!"

"That's right," answered Conover, secure in his knowledge of boyish capacity. "If that little boy there can eat thirty-two I'll make them all day free to the school. That's what I said, and what I say goes—and that's what I say now."

Hickey and Doc Macnooder whispered the last instructions in Smeed's ear.

"Cut out the syrup."

"Loosen your belt."

"Eat slowly."

In a low room, with the white rafters impending over his head, beside a basement window flanked with geraniums, little Smeed sat down to battle for the honor of the Dickinson and the record of the school. Directly under his eyes, carved on the wooden table, a name challenged him, standing out of the numerous initials—Guzzler Wilkins.

"I'll keep count," said Hickey. "Macnooder and Turkey, watch the pancakes."

"Regulation size, Conover," cried that cautious Red Dog; "no doubling now. All fair and above board."

"All right, Hickey, all right," said Conover, leering wickedly from the door; "if that little grasshopper can do it, you get the cakes."

"Now, Hungry," said Turkey, clapping Smeed on the shoulder. "Here is where you get your chance. Remember, Kid, old sport, it's for the Dickinson."

Smeed heard in ecstasy; it was just the way Turkey talked to the eleven on the eve of a match. He nodded his head with a grim little shake and smiled nervously at the thirty-odd Dickinsonians who formed around him a pit of expectant and hungry boyhood from the floor to the ceiling.

"All ready!" sang out Turkey, from the doorway.

"Six pancakes!"

"Six it is," replied Hickey, chalking up a monster 6 on the slate that swung from the rafters. The pancakes placed before the ravenous Smeed vanished like snowflakes on a July lawn.

A cheer went up, mingled with cries of caution.

"Not so fast."

"Take your time."

"Don't let them be too hot."

"Not too hot, Hickey!"

Macnooder was instructed to watch carefully over the temperature as well as the dimensions.

"Ready again," came the cry.

"Ready—how many?"

"Six more."

"Six it is," said Hickey, adding a second figure to the score. "Six and six are twelve."

The second batch went the way of the first.

"Why, that boy is starving," said Conover, opening his eyes.

"Sure he is," said Hickey. "He's eating way back in last week—he hasn't had a thing for ten days."

"Six more," cried Macnooder.

"Six it is," answered Hickey. "Six and twelve is eighteen."

"Eat them one at a time, Hungry."

"No, let him alone."

"He knows best."

"Not too fast, Hungry, not too fast."

"Eighteen for Hungry, eighteen. Hurrah!"

"Thirty-two is a long ways to go," said Conover, gazing apprehensively at the little David who had come so impudently into his domain; "fourteen pancakes is an awful lot."

"Shut up, Conover."

"No trying to influence him there."

"Don't listen to him, Hungry."

"He's only trying to get you nervous."

"Fourteen more, Hungry—fourteen more."

"Ready again," sang out Macnooder.

"Ready here."

"Three pancakes."

"Three it is," responded Hickey. "Eighteen and three is twenty-one."

But a storm of protest arose.

"Here, that's not fair!"

"I say, Hickey, don't let them do that."

"I say, Hickey, it's twice as hard that way."

"Oh, go on."

"Sure it is."

"Of course it is."

"Don't you know that you can't drink a glass of beer if you take it with a teaspoon?"

"That's right, Red Dog's right! Six at a time."

"Six at a time!"

A hurried consultation was now held and the reasoning approved. Macnooder was charged with the responsibility of seeing to the number as well as the temperature and dimensions.

Meanwhile Smeed had eaten the pancakes.

"Coming again!"

"All ready here."

"Six pancakes!"

"Six," said Hickey; "twenty-one and six is twenty-seven."

"That'll beat Guzzler Wilkins."

"So it will."

"Five more makes thirty-two."

"Easy, Hungry, easy."

"Hungry's done it; he's done it."

"Twenty-seven and the record!"

"Hurrah!"

At this point Smeed looked about anxiously.

"It's pretty dry," he said, speaking for the first time.

Instantly there was a panic. Smeed was reaching his limit—a groan went up.

"Oh, Hungry."

"Only five more."

"Give him some water."

"Water, you loon; do you want to end him?"

"Why?"

"Water'll swell up the pancakes, crazy."

"No water, no water."

Hickey approached his man with anxiety.

"What is it, Hungry? Anything wrong?" he said tenderly.

"No, only it's a little dry," said Smeed, unmoved. "I'm all right, but I'd like just a drop of syrup now."

The syrup was discussed, approved and voted.

"You're sure you're all right," said Hickey.

"Oh, yes."

Conover, in the last ditch, said carefully:

"I don't want no fits around here."

A cry of protest greeted him.

"Well, son, that boy can't stand much more. That's just like the Guzzler. He was taken short and we had to work over him for an hour."

"Conover, shut up!"

"Conover, you're beaten."

"Conover, that's an old game."

"Get out."

"Shut up."

"Fair play."

"Fair play! Fair play!"

A new interruption came from the kitchen. Macnooder claimed that Mrs. Conover was doubling the size of the cakes. The dish was brought. There was no doubt about it. The cakes were swollen. Pandemonium broke loose. Conover capitulated, the cakes were rejected.

"Don't be fazed by that," said Hickey warningly to Smeed.

"I'm not," said Smeed.

"All ready," came Macnooder's cry.

"Ready here."

"Six pancakes!"

"Regulation size?"

"Regulation."

"Six it is," said Hickey, at the slate. "Six and twenty-seven is thirty-three."

"Wait a moment," sang out the Butcher. "He has only to eat thirty-two."

"That's so—take one off."

"Give him five, Hickey—five only."

"If Hungry says he can eat six," said Hickey, firmly, glancing at his protégé, "he can. We're out for big things. Can you do it, Hungry?"

And Smeed, fired with the heroism of the moment, answered in disdainful simplicity:

"Sure!"

A cheer that brought two Davis House boys running in greeted the disappearance of the thirty-third. Then everything was forgotten in the amazement of the deed.

"Please, I'd like to go on," said Smeed.

"Oh, Hungry, can you do it?"

"Really?"

"You're goin' on?"

"Holy cats!"

"How'll you take them?" said Hickey, anxiously.

"I'll try another six," said Smeed, thoughtfully, "and then we'll see."

Conover, vanquished and convinced, no longer sought to intimidate him with horrid suggestions.

"Mr. Smeed," he said, giving him his hand in admiration, "you go ahead; you make a great record."

"Six more," cried Macnooder.

"Six it is," said Hickey, in an awed voice; "six and thirty-three makes thirty-nine!"

Mrs. Conover and Macnooder, no longer antagonists, came in from the kitchen to watch the great spectacle. Little Smeed alone, calm and unconscious, with the light of a great ambition on his forehead, ate steadily, without vacillation.

"Gee, what a stride!"

"By Jiminy, where does he put it?" said Conover, staring helplessly.

"Holy cats!"

"Thirty-nine—thirty-nine pancakes—gee!!!"

"Hungry," said Hickey, entreatingly, "do you think you could eat another—make it an even forty?"

"Three more," said Smeed, pounding the table with a new authority. This time no voice rose in remonstrance. The clouds had rolled away. They were in the presence of a master.

"Pancakes coming."

"Bring them in!"

"Three more."

"Three it is," said Hickey, faintly. "Thirty-nine and three makes forty-two—forty-two. Gee!"

In profound silence the three pancakes passed regularly from the plate down the throat of little Smeed. Forty-two pancakes!

"Three more," said Smeed.

Doc Macnooder rushed in hysterically.

"Hungry, go the limit—the limit! If anything happens I'll bleed you."

"Shut up, Doc!"

"Get out, you wild man."

Macnooder was sent ignominiously back into the kitchen, with the curses of the Dickinson, and Smeed assured of their unfaltering protection.

"Three more," came the cry from the chastened Macnooder.

"Three it is," said Hickey. "Forty-two and three makes—forty-five."

"Holy cats!"

Still little Smeed, without appreciable abatement of hunger, continued to eat. A sense of impending calamity and alarm began to spread. Forty-five pancakes, and still eating! It might turn into a tragedy.

"Say, bub—say, now," said Hickey, gazing anxiously down into the pointed face, "you've done enough—don't get rash."

"I'll stop when it's time," said Smeed; "bring 'em on now, one at a time."

"Forty-six, forty-seven, forty-eight, forty-nine!"

Suddenly, at the moment when they expected him to go on forever, little Smeed stopped, gazed at his plate, then at the fiftieth pancake, and said:

"That's all."

Forty-nine pancakes! Then, and only then, did they return to a realization of what had happened. They cheered Smeed, they sang his praises, they cheered again, and then, pounding the table, they cried, in a mighty chorus:

"We want pancakes!"

"Bring us pancakes!"

"Pancakes, pancakes, we want pancakes!"

Twenty minutes later, Red Dog and the Egghead, fed to bursting, rolled out of Conover's, spreading the uproarious news.

"Free pancakes! Free pancakes!"

The nearest houses, the Davis and the Rouse, heard and came with a rush.

Red Dog and the Egghead staggered down into the village and over to the circle of houses, throwing out their arms like returning bacchanalians.

"Free pancakes!"

"Hungry Smeed's broken the recod!"

"Pancakes at Conover's—free pancakes!"

The word jumped from house to house, the campus was emptied in a trice. The road became choked with the hungry stream that struggled, fought, laughed and shouted as it stormed to Conover's.

"Free pancakes! Free pancakes!"

"Hurrah for Smeed!"

"Hurrah for Hungry Smeed!!"

The Freshest Boy

By F. SCOTT FITZGERALD

IT WAS a hidden Broadway restaurant in the dead of the night, and a brilliant and mysterious group of society people, diplomats and members of the underworld were there. A few minutes ago the sparkling wine had been flowing and a girl had been dancing gaily upon a table, but now the whole crowd were hushed and breathless. All eyes were fixed upon the masked but well-groomed man in the dress suit and opera hat who stood nonchalantly in the door.

"Don't move, please," he said, in a well-bred, cultivated voice that had, nevertheless, a ring of steel in it. "This thing in my hand might—go off."

His glance roved from table to table—fell upon the malignant man higher up with his pale saturnine face, upon Heatherly, the suave secret agent from a foreign power, then rested a little longer, a little more softly perhaps, upon the table where the girl with dark hair and dark tragic eyes sat alone.

"Now that my purpose is accomplished, it might interest you to know who I am." There was a gleam of expectation in every eye. The breast of the dark-eyed girl heaved faintly and a tiny burst of subtle French perfume rose into the air. "I am none other than that elusive gentleman, Basil Lee, better known as the Shadow."

Taking off his well-fitting opera hat, he bowed ironically from the waist. Then, like a flash, he turned and was gone into the night.

"You get up to New York only once a month," Lewis Crum was saying, "and then you have to take a master along."

Slowly, Basil Lee's glazed eyes returned from the barns and billboards of the Indiana countryside to the interior of the Broadway Limited. The hypnosis of the swift telegraph poles faded and Lewis Crum's stolid face took shape against the white slip-cover of the opposite bench.

"I'd just duck the master when I got to New York," said Basil.

"Yes, you would!"

"I bet I would."

"You try it and you'll see."

"What do you mean saying I'll see, all the time, Lewis? What'll I see?" His very bright dark-blue eyes were at this moment fixed upon his companion with boredom and impatience. The two had nothing in common except their age, which was fifteen, and the lifelong friendship of their fathers—which is less than nothing. Also they were bound from the same Middle Western city for Basil's first and Lewis' second year at the same Eastern school.

But, contrary to all the best traditions, Lewis the veteran was miserable and Basil the neophyte was happy. Lewis hated school. He had grown entirely dependent on the stimulus of a hearty vital mother, and as he felt her slipping farther and farther away from him, he plunged deeper into misery and homesickness. Basil, on the other hand, had lived with such intensity on so many stories of boarding-school life that, far from being homesick, he had glad feeling of recognition and familiarity. Indeed, it was with some sense of doing the appropriate thing, having the traditional roughhouse, that he had thrown Lewis' comb off the train at Milwaukee last night for no reason at all.

To Lewis, Basil's ignorant enthusiasm was distasteful—his instinctive attempt to dampen it had contributed to the mutual irritation.

"I'll tell you what you'll see," he said ominously. "They'll catch you smoking and put you on bounds."

"No, they won't, because I won't be smoking. I'll be in training for football."

"Football! Yeah! Football!"

"Honestly, Lewis, you don't like anything, do you?"

"I don't like football. I don't like to go out and get a crack in the eye." Lewis spoke aggressively, for his mother had canonized all his timidities as common sense. Basil's answer, made with what he considered kindly intent, was the sort of remark that creates lifelong enmities.

"You'd probably be a lot more popular in school if you played football," he suggested patronizingly.

Lewis did not consider himself unpopular. He did not think of it in that way at all. He was astounded.

"You wait!" he cried furiously. "They'll take all that freshness out of you."

"Clam yourself," said Basil, coolly plucking at the creases of his first long trousers. "Just clam yourself."

"I guess everybody knows you were the freshest boy at the Country Day!"

"Clam yourself," repeated Basil, but with less assurance. "Kindly clam yourself."

"I guess I know what they had in the school paper about you—"

Basil's own coolness was no longer perceptible.

"If you don't clam yourself," he said darkly, "I'm going to throw your brushes off the train too."

The enormity of this threat was effective. Lewis sank back in his seat, snorting and muttering, but undoubtedly calmer. His reference had been to one of the most shameful passages in his companion's life. In a periodical issued by the boys of Basil's late school there had appeared, under the heading Personals:

If someone will please poison young Basil, or find some other means to stop his mouth, the school at large and myself will be much obliged.

The two boys sat there fuming wordlessly at each other. Then, resolutely, Basil tried to reinter this unfortunate souvenir of the past. All that was behind him now. Perhaps he had been a little fresh, but he was making a new start. After a moment, the memory passed and with it the train and Lewis' dismal presence—the breath of the East came sweeping over him again with a vast nostalgia. A voice called him out of the fabled world; a man stood beside him with a hand on his sweater-clad shoulder.

"Lee!"

"Yes, sir."

"It all depends on you now. Understand?"

"Yes, sir."

"All right," the coach said, "go in and win."

Basil tore the sweater from his stripling form and dashed out on the field. There were two minutes to play and the score was 3 to 0 for the enemy, but at the sight of young Lee, kept out of the game all year by a malicious plan of Dan Haskins, the school bully, and weasel Weems, his toady, a thrill of hope went over the St. Regis stand.

"33-12-16-22!" barked Midget Brown, the diminutive little quarterback. It was his signal——

"Oh, gosh!" Basil spoke aloud, forgetting the late unpleasantness. "I wish we'd get there before tomorrow."

II

ST. REGIS SCHOOL, EASTCHESTER,
November 18, 19——

DEAR MOTHER: There is not much to say today, but I thought I would write you about my allowance. All the boys have a bigger allowance than me, because there are a lot of little things I have to get, such as shoe laces, etc. School is still very nice and am having a fine time, but football is over and there is not much to do. I am going to New York this week to see a show. I do not know yet what it will be, but probably the Quaker Girl or little boy Blue as they are both very good. Dr. Bacon is very nice and there's a good phycission in the village. No more now as I have to study Algebra.

Your Affectionate Son,
BASIL D. LEE.

As he put the letter in its envelope, a wizened little boy came into the deserted study hall where he sat and stood staring at him.

"Hello," said Basil, frowning.

"I been looking for you," said the little boy, slowly and judicially. "I looked all over—up in your room and out in the gym, and they said you probably might of sneaked off in here."

"What do you want?" Basil demanded.

"Hold your horses, Bossy."

Basil jumped to his feet. The little boy retreated a step.

"Go on, hit me!" he chirped nervously. "Go on, hit me, cause I'm just half your size—Bossy."

Basil winced. "You call me that again and I'll spank you."

"No, you won't spank me. Brick Wales said if you ever touched any of us—"

"But I never did touch any of you."

"Didn't you chase a lot of us one day and didn't Brick Wales—"

"Oh, what do you want?" Basil cried in desperation.

"Dr. Bacon wants you. They sent me after you and somebody said maybe you sneaked in here."

Basil dropped his letter in his pocket and walked out—the little boy and his invective following him through the door. He traversed a long corridor, muggy with that odor best described as the smell of stale caramels that is so peculiar to boys' schools, ascended a stairs and knocked at an unexceptional but formidable door.

Dr. Bacon was at his desk. He was a handsome, redheaded Episcopal clergyman of fifty whose original real interest in boys was now tempered by the flustered cynicism which is the fate of all headmasters and settles on them like green mold. There were certain preliminaries before Basil was asked to sit down—gold-rimmed glasses had to be hoisted up from nowhere by a black cord and fixed on Basil to be sure that he was not an impostor; great masses of paper on the desk had to be shuffled through, not in search of anything but as a man nervously shuffles a pack of cards.

"I had a letter from your mother this morning—ah—Basil." The use of his first name had come to startle Basil. No one else in school had yet called him anything but Bossy or Lee. "She feels that your marks have been poor. I believe you have been sent here at a certain amount of—ah—sacrifice and she expects—"

Basil's spirit writhed with shame, not at his poor marks but that his financial inadequacy should be so bluntly stated. He knew that he was one of the poorest boys in a rich boys' school.

Perhaps some dormant sensibility in Dr. Bacon became aware of his discomfort; he shuffled through the papers once more and began on a new note.

"However, that was not what I sent for you about this afternoon. You applied last week for permission to go to New York on Saturday, to a matinée. Mr. Davis tells me that for almost the first time since school opened you will be off bounds tomorrow."

"Yes, sir."

"That is not a good record. However, I would allow you to go to New York if it could be arranged. Unfortunately, no masters are available this Saturday."

Basil's mouth dropped ajar. "Why, I—why, Dr. Bacon, I know two parties that are going. Couldn't I go with one of them?"

Dr. Bacon ran through all his papers very quickly. "Unfortunately, one is composed of slightly older boys and the other group made arrangements some weeks ago."

"How about the party that's going to the *Quaker Girl* with Mr. Dunn?"

"It's that party I speak of. They feel that their arrangements are complete and they have purchased seats together."

Suddenly Basil understood. At the look in his eye Dr. Bacon went on hurriedly:

"There's perhaps one thing I can do. Of course there must be several boys in the party so that the expenses of the master can be divided up among all. If you can find two other boys who would like to make up a party, and let me have their names by five o'clock, I'll send Mr. Rooney with you."

"Thank you," Basil said.

Dr. Bacon hesitated. Beneath the cynical incrustations of many years an instinct stirred to look into the unusual case of this boy and find out what made him the most detested boy in school. Among boys and masters there seemed to exist an extraordinary hostility toward him, and though Dr. Bacon had dealt with many sorts of schoolboy crimes, he had neither by himself nor with the aid of trusted sixth-formers been able to lay his hands on its underlying cause. It was probably no single thing, but a combination of things; it was most probably one of those intangible questions of personality. Yet he remembered that when he first saw Basil he had considered him unusually prepossessing.

He sighed. Sometimes these things worked themselves out. He wasn't one to rush in clumsily. "Let us have a better report to send home next month, Basil."

"Yes, sir."

Basil ran quickly downstairs to the recreation room. It was Wednesday and most of the boys had already gone into the village of Eastchester, whither Basil, who was still on bounds, was forbidden to follow. When he looked at those still scattered about the pool tables and piano, he saw that it was going to be difficult to get anyone to go with him at all. For Basil was quite conscious that he was the most unpopular boy at school.

It had begun almost immediately. One day, less than a fortnight after he came, a crowd of the smaller boys, perhaps urged on to it, gathered suddenly around him and began calling him Bossy. Within the next week he had two fights, and both times the crowd was vehemently and eloquently with the other boy. Soon after, when he was merely shoving indiscriminately, like everyone else, to get into the dining room, Carver, the captain of the football team, turned about and, seizing him by the back of the neck, held him and dressed him down savagely. He joined a group innocently at the piano and was told, "Go on away. We don't want you around."

After a month he began to realize the full extent of his unpopularity. It shocked him. One day after a particularly bitter humiliation he went up to his room and cried. He tried to keep out of the way for a while, but it didn't help. He was accused of sneaking off here and there, as if bent on a series of nefarious errands. Puzzled and wretched, he looked at his face in the glass, trying to discover there the secret of their dislike—in the expression of his eyes, his smile.

He saw now that in certain ways he had erred at the outset—he had boasted, he had been considered yellow at football, he had pointed out people's mistakes to them, he had shown off his rather extraordinary fund of general information in class. But he had tried to do better and couldn't understand his failure to atone. It must be too late. He was queered forever.

He had, indeed, become the scapegoat, the immediate villain, the sponge which absorbed all malice and irritability abroad—just as the most frightened person in a party seems to absorb all the others' fear, seems to be afraid for them all. His situation was not helped by the fact, obvious to all, that the supreme self-confidence with which he had come to St. Regis in September was thoroughly broken. Boys taunted him with impunity who would not have dared raise their voices to him several months before.

This trip to New York had come to mean everything to him—surcease from the misery of his daily life as well as a glimpse into the long-awaited heaven of romance. Its postponement for week after week due to his sins —he was constantly caught reading after lights, for example, driven by his wretchedness into such vicarious escapes from reality—had deepened his longing until it was a burning hunger. It was unbearable that he should not go, and he told over the short list of those whom he might get to accompany him. The possibilities were Fat Gaspar, Treadway, and Bugs Brown. A quick journey to their rooms showed that they had all availed themselves of the Wednesday permission to go into Eastchester for the afternoon.

Basil did not hesitate. He had until five o'clock and his only chance was to go after them. It was not the first time he had broken bounds, though the last attempt had ended in disaster and an extension of his confinement.

In his room, he put on a heavy sweater—an overcoat was a betrayal of intent—replaced his jacket over it and hid a cap in his back pocket. Then he went downstairs and with an elaborately careless whistle struck out across the lawn for the gymnasium. Once there, he stood for a while as if looking in the windows, first the one close to the walk, then one near the corner of the building. From here he moved quickly, but not too quickly, into a grove of lilacs. Then he dashed around the corner, down a long stretch of lawn that was blind from all windows and, parting the strands of a wire fence, crawled through and stood upon the ground of a neighboring estate. For the moment he was free. He put on his cap against the chilly November wind, and set out along the half-mile road to town.

Eastchester was a suburban farming community, with a small shoe factory. The institutions which pandered to the factory workers were the ones patronized by the boys—a movie house, a quick-lunch wagon on wheels known as the Dog and the Bostonian Candy Kitchen. Basil tried the Dog first and happened immediately upon a prospect.

This was Bugs Brown, a hysterical boy, subject to fits and strenuously avoided. Years later he became a brilliant lawyer, but at that time he was considered by the boys of St. Regis to be a typical lunatic because of his peculiar series of sounds with which he assuaged his nervousness all day long.

He consorted with boys younger than himself, who were without the prejudices of their elders, and was in the company of several when Basil came in.

"Who-ee!" he cried. "Ee-ee-ee!" He put his hand over his mouth and bounced it quickly, making a wah-wah-wah sound. "It's Bossy Lee! It's Bossy Lee! It's Boss-Boss-Boss-Boss-Bossy Lee!"

"Wait a minute, Bugs," said Basil anxiously, half afraid that Bugs would go finally crazy before he could persuade him to come to town. "Say, Bugs, listen. Don't, Bugs—wait a minute. Can you come up to New York Saturday afternoon?"

"Whe-ee-ee!" cried Bugs to Basil's distress. "Whee-ee-ee!"

"Honestly, Bugs, tell me, can you? We could go up together if you could go."

"I've got to see a doctor," said Bugs, suddenly calm. "He wants to see how crazy I am."

"Can't you have him see about it some other day?" said Basil without humor.

"Whee-ee-ee!" cried Bugs.

"All right then," said Basil hastily. "Have you seen Fat Gaspar in town?"

Bugs was lost in shrill noise, but someone had seen Fat; Basil was directed to the Bostonian Candy Kitchen.

This was a gaudy paradise of cheap sugar. Its odor, heavy and sickly and calculated to bring out a sticky sweat upon an adult's palms, hung suffocatingly over the whole vicinity and met one like a strong moral dissuasion at the door. Inside, beneath a pattern of flies, material as black point lace, a line of boys sat eating heavy dinners of banana splits, maple nut, and chocolate marshmallow nut sundaes. Basil found Fat Gaspar at a table on the side.

Fat Gaspar was at once Basil's most unlikely and most ambitious quest. He was considered a nice fellow—in fact he was so pleasant that he had been courteous to Basil and had spoken to him politely all fall. Basil realized that he was like that to everyone, yet it was just possible that Fat liked him, as people used to in the past, and he was driven desperately to take a chance. But it was undoubtedly a presumption, and as he approached the table and saw the stiffened faces which the other two boys turned toward him, Basil's hope diminished.

"Say, Fat—" he said, and hesitated. Then he burst forth suddenly. "I'm on bounds, but I ran off because I had to see you. Dr. Bacon told me I could go to New York Saturday if I could get two other boys to go. I asked Bugs Brown and he couldn't go, and I thought I'd ask you."

He broke off, furiously embarrassed, and waited. Suddenly the two boys with Fat burst into a shout of laughter.

"Bugs wasn't crazy enough!"

Fat Gaspar hesitated. He couldn't go to New York Saturday and ordinarily he would have refused without offending. He had nothing against Basil; nor, indeed, against anybody; but boys have only a certain resistance to public opinion and he was influenced by the contemptuous laughter of the others.

"I don't want to go," he said indifferently. "Why do you want to ask *me?*"

Then, half in shame, he gave a deprecatory little laugh and bent over his ice cream.

"I just thought I'd ask you," said Basil.

Turning quickly away, he went to the counter and in a hollow and unfamiliar voice ordered a strawberry sundae. He ate it mechanically, hearing occasional whispers and snickers from the table behind. Still in a daze, he started to walk out without paying his check, but the clerk called him back and he was conscious of more derisive laughter.

For a moment he hesitated whether to go back to the table and hit one of those boys in the face, but he saw nothing to be gained. They would say the truth—that he had done it because he couldn't get anybody to go to New York. Clenching his fists with impotent rage, he walked from the store.

He came immediately upon his third prospect, Treadway. Treadway had entered St. Regis late in the year and had been put in to room with Basil the week before. The fact that Treadway hadn't witnessed his humiliations of the autumn encouraged Basil to behave naturally toward him, and their relations had been, if not intimate, at least tranquil.

"Hey, Treadway," he cried, still excited from the affair in the Bostonian, "can you come up to New York to a show Saturday afternoon?"

He stopped, realizing that Treadway was in the company of Brick Wales, a boy he had had a fight with and one of his bitterest enemies. Looking from one to the other, Basil saw a look of impatience in Treadway's face and a faraway expression in Brick Wales's, and he realized what must have been happening. Treadway, making his way into the life of the school, had just been enlightened as to the status of his roommate. Like Fat Gaspar, rather than acknowledge himself eligible to such an intimate request, he preferred to cut their friendly relations short.

"Not on your life," he said briefly. "So long." The two walked past him into the candy kitchen.

Had these slights, so much the bitterer for their lack of passion, been visited upon Basil in September, they would have been unbearable. But since then he had developed a shell of hardness which, while it did not add to his attractiveness, spared him certain delicacies of torture. In misery enough, and despair and self-pity, he went the other way along the street for a little distance until he could control the violent contortions of his face. Then, taking a roundabout route, he started back to school.

He reached the adjoining estate, intending to go back the way he had come. Halfway through a hedge, he heard footsteps approaching along the sidewalk and stood motionless, fearing the proximity of masters. Their voices grew nearer and louder; before he knew it he was listening with horrified fascination:

"—so, after he tried Bugs Brown, the poor nut asked Fat Gaspar to go with him and Fat said, 'What do you ask me for?' It serves him right if he couldn't get anybody at all."

It was the dismal but triumphant voice of Lewis Crum.

III

Up in his room, Basil found a package lying on his bed. He knew its contents and for a long time he had been eagerly expecting it, but such was his depression that he opened it listlessly. It was a series of eight color reproductions of Harrison Fisher girls "on glossy paper, without printing or advertising matter and suitable for framing."

The pictures were named Dora, Marguerite, Babette, Lucille, Gretchen, Rose, Katherine and Mina. Two of them—Marguerite and Rose—Basil looked at, slowly tore up and dropped in the wastebasket, as one who disposes of the inferior pups from a litter. The other six he pinned at intervals around the room. Then he lay down on his bed and regarded them.

Dora, Lucille and Katherine were blonde; Gretchen was medium;

Babette and Mina were dark. After a few minutes, he found that he was looking oftenest at Dora and Babette and, to a lesser extent, at Gretchen, though the latter's Dutch cap seemed unromantic and precluded the element of mystery. Babette, a dark little violet-eyed beauty in a tight-fitting hat, attracted him most; his eyes came to rest on her at last.

"Babette," he whispered to himself—"beautiful Babette."

The sound of the word, so melancholy and suggestive, like "Vilia" or "I'm happy at Maxim's" on the phonograph, softened him and, turning over on his face, he sobbed into the pillow. He took hold of the bed rails over his head and, sobbing and straining, began to talk to himself brokenly—how he hated them and whom he hated—he listed a dozen—and what he would do to them when he was great and powerful. In previous moments like these he had always rewarded Fat Gaspar for his kindness, but now he was like the rest. Basil set upon him, pummeling him unmercifully, or laughed sneeringly when he passed him blind and begging on the street.

He controlled himself as he heard Treadway come in, but did not move or speak. He listened as the other moved about the room, and after a while became conscious that there was an unusual opening of closets and bureau drawers. Basil turned over, his arm concealing his tear-stained face. Treadway had an armful of shirts in his hand.

"What are you doing?" Basil demanded.

His roommate looked at him stonily. "I'm moving in with Wales," he said.

"Oh!"

Treadway went on with his packing. He carried out a suitcase full, then another, took down some pennants and dragged his trunk into the hall. Basil watched him bundle his toilet things into a towel and take one last survey about the room's new barrenness to see if there was anything forgotten.

"Good-by," he said to Basil, without a ripple of expression on his face.

"Good-by."

Treadway went out. Basil turned over once more and choked into the pillow.

"Oh, poor Babette!" he cried huskily. "Poor little Babette! Poor little Babette!"

Babette, svelte and piquant, looked down at him coquettishly from the wall.

IV

Dr. Bacon, sensing Basil's predicament and perhaps the extremity of his misery, arranged it that he should go into New York, after all. He went in the company of Mr. Rooney, the football coach and history teacher. At twenty Mr. Rooney had hesitated for some time between joining the police force and having his way paid through a small New England college; in fact he was a hard specimen and Dr. Bacon was planning to get rid of him at Christmas. Mr. Rooney's contempt for Basil was founded on the latter's ambiguous and unreliable conduct on the football field during the past season—he had consented to take him to New York for reasons of his own.

Basil sat meekly beside him on the train, glancing past Mr. Rooney's bulky body at the Sound and the fallow fields of Westchester County. Mr. Rooney finished his newspaper, folded it up and sank into a moody silence. He had eaten a large breakfast and the exigencies of time had not allowed him to work it off with exercise. He remembered that Basil was a fresh boy, and it was time he did something fresh and could be called to account. This reproachless silence annoyed him.

"Lee," he said suddenly, with a thinly assumed air of friendly interest, "why don't you get wise to yourself?"

"What, sir?" Basil was startled from his excited trance of this morning.

"I said why don't you get wise to yourself?" said Mr. Rooney in a somewhat violent tone. "Do you want to be the butt of the school all your time here?"

"No, I don't." Basil was chilled. Couldn't all this be left behind for just one day?

"You oughtn't to get so fresh all the time. A couple of times in history class I could just about have broken your neck." Basil could think of no appropriate answer. "Then out playing football," continued Mr. Rooney "—you didn't have any nerve. You could play better than a lot of 'em when you wanted, like that day against the Pomfret seconds, but you lost your nerve."

"I shouldn't have tried for the second team," said Basil. "I was too light. I should have stayed on the third."

"You were yellow, that was all the trouble. You ought to get wise to yourself. In class, you're always thinking of something else. If you don't study, you'll never get to college."

"I'm the youngest boy in the fifth form," Basil said rashly.

"You think you're pretty bright, don't you?" He eyed Basil ferociously. Then something seemed to occur to him that changed his attitude and they rode for a while in silence. When the train began to run through the thickly clustered communities near New York, he spoke again in a milder voice and with an air of having considered the matter for a long time:

"Lee, I'm going to trust you."

"Yes, sir."

"You go and get some lunch and then go on to your show. I've got some business of my own I got to attend to, and when I've finished I'll try to get to the show. If I can't, I'll anyhow meet you outside." Basil's heart leaped up. "Yes, sir."

"I don't want you to open your mouth about this at school—I mean, about me doing some business of my own."

"No, sir."

"We'll see if you can keep your mouth shut for once," he said, making it fun. Then he added, on a note of moral sternness, "And no drinks, you understand that?"

"Oh, no, sir!" The idea shocked Basil. He had never tasted a drink, nor even contemplated the possibility, save the intangible and non-alcoholic champagne of his café dreams.

On the advice of Mr. Rooney he went for luncheon to the Manhattan Hotel, near the station, where he ordered a club sandwich, French fried potatoes and a chocolate parfait. Out of the corner of his eye he watched the nonchalant, debonair, blasé New Yorkers at neighboring tables, investing them with a romance by which these possible fellow citizens of his from the Middle West lost nothing. School had fallen from him like a burden; it was no more than an unheeded clamor, faint and far away. He even delayed opening the letter from the morning's mail which he found in his pocket, because it was addressed to him at school.

He wanted another chocolate parfait, but being reluctant to bother the busy waiter any more, he opened the letter and spread it before him instead. It was from his mother:

Dear Basil: This is written in great haste, as I didn't want to frighten you by telegraphing. Grandfather is going abroad to take the waters and he wants you and me to come too. The idea is that you'll go to school at Grenoble or Montreux for the rest of the year and learn the languages and we'll be close by. That is, if you want to. I know how you like St. Regis and playing football and baseball, and of course there would be none of that; but on the other hand, it would be a nice change, even if it postponed your entering Yale by an extra year. So, as usual, I want you to do just as you like. We will be leaving home almost as soon as you get this and will come to the Waldorf in New York, where you can come in and see us for a few days, even if you decide to stay. Think it over, dear.

With love to my dearest boy,
Mother

Basil got up from his chair with a dim idea of walking over to the Waldorf and having himself locked up safely until his mother came. Then, impelled to some gesture, he raised his voice and in one of his first basso notes called boomingly and without reticence for the waiter. No more St. Regis! No more St. Regis! He was almost strangling with happiness.

"Oh, gosh!" he cried to himself. "Oh, golly! Oh, gosh! Oh, gosh!" No more Dr. Bacon and Mr. Rooney and Brick Wales and Fat Gaspar. No more Bugs Brown and on bounds and being called Bossy. He need no longer hate them, for they were impotent shadows in the stationary world that he was sliding away from, sliding past, waving his hand. "Good-by!" he pitied them. "Good-by!"

It required the din of Forty-second Street to sober his maudlin joy. With his hand on his purse to guard against the omnipresent pickpocket, he moved cautiously toward Broadway. What a day! He would tell Mr. Rooney— Why, he needn't ever go back! Or perhaps it would be better to go back and let them know what he was going to do, while they went on and on in the dismal, dreary round of school.

He found the theater and entered the lobby with its powdery feminine atmosphere of a matinee. As he took out his ticket, his gaze was caught and held by a sculptured profile a few feet away. It was of a well-built blond young man of about twenty with a strong chin and direct gray eyes. Basil's brain spun wildly for a moment and then came to rest upon a name—more than a name—upon a legend, a sign in the sky. What a day! He had never seen the young man before, but from a thousand pictures he knew beyond the possibility of a doubt that it was Ted Fay, the Yale football captain, who had almost singlehanded beaten Harvard and Princeton last fall. Basil felt a sort of exquisite pain. The profile turned away; the crowd revolved; the hero disappeared. But Basil would know all through the next hours that Ted Fay was here too.

In the rustling, whispering, sweet-smelling darkness of the theater he read the program. It was the show of all shows that he wanted to see, and until the curtain actually rose the program itself had a curious sacredness—a prototype of the thing itself. But when the curtain rose it became waste paper to be dropped carelessly to the floor.

Act I. *The Village Green of a Small Town near New York.*

It was too bright and blinding to comprehend all at once, and it went so fast that from the very first Basil felt he had missed things; he would make his mother take him again when she came—next week—tomorrow.

An hour passed. It was very sad at this point—a sort of gay sadness, but sad. The girl—the man. What kept them apart even now? Oh, those tragic errors and misconceptions. So sad. Couldn't they look into each other's eyes and *see?*

In a blaze of light and sound, of resolution, anticipation and imminent trouble, the act was over.

He went out. He looked for Ted Fay and thought he saw him leaning rather moodily on the plush wall at the rear of the theater, but he could not be sure. He bought cigarettes and lit one, but fancying at the first puff that he heard a blare of music he rushed back inside.

Act II. *The Foyer of the Hotel Astor.*

Yes, she was, indeed, like that song—a Beautiful Rose of the Night. The waltz buoyed her up, brought her with it to a point of aching beauty and then let her slide back to life across its last bars as a leaf slants to earth across the air. The high life of New York! Who could blame her if she was carried away by the glitter of it all, vanishing into the bright morning of the amber window borders or into distant and entrancing music as the door opened and closed that led to the ballroom? The toast of the shining town.

Half an hour passed. Her true love brought her roses like herself and she threw them scornfully at his feet. She laughed and turned to the other, and danced—danced madly, wildly. Wait! That delicate treble among the thin horns, the low curving note from the great strings. There it was again, poignant and aching, sweeping like a great gust of emotion across the stage, catching her again like a leaf helpless in the wind:

> Rose—Rose—Rose of the night,
> When the spring moon is bright you'll be fair—

A few minutes later, feeling oddly shaken and exalted, Basil drifted outside with the crowd. The first thing upon which his eyes fell was the almost forgotten and now curiously metamorphosed specter of Mr. Rooney.

Mr. Rooney had, in fact, gone a little to pieces. He was, to begin with, wearing a different and much smaller hat than when he left Basil at noon. Secondly, his face had lost its somewhat gross aspect and turned a pure and even delicate white, and he was wearing his necktie and even portions of his shirt on the outside of his unaccountably wringing-wet overcoat. How, in the short space of four hours, Mr. Rooney had got himself in such shape is explicable only by the pressure of confinement in a boys' school upon a fiery outdoor spirit. Mr. Rooney was born to toil under the clear light of heaven and, perhaps half consciously, he was headed toward his inevitable destiny.

"Lee, " he said dimly, "you ought to get wise to y'self. I'm going to put you wise y'self."

To avoid the ominous possibility of being put wise to himself in the lobby, Basil uneasily changed the subject.

"Aren't you coming to the show?" he asked, flattering Mr. Rooney by implying that he was in any condition to come to the show. "It's a wonderful show."

Mr. Rooney took off his hat, displaying wringing-wet matted hair. A picture of reality momentarily struggled for development in the back of his brain.

"We got to get back to school," he said in a somber and unconvinced voice.

"But there's another act," protested Basil in horror. "I've got to stay for the last act."

Swaying, Mr. Rooney looked at Basil, dimly realizing that he had put himself in the hollow of this boy's hand.

"All righ'," he admitted. "I'm going to get somethin' to eat. I'll wait for you next door."

He turned abruptly, reeled a dozen steps and curved dizzily into a bar adjoining the theater. Considerably shaken, Basil went back inside.

Act III. *The Roof Garden of Mr. Van Astor's House. Night.*

Half an hour passed. Everything was going to be all right, after all. The comedian was at his best now, with the glad appropriateness of laughter after tears, and there was a promise of felicity in the bright tropical sky. One lovely plaintive duet, and then abruptly the long moment of incomparable beauty was over.

Basil went into the lobby and stood in thought while the crowd passed out. His mother's letter and the show had cleared his mind of bitterness and vindictiveness—he was his old self and he wanted to do the right thing. He wondered if it was the right thing to get Mr. Rooney back to school. He walked toward the saloon, slowed up as he came to it and, gingerly opening the swinging door, took a quick peer inside. He saw only that Mr. Rooney was not one of those drinking at the bar. He walked down the street a little way, came back and tried again. It was as if he thought the doors were teeth to bite him, for he had the old-fashioned Middle Western boy's horror of the saloon. The third time he was successful. Mr. Rooney was sound asleep at a table in the back of the room.

Outside again Basil walked up and down, considering. He would give Mr. Rooney half an hour. If, at the end of that time, he had not come out, he would go back to school. After all, Mr. Rooney had laid for him ever since football season—Basil was simply washing his hands of the whole affair, as in a day or so he would wash his hands of school.

He had made several turns up and down, when, glancing up an alley that ran beside the theater his eye was caught by the sign, Stage Entrance. He could watch the actors come forth.

He waited. Women streamed by him, but those were the days before Glorification and he took these drab people for wardrobe women or something. Then suddenly a girl came out and with her a man, and Basil turned and ran a few steps up the street as if afraid they would recognize him—and ran back, breathing as if with a heart attack—for the girl, a radiant little beauty of nineteen, was Her and the young man by her side was Ted Fay.

Arm in arm, they walked past him, and irresistibly Basil followed. As they walked, she leaned toward Ted Fay in a way that gave them a fascinating air of intimacy. They crossed Broadway and turned into the Knickerbocker Hotel, and twenty feet behind them Basil followed, in time to see them go into a long room set for afternoon tea. They sat at a table for two, spoke vaguely to a waiter, and then, alone at last, bent eagerly toward each other. Basil saw that Ted Fay was holding her gloved hand.

The tearoom was separated only by a hedge of potted firs from the main corridor. Basil went along this to a lounge which was almost up against their table and sat down.

Her voice was low and faltering, less certain than it had been in the play, and very sad: "Of course I do, Ted." For a long time, as their conversation continued, she repeated "Of course I do" or "But I do, Ted." Ted Fay's remarks were too low for Basil to hear.

"—says next month, and he won't be put off any more. . . . I do in a way, Ted. It's hard to explain, but he's done everything for Mother and me. . . . There's no use kidding myself. It was a foolproof part and any girl he gave it to was made right then and there. . . . He's been awfully thoughtful. He's done everything for me."

Basil's ears were sharpened by the intensity of his emotion; now he could hear Ted Fay's voice too:

"And you say you love me."

"But don't you see I promised to marry him more than a year ago."

"Tell him the truth—that you love me. Ask him to let you off."

"This isn't musical comedy, Ted."

"That was a mean one," he said bitterly.

"I'm sorry, dear, Ted darling, but you're driving me crazy going on this way. You're making it so hard for me."

"I'm going to leave New Haven, anyhow."

"No, you're not. You're going to stay and play baseball this spring. Why, you're an ideal to all those boys! Why, if you—"

He laughed shortly. "You're a fine one to talk about ideals."

"Why not? I'm living up to my responsibility to Beltzman; you've got to make up your mind just like I have—that we can't have each other."

"Jerry! Think what you're doing! All my life, whenever I hear that waltz—"

Basil got to his feet and hurried down the corridor, through the lobby and out of the hotel. He was in a state of wild emotional confusion. He did not understand all he had heard, but from his clandestine glimpse into the privacy of these two, with all the world that his short experience could conceive of at their feet, he had gathered that life for everybody was a struggle, sometimes magnificent from a distance, but always difficult and surprisingly simple and a little sad.

They would go on. Ted Fay would go back to Yale, put her picture in his bureau drawer and knock out home runs with the bases full this spring—at 8:30 the curtain would go up and She would miss something warm and young out of her life, something she had had this afternoon.

It was dark outside and Broadway was a blazing forest fire as Basil walked slowly along toward the point of brightest light. He looked up at the great intersecting planes of radiance with a vague sense of approval and possession. He would see it a lot now, lay his restless heart upon this greater restlessness of a nation—he would come whenever he could get off from school.

But that was all changed—he was going to Europe. Suddenly Basil realized that he wasn't going to Europe. He could not forego the molding of his own destiny just to alleviate a few months of pain. The conquest of the successive worlds of school, college and New York—why, that was his true dream that he had carried from boyhood into adolescence, and because of the jeers of a few boys he had been about to abandon it and run ignominiously up a back alley! He shivered violently, like a dog coming out of the water, and simultaneously he was reminded of Mr. Rooney.

A few minutes later he walked into the bar, past the quizzical eyes of the bartender and up to the table where Mr. Rooney still sat asleep. Basil shook him gently, then firmly. Mr. Rooney stirred and perceived Basil.

"G'wise to yourself," he muttered drowsily. "G'wise to yourself an' let me alone."

"I am wise to myself," said Basil. "Honest, I am wise to myself, Mr. Rooney. You got to come with me into the washroom and get cleaned up, and then you can sleep on the train again, Mr. Rooney. Come on, Mr. Rooney, please—"

V

It was a long hard time. Basil got on bounds again in December and wasn't free again until March. An indulgent mother had given him no habits of work and this was almost beyond the power of anything but life itself to remedy, but he made numberless new starts and failed and tried again.

He made friends with a new boy named Maplewood after Christmas, but they had a silly quarrel; and through the winter term, when a boys' school is shut in with itself and only partly assuaged from its natural savagery by indoor sports, Basil was snubbed and slighted a good deal for his real and imaginary sins, and he was much alone. But on the other hand, there was Ted Fay, and Rose of the Night on the phonograph— "All my life whenever I hear that waltz"—and the remembered lights of New York, and the thought of what he was going to do in football next autumn and the glamorous mirage of Yale and the hope of spring in the air.

Fat Gaspar and a few others were nice to him now. Once when he and Fat walked home together by accident from downtown they had a long talk about actresses—a talk that Basil was wise enough not to presume upon afterward. The smaller boys suddenly decided that they approved of him, and a master who had hitherto disliked him put his hand on his shoulder walking to a class one day. They would all forget eventually—maybe during the summer. There would be new fresh boys in September; he would have a clean start next year.

One afternoon in February, playing basketball, a great thing happened. He and Brick Wales were at forward on the second team and in the fury of the scrimmage the gymnasium echoed with sharp slapping contacts and shrill cries.

"Here yar!"

"Bill! Bill!"

Basil had dribbled the ball down the court and Brick Wales, free, was crying for it.

"Here yar! Lee! Hey! Lee-y!"

Lee-y!

Basil flushed and made a poor pass. He had been called by a nickname. It was a poor makeshift, but it was something more than the stark bareness of his surname or a term of derision. Brick Wales went on playing, unconscious that he had done anything in particular or that he had contributed to the events by which another boy was saved from the army of the bitter, the selfish, the neurasthenic and the unhappy. It isn't given to us to know those rare moments when people are wide open and the lightest touch can wither or heal. A moment too late and we can never reach them any more in this world. They will not be cured by our most efficacious drugs or slain with our sharpest swords.

"Lee-y!" It could scarcely be pronounced. But Basil took it to bed with him that night, and thinking of it, holding it to him happily to the last, fell easily to sleep.

VII

✿ ✿ ✿

Where There's a Thrill ...

The Hands of Mr. Ottermole

By THOMAS BURKE

At six o'clock of a January evening Mr. Whybrow was walking home through the cobweb alleys of London's East End. He had left the golden clamor of the great High Street to which the tram had brought him from the river and his daily work, and was now in the chessboard of byways that is called Mallon End. None of the rush and gleam of the High Street trickled into these byways. A few paces south—a flood tide of life, foaming and beating. Here—only slow-shuffling figures and muffled pulses. He was in the sink of London, the last refuge of European vagrants.

As though in tune with the street's spirit, he too walked slowly, with head down. It seemed that he was pondering some pressing trouble, but he was not. He had no trouble. He was walking slowly because he had been on his feet all day, and he was bent in abstraction because he was wondering whether the Missis would have herrings for his tea, or haddock; and he was trying to decide which would be the more tasty on a night like this. A wretched night it was, of damp and mist, and the mist wandered into his throat and his eyes, and the damp had settled on pavement and roadway, and where the sparse lamplight fell it sent up a greasy sparkle that chilled one to look at. By contrast it made his speculations more agreeable, and made him ready for that tea—whether herring or haddock. His eye turned from the glum bricks that made his horizon, and went forward half a mile. He saw a gaslit kitchen, a flamy fire and a spread tea table. There was toast in the hearth and a singing kettle on the side and a piquant effusion of herrings, or maybe of haddock, or perhaps sausages. The vision gave his aching feet a throb of energy. He shook imperceptible damp from his shoulders, and hastened towards its reality.

But Mr. Whybrow wasn't going to get any tea that evening—or any other evening. Mr. Whybrow was going to die. Somewhere within a hundred yards of him another man was walking: a man much like Mr. Whybrow and much like any other man, but without the only quality that enables mankind to live peaceably together and not as madmen in a jungle. A man with a dead heart eating into itself and bringing forth the foul organisms that arise from death and corruption. And that thing in man's shape, on a whim or a settled idea—one cannot know—had said within himself that Mr. Whybrow should never taste another herring. Not that Mr. Whybrow had injured him. Not that he had any dislike of Mr. Whybrow. Indeed, he knew nothing of him save as a familiar figure about the streets. But, moved by a force that had taken possession of his empty cells, he had picked on Mr. Whybrow with that blind choice that makes us pick one restaurant table that has nothing to mark it from four or five other tables, or one apple from a dish of half a dozen equal apples; or that drives Nature to send a cyclone upon one corner of this planet, and destroy five hundred lives in that corner, and leave another five hundred in the same corner unharmed. So this man had picked on Mr. Whybrow, as he might have picked on you or me, had we been within his daily observation; and even now he was creeping through the blue-toned streets, nursing his large white hands, moving ever closer to Mr. Whybrow's tea table, and so closer to Mr. Whybrow himself.

He wasn't, this man, a bad man. Indeed, he had many of the social and amiable qualities, and passed as a respectable man, as most successful criminals do. But the thought had come into his moldering mind that he would like to murder somebody, and, as he held no fear of God or man, he was going to do it, and would then go home to *his* tea. I don't say that flippantly, but as a statement of fact. Strange as it may seem to the humane, murderers must and do sit down to meals after a murder. There is no reason why they shouldn't, and many reasons why they should. For one thing, they need to keep their physical and mental vitality at full beat for the business of covering their crime. For another, the strain of their effort makes them hungry, and satisfaction at the accomplishment of a desired thing brings a feeling of relaxation towards human pleasures. It is accepted among non-murderers that the murderer is always overcome by fear for his safety and horror at his act; but this type is rare. His own safety is, of course, his immediate concern, but vanity is a marked quality of most murderers, and that, together with the thrill of conquest, makes him confident that he can secure it, and when he has restored his strength with food he goes about securing it as a young hostess goes about the arranging of her first big dinner—a little anxious, but no more. Criminologists and detectives tell us that *every* murderer, however intelligent or cunning, always makes one slip in his tactics—one little slip that brings the affair home to him. But that is only half true. It is true only of the murderers who are caught. Scores of murderers are not caught: therefore scores of murderers do not make any mistake at all. This man didn't.

As for horror or remorse, prison chaplains, doctors and lawyers have told us that of murderers they have interviewed under condemnation and the shadow of death, only one here and there has expressed any contrition for his act, or shown any sign of mental misery. Most of them display

only exasperation at having been caught when so many have gone undiscovered, or indignation at being condemned for a perfectly reasonable act.
However normal and humane they may have been before the murder,
they are utterly without conscience after it. For what is conscience? Simply
a polite nickname for superstition, which is a polite nickname for fear.
Those who associate remorse with murder are, no doubt, basing their ideas
on the world legend of the remorse of Cain, or are projecting their own
frail minds into the mind of the murderer, and getting false reactions.
Peaceable folk cannot hope to make contact with this mind, for they are
not merely different in mental type from the murderer: they are different
in their personal chemistry and construction. Some men can and do kill,
not one man, but two or three, and go calmly about their daily affairs.
Other men could not, under the most agonizing provocation, bring themselves even to wound. It is men of this sort who imagine the murderer
in torments of remorse and fear of the law, whereas he is actually sitting
down to his tea.

The man with the large white hands was as ready for his tea as Mr.
Whybrow was, but he had something to do before he went to it. When
he had done that something, and made no mistake about it, he would be
even more ready for it, and would go to it as comfortably as he went to
it the day before, when his hands were stainless.

Walk on, then, Mr. Whybrow, walk on; and as you walk, look your
last upon the familiar features of your nightly journey. Follow your jack-
o'-lantern tea table. Look well upon its warmth and color and kindness;
feed your eyes with it, and tease your nose with its gentle domestic odors;
for you will never sit down to it. Within ten minutes' pacing of you a
pursuing phantom has spoken in his heart, and you are doomed. There
you go—you and phantom—two nebulous dabs of mortality, moving
through green air along pavements of powder blue, the one to kill, the
other to be killed. Walk on. Don't annoy your burning feet by hurrying,
for the more slowly you walk, the longer you will breathe the green air
of this January dusk, and see the dreamy lamplight and the little shops,
and hear the agreeable commerce of the London crowd and the haunting
pathos of the street organ. These things are dear to you, Mr. Whybrow.
You don't know it now, but in fifteen minutes you will have two seconds
in which to realize how inexpressibly dear they are.

Walk on, then, across this crazy chessboard. You are in Lagos Street
now, among the tents of the wanderers of eastern Europe. A minute or
so, and you are in Loyal Lane, among the lodging houses that shelter the
useless and the beaten of London's camp followers. The lane holds the
smell of them, and its soft darkness seems heavy with the wail of the
futile. But you are not sensitive to impalpable things, and you plod
through it, unseeing, as you do every evening, and come to Blean Street,
and plod through that. From basement to sky rise the tenements of an

alien colony. Their windows slot the ebony of their walls with lemon. Behind those windows strange life is moving, dressed with forms that are not of London or of England, yet, in essence, the same agreeable life that you have been living, and tonight will live no more. From high above you comes a voice crooning *The Song of Katta.* Through a window you see a family keeping a religious rite. Through another you see a woman pouring out tea for her husband. You see a man mending a pair of boots; a mother bathing her baby. You have seen all these things before, and never noticed them. You do not notice them now, but if you knew that you were never going to see them again, you would notice them. You never *will* see them again, not because your life has run its natural course, but because a man whom you have often passed in the street has at his own solitary pleasure decided to usurp the awful authority of nature, and destroy you. So perhaps it's as well that you don't notice them, for your part in them is ended. No more for you these pretty moments of our earthly travail: only one moment of terror, and then a plunging darkness.

Closer to you this shadow of massacre moves, and now he is twenty yards behind you. You can hear his footfall, but you do not turn your head. You are familiar with footfalls. You are in London, in the easy security of your daily territory, and footfalls behind you, your instinct tells you, are no more than a message of human company.

But can't you hear something in those footfalls—something that goes with a widdershins beat? Something that says: *Look out, look out. Beware, beware.* Can't you hear the very syllables of *mur-der-er, mur-der-er?* No; there is nothing in footfalls. They are neutral. The foot of villainy falls with the same quiet note as the foot of honesty. But those footfalls, Mr. Whybrow, are bearing on to you a pair of hands, and there *is* something in hands. Behind you that pair of hands is even now stretching its muscles in preparation for your end. Every minute of your days you have been seeing human hands. Have you ever realized the sheer horror of hands—those appendages that are a symbol for our moments of trust and affection and salutation? Have you thought of the sickening potentialities that lie within the scope of that five-tentacled member? No, you never have; for all the human hands that you have seen have been stretched to you in kindness or fellowship. Yet, though the eyes can hate, and the lips can sting, it is only that dangling member that can gather the accumulated essence of evil, and electrify it into currents of destruction. Satan may enter into man by many doors, but in the hands alone can he find the servants of his will.

Another minute, Mr. Whybrow, and you will know all about the horror of human hands.

You are nearly home now. You have turned into your street—Caspar Street—and you are in the center of the chessboard. You can see the front window of your little four-roomed house. The street is dark, and its three lamps give only a smut of light that is more confusing than darkness. It is dark—empty, too. Nobody about; no lights in the front parlors of the houses, for the families are at tea in their kitchens; and only a random glow in a few upper rooms occupied by lodgers. Nobody about but you and your following companion, and you don't notice him. You see him so often that he is never seen. Even if you turned your head and saw him, you would only say "Good evening" to him, and walk on. A suggestion that he was a possible murderer would not even make you laugh. It would be too silly.

And now you are at your gate. And now you have found your door key. And now you are in, and hanging up your hat and coat. The Missis has just called a greeting from the kitchen, whose smell is an echo of that greeting (herrings!) and you have answered it, when the door shakes under a sharp knock.

Go away, Mr. Whybrow. Go away from that door. Don't touch it. Get right away from it. Get out of the house. Run with the Missis to the back garden, and over the fence. Or call the neighbors. But don't touch that door. Don't, Mr. Whybrow, don't open . . .

Mr. Whybrow opened the door.

That was the beginning of what became known as London's Strangling Horrors. Horrors they were called because they were something more than murders: they were motiveless, and there was an air of black magic about them. Each murder was committed at a time when the street where the bodies were found was empty of any perceptible or possible murderer. There would be an empty alley. There would be a policeman at its end. He would turn his back on the empty alley for less than a minute. Then he would look round and run into the night with news of another strangling. And in any direction he looked nobody to be seen and no report to be had of anybody being seen. Or he would be on duty in a long-quiet street, and suddenly be called to a house of dead people whom a few seconds earlier he had seen alive. And, again, whichever way he looked nobody to be seen; and although police whistles put an immediate cordon around the area, and searched all houses, no possible murderer to be found.

The first news of the murder of Mr. and Mrs. Whybrow was brought by the station sergeant. He had been walking through Caspar Street on his way to the station for duty, when he noticed the open door of No. 98. Glancing in, he saw by the gaslight of the passage a motionless body on the floor. After a second look he blew his whistle, and when the constables answered him he took one to join him in a search of the house, and sent others to watch all neighboring streets, and make inquiries at adjoining houses. But neither in the house nor in the streets was anything found to indicate the murderer. Neighbors on either side, and opposite, were questioned, but they had seen nobody about, and had heard nothing. One had heard Mr. Whybrow come home—the scrape of his latchkey in the door was so regular an evening sound, he said, that you could set your watch by it for half-past six—but he had heard nothing more than the sound of the opening door until the sergeant's whistle. Nobody had been seen to enter the house or leave it, by front or back, and the necks of the dead people carried no fingerprints or other traces. A nephew was called in to go over the house, but he could find nothing missing; and anyway his uncle possessed nothing worth stealing. The little money in the house was untouched, and there were no signs of any disturbance of the property, or even of struggle. No signs of anything but brutal and wanton murder.

Mr. Whybrow was known to neighbors and workmates as a quiet, likable, home-loving man; such a man as could not have any enemies. But, then, murdered men seldom have. A relentless enemy who hates a man to the point of wanting to hurt him seldom wants to murder him, since to do that puts him beyond suffering. So the police were left with an impossible situation: no clue to the murderer and no motive for the murders; only the fact that they had been done.

The first news of the affair sent a tremor through London generally, and an electric thrill through all Mallon End. Here was a murder of two inoffensive people, not for gain and not for revenge; and the murderer, to whom, apparently, killing was a casual impulse, was at large. He had left no traces, and, provided he had no companions, there seemed no reason why he should not remain at large. Any clearheaded man who stands alone, and has no fear of God or man, can, if he chooses, hold a city, even a nation, in subjection; but your everyday criminal is seldom clear-headed, and dislikes being lonely. He needs, if not the support of confederates, at least somebody to talk to; his vanity needs the satisfaction of perceiving at first hand the effect of his work. For this he will frequent bars and coffee shops and other public places. Then, sooner or later, in a glow of comradeship, he will utter the one word too much; and the nark, who is everywhere, has an easy job.

But though the doss houses and saloons and other places were "combed" and set with watches, and it was made known by whispers that good money and protection were assured to those with information, nothing attaching to the Whybrow case could be found. The murderer clearly had no friends and kept no company. Known men of this type were called up and questioned, but each was able to give a good account of himself; and in a few days the police were at a dead end. Against the constant public gibe that the thing had been done almost under their noses, they became restive, and for four days each man of the force was working his daily beat under a strain. On the fifth day they became still more restive.

It was the season of annual teas and entertainments for the children of the Sunday schools, and on an evening of fog, when London was a world of groping phantoms, a small girl, in the bravery of best Sunday frock and shoes, shining face and new-washed hair, set out from Logan Passage for St. Michael's Parish Hall. She never got there. She was not actually dead until half-past six, but she was as good as dead from the moment she left her mother's door. Somebody like a man, pacing the street from which the Passage led, saw her come out; and from that moment she was dead. Through the fog somebody's large white hands reached after her, and in fifteen minutes they were about her.

At half-past six a whistle screamed trouble, and those answering it found the body of little Nellie Vrinoff in a warehouse entry in Minnow Street. The sergeant was first among them, and he posted his men to useful points, ordering them here and there in the tart tones of repressed rage, and berating the officer whose beat the street was. "I saw you, Magson, at the end of the lane. What were you up to there? You were there ten minutes before you turned." Magson began an explanation about keeping an eye on a suspicious-looking character at that end, but the sergeant cut him short: "Suspicious characters be damned. You don't want to look for suspicious characters. You want to look for *murderers*. Messing about . . . and then this happens right where you ought to be. Now think what they'll say."

With the speed of ill news came the crowd, pale and perturbed; and on the story that the unknown monster had appeared again, and this time to a child, their faces streaked the fog with spots of hate and horror. But then came the ambulance and more police, and swiftly they broke up the crowd; and as it broke the sergeant's thought was thickened into words, and from all sides came low murmurs of "Right under their noses." Later inquiries showed that four people of the district, above suspicion, had passed that entry at intervals of seconds before the murder, and seen nothing and heard nothing. None of them had passed the child alive or seen her dead. None of them had seen anybody in the street except themselves. Again the police were left with no motive and with no clue.

And now the district, as you will remember, was given over, not to panic, for the London public never yields to that, but to apprehension and dismay. If these things were happening in their familiar streets, then anything might happen. Wherever people met—in the streets, the markets and the shops—they debated the one topic. Women took to bolting their windows and doors at the first fall of dusk. They kept their children closely under their eye. They did their shopping before dark, and watched anxiously, while pretending they weren't watching, for the return of their husbands from work. Under the Cockney's semihumorous resignation to disaster, they hid an hourly foreboding. By the whim of one man with a pair of hands the structure and tenor of their daily life were shaken, as they always can be shaken by any man contemptuous of humanity and fearless of its laws. They began to realize that the pillars that supported the peaceable society in which they lived were mere straws that anybody could snap; that laws were powerful only so long as they were obeyed; that the police were potent only so long as they were feared. By the power of his hands this one man had made a whole community do something new: he had made it think, and left it gasping at the obvious.

And then, while it was yet gasping under his first two strokes, he made his third. Conscious of the horror that his hands had created, and hungry as an actor who has once tasted the thrill of the multitude, he made fresh advertisement of his presence; and on Wednesday morning, three days after the murder of the child, the papers carried to the breakfast tables of England the story of a still more shocking outrage.

At 9:32 on Tuesday night a constable was on duty in Jarnigan Road, and at that time spoke to a fellow officer named Petersen at the top of Clemming Street. He had seen this officer walk down that street. He could swear that the street was empty at that time, except for a lame boot-black whom he knew by sight, and who passed him and entered a tenement on the side opposite that on which his fellow-officer was walking. He had the habit, as all constables had just then, of looking constantly behind him and around him, whichever way he was walking, and he was certain that the street was empty. He passed his sergeant at 9:33, saluted him, and answered his inquiry for anything seen. He reported that he had seen nothing, and passed on. His beat ended at a short distance from Clemming Street, and, having paced it, he turned and came again at 9:34 to the top of the street. He had scarcely reached it before he heard the hoarse voice of the sergeant: "Gregory! You there? Quick. Here's another. My God, it's Petersen! Garroted. Quick, call 'em up!"

That was the third of the Strangling Horrors, of which there were to be a fourth and a fifth; and the five horrors were to pass into the unknown and unknowable. That is, unknown as far as authority and the public were concerned. The identity of the murderer *was* known, but to two men only. One was the murderer himself; the other was a young journalist.

This young man, who was covering the affairs for his paper, the *Daily Torch,* was no smarter than the other zealous newspaper men who were hanging about these byways in the hope of a sudden story. But he was patient, and he hung a little closer to the case than the other fellows, and by continually staring at it he at last raised the figure of the murderer like a genie from the stones on which he had stood to do his murders.

After the first few days the men had given up any attempt at exclusive stories, for there was none to be had. They met regularly at the police station, and what little information there was they shared. The officials were agreeable to them, but no more. The sergeant discussed with them the details of each murder; suggested possible explanations of the man's methods; recalled from the past those cases that had some similarity; and on the matter of motive reminded them of the motiveless Neil Cream and the wanton John Williams, and hinted that work was being done which would soon bring the business to an end; but about that work he would not say a word. The Inspector, too, was gracefully garrulous on the thesis of Murder, but whenever one of the party edged the talk towards what was being done in this immediate matter, he glided past it. Whatever the officials knew, they were not giving it to newspapermen. The business had fallen heavily upon them, and only by a capture made by their own efforts could they rehabilitate themselves in official and public esteem. Scotland Yard, of course, was at work, and had all the station's material; but the station's hope was that they themselves would have the honor of settling the affair; and however useful the co-operation of the Press might be in other cases, they did not want to risk a defeat by a premature disclosure of their theories and plans.

So the sergeant talked at large, and propounded one interesting theory after another, all of which the newspapermen had thought of themselves.

The young man soon gave up these morning lectures on the Philosophy of Crime, and took to wandering about the streets and making bright stories out of the effect of the murders on the normal life of the people. A melancholy job made more melancholy by the district. The littered roadways, the crestfallen houses, the bleared windows—all held the acid misery that evokes no sympathy: the misery of the frustrated poet. The misery was the creation of the aliens, who were living in this makeshift fashion because they had no settled homes, and would neither take the trouble to make a home where they *could* settle, nor get on with their wandering.

There was little to be picked up. All he saw and heard were indignant faces, and wild conjectures of the murderer's identity and of the secret of his trick of appearing and disappearing unseen. Since a policeman himself had fallen a victim, denunciations of the force had ceased, and the unknown was now invested with a cloak of legend. Men eyed other men, as though thinking: It might be *him*. It might be *him*. They were no longer looking for a man who had the air of a Madame Tussaud murderer; they were looking for a man, or perhaps some harridan woman, who had done these particular murders. Their thoughts ran mainly on the foreign set. Such ruffianism could scarcely belong to England, nor could the bewildering cleverness of the thing. So they turned to Roumanian gipsies and Turkish carpet sellers. There, clearly, would be found the "warm" spot. These Eastern fellows—they knew all sorts of tricks, and they had no real religion—nothing to hold them within bounds. Sailors returning from those parts had told tales of conjurors who made themselves invisible; and there were tales of Egyptian and Arab potions that were used for abysmally queer purposes. Perhaps it *was* possible to them;

you never knew. They were so slick and cunning, and they had such gliding movements; no Englishman could melt away as they could. Almost certainly the murderer would be found to be one of that sort—with some dark trick of his own—and just because they were sure that he *was* a magician, they felt that it was useless to look for him. He was a power, able to hold them in subjection and to hold himself untouchable. Superstition, which so easily cracks the frail shell of reason, had got into them. He could do anything he chose: he would never be discovered. These two points they settled, and they went about the streets in a mood of resentful fatalism.

They talked of their ideas to the journalist in half tones, looking right and left, as though HE might overhear them and visit them. And though all the district was thinking of him and ready to pounce upon him, yet, so strongly had he worked upon them, that if any man in the street—say, a small man of commonplace features and form—had cried "*I* am the Monster!" would their stifled fury have broken into flood and have borne him down and engulfed him? Or would they not suddenly have seen something unearthly in that everyday face and figure, something unearthly in his everyday boots, something unearthly about his hat, something that marked him as one whom none of their weapons could alarm or pierce? And would they not momentarily have fallen back from this devil, as the devil fell back from the Cross made by the sword of Faust, and so have given him time to escape? I do not know; but so fixed was their belief in his invincibility that it is at least likely that they would have made this hesitation, had such an occasion arisen. But it never did. Today this commonplace fellow, his murder lust glutted, is still seen and observed among them as he was seen and observed all the time; but because nobody then dreamt, or now dreams, that he was what he was, they observed him then, and observe him now, as people observe a lamppost.

Almost was their belief in his invincibility justified; for, five days after the murder of the policeman Petersen, when the experience and inspiration of the whole detective force of London were turned towards his identification and capture, he made his fourth and fifth strokes.

At nine o'clock that evening, the young newspaperman, who hung about every night until his paper was away, was strolling along Richards Lane. Richards Lane is a narrow street, partly a stall market, and partly residential. The young man was in the residential section, which carries on one side small working-class cottages, and on the other the wall of a railway goods yard. The great wall hung a blanket of shadow over the lane, and the shadow and the cadaverous outline of the now deserted market stalls gave it the appearance of a living lane that had been turned to frost in the moment between breath and death. The very lamps, that elsewhere were nimbuses of gold, had here the rigidity of gems. The journalist, feeling this message of frozen eternity, was telling himself that he was tired of the whole thing, when in one stroke the frost was broken. In the moment between one pace and another silence and darkness were racked by a high scream and through the scream a voice: "Help! help! *He's here!*"

Before he could think what movement to make, the lane came to life. As though its invisible populace had been waiting on that cry, the door of every cottage was flung open, and from them and from the alleys poured shadowy figures bent in question-mark form. For a second or so they stood as rigid as the lamps; then a police whistle gave them direction, and the flock of shadows sloped up the street. The journalist followed them, and others followed him. From the main street and from surrounding streets they came, some risen from unfinished suppers, some disturbed in their ease of slippers and shirt sleeves, some stumbling on infirm limbs, and some upright, and armed with pokers or the tools of their trade. Here and there above the wavering cloud of heads moved the bold helmets of policemen. In one dim mass they surged upon a cottage whose doorway was marked by the sergeant and two constables; and voices of those behind urged them on with "Get in! Find him! Run round the back! Over the wall!" and those in front cried: "Keep back! Keep back!"

And now the fury of a mob held in thrall by unknown peril broke loose. He was here—on the spot. Surely this time he *could not* escape. All minds were bent upon the cottage; all energies thrust towards its doors and windows and roof; all thought was turned upon one unknown man and his extermination. So that no one man saw any other man. No man saw the narrow, packed lane and the mass of struggling shadows, and all forgot to look among themselves for the monster who never lingered upon his victims. All forgot, indeed, that they, by their mass crusade of vengeance, were affording him the perfect hiding place. They saw only the house, and they heard only the rending of woodwork and the smash of glass at back and front, and the police giving orders or crying with the chase; and they pressed on.

But they found no murderer. All they found was news of murder and a glimpse of the ambulance, and for their fury there was no other object than the police themselves, who fought against this hampering of their work.

The journalist managed to struggle through to the cottage door, and to get the story from the constable stationed there. The cottage was the home of a pensioned sailor and his wife and daughter. They had been at supper, and at first it appeared that some noxious gas had smitten all three in mid-action. The daughter lay dead on the hearthrug, with a piece of bread and butter in her hand. The father had fallen sideways from his chair, leaving on his plate a filled spoon of rice pudding. The mother lay half under the table, her lap filled with the pieces of a broken cup and splashes of cocoa. But in three seconds the idea of gas was dismissed. One glance at their necks showed that this was the Strangler again; and the police stood and looked at the room and momentarily shared the fatalism of the public. They were helpless.

This was his fourth visit, making seven murders in all. He was to do, as you know, one more—and to do it that night; and then he was to pass into history as the unknown London horror, and return to the decent life that he had always led, remembering little of what he had done, and worried not at all by the memory. Why did he stop? Impossible to say. Why did he begin? Impossible again. It just happened like that; and if he thinks at all of those days and nights, I surmise that he thinks of them as we think of foolish or dirty little sins that we committed in childhood. We say that they were not really sins, because we were not then consciously ourselves: we had not come to realization; and we look back at that foolish little creature that we once were, and forgive him because he didn't know. So, I think, with this man.

There are plenty like him. Eugene Aram, after the murder of Daniel Clarke, lived a quiet, contented life for fourteen years, unhaunted by his crime and unshaken in his self-esteem. Dr. Crippen murdered his wife, and then lived pleasantly with his mistress in the house under whose floor he had buried the wife. Constance Kent, found Not Guilty of the murder of her young brother, led a peaceful life for five years before she confessed. George Joseph Smith and William Palmer lived amiably among their fellows untroubled by fear or by remorse for their poisonings and drownings. Charles Peace, at the time he made his one unfortunate essay, had settled down into a respectable citizen with an interest in antiques. It happened that, after a lapse of time, these men were discovered, but more murderers than we guess are living decent lives today, and will die in decency, undiscovered and unsuspected. As this man will.

But he had a narrow escape, and it was perhaps this narrow escape that brought him to a stop. The escape was due to an error of judgment on the part of the journalist.

As soon as he had the full story of the affair, which took some time, he spent fifteen minutes on the telephone, sending the story through, and at the end of the fifteen minutes, when the stimulus of the business had left him, he felt physically tired and mentally disheveled. He was not yet free to go home; the paper would not go away for another hour; so he turned into a bar for a drink and some sandwiches.

It was then, when he had dismissed the whole business from his mind, and was looking about the bar and admiring the landlord's taste in watch chains and his air of domination, and was thinking that the landlord of a well-conducted tavern had a more comfortable life than a newspaperman, that his mind received from nowhere a spark of light. He was not thinking about the Strangling Horrors; his mind was on his sandwich.

As a public-house sandwich, it was a curiosity. The bread had been thinly cut, it was buttered, and the ham was not two months' stale; it was ham as it should be. His mind turned to the inventor of this refreshment, the Earl of Sandwich, and then to George the Fourth, and then to the Georges, and to the legend of that George who was worried to know how the apple got into the apple dumpling. He wondered whether George would have been equally puzzled to know how the ham got into the ham sandwich, and how long it would have been before it occurred to him that the ham could not have got there unless somebody had put it there. He got up to order another sandwich, and in that moment a little active corner of his mind settled the affair. If there was ham in his sandwich, somebody must have put it there. If seven people had been murdered, somebody must have been there to murder them. There was no airplane or automobile that would go into a man's pocket; therefore that somebody must have escaped either by running away or standing still; and again therefore—

He was visualizing the front-page story that his paper would carry if his theory were correct, and if—a matter of conjecture—his editor had the necessary nerve to make a bold stroke, when a cry of "Time, gentlemen, please! All out!" reminded him of the hour. He got up and went out into a world of mist, broken by the ragged disks of roadside puddles and the streaming lightning of motor buses. He was certain that he had *the* story, but, even if it were proved, he was doubtful whether the policy of his paper would permit him to print it. It had one great fault. It was truth, but it was impossible truth. It rocked the foundations of everything that newspaper readers believed and that newspaper editors helped them to believe. They might believe that Turkish carpet sellers had the gift of making themselves invisible. They would not believe this.

As it happened, they were not asked to, for the story was never written. As his paper had by now gone away, and as he was nourished by his refreshment and stimulated by his theory, he thought he might put in an extra half hour by testing that theory. So he began to look about for the man he had in mind—a man with white hair, and large white hands; otherwise an everyday figure whom nobody would look twice at. He wanted to spring his idea on this man without warning, and he was going to place himself within reach of a man armored in legends of dreadfulness and grue. This might appear to be an act of supreme courage—that one man, with no hope of immediate outside support, should place himself at the mercy of one who was holding a whole parish in terror. But it wasn't. He didn't think about the risk. He didn't think about his duty to his employers or loyalty to his paper. He was moved simply by an instinct to follow a story to its end.

He walked slowly from the tavern and crossed into Fingal Street, making for Deever Market, where he had hope of finding his man. But his journey was shortened. At the corner of Lotus Street he saw him—or a man who looked like him. This street was poorly lit, and he could see little of the man: but he *could* see white hands. For some twenty paces he stalked him; then drew level with him; and at a point where the arch of a railway crossed the street, he saw that this was his man. He approached him with the current conversational phrase of the district: "Well, seen anything of the murderer?" The man stopped to look sharply at him; then, satisfied that the journalist was not the murderer, said:

"Eh? No, nor's anybody else, curse it. Doubt if they ever will."

"I don't know. I've been thinking about them, and I've got an idea."

"So?"

"Yes. Came to me all of a sudden. Quarter of an hour ago. And I'd felt that we'd all been blind. It's been staring us in the face."

The man turned again to look at him, and the look and the movement held suspicion of this man who seemed to know so much. "Oh? Has it? Well, if you're so sure, why not give us the benefit of it?"

"I'm going to." They walked level, and were nearly at the end of the little street where it meets Deever Market, when the journalist turned casually to the man. He put a finger on his arm. "Yes, it seems to me quite simple now. But there's still one point I don't understand. One little thing I'd like to clear up. I mean the motive. Now, as man to man, tell me, Sergeant Ottermole, just *why* did you kill all those inoffensive people?"

The sergeant stopped, and the journalist stopped. There was just enough light from the sky, which held the reflected light of the continent of London, to give him a sight of the sergeant's face, and the sergeant's face was turned to him with a wide smile of such urbanity and charm that the journalist's eyes were frozen as they met it. The smile stayed for some seconds. Then said the sergeant: "Well, to tell you the truth, Mr. Newspaper Man, I don't know. I really don't know. In fact, I've been worried about it myself. But I've got an idea—just like you. Everybody knows that we can't control the workings of our minds. Don't they? Ideas come into our minds without asking. But everybody's supposed to be able to control his body. Why? Eh? We get our minds from lord-knows-where— from people who were dead hundreds of years before we were born. Mayn't we get our bodies in the same way? Our faces—our legs—our heads—they aren't completely ours. We don't make 'em. They come to us. And couldn't ideas come into our bodies like ideas come into our minds? Eh? Can't ideas live in nerve and muscle as well as in brain? Couldn't it be that parts of our bodies aren't really us, and couldn't ideas come into those parts all of a sudden, like ideas come into—into"—he shot his arms out, showing the great white-gloved hands and hairy wrists; shot them out so swiftly to the journalist's throat that his eyes never saw them—"into *my hands!*"

Thus I Refute Beelzy

By JOHN COLLIER

"There goes the tea bell," said Mrs. Carter. "I hope Simon hears it."

They looked out from the window of the drawing room. The long garden, agreeably neglected, ended in a waste plot. Here a little summerhouse was passing close by beauty on its way to complete decay. This was Simon's retreat. It was almost completely screened by the tangled branches of the apple tree and the pear tree, planted too close together, as they always are in the suburbs. They caught a glimpse of him now and then, as he strutted up and down, mouthing and gesticulating, performing all the solemn mumbo-jumbo of small boys who spend long afternoons at the forgotten ends of long gardens.

"There he is, bless him!" said Betty.

"Playing his game," said Mrs. Carter. "He won't play with the other children any more. And if I go down there—the temper! And comes in tired out!"

"He doesn't have his sleep in the afternoons?" asked Betty.

"You know what Big Simon's ideas are," said Mrs. Carter. " 'Let him choose for himself,' he says. That's what he chooses, and he comes in as white as a sheet."

"Look! He's heard the bell," said Betty. The expression was justified, though the bell had ceased ringing a full minute ago. Small Simon stopped in his parade exactly as if its tiny dingle had at that moment reached his ear. They watched him perform certain ritual sweeps and scratchings with his little stick, and come lagging over the hot and flaggy grass toward the house.

Mrs. Carter led the way down to the playroom, or garden room, which was also the tearoom for hot days. It had been the huge scullery of this tall Georgian house. Now the walls were cream-washed, there was coarse blue net in the windows, canvas-covered armchairs on the stone floor, and a reproduction of Van Gogh's "Sunflowers" over the mantelpiece.

Small Simon came drifting in, and accorded Betty a perfunctory greet-

ing. His face was an almost perfect triangle, pointed at the chin, and he
was paler than he should have been. "The little elf-child!" cried Betty.

Simon looked at her. "No," said he.

At that moment the door opened, and Mr. Carter came in, rubbing his
hands. He was a dentist, and washed them before and after everything
he did. "You!" said his wife. "Home already!"

"Not unwelcome, I hope," said Mr. Carter, nodding to Betty. "Two
people canceled their appointments; I decided to come home. I said, I
hope I am not unwelcome."

"Silly!" said his wife. "Of course not."

"Small Simon seems doubtful," continued Mr. Carter. "Small Simon,
are you sorry to see me at tea with you?"

"No, Daddy."

"No, what?"

"No, Big Simon."

"That's right. Big Simon and Small Simon. That sounds more like
friends, doesn't it? At one time little boys had to call their father 'sir.' If
they forgot—a good spanking. On the bottom, Small Simon! On the bottom!" said Mr. Carter, washing his hands once more with his invisible
soap and water.

The little boy turned crimson with shame or rage.

"But now, you see," said Betty, to help, "you can call your father whatever you like."

"And what," asked Mr. Carter, "has Small Simon been doing this afternoon? While Big Simon has been at work."

"Nothing," muttered his son.

"Then you have been bored," said Mr. Carter. "Learn from experience,
Small Simon. Tomorrow, do something amusing, and you will not be
bored. I want him to learn from experience, Betty. That is my way, the
new way."

"I have learned," said the boy, speaking like an old, tired man, as little
boys so often do.

"It would hardly seem so," said Mr. Carter, "if you sit on your behind
all the afternoon, doing nothing. Had *my* father caught me doing nothing, I should not have sat very comfortably."

"He played," said Mrs. Carter.

"A bit," said the boy, shifting on his chair.

"Too much," said Mrs. Carter. "He comes in all nervy and dazed. He
ought to have his rest."

"He is six," said her husband. "He is a reasonable being. He must
choose for himself. But what game is this, Small Simon, that is worth
getting nervy and dazed over? There are very few games as good as all
that."

"It's nothing," said the boy.

"Oh, come," said his father. "We are friends, are we not? You can tell me. I was a Small Simon once, just like you, and played the same games you play. Of course there were no airplanes in those days. With whom do you play this fine game? Come on, we must all answer civil questions, or the world would never go round. With whom do you play?"

"Mr. Beelzy," said the boy, unable to resist.

"Mr. Beelzy?" said his father, raising his eyebrows inquiringly at his wife.

"It's a game he makes up," said she.

"Not makes up!" cried the boy. "Fool!"

"That is telling stories," said his mother. "And rude as well. We had better talk of something different."

"No wonder he is rude," said Mr. Carter, "if you say he tells lies, and then insist on changing the subject. He tells you his fantasy: you implant a guilt feeling. What can you expect? A defense mechanism. Then you get a real lie."

"Like in *These Three*," said Betty. "Only different, of course. *She* was an unblushing little liar."

"I would have made her blush," said Mr. Carter, "in the proper part of her anatomy. But Small Simon is in the fantasy stage. Are you not, Small Simon? You just make things up."

"No, I don't," said the boy.

"You do," said his father. "And because you do, it is not too late to reason with you. There is no harm in a fantasy, old chap. There is no harm in a bit of make-believe. Only you have to know the difference between daydreams and real things, or your brain will never grow. It will never be the brain of a Big Simon. So come on. Let us hear about this Mr. Beelzy of yours. Come on. What is he like?"

"He isn't like anything," said the boy.

"Like nothing on earth?" said his father. "That's a terrible fellow."

"I'm not frightened of him," said the child, smiling. "Not a bit."

"I should hope not," said his father. "If you were, you would be frightening yourself. I am always telling people, older people than you are, that they are just frightening themselves. Is he a funny man? Is he a giant?"

"Sometimes he is," said the little boy.

"Sometimes one thing, sometimes another," said his father. "Sounds pretty vague. Why can't you tell us just what he's like?"

"I love him," said the small boy. "He loves me."

"That's a big word," said Mr. Carter. "That might be better kept for real things, like Big Simon and Small Simon."

"He is real," said the boy, passionately. "He's not a fool. He's real."

"Listen," said his father. "When you go down the garden there's nobody there. Is there?"

"No," said the boy.

"Then you think of him, inside your head, and he comes."

"No," said Small Simon. "I have to make marks. On the ground. With my stick."

"That doesn't matter."

"Yes, it does."

"Small Simon, you are being obstinate," said Mr. Carter. "I am trying to explain something to you. I have been longer in the world than you have, so naturally I am older and wiser. I am explaining that Mr. Beelzy is a fantasy of yours. Do you hear? Do you understand?"

"Yes, Daddy."

"He is a game. He is a let's-pretend."

The little boy looked down at his plate, smiling resignedly.

"I hope you are listening to me," said his father. "All you have to do is to say, 'I have been playing a game of let's-pretend. With someone I make up, called Mr. Beelzy.' Then no one will say you tell lies, and you will know the difference between dreams and reality. Mr. Beelzy is a day-dream."

The little boy still stared at his plate.

"He is sometimes there and sometimes not there," pursued Mr. Carter. "Sometimes he's like one thing, sometimes another. You can't really see him. Not as you see me. I am real. You can't touch him. You can touch me. I can touch you." Mr. Carter stretched out his big, white, dentist's hand, and took his little son by the nape of the neck. He stopped speaking for a moment and tightened his hand. The little boy sank his head still lower.

"Now you know the difference," said Mr. Carter, "between a pretend and a real thing. You and I are one thing; he is another. Which is the pretend? Come on. Answer me. What is the pretend?"

"Big Simon and Small Simon," said the little boy.

"Don't!" cried Betty, and at once put her hand over her mouth, for why should a visitor cry "Don't!" when a father is explaining things in a scientific and modern way? Besides, it annoys the father.

"Well, my boy," said Mr. Carter, "I have said you must be allowed to learn from experience. Go upstairs. Right up to your room. You shall learn whether it is better to reason, or to be perverse and obstinate. Go up. I shall follow you."

"You are not going to beat the child?" cried Mrs. Carter.

"No," said the little boy. "Mr. Beelzy won't let him."

"Go on up with you!" shouted his father.

Small Simon stopped at the door. "He said he wouldn't let anyone hurt me," he whimpered. "He said he'd come like a lion, with wings on, and eat them up."

"You'll learn how real he is!" shouted his father after him. "If you can't learn it at one end, you shall learn it at the other. I'll have your breeches down. I shall finish my cup of tea first, however," said he to the two women.

Neither of them spoke. Mr. Carter finished his tea, and unhurriedly left the room, washing his hands with his invisible soap and water.

Mrs. Carter said nothing. Betty could think of nothing to say. She wanted to be talking for she was afraid of what they might hear.

Suddenly it came. It seemed to tear the air apart. "Good God!" she cried. "What was that? He's hurt him." She sprang out of her chair, her silly eyes flashing behind her glasses. "I'm going up there!" she cried, trembling.

"Yes, let us go up," said Mrs. Carter. "Let us go up. That was not Small Simon."

It was on the second-floor landing that they found the shoe, with the man's foot still in it, like that last morsel of a mouse which sometimes falls unnoticed from the side of the jaws of the cat.

Sredni Vashtar

By SAKI (H. H. MUNRO)

CONRADIN was ten years old, and the doctor had pronounced his professional opinion that the boy would not live another five years. The doctor was silky and effete, and counted for little, but his opinion was endorsed by Mrs. De Ropp, who counted for nearly everything. Mrs. De Ropp was Conradin's cousin and guardian, and in his eyes she represented those three-fifths of the world that are necessary and disagreeable and real; the other two-fifths, in perpetual antagonism to the foregoing, were summed up in himself and his imagination. One of these days Conradin supposed he would succumb to the mastering pressure of wearisome necessary things—such as illnesses and coddling restrictions and drawn-out dullness. Without his imagination, which was rampant under the spur of loneliness, he would have succumbed long ago.

Mrs. De Ropp would never, in her honestest moments, have confessed to herself that she disliked Conradin, though she might have been dimly aware that thwarting him "for his good" was a duty which she did not find particularly irksome. Conradin hated her with a desperate sincerity which he was perfectly able to mask. Such few pleasures as he could contrive for himself gained an added relish from the likelihood that they would be displeasing to his guardian, and from the realm of his imagination she was locked out—an unclean thing, which should find no entrance.

In the dull, cheerless garden, overlooked by so many windows that were ready to open with a message not to do this or that, or a reminder that medicines were due, he found little attraction. The few fruit trees that it contained were set jealously apart from his plucking, as though they were rare specimens of their kind blooming in an arid waste; it would probably have been difficult to find a market gardener who would have offered ten shillings for their entire yearly produce. In a forgotten corner, however, almost hidden behind a dismal shrubbery, was a disused tool shed of respectable proportions, and within its walls Conradin found a haven, something that took on the varying aspects of a playroom and a cathedral. He had peopled it with a legion of familiar phantoms, evoked partly from fragments of history and partly from his own brain, but it also boasted two inmates of flesh and blood. In one corner lived a ragged-plumaged Houdan hen, on which the boy lavished an affection that had scarcely another outlet. Further back in the gloom stood a large hutch, divided into two compartments, one of which was fronted with close iron bars. This was the abode of a large polecat-ferret, which a friendly butcher boy had once smuggled, cage and all, into its present quarters, in exchange for a long-secreted hoard of small silver. Conradin was dreadfully afraid of the lithe, sharp-fanged beast, but it was his most treasured possession. Its very presence in the tool shed was a secret and fearful joy, to be kept scrupulously from the knowledge of the Woman, as he privately dubbed his cousin. And one day, out of Heaven knows what material, he spun the beast a wonderful name, and from that moment it grew into a god and a religion. The Woman indulged in religion once a week at a church near by, and took Conradin with her, but to him the church service was an alien rite in the House of Rimmon. Every Thursday, in the dim and musty silence of the tool shed, he worshiped with mystic and elaborate ceremonial before the wooden hutch where dwelt Sredni Vashtar, the great ferret. Red flowers in their season and scarlet berries in the winter-time were offered at his shrine, for he was a god who laid some special stress on the fierce impatient side of things, as opposed to the Woman's religion, which, as far as Conradin could observe, went to great lengths in the contrary direction. And on great festivals powdered nutmeg was strewn in front of his hutch, an important feature of the offering being that the nutmeg had to be stolen. These festivals were of irregular occurrence, and were chiefly appointed to celebrate some passing event. On one occasion, when Mrs. De Ropp suffered from acute toothache for three days, Conradin kept up the festival during the entire three days, and almost succeeded in persuading himself that Sredni Vashtar was personally responsible for the toothache. If the malady had lasted for another day the supply of nutmeg would have given out.

The Houdan hen was never drawn into the cult of Sredni Vashtar. Conradin had long ago settled that she was Anabaptist. He did not pretend to have the remotest knowledge as to what an Anabaptist was, but he privately hoped that it was dashing and not very respectable. Mrs. De Ropp was the ground plan on which he based and detested all respectability.

After a while Conradin's absorption in the tool shed began to attract the notice of his guardian. "It is not good for him to be pottering down there in all weathers," she promptly decided, and at breakfast one morning she announced that the Houdan hen had been sold and taken away overnight. With her shortsighted eyes she peered at Conradin, waiting for an outbreak of rage and sorrow, which she was ready to rebuke with a flow of excellent precepts and reasoning. But Conradin said nothing: there was nothing to be said. Something perhaps in his white set face gave her a momentary qualm, for at tea that afternoon there was toast on the table, a delicacy which she usually banned on the ground that it was bad for him; also because the making of it "gave trouble," a deadly offense in the middle-class feminine eye.

"I thought you liked toast," she exclaimed, with an injured air, observing that he did not touch it.

"Sometimes," said Conradin.

In the shed that evening there was an innovation in the worship of the hutch god. Conradin had been wont to chant his praises; tonight he asked a boon.

"Do one thing for me, Sredni Vashtar."

The thing was not specified. As Sredni Vashtar was a god he must be supposed to know. And, choking back a sob as he looked at that other empty corner, Conradin went back to the world he so hated.

And every night, in the welcome darkness of his bedroom, and every evening in the dusk of the tool shed, Conradin's bitter litany went up: "Do one thing for me, Sredni Vashtar."

Mrs. De Ropp noticed that the visits to the shed did not cease, and one day she made a further journey of inspection.

"What are you keeping in that locked hutch?" she asked. "I believe it's guinea pigs. I'll have them all cleared away."

Conradin shut his lips tight, but the Woman ransacked his bedroom till she found the carefully hidden key, and forthwith marched down to the shed to complete her discovery. It was a cold afternoon, and Conradin had been bidden to keep to the house. From the furtherest window of the dining room the door of the shed could just be seen beyond the corner of the shrubbery, and there Conradin stationed himself. He saw the Woman enter, and then he imagined her opening the door of the sacred hutch and peering down with her shortsighted eyes into the thick straw bed where his god lay hidden. Perhaps she would prod at the straw in her clumsy impatience. And Conradin fervently breathed his prayer for the last time. But he knew as he prayed that he did not believe. He knew that the Woman would come out presently with that pursed smile he loathed so well on her face, and that in an hour or two the gardener would carry away his wonderful god, a god no longer, but a simple brown ferret in a hutch. And he knew that the Woman would triumph always as she triumphed now, and that he would grow ever more sickly under her pestering and domineering and superior wisdom, till one day nothing would matter much more with him, and the doctor would be proved right. And in the sting and misery of his defeat, he began to chant loudly and defiantly the hymn of his threatened idol:

> Sredni Vashtar went forth,
> His thoughts were red thoughts and his teeth were white.

His enemies called for peace, but he brought them death.
Sredni Vashtar the Beautiful.

And then of a sudden he stopped his chanting and drew closer to the windowpane. The door of the shed still stood ajar as it had been left, and the minutes were slipping by. They were long minutes, but they slipped by nevertheless. He watched the starlings running and flying in little parties across the lawn; he counted them over and over again, with one eye always on that swinging door. A sour-faced maid came in to lay the table for tea, and still Conradin stood and waited and watched. Hope had crept by inches into his heart, and now a look of triumph began to blaze in his eyes that had only known the wistful patience of defeat. Under his breath, with a furtive exultation, he began once again the paean of victory and devastation. And presently his eyes were rewarded: out through that doorway came a long, low, yellow-and-brown beast, with eyes a-blink at the waning daylight, and dark wet stains around the fur of jaws and throat. Conradin dropped on his knees. The great polecat-ferret made its way down to a small brook at the foot of the garden, drank for a moment, then crossed a little plank bridge and was lost to sight in the bushes. Such was the passing of Sredni Vashtar.

"Tea is ready," said the sour-faced maid; "where is the mistress?"

"She went down to the shed some time ago," said Conradin.

And while the maid went to summon her mistress to tea, Conradin fished a toasting fork out of the sideboard drawer and proceeded to toast himself a piece of bread. And during the toasting of it and the buttering of it with much butter and the slow enjoyment of eating it, Conradin listened to the noises and silences which fell in quick spasms beyond the dining-room door. The loud foolish screaming of the maid, the answering chorus of wondering ejaculations from the kitchen region, the scuttering footsteps and hurried embassies for outside help, and then, after a lull, the scared sobbings and the shuffling tread of those who bore a heavy burden into the house.

"Whoever will break it to the poor child? I couldn't for the life of me!" exclaimed a shrill voice. And while they debated the matter among themselves, Conradin made himself another piece of toast.

Coroner's Inquest

By MARC CONNELLY

"WHAT is your name?"

"Frank Wineguard."

"Where do you live?"

"A hundred and eighty-five West Fifty-fifth Street."

"What is your business?"

"I'm stage manager for *Hello, America.*"

"You were the employer of James Dawle?"

"In a way. We both worked for Mr. Bender, the producer, but I have charge backstage."

"Did you know Theodore Robel?"

"Yes sir."

"Was he in your company too?"

"No sir. I met him when we started rehearsals. That was about three months ago, in June. We sent out a call for midgets and he and Jimmy showed up together, with a lot of others. Robel was too big for us. I didn't see him again until we broke into their room Tuesday."

"You discovered their bodies?"

"Yes sir. Mrs. Pike, there, was with me."

"You found them both dead?"

"Yes sir."

"How did you happen to be over in Jersey City?"

"Well, I'd called up his house at curtain time Monday night when I found Jimmy hadn't shown up for the performance. Mrs. Pike told me they were both out, and I asked her to have either Jimmy or Robel call me when they came in. Then Mrs. Pike called me Tuesday morning and said she tried to get into the room but she'd found the door was bolted. She said all her other roomers were out and she was alone and scared.

"I'd kind of suspected something might be wrong. So I said to wait and I'd come over. Then I took the tube over and got there about noon. Then we went up and I broke down the door."

"Did you see this knife there?"

"Yes sir. It was on the floor, about a foot from Jimmy."

"You say you suspected something was wrong. What do you mean by that?"

"I mean I felt something might have happened to Jimmy. Nothing like this, of course. But I knew he'd been feeling very depressed lately, and I knew Robel wasn't helping to cheer him up any."

"You mean that they had had quarrels?"

"No sir. They just both had the blues. Robel had had them for a long time. Robel was Jimmy's brother-in-law. He'd married Jimmy's sister—she was a midget too—about five years ago, but she died a year or so later. Jimmy had been living with them and after the sister died he and Robel took a room in Mrs. Pike's house together."

"How did you learn this?"

"Jimmy and I were pretty friendly at the theater. He was a nice little fellow and seemed grateful that I'd given him his job. We'd only needed one midget for an oriental scene in the second act and the agencies had sent about fifteen. Mr. Gehring, the director, told me to pick one of them as he was busy and I picked Jimmy because he was the littlest.

"After I got to know him he told me how glad he was I'd given him the job. He hadn't worked for nearly a year. He wasn't little enough to be a featured midget with circuses or in museums so he had to take whatever came along. Anyway, we got to be friendly and he used to tell me about his brother-in-law and all."

"He never suggested that there might be ill feeling between him and his brother-in-law?"

"No sir. I don't imagine he'd ever had any words at all with Robel. As a matter of fact from what I could gather I guess Jimmy had quite a lot of affection for him and he certainly did everything he could to help him. Robel was a lot worse off than Jimmy. Robel hadn't worked for a couple of years and Jimmy practically supported him. He used to tell me how Robel had been sunk ever since he got his late growth."

"His what?"

"His late growth. I heard it happens among midgets often, but Jimmy told me about it first. Usually a midget will stay as long as he lives at whatever height he reaches when he's fourteen or fifteen, but every now and then one of them starts growing again just before he's thirty, and he can grow a foot or even more in a couple of years. Then he stops growing for good. But of course he don't look so much like a midget any more.

"That's what had happened to Robel about three years ago. Of course he had trouble getting jobs and it hit him pretty hard.

"From what Jimmy told me and from what Mrs. Pike says, I guess he used to talk about it all the time. Robel used to come over and see his agent in New York twice a week, but there was never anything for him. Then he'd go back to Jersey City. Most of the week he lived alone because after the show started Jimmy often stayed in New York with a cousin or somebody that lived uptown.

"Lately Robel hadn't been coming over to New York at all. But every Saturday night Jimmy would go over to Jersey City and stay till Monday with him, trying to cheer him up. Every Sunday they'd take a walk and go to a movie. I guess as they walked along the street Robel realized most the difference in their heights. And I guess that's really why they're both dead now."

"How do you mean?"

"Well, as I told you, Jimmy would try to sympathize with Robel and cheer him up. He and Robel both realized that Jimmy was working and supporting them and that Jimmy would probably keep right on working, according to the ordinary breaks of the game, while Robel would always be too big. It simply preyed on Robel's mind.

"And then three weeks ago Monday Jimmy thought he saw the ax fall.

"I was standing outside the stage door—it was about seven-thirty—and Jimmy came down the alley. He looked down in the mouth, which I thought was strange, seeing that he usually used to come in swinging his little cane and looking pretty cheerful. I said, 'How are you feeling, Jimmy?' and he said, 'I don't feel so good, Mr. Wineguard.' So I said, 'Why, what's the matter, Jimmy?' I could see there really was something the matter with him by this time.

" 'I'm getting scared,' he said, and I says, 'Why?'

" 'I'm starting to grow again,' he says. He said it the way you'd say you just found out you had some disease that was going to kill you in a week. He looked like he was shivering.

" 'Why, you're crazy, Jimmy,' I says, 'you ain't growing.'

" 'Yes, I am,' he says. 'I'm thirty-one and it's that late growth like my brother-in-law has. My father had it, but his people had money, so it didn't make much difference to him. It's different with me. I've got to keep working.'

"He went on like that for a while and then I tried to kid him out of it.

" 'You look all right to me,' I said. 'How tall have you been all along?'

" 'Thirty-seven inches,' he says. So I says, 'Come on into the prop room and I'll measure you.'

"He backed away from me. 'No,' he says, 'I don't want to know how much it is.' Then he went up to the dressing room before I could argue with him.

"All week he looked awful sunk. When he showed up the next Monday evening he looked almost white.

"I grabbed him as he was starting upstairs to make up.

" 'Come on out of it,' I says. I thought he'd make a break and try to get away from me, but he didn't. He just sort of smiled as if I didn't understand. Finally he says, 'It ain't any use, Mr. Wineguard.'

" 'Listen,' I says, 'you've been over with that brother-in-law of yours, haven't you?' He said yes, he had. 'Well,' I says, 'that's what's bothering you. From what you tell me about him he's talked about his own tough luck so much that he's given you the willies too. Stay away from him the end of this week.'

"He stood there for a second without saying anything. Then he says, 'That wouldn't do any good. He's all alone over there and he needs company. Anyway, it's all up with me, I guess. I've grown nearly two inches already.'

"I looked at him. He was pretty pathetic, but outside of that there wasn't any change in him as far as I could see.

"I says, 'Have you been measured?' He said he hadn't. Then I said, 'Then how do you know? Your clothes fit you all right, except your pants, and as a matter of fact they seem a little longer.'

" 'I fixed my suspenders and let them down a lot farther,' he says. 'Besides, they were always a little big for me.'

" 'Let's make sure,' I says. 'I'll get a yardstick and we'll make absolutely sure.'

"But I guess he was too scared to face things. He wouldn't do it.

"He managed to dodge me all week. Then last Saturday night I ran into him as I was leaving the theater. I asked him if he felt any better.

" 'I feel all right,' he says. He really looked scared to death.

"That's the last time I saw him before I went over to Jersey City after Mrs. Pike phoned me Tuesday."

"Patrolman Gorlitz has testified that the bodies were in opposite ends of the room when he arrived. They were in that position when you forced open the door?"

"Yes sir."

"The medical examiner has testified that they were both dead of knife wounds, apparently from the same knife. Would you assume the knife had fallen from Dawle's hand as he fell?"

"Yes sir."

"Has it been your purpose to suggest that both men were driven to despondency by a fear of lack of employment for Dawle, and that they might have committed suicide?"

"No sir. I don't think anything of the kind."

"What do you mean?"

"Well, when Mrs. Pike and I went in the room and I got a look at the knife, I said to Mrs. Pike that that was a funny kind of a knife for them to have in the room. You can see it's a kind of a butcher knife. Then Mrs. Pike told me it was one that she'd missed from her kitchen a few weeks before. She'd never thought either Robel or Jimmy had taken it. It struck me as funny Robel or Jimmy had stolen it too. Then I put two and two together and found out what really happened. Have you got the little broken cane that was lying on the bed?"

"Is this it?"

"Yes sir. Well, I'd never been convinced by Jimmy that he was really growing. So when Mrs. Pike told me about the knife I started figuring. I figured that about five minutes before that knife came into play Jimmy must have found it, probably by accident."

"Why by accident?"

"Because Robel had gone a little crazy, I guess. He'd stolen it and kept it hidden from Jimmy. And when Jimmy found it he wondered what Robel had been doing with it. Then Robel wouldn't tell him and Jimmy found out for himself. Or maybe Robel did tell him. Anyway, Jimmy looked at the cane. It was the one he always carried. He saw where, when Jimmy wasn't looking, Robel had been cutting little pieces off the end of it!"

Treasure Trove

By F. TENNYSON JESSE

SUMMER stayed late that year, and it was not until the last day of October that Brandon realized it had gone. Then a storm sprang up which went sweeping over the marshes, ruffling the still, gray waters of the meres and inlets, and rending the leaves from the twisted trees. After it had passed the warmth had gone from the air and only a pale, wintry sunshine lay pure and chill over the fen land. A few leaves still clung to the elms that grew about the farm place, he heard the cawing of the rooks about their nests, which showed black amid the bare branches.

Brandon felt for the moment the classic melancholy appropriate to the dying year, annual reminder of the autumn that approaches to every man. But the next moment, turning his head to look the way he had come, he saw that between the pale brown masses of the reeds the waters were a cold, bright blue, and the crystalline notes of the robin, practicing for its winter song, came to his ear. Beauty still lived in this fenny country and his heart responded gratefully.

He went across the muddy yard and met his friend Miles in the doorway of the farmhouse. Dear, good Miles—sun or rain, summer or winter, held very little message for him that was not strictly utilitarian. But Miles's ruddy, outdoor face seemed somehow to have lost its usual cheerfulness of outlook, though it would certainly not be because of anything to do with some allegorical message of the dying summer.

"Have you seen Tom and Jack?" asked Miles. "They were supposed to be plowing in the five-acre today, and they're not to be found. They're so dependable as a rule."

"Tom and Jack? No. It doesn't matter, does it? I suppose they're harrowing or mulching or marling or sowing or some other of the many processes that you indulge in."

The strange expression on his host's face had not lightened.

"They've been queer," he said, "darn queer, for two days now, ever since they found that cursed treasure while plowing the reclaimed piece of waste land over by the big dike. This morning they looked so queerly at each other I didn't quite like them going out together. There's something odd about it, Bill. I don't like it."

Brandon smiled and began to stuff his pipe.

"Nonsense, what could be wrong with your men?" he said. "It won't be the first time a little bit of money has gone to a man's head. They'll get over it, you'll see."

But to himself he was thinking that it was a bit queer all the same. Everyone knew Tom and Jack; they were the famous friends of the village. Damon and Pythias weren't in it when it came to friendship. They had been to the same Council school as boys, been in the same footer team in the winter, same cricket team in the summer, skated together, gone duck shooting together, gone fishing together, fought in the same regiment through the war and had even married twin sisters, and as far as anyone knew there had never been a wry word between them. They were not men of any special ability which would have caused them to grow away from the class of life into which they had been born, but in that class they were easily first in their district. Honest, decent, intelligent men, a little slow in the processes of their thoughts, perhaps, but none the less shrewd and sound for that. Tom a year younger, slightly built and active, Jack heavy compared with his friend, but strong as a bull. Tom might be quick in his temper, but it was soon over. Jack had the serenity that often goes with men of his large build. It seemed sad and a little odd that a few, dirty, antique coins should have been able to come between them.

"Why don't you tell them," he suggested to Miles, "that their old coins are probably worth very little?"

"I have," said Miles. "But you know what these people are, they always imagine anything they dig up must be of immense value and that the British Museum would buy it for a large sum. I can understand that part of it, what I can't understand is that they should begin to quarrel over it. I should have thought they'd have been only too glad to share it, however much or little it's worth. Besides, their working hours are not over yet, and I've never known them to down tools until the right hour, generally not till after it, they're the real old-fashioned kind that doesn't like to leave a job half done."

Scarcely had he said this when one of the maidservants came running from the passage at his back, calling to him in a loud and frightened voice:

"Come quick, sir, Tom and Jack be fighting in the barn, they're killing each other. . . ."

Miles turned and ran through the house, out into the front garden and across it, Brandon at his heels.

The big barn stood on the slope of the field beyond, a wooden building, black with pitch, with a red fluted roof. Beside it the straw ricks gleamed golden in the late sunshine. The two men ran up the slope of the field where the trodden turf was heavy and greasy to their feet and Brandon, outstepping his more elderly host, burst through into the barn.

For the first moment it all seemed very dark to him, a darkness filled with dust motes that wreathed like steam in the rays shining through the doorway. The smell of cattle and trodden earth, and of the sweet stored hay, filled the dimness; rafters and rough wooden pillars stood out in the gloom. Then, as sight grew clear, his ears became aware of a horrible sound of sobbing that rose and fell, and the thud of blows. Two men were fighting, backward and forward, on the earthy floor. As Miles and Brandon sprang forward, the bigger man, who was winning, rained blows upon either side of his opponent's head, and the smaller man, from whom came the noise of sobbing, suddenly crumpled up and fell to the floor, where he lay still.

"Good God, man!" cried Miles, hanging on to the big fellow's arm. "You must be mad, you might kill him."

The man turned a ravaged face to his master.

"I shouldn't care if I had, the dirty hound!" he said. "He's a thief, that's what he is."

"Tom a thief! Nonsense. Why, you'd have fought anybody else who said as much."

"Aye, I *would* have," said the man, "but not now. . . . He's stolen all the money we dug up in the new field. He's hidden it away somewhere and won't say where. He's just lying and saying he hasn't got it."

Brandon had knelt down beside the unconscious Tom, whose face was running with blood; now he looked up and said:

"Well, you've nearly killed him. Even if it's true, you ought to be ashamed of yourself, and I don't believe it *is* true, Tom wouldn't do a thing like that. By God, Miles, look at his fists. Open your fists."

And he got up and advanced on Jack, who stood staring sullenly at him, his clenched fists still held before him. Jack offered no resistance as his master and Brandon pulled his fingers apart and discovered, clenched in each hand, a ragged flint stone, the ends dripping with Tom's blood. Brandon, looking at Jack's glazed eyes, said nothing; it would be little use saying anything, he felt, to a man as changed from the self they all knew as this man was. Instead, he said to Miles:

"We must get Tom out of this, you and Jack pick him up while I have a look around."

With surprising docility Jack bent down and picked up gently the head he had ill-treated, and he and Miles between them carried the unconscious man out through the ray of sunlight into the air.

Brandon sat down on an upturned bucket near at hand, he felt sick and ill at the sight of the blood, an idiosyncrasy of his, so unconquerable that he had ceased to be ashamed of it. It seemed to him that the dim air of the barn was laden still with the violent passions that had been released there, that the element of strangeness in this sudden hatred sickened the very sunlight that slanted in upon the spot trodden by the men's struggling feet.

Brandon was not normally a supersensitive man, but all his life he had been the prey of moments which had taken and shaken him oddly, moments when he had seemed not through any superior gifts of his own, but because of some outer compulsion, to be aware of more than most men, of more than, ordinarily, he would have been aware of himself. Usually these strange spaces of clarity were prefaced by an unaccountable aspect of external things; a familiar tree or bookshelf would take on a look that he could only describe to himself as "tilted," as though the angle of the visible world had started off in a new direction, pointing toward an unknown dimension; as though the tree or bookshelf had lost, all of a sudden, its treeness or furniturehood, and become a wedge thrust into space. At the time this would seem all right to him, only afterwards, looking back, his senses still giddy, he would realize the different tilt. And, cutting across this new space, there would come a wedge of light, tilted at the same new angle, which for the moment was the right angle, and in it he would be aware of, rather than see, a new and more complete aspect of something he had only imperfectly known before. A friend's motive for doing what had to him previously seemed inexplicable; the solution to some riddle in the history lecture he was working out; or sometimes even a fresh light upon a matter which had no earthly connection, as far as he knew, with himself.

He was almost hypnotized into this feeling now, as he sat there in the barn, but he shook off the dizzying sensation, like the familiar pins and needles of the children, that was stealing over him, and told himself it was due to the upset of his nerves and to the angle of the shaft of light that streamed in at the door. He got to his feet and as he did so he caught sight of a battered felt hat lying against the wall of the barn. He went over to it to take it up, he recognized it as Tom's by its peculiar light-gray color and by the bluejay's feather stuck in the band. He bent to pick it up, but to his surprise it was so unexpectedly heavy in his hand that he almost dropped it. He ran his fingers behind the head lining of the crown; wrapped in a thin piece of stuff he felt the uneven surfaces of coins. So Tom had lied after all . . . he had concealed the coins. Brandon felt as when he had seen the flints concealed in Jack's fists.

He picked up the hat, and went heavily out of the barn with the hat carried between his two hands. He crossed the garden and went into the little room outside the front door which Miles used as his office.

Brandon closed the door and sat down at the table, pushing away papers and ledgers to make a clear space in front of him. Then he turned the hat up, and pulled out the pack of coins which lay, snakelike, curled round the crown. He unfolded the strip of soiled silk handkerchief and poured the coins out on to the table before him. There they lay, the source of all the trouble between Tom and Jack, a mere handful of dirty, almost shapeless coins. Brandon looked at them curiously. They were so old and battered he could only just make out the head of a Cæsar—which, he knew not, but the Roman look of it was unmistakable. It seemed incredible that through these coins, the passion of envy, mounting murder high, had come into being. . . . He scraped the coins together in his two hands.

And then, as he sat there, the strange sensation came flooding over him, drenching him, as it were, to the tips of his fingers and toes, so that he felt he could not move if the house caught fire about him. He felt very cold, in spite of the tingling that pervaded him, and he knew—how, he could not have told—that he was holding in his palms things so evil that his very flesh revolted, things so evil that whenever they were discovered and rediscovered by men they brought evil in their train. He knew, with a dreadful clearness in the midst of this dark red mist, that these things had been turned up by the plowshare, or dragged from the sea, or cast upon beaches throughout the years, and whosoever found them knew desolation and decay of everything that had been his until then. There beat at him persistently the knowledge that he must take these things out and throw them away in the place where it was least likely they would be found for generations to come. He must weight them heavily and cast them out to sea, or throw them into the still waters of some disused pit.

He struggled violently against the feeling of horror that held him, because he wished to see about this business as soon as might be, and by a violent effort of the will he pulled himself back into the present. The evening sun was still shining into the little room. Shaking, but with the tingling slowly growing less all over his body, he drew his hands away from the clustering coins and let them fall upon the table. He passed his palm across his wet forehead and told himself that in another moment or so he would be able to do what he had to do, and quite soon he stood up, his steady self again, although not denying he had been shaken.

It was suddenly that the dreadful idea took him. Putting out his hand he began to count the coins; he counted three times, always hoping that in his hurry he might have erred, but count as he would, the battered pieces of silver numbered thirty. Brandon leaped up, and drew away from the table, his hands shaking. He found himself saying in a dreadful whisper: "Thirty pieces of silver . . . thirty pieces . . . of silver."

The Most Dangerous Game

By RICHARD CONNELL

"OFF THERE to the right—somewhere—is a large island," said Whitney. "It's rather a mystery—"

"What island is it?" Rainsford asked.

"The old charts called it Ship-Trap Island," Whitney replied. "A suggestive name, isn't it? Sailors have a curious dread of the place. I don't know why. Some superstition—"

"Can't see it," remarked Rainsford, trying to peer through the dank tropical night that pressed its thick warm blackness in upon the yacht.

"You've good eyes," said Whitney with a laugh, "and I've seen you pick off a moose moving in the brown fall bush at four hundred yards, but even you can't see four miles or so through a moonless Caribbean night."

"Nor four yards," admitted Rainsford. "Ugh! It's like moist black velvet."

"It will be light enough in Rio," promised Whitney. "We should make it in a few days. I hope the jaguar guns have come from Purdey's. We should have some good hunting up the Amazon. Great sport, hunting."

"The best sport in the world," agreed Rainsford.

"For the hunter," amended Whitney. "Not for the jaguar."

"Don't talk rot, Whitney. You're a big-game hunter, not a philosopher. Who cares how a jaguar feels?"

"Perhaps the jaguar does."

"Bah! They've no understanding."

"Even so, I rather think they understand one thing—fear. The fear of pain and the fear of death."

"Nonsense," laughed Rainsford. "This hot weather is making you soft, Whitney. Be a realist. The world is made up of two classes—the hunters and the huntees. Luckily you and I are hunters. Do you think we have passed that island yet?"

"I can't tell in the dark. I hope so."

"Why?"

"The place has a reputation—a bad one."

"Cannibals?"

"Hardly. Even cannibals wouldn't live in such a God-forsaken place. But it's gotten into sailor lore, somehow. Didn't you notice that the crew's nerves seemed a bit jumpy today?"

"They were a bit strange, now you mention it. Even Captain Neilson."

"Yes, even that tough-minded old Swede, who'd go up to the devil himself and ask him for a light. Those fishy blue eyes held a look I never saw there before. All I could get out of him was: 'This place has an evil name among seafaring men, sir.' Then he said, gravely: 'Don't you feel anything?' Now you mustn't laugh but I did feel a sort of chill, and there wasn't a breeze. What I felt was a—a mental chill, a sort of dread."

"Pure imagination," said Rainsford. "One superstitious sailor can taint a whole ship's company with his fear."

"Maybe. Sometimes I think sailors have an extra sense which tells them when they are in danger . . . anyhow I'm glad we are getting out of this zone. Well, I'll turn in now, Rainsford."

"I'm not sleepy. I'm going to smoke another pipe on the after deck."

There was no sound in the night as Rainsford sat there but the muffled throb of the yacht's engine and the swish and ripple of the propeller.

Rainsford, reclining in a steamer chair, puffed at his favorite briar. The sensuous drowsiness of the night was on him. "It's so dark," he thought, "that I could sleep without closing my eyes; the night would be my eyelids—"

An abrupt sound startled him. Off to the right he heard it, and his ears, expert in such matters, could not be mistaken. Again he heard the sound, and again. Somewhere, off in the blackness, someone had fired a gun three times.

Rainsford sprang up and moved quickly to the rail, mystified. He strained his eyes in the direction from which the reports had come, but it was like trying to see through a blanket. He leaped upon the rail and balanced himself there, to get greater elevation; his pipe, striking a rope, was knocked from his mouth. He lunged for it; a short, hoarse cry came from his lips as he realized he had reached too far and had lost his balance. The cry was pinched off short as the blood-warm waters of the Caribbean Sea closed over his head.

He struggled to the surface and cried out, but the wash from the speeding yacht slapped him in the face and the salt water in his open mouth made him gag and strangle. Desperately he struck out after the receding lights of the yacht, but he stopped before he had swum fifty feet. A certain cool-headedness had come to him for this was not the first time he had been in a tight place. There was a chance that his cries could be heard by someone aboard the yacht, but that chance was slender and grew more slender as the yacht raced on. He wrestled himself out of his clothes and shouted with all his power. The lights of the boat became faint and vanishing fireflies; then they were blotted out by the night.

Rainsford remembered the shots. They had come from the right, and doggedly he swam in that direction, swimming slowly, conserving his strength. For a seemingly endless time he fought the sea. He began to count his strokes; he could do possibly a hundred more and then—

He heard a sound. It came out of the darkness, a high, screaming sound, the cry of an animal in an extremity of anguish and terror. He did not know what animal made the sound. With fresh vitality he swam towards it. He heard it again; then it was cut short by another noise, crisp, staccato.

"Pistol shot," muttered Rainsford, swimming on.

Ten minutes of determined effort brought to his ears the most welcome sound he had ever heard, the breaking of the sea on a rocky shore. He was almost on the rocks before he saw them; on a night less calm he would have been shattered against them. With his remaining strength he dragged himself from the swirling waters. Jagged crags appeared to jut into the opaqueness; he forced himself up hand over hand. Gasping, his hands raw, he reached a flat place at the top. Dense jungle came down to the edge of the cliffs, and careless of everything but his weariness Rainsford flung himself down and tumbled into the deepest sleep of his life.

When he opened his eyes he knew from the position of the sun that it was late in the afternoon. Sleep had given him vigor; a sharp hunger was picking at him.

"Where there are pistol shots there are men. Where there are men there is food," he thought; but he saw no sign of a trail through the closely knit web of weeds and trees; it was easier to go along the shore. Not far from where he had landed, he stopped.

Some wounded thing, by the evidence a large animal, had crashed about in the underwood. A small glittering object caught Rainsford's eye and he picked it up. It was an empty cartridge.

"A twenty-two," he remarked. "That's odd. It must have been a fairly large animal, too. The hunter had his nerve with him to tackle it with a light gun. It is clear the brute put up a fight. I suppose the first three shots I heard were when the hunter flushed his quarry and wounded it. The last shot was when he trailed it here and finished it."

He examined the ground closely and found what he had hoped to find —the print of hunting boots. They pointed along the cliff in the direction he had been going. Eagerly he hurried along, for night was beginning to settle down on the island.

Darkness was blacking out sea and jungle before Rainsford sighted the lights. He came upon them as he turned a crook in the coast line, and his first thought was that he had come upon a village as there were so many lights. But as he forged along he saw that all the lights were in one building—a château on a high bluff.

"Mirage," thought Rainsford. But the stone steps were real enough. He lifted the knocker and it creaked up stiffly as if it had never before been used.

The door, opening, let out a river of glaring light. A tall man, solidly built and black-bearded to the waist, stood facing Rainsford with a revolver in his hand.

"Don't be alarmed," said Rainsford, with a smile that he hoped was disarming. "I'm no robber. I fell off a yacht. My name is Sanger Rainsford of New York City."

The man gave no sign that he understood the words or had even heard them. The menacing revolver pointed as rigidly as if the giant were a statue.

Another man was coming down the broad, marble steps, an erect slender man in evening clothes. He advanced and held out his hand.

In a cultivated voice marked by a slight accent which gave it added precision and deliberateness, he said: "It is a great pleasure and honor to welcome Mr. Sanger Rainsford, the celebrated hunter, to my home."

Automatically Rainsford shook the man's hand.

"I've read your book about hunting snow leopards in Tibet," explained the man. "I am General Zaroff."

Rainsford's first impression was that the man was singularly handsome; his second, that there was a bizarre quality about the face. The general was a tall man past middle age, for his hair was white; but his eyebrows and mustache were black. His eyes, too, were black and very bright. He had the face of a man used to giving orders. Turning to the man in uniform he made a sign. The fellow put away his pistol, saluted, withdrew.

"Ivan is an incredibly strong fellow," remarked the general, "but he has the misfortune to be deaf and dumb. A simple fellow, but a bit of a savage."

"Is he Russian?"

"A Cossack," said the general, and his smile showed red lips and pointed teeth. "So am I.

"Come," he said, "we shouldn't be chatting here. You want clothes, food, rest. You shall have them. This is a most restful spot."

Ivan had reappeared and the general spoke to him with lips that moved but gave forth no sound.

"Follow Ivan if you please, Mr. Rainsford. I was about to have my dinner, but will wait. I think my clothes will fit you."

It was to a huge beam-ceilinged bedroom with a canopied bed large enough for six men that Rainsford followed the man. Ivan laid out an evening suit and Rainsford as he put it on noticed that it came from a London tailor.

"Perhaps you were surprised," said the general as they sat down to dinner in a room which suggested a baronial hall of feudal times, "that I recognized your name; but I read all books on hunting published in English, French and Russian. I have but one passion in life, and that is the hunt."

"You have some wonderful heads here," said Rainsford, glancing at the walls. "That Cape buffalo is the largest I ever saw."

"Oh, that fellow? He charged me, hurled me against a tree and fractured my skull. But I got the brute."

"I've always thought," said Rainsford, "that the Cape buffalo is the most dangerous of all big game."

For a moment the general did not reply, then he said slowly: "No, the Cape buffalo is not the most dangerous." He sipped his wine. "Here in my preserve on this island I hunt more dangerous game."

"Is there big game on this island?"

The general nodded. "The biggest."

"Really?"

"Oh, it isn't here naturally. I have to stock the island."

"What have you imported, General? Tigers?"

The general grinned. "No, hunting tigers ceased to interest me when I exhausted their possibilities. No thrill left in tigers, no real danger. I live for danger, Mr. Rainsford."

The general took from his pocket a gold cigarette case and offered his guest a long black cigarette with a silver tip; it was perfumed and gave off a smell like incense.

"We will have some capital hunting, you and I," said the general.

"But what game—" began Rainsford.

"I'll tell you. You will be amused, I know. I think I may say in all modesty, that I have done a rare thing. I have invented a new sensation. May I pour you another glass of port?"

"Thank you, General."

The general filled both glasses and said: "God makes some men poets. Some he makes kings, some beggars. Me he made a hunter. But after years of enjoyment I found that the hunt no longer fascinated me. You can perhaps guess why?"

"No—why?"

"Simply this, hunting had ceased to be what you call a 'sporting proposition.' I always got my quarry . . . always . . . and there is no greater bore than perfection."

The general lit a fresh cigarette.

"The animal has nothing but his legs and his instinct. Instinct is no match for reason. When I realized this, it was a tragic moment for me."

Rainsford leaned across the table, absorbed in what his host was saying.

"It came to me as an inspiration what I must do."

"And that was?"

"I had to invent a new animal to hunt."

"A new animal? You are joking."

"I never joke about hunting. I needed a new animal. I found one. So I bought this island, built this house, and here I do my hunting. The island is perfect for my purpose—there are jungles with a maze of trails in them, hills, swamps—"

"But the animal, General Zaroff?"

"Oh," said the general, "it supplies me with the most exciting hunting in the world. Every day I hunt, and I never grow bored now, for I have a quarry with which I can match my wits."

Rainsford's bewilderment showed in his face.

"I wanted the ideal animal to hunt, so I said, 'What are the attributes of an ideal quarry?' and the answer was, of course: 'It must have courage, cunning, and, above all, it must be able to reason.'"

"But no animal can reason," objected Rainsford.

"My dear fellow," said the general, "there is one that can."

"But you can't mean—"

"And why not?"

"I can't believe you are serious, General Zaroff. This is a grisly joke."

"Why should I not be serious? I am speaking of hunting."

"Hunting? Good God, General Zaroff, what you speak of is murder."

The general regarded Rainsford quizzically. "Surely your experiences in the war—"

"Did not make me condone cold-blooded murder," finished Rainsford stiffly.

Laughter shook the general. "I'll wager you'll forget your notions when you go hunting with me. You've a genuine new thrill in store for you, Mr. Rainsford."

"Thank you, I am a hunter, not a murderer."

"Dear me," said the general, quite unruffled, "again that unpleasant word; but I hunt the scum of the earth—sailors from tramp ships—lascars, blacks, Chinese, whites, mongrels."

"Where do you get them?"

The general's left eyelid fluttered down in a wink. "This island is called Ship-Trap. Come to the window with me."

Rainsford went to the window and looked out towards the sea.

"Watch! Out there!" exclaimed the general, as he pressed a button. Far out Rainsford saw a flash of lights. "They indicate a channel where there's none. Rocks with razor edges crouch there like a sea monster. They can crush a ship like a nut. Oh, yes, that is electricity. We try to be civilized."

"Civilized? And you shoot down men?"

"But I treat my visitors with every consideration," said the general in

his most pleasant manner. "They get plenty of good food and exercise.
They get into splendid physical condition. You shall see for yourself tomorrow."

"What do you mean?"

"We'll visit my training school," smiled the general. "It is in the cellar.
I have about a dozen there now. They're from the Spanish bark, *Sanlucar,*
which had the bad luck to go on the rocks out there. An inferior lot, I
regret to say, and more accustomed to the deck than the jungle."

He raised his hand and Ivan brought thick Turkish coffee. "It is a
game, you see," pursued the general blandly. "I suggest to one of them
that we go hunting. I give him three hours' start. I am to follow, armed
only with a pistol of smallest caliber and range. If my quarry eludes me
for three whole days, he wins the game. If I find him"—the general
smiled—"he loses."

"Suppose he refuses to be hunted?"

"I give him the option. If he does not wish to hunt I turn him over to
Ivan. Ivan once served as official knouter to the Great White Tsar and
he has his own ideas of sport. Invariably they choose the hunt."

"And if they win?"

The smile on the general's face widened. "To date I have not lost."

Then he added, hastily: "I don't wish you to think me a braggart, Mr.
Rainsford, and one did almost win. I eventually had to use the dogs."

"The dogs?"

"This way, please. I'll show you."

The general led the way to another window. The lights sent a flickering illumination that made grotesque patterns on the courtyard below,
and Rainsford could see a dozen or so huge black shapes moving about.
As they turned towards him he caught the green glitter of eyes.

"They are let out at seven every night. If anyone should try to get into
my house—or out of it—something regrettable would happen to him. And
now I want to show you my new collection of heads. Will you come to
the library?"

"I hope," said Rainsford, "that you will excuse me tonight. I'm really
not feeling at all well."

"Ah, indeed? You need a good restful night's sleep. Tomorrow you'll
feel like a new man. Then we'll hunt, eh? I've one rather promising
prospect—"

Rainsford was hurrying from the room.

"Sorry you can't go with me tonight," called the general. "I expect
rather fair sport. A big, strong black. He looks resourceful—"

The bed was good and Rainsford was tired, but nevertheless he could
not sleep, and had only achieved a doze when, as morning broke, he
heard, far off in the jungle, the faint report of a pistol.

General Zaroff did not appear till luncheon. He was solicitous about

Rainsford's health. "As for me," he said, "I do not feel so well. The hunting was not good last night. He made a straight trail that offered no problems at all."

"General," said Rainsford firmly, "I want to leave the island at once."

He saw the dead black eyes of the general on him studying him. The eyes suddenly brightened. "Tonight," said he, "we will hunt—you and I."

Rainsford shook his head. "No, General," he said, "I will not hunt."

The general shrugged his shoulders. "As you wish. The choice rests with you, but I would suggest that my idea of sport is more diverting than Ivan's."

"You don't mean—" cried Rainsford.

"My dear fellow," said the general, "have I not told you I always mean what I say about hunting? This is really an inspiration. I drink to a foeman worthy of my steel at last."

The general raised his glass, but Rainsford sat staring at him. "You'll find this game worth playing," the general said, enthusiastically. "Your brain against mine. Your woodcraft against mine. Your strength and stamina against mine. Outdoor chess! And the stake is not without value, eh?"

"And if I win—" began Rainsford huskily.

"If I do not find you by midnight of the third day, I'll cheerfully acknowledge myself defeated," said General Zaroff. "My sloop will place you on the mainland near a town."

The general read what Rainsford was thinking.

"Oh, you can trust me," said the Cossack. "I will give you my word as a gentleman and a sportsman. Of course, you, in turn, must agree to say nothing of your visit here."

"I'll agree to nothing of the kind."

"Oh, in that case—but why discuss that now? Three days hence we can discuss it over a bottle of Veuve Cliquot, unless—"

The general sipped his wine.

Then a businesslike air animated him. "Ivan," he said, "will supply you with hunting clothes, food, a knife. I suggest you wear moccasins; they leave a poorer trail. I suggest, too, that you avoid the big swamp in the southeast corner of the island. We call it Death Swamp. There's quicksand there. One foolish fellow tried it. The deplorable part of it was that Lazarus followed him. You can't imagine my feelings, Mr. Rainsford, I loved Lazarus; he was the finest hound in my pack. Well, I must beg you to excuse me now. I always take a siesta after lunch. You'll hardly have time for a nap, I fear. You'll want to start, no doubt. I shall not follow until dusk. Hunting at night is so much more exciting than by day, don't you think? Au revoir, Mr. Rainsford, au revoir."

As General Zaroff, with a courtly bow strolled from the room, Ivan entered by another door. Under one arm he carried hunting clothes, a haversack of food, a leathern sheath containing a long-bladed hunting knife; his right hand rested on a cocked revolver thrust in the crimson sash about his waist. . . .

Rainsford had fought his way through the bush for two hours, but at length he paused, saying to himself through tight teeth, "I must keep my nerve."

He had not been entirely clearheaded when the château gates closed behind him. His first idea was to put distance between himself and General Zaroff and, to this end, he had plunged along, spurred by the sharp rowels of something approaching panic. Now, having got a grip on himself he had stopped to take stock of himself and the situation.

Straight flight was futile for it must inevitably bring him to the sea. Being in a picture with a frame of water, his operations, clearly, must take place within that frame.

"I'll give him a trail to follow," thought Rainsford, striking off from the path into trackless wilderness. Recalling the lore of the fox hunt and the dodges of the fox, he executed a series of intricate loops, doubling again and again on his trail. Night found him leg-weary, with hands and face lashed by the branches. He was on a thickly wooded ridge. As his need for rest was imperative, he thought: "I have played the fox, now I must play the cat of the fable."

A big tree with a thick trunk and outspread branches was near by, and, taking care to leave no marks, he climbed into the crotch and stretched out on one of the broad limbs. Rest brought him new confidence and almost a feeling of security.

An apprehensive night crawled slowly by like a wounded snake. Towards morning, when a dingy gray was varnishing the sky, the cry of a startled bird focused Rainsford's attention in its direction. Something was coming through the bush, coming slowly, carefully, coming by the same winding way that Rainsford had come. He flattened himself against the bough and, through a screen of leaves almost as thick as tapestry, watched.

It was General Zaroff. He made his way along, with his eyes fixed in concentration on the ground. He paused, almost beneath the tree, dropped to his knees and studied the ground. Rainsford's impulse was to leap on him like a panther, but he saw that the general's right hand held a small automatic.

The hunter shook his head several times as if he were puzzled. Then, straightening himself he took from his case one of his black cigarettes; its pungent incense-like smoke rose to Rainsford's nostrils.

Rainsford held his breath. The general's eyes had left the ground and were traveling inch by inch up the tree. Rainsford froze, every muscle tensed for a spring. But the sharp eyes of the hunter stopped before they reached the limb where Rainsford lay. A smile spread over his brown face. Very deliberately he blew a smoke ring into the air; then he turned his back on the tree and walked carelessly away along the trail he had come. The swish of the underbrush against his hunting boots grew fainter and fainter.

The pent-up air burst hotly from Rainsford's lungs. His first thought made him feel sick and numb. The general could follow a trail through the woods at night; he could follow an extremely difficult trail; he must have uncanny powers; only by the merest chance had he failed to see his quarry.

Rainsford's second thought was more terrible. It sent a shudder through him. Why had the general smiled? Why had he turned back?

Rainsford did not want to believe what his reason told him was true—the general was playing with him, saving him for another day's sport. The Cossack was the cat; he was the mouse. Then it was that Rainsford knew the meaning of terror.

"I will not lose my nerve," he told himself, "I will not."

Sliding down from the tree, he set off into the woods. Three hundred yards from his hiding place he stopped where a huge dead tree leaned precariously on a smaller, living one. Throwing off his sack of food, he took his knife from its sheath and set to work.

When the job was finished, he threw himself down behind a fallen log a hundred feet away. He did not have to wait long. The cat was coming back to play with the mouse.

Following the trail with the sureness of a bloodhound came General Zaroff. Nothing escaped those searching black eyes, no crushed blade of grass, no bent twig, no mark, no matter how faint, in the moss. So intent was the Cossack on his stalking that he was upon the thing Rainsford had made before he saw it. His foot touched the protruding bough that was the trigger. Even as he touched it, the general sensed his danger, and leaped back with the agility of an ape. But he was not quite quick enough; the dead tree, delicately adjusted to rest on the cut living one, crashed down and struck the general a glancing blow on the shoulder as it fell; but for his alertness he must have been crushed beneath it. He staggered but he did not fall; nor did he drop his revolver. He stood there, rubbing his injured shoulder, and Rainsford, with fear again gripping his heart, heard the general's mocking laugh ring through the jungle.

"Rainsford," called the general, "if you are within sound of my voice let me congratulate you. Not many men know how to make a Malay man catcher. Luckily for me I, too, have hunted in Malacca. You are proving interesting, Mr. Rainsford. I am now going to have my wound dressed; it is only a slight one. But I shall be back. I shall be back."

When the general, nursing his wounded shoulder, had gone, Rainsford again took up his flight. It was flight now, and it carried him on for some hours. Dusk came, then darkness, and still he pressed on. The ground grew softer under his moccasins; the vegetation grew ranker, denser; insects bit him savagely. He stepped forward and his foot sank into ooze. He tried to wrench it back, but the mud sucked viciously at his foot as if it had been a giant leech. With a violent effort he tore his foot loose. He knew where he was now. Death Swamp and its quicksand.

The softness of the earth had given him an idea. Stepping back from the quicksand a dozen feet, he began, like some huge prehistoric beaver, to dig.

Rainsford had dug himself in, in France, when a second's delay would have meant death. Compared to his digging now, that had been a placid pastime. The pit grew deeper; when it was above his shoulders he climbed out and from some hard saplings cut stakes, sharpening them to a fine point. These stakes he planted at the bottom of the pit with the points up. With flying fingers he wove a rough carpet of weeds and branches and with it covered the mouth of the pit. Then, wet with sweat and aching with tiredness, he crouched behind the stump of a lightning-blasted tree.

By the padding sound of feet on the soft earth he knew his pursuer was coming. The night breeze brought him the perfume of the general's cigarette. It seemed to the hunted man that the general was coming with unusual swiftness; that he was not feeling his way along, foot by foot. Rainsford, from where he was crouching, could not see the general, neither could he see the pit. He lived a year in a minute. Then he heard the sharp crackle of breaking branches as the cover of the pit gave way; heard the sharp scream of pain as the pointed stakes found their mark. Then he cowered back. Three feet from the pit a man was standing with an electric torch in his hand.

"You've done well, Rainsford," cried the general. "Your Burmese tiger pit has claimed one of my best dogs. Again you score. I must now see what you can do against my whole pack. I'm going home for a rest now. Thank you for a most amusing evening."

At daybreak Rainsford, lying near the swamp, was awakened by a distant sound, faint and wavering, but he knew it for the baying of a pack of hounds.

Rainsford knew he could do one of two things. He could stay where he was. That was suicide. He could flee. That was postponing the inevitable. For a moment, he stood there thinking. An idea that held a wild chance came to him, and, tightening his belt, he headed away from the swamp.

The baying of the hounds drew nearer, nearer. Rainsford climbed a tree. Down a watercourse, not a quarter of a mile away, he could see the bush moving. Straining his eyes, he saw the lean figure of General Zaroff. Just ahead of him Rainsford made out another figure, with wide shoulders, which surged through the jungle reeds. It was the gigantic Ivan and he seemed to be pulled along. Rainsford realized that he must be holding the pack in leash.

They would be on him at any moment now. His mind worked frantically, and he thought of a native trick he had learned in Uganda. Sliding down the tree, he caught hold of a springy young sapling and to it fastened his hunting knife, with the blade pointing down the trail. With a bit of wild grapevine he tied back the sapling . . . and ran for his life. As the hounds hit the fresh scent, they raised their voices and Rainsford knew how an animal at bay feels.

He had to stop to get his breath. The baying of the hounds stopped abruptly, and Rainsford's heart stopped, too. They must have reached the knife.

Shinning excitedly up a tree he looked back. His pursuers had stopped. But the hope in Rainsford's brain died for he saw that General Zaroff was still on his feet. Ivan, however, was not. The knife, driven by the recoil of the springing tree, had not wholly failed.

Hardly had Rainsford got back to the ground when, once more, the pack took up the cry.

"Nerve, nerve, nerve!" he panted to himself as he dashed along. A blue gap showed through the trees dead ahead. The hounds drew nearer. Rainsford forced himself on towards that gap. He reached the sea, and across a cove could see the gray stone of the château. Twenty feet below him the sea rumbled and hissed. Rainsford hesitated. He heard the hounds. Then he leaped far out into the water.

When the general and his pack reached the opening, the Cossack stopped. For some moments he stood regarding the blue-green expanse of water. Then he sat down, took a drink of brandy from a silver flask, lit a perfumed cigarette, and hummed a bit from *Madame Butterfly*.

General Zaroff ate an exceedingly good dinner in his great paneled hall that evening. With it he had a bottle of Pol Roger and half a bottle of Chambertin. Two slight annoyances kept him from perfect enjoyment. One was that it would be difficult to replace Ivan; the other, that his quarry had escaped him. Of course—so thought the general, as he tasted his after-dinner liqueur—the American had not played the game.

To soothe himself, he read in his library from the works of Marcus Aurelius. At ten he went to his bedroom. He was comfortably tired, he said to himself, as he turned the key of his door. There was a little moonlight, so before turning on the light he went to the window and looked down on the courtyard. He could see the great hounds, and he called: "Better luck another time." Then he switched on the light.

A man who had been hiding in the curtains of the bed, was standing before him.

"Rainsford!" screamed the general. "How in God's name did you get here?"

"Swam. I found it quicker than walking through the jungle."

The other sucked in his breath and smiled. "I congratulate you. You have won the game."

Rainsford did not smile. "I am still a beast at bay," he said, in a low, hoarse voice. "Get ready, General Zaroff."

The general made one of his deepest bows. "I see," he said. "Splendid. One of us is to furnish a repast for the hounds. The other will sleep in this very excellent bed. On guard, Rainsford. . . ."

He had never slept in a better bed, Rainsford decided.

The World the Children Made

By RAY BRADBURY

"GEORGE, I wish you'd look at the nursery."

"What's wrong with it?"

"I don't know."

"Well, then."

"I just want you to look at it, is all, or call a psychologist in to look at it."

"What would a psychologist want with a nursery?"

"You know very well what he'd want." His wife paused in the middle of the kitchen and watched the stove busy humming to itself, making supper for four. "It's just that the nursery is different now than it was."

"All right, let's have a look."

They walked down the hall of their sound-proofed Happylife Home, which had cost them thirty thousand dollars installed, this house which clothed and fed and rocked them to sleep and played and sang and was good to them. Their approach sensitized a switch somewhere and the nursery light flicked on when they came within ten feet of it. Similarly, behind them in the halls lights went on and off as they left them behind, with a soft automaticity.

"Well," said George Hadley.

They stood on the thatched floor of the nursery. It was forty feet across by forty feet long and thirty feet high; it had cost half again as much as the rest of the house. "But nothing's too good for our children," George had said.

The nursery was silent. It was empty as a jungle glade at hot high noon. The walls were blank and two-dimensional. Now, as George and Lydia Hadley stood in the center of the room, the walls began to purr and recede into crystalline distance, it seemed, and presently an African veld appeared in three dimensions, on all sides, in color, reproduced to the final pebble and bit of straw. The ceiling above them became a deep sky with a hot yellow sun.

George Hadley felt the perspiration start on his brow. "Let's get out of this sun," he said. "This is a little too real. But I don't see anything wrong."

"Wait a moment; you'll see," said his wife.

Now the hidden odorophonics were beginning to blow a wind of odor at the two people in the middle of the baked veldland. The hot straw smell of lion grass, the cool green smell of the hidden water hole, the great rusty smell of animals, the smell of dust like a red paprika in the hot air. And now the sounds—the thump of distant antelope feet on grassy sod, the papery rustling of vultures. A shadow passed through the sky. The shadow flickered on George Hadley's upturned, sweating face.

"Filthy creatures," he heard his wife say.

"The vultures."

"You see, there are the lions, far over that way. Now they're on their way to the water hole. They've just been eating," said Lydia. "I don't know what."

"Some animal." George Hadley put his hand up to shield off the burning light from his squinted eyes. "A zebra or a baby giraffe maybe."

"Are you sure?" His wife sounded peculiarly tense.

"No, it's a little late to be sure," he said, amused. "Nothing over there I can see but cleaned bone, and the vultures dropping for what's left."

"Did you hear that scream?" she asked.

"No."

"About a minute ago?"

"Sorry, no."

The lions were coming. And again, George Hadley was filled with admiration for the mechanical genius who had conceived this room. A miracle of efficiency selling for an absurdly low price. Every home should have one. Oh, occasionally they frightened you with their clinical accuracy, they startled you, they gave you a twinge, but most of the time what fun for everyone, not only your own son and daughter but for yourself. When you felt like a quick jaunt to a foreign land, a quick change of scenery—well, here it was.

And here were the lions now, fifteen feet away—so real, so feverishly and startlingly real that you could feel the prickling fur on your hand, and your mouth was stuffed with the dusty upholstery smell of their heated pelts, and the yellow of them was in your eyes like the yellow of an exquisite French tapestry, the yellow of lions and summer grass, and the sound of the matted lion lungs exhaling on the silent noontide, and the smell of meat from the panting, dripping mouths.

The lions stood looking at George and Lydia Hadley with terrible green-yellow eyes.

"Watch out!" screamed Lydia.

The lions came running at them. Lydia bolted and ran. Instinctively, George sprang after her. Outside, in the hall, with the door slammed, he was laughing and she was crying, and they both stood appalled at the other's reaction.

"George!"

"Lydia! Oh, my dear poor sweet Lydia!"

"They almost got us!"

"Walls, Lydia, remember; crystal walls, that's all they are. Oh, they look real, I must admit; Africa in your parlor, but it's all dimensional superreactionary, supersensitive color film and mental-tape film behind glass screens. It's all odorophonics and sonics, Lydia. Here's my handkerchief."

"I'm afraid." She came to him and put her body against him and cried steadily. "Did you see? Did you feel? It's too real."

"Now, Lydia—"

"You've got to tell Wendy and Peter not to read any more on Africa."

"Of course, of course." He patted her.

"Promise?"

"Sure."

"And lock the nursery for a few days until I get my nerves settled."

"You know how difficult Peter is about that. When I punished him a month ago by locking the nursery for even a few hours, the tantrum he threw. And Wendy too. They live for the nursery."

"It's got to be locked, that's all there is to it."

"All right." Reluctantly he locked the huge door. "You've been working too hard. You need a rest."

"I don't know, I don't know," she said, blowing her nose and sitting down in a chair that immediately began to rock and comfort her. "Maybe I don't have enough to do. Maybe I have time to think too much. Why don't we shut the whole house off for a few days and take a vacation?"

"You mean you want to fry my eggs for me?"

"Yes." She nodded.

"And darn my socks?"

"Yes." A frantic, watery-eyed nodding.

"And sweep the house?"

"Yes, yes; oh, yes!"

"But I thought that's why we bought this house—so we wouldn't have to do anything?"

"That's just it. I feel like I don't belong here. The house is wife and mother now, and nursemaid. Can I compete with an African veld? Can I give a bath and scrub to the children as efficiently or quickly as the automatic scrub bath can? I cannot. And it isn't just me. It's you. You've been awfully nervous lately."

"I suppose I have been smoking too much."

"You look as if you didn't know what to do with yourself in this house, either. You smoke a little more every morning and drink a little more

every afternoon and need a little more sedative every night. You're beginning to feel unnecessary too."

"Am I?" He paused and tried to feel into himself to see what was really
there.

"Oh, George!" She looked beyond him at the nursery door. "Those
lions can't get out of there, can they?"

He looked at the door and saw it tremble as if something had jumped
against it from the other side.

"Of course not," he said.

At dinner they ate alone, for Wendy and Peter were at a special plastic
carnival across town and had televised home to say they'd be late, to go
ahead eating. So George Hadley, bemused, sat watching the dining-room
table produce warm dishes of food from its mechanical interior.

"We forgot the ketchup," he said.

"Sorry," said a small voice within the table, and ketchup appeared.

As for the nursery, thought George Hardley, it wouldn't hurt for the
children to be locked out of it a while. Too much of anything wasn't good
for anyone. And it was clearly indicated that the children had been spending a little too much time on Africa. That sun. He could feel it on his
neck, still, like a hot paw. And the lions. And the smell of blood. Remarkable how the nursery caught the telepathic emanations of the children's
minds and created life to fill their every desire. The children thought
lions, and there were lions. The children thought zebras, and there were
zebras. Sun, sun. Giraffes, giraffes. Death, and death.

Death thoughts. They were awfully young, Wendy and Peter, for death
thoughts. Or no, you were never too young, really. Long before you knew
what death was you were wishing it on someone else. When you were two
years old you were shooting people with cap pistols.

But this—the long hot African veld, the awful death in the jaws of a
lion. And repeated again and again.

"Where are you going?"

He didn't answer Lydia. Preoccupied, he let the lights glow softly on
ahead of him, extinguish behind him as he padded to the nursery door.
He listened against it. Far away, a lion roared.

He unlocked the door and opened it. Just before he stepped inside, he
heard a faraway scream. And then another roar from the lions, which subsided quickly. He stepped into Africa. How many times in the last year
had he opened this door and found Wonderland, Alice, the Mock Turtle,
or Aladdin and his magic lamp. But now, this yellow hot Africa, this bake
oven with murder in the heat. Perhaps Lydia was right. Perhaps they
needed a little vacation from this fantasy which was growing a bit too
real for ten-year-old children. It was all right to exercise one's mind with
gymnastic fantasies, but when the lively child mind settled on one pat-

tern— It seemed that at a distance, for the past month, he had heard lions roaring and smelled their strong odor seeping as far away as his study door. But, being busy, he had paid it no attention.

George Hadley stood on the African grassland alone. The lions looked up from their feeding, watching him. The only flaw to the illusion was the open door through which he could see his wife, far down the dark hall, like a framed picture, eating abstractedly.

"Go away," he said to the lions.

They did not go.

He knew the principle of the room exactly. You sent out your thoughts. Whatever you thought would appear.

"Let's have the Emerald City of Oz!" he snapped.

The veld land remained, the lions remained.

"Come on, room! I demand Oz!"

Nothing happened.

"Oz!"

He went back to dinner. "The fool room's out of order," he said. "It won't respond."

"Or—"

"Or what?"

"Or it can't change," said Lydia, "because the children have thought about Africa and lions and killing so many days that the room's in a rut."

"Could be."

"Or Peter's set it to remain that way."

"Set it?"

"He may have got into the machinery and fixed something."

"Peter doesn't know machinery."

"He's a wise one for ten; that I.Q. of his—"

"Nevertheless—"

"Hello, Mom. . . . Hello, Dad."

The Hadleys turned. Wendy and Peter were coming in the front door, cheeks like peppermint candy, eyes like bright blue agate marbles, a smell of ozone on their jumps from their trip in the helicopter.

"You're just in time for supper," said both parents.

"We're full of strawberry ice cream and hot dogs," said the children, holding hands. "But we'll sit and watch."

"Yes, come tell us about the nursery," said George Hadley.

The brother and sister blinked at him and then at each other. "Nursery?"

"All about Africa and everything," said the father, with false joviality.

"I don't understand," said Peter.

"Your mother and I were just traveling through Africa with rod and reel; Tom Swift and his Electric Lion," said George Hardley.

"There's no Africa in the nursery," said Peter simply.

"Oh, come now; we know better."

"I don't remember any Africa," said Peter to Wendy. "Do you?"

"No."

"Run see and come tell."

She obeyed.

"Wendy, come back here!" said George Hadley, but she was gone. Too late, he realized he had forgotten to lock the nursery door after his last inspection.

"Wendy'll look and come tell us," said Peter.

"She doesn't have to tell me. I've seen it."

"I'm sure you're mistaken, Father."

"I'm not, Peter. Come along, now."

But Wendy was back. "It's not Africa," she said breathlessly.

"We'll see about this," said George Hadley, and they all walked down the hall together and opened the nursery door.

There was a green, lovely forest, a lovely river, a purple mountain. The African veld land was gone. The lions were gone. Only Rima was here now, singing a song so beautiful that it brought tears to their eyes.

George Hadley looked in at the changed scene. "Go to bed," he said to the children.

They opened their mouths.

"You heard me," he said.

They went off to the air closet, where a wind sucked them like brown leaves up the flue to their slumber rooms.

George Hadley walked through the singing glade and picked up something that lay in the corner near where the lions had been. He walked slowly back to his wife.

"What is that?" she asked.

"An old wallet of mine," he said.

He showed it to her. The smell of hot grass was on it and the smell of a lion. There were drops of saliva on it, it had been chewed, and there were blood smears on both sides.

He closed the nursery door and locked it.

In the middle of the night he was still awake and he knew his wife was awake. "Do you think Wendy changed it?" she said at last in the dark room.

"Of course."

"Made it from a veld into a forest and put Rima there instead of lions?"

"Yes."

"Why?"

"I don't know. But it's staying locked until I find out."

"How did your wallet get there?"

"It was part of the game, I suppose."

"What's going on?"

"I don't know anything," he said, "except that I'm beginning to be sorry we bought that room for the children. If the children are neurotic at all, a room like that—"

"It's supposed to help them work off their neuroses in a healthful way."

"I'm starting to wonder." He stared at the ceiling.

"We've given the children everything they ever wanted. Is this our reward—secrecy, disobedience?"

"They've been acting funny ever since you forbade them to take the Rocket to New York a few months ago."

"They're not old enough to do that alone, I explained."

"Nevertheless, I've noticed they're decidedly cool toward us since."

"I think I'll have David McClean come tomorrow morning to have a look at Africa."

"But it's not Africa now; it's Green Mansions country and Rima."

"I have a feeling it'll be Africa again before then."

A moment later they heard the screams. Two screams. Two people screaming from downstairs. And then a roar of lions.

"Wendy and Peter aren't in their rooms," said his wife.

He lay in his bed with his beating heart. "No," he said. "They've broken into the nursery."

"Those screams—they sound familiar."

"Do they?"

"Yes, awfully."

And although their beds tried very hard, the two adults couldn't be rocked asleep for another hour. A smell of cats was in the night air.

"Father?" said Peter.

"Yes." George Hadley glanced up from breakfast.

Peter looked at his shoes. He never looked at his father any more, nor at his mother. "You aren't going to lock up the nursery for good, are you?"

"That all depends."

"On what?" snapped Peter.

"On you and your sister. If you intersperse this Africa with a little variety—oh, Sweden perhaps, or Denmark or China."

"What's wrong with Africa, Father?"

"Oh, so now you admit you have been conjuring up Africa, do you?"

"I wouldn't want the nursery locked up," said Peter coldly. "Ever."

"Matter of fact, we're thinking of turning the whole house off for about a month. Live sort of a carefree one-for-all existence."

"That sounds dreadful! Would I have to tie my own shoes instead of letting the shoe tier do it? And brush my own teeth and comb my hair and give myself a bath?"

"It would be fun for a change, don't you think?"

"No, it would be horrid. I didn't like it when you took out the picture painter last month."

"That's because I wanted you to learn to paint all by yourself, son."

"I don't want to do anything but look and listen and smell. What else is there to do?"

"All right, go play in Africa."

"Will you shut off the house sometime soon?"

"We're considering it."

"I don't think you'd better consider it any more, Father."

"I won't have any threats from my son!"

"Very well." Peter strolled off to the nursery.

"Am I on time?" said David McClean.

"Breakfast?" asked George Hadley.

"Thanks, had some. What's the trouble?"

"David, you're a psychologist."

"I should hope so."

"Well, then, have a look at our nursery. You saw it a year ago when you dropped by. Did you notice anything peculiar about it then?"

"Can't say I did. The usual violences, a tendency toward a slight paranoia here or there, usual in children because they feel persecuted by parents constantly, but oh, really nothing."

They walked down the hall. "I locked the nursery up," explained the father, "and the children broke into it during the night. I let them stay so they could form the patterns for you to see."

There was a terrible screaming from the nursery.

"There it is," said George Hadley. "See what you make of it."

They walked in on the children without rapping. The screams had faded. The lions were feeding.

"Run outside a moment, children," said George Hadley. . . . "No, don't change the mental combination. Leave the walls as they are. Get!"

With the children gone, the two men stood studying the lions clustered at a distance, eating with great relish whatever it was they had caught.

"I wish I knew what it was," said George Hadley. "Sometimes I can almost see. Do you think if I brought high-powered glasses here and—"

"Hardly." He turned to study all four walls. "How long has this been going on?"

"A little over a month."

"It certainly doesn't feel good."

"I want facts, not feelings."

"My dear George, a psychologist never saw a fact in his life. He only hears about feelings, vague things. This doesn't feel good, I tell you. Trust my hunches and my instincts. I have a nose for something bad. This is very bad. My advice to you is to have the whole room torn down and your children brought to me every day for the next year for treatment."

"Is it that bad?"

"I'm afraid so. One of the original uses of these nurseries was so that we could study the patterns left on the walls by the child's mind, study at our leisure, and help the child. In this case however, the room has become a channel toward . . . destructive thoughts, instead of a release away from them."

"Didn't you sense this before?"

"I sensed only that you had spoiled your children more than most. And now you're letting them down in some way. What way?"

"I wouldn't let them go to New York."

"What else?"

"I've taken away a few machines from the house and threatened them, a month ago, with closing up the nursery unless they did their homework. I did close it for a few days to show I meant business."

"Ah-ha!"

"Does that mean anything?"

"Everything. Where before they had a Santa Claus, now they have a Scrooge. Children prefer Santas. You've let this room and this house replace you and your wife in your children's affections. This room is their mother and father, far more important in their lives than their real parents. And now you come along and want to shut it off. No wonder there's hatred here. You can feel it coming out of the sky. Feel that sun. George, you'll have to change your life. Like too many others, you've built it around creature comforts. Why, you'd starve tomorrow if something went wrong in your kitchen. You wouldn't know how to tap an egg. Nevertheless, turn everything off. Start new. It'll take time. But we'll make good children out of bad in a year; wait and see."

"But won't the shock be too much for the children, shutting the room up abruptly for good?"

"I don't want them going any deeper into this, that's all."

The lions were finished with their red feast. The lions were standing on the edge of the clearing, watching the two men.

"Now *I'm* feeling persecuted," said McClean. "Let's get out of here. I never have cared for these rooms. Make me nervous."

"The lions look real, don't they?" said George Hadley. "I don't suppose there's any way—"

"What?"

"—that they could *become* real?"

"Not that I know."

"Some flaw in the machinery, a tampering or something?"

"No."

They went to the door.

"I don't imagine the room will like being turned off," said the father.

"Nothing ever likes to die, even a room."

"I wonder if it hates me for wanting to switch it off?"

"Paranoia is thick around here today," said David McClean. "You can follow it like a spoor. Hello." He bent and picked up a bloody scarf. "This yours?"

"No." George Hadley's face was rigid. "It belongs to Lydia."

They went to the fuse box together and threw the switch that killed the nursery.

The two children were in hysterics. They screamed and pranced and threw things. They yelled and sobbed and swore and jumped at the furniture.

"George," said Lydia Hadley, "turn on the nursery, just for a few moments. You can't be so abrupt.

"No."

"You can't be so cruel."

"Lydia, it's off, and it stays off. And the whole house dies as of here and now. The more I see of the mess we've put ourselves in, the more it sickens me. We've been contemplating our mechanical, electronic navels for too long. Lord, how we need a breath of honest air!"

And he marched about the house turning off the voice clocks, the stoves, the heaters, the shoe shiners, the shoe lacers, the body scrubbers and swabbers and massagers, and every other machine he could put his hand to.

The house was full of dead bodies, it seemed. It felt like a mechanical cemetery. So silent. None of the humming hidden energy of machines waiting to function at the tap of a button.

"Don't let them do it!" wailed Peter at the ceiling, as if he were talking to the house, the nursery. "Don't let Father kill everything!" He turned to his father. "Oh, I hate you!"

"Insults won't get you anywhere."

"I wish you were dead!"

"We were, for a long while. Now we're really going to start living. Instead of being handled and massaged, we're going to live."

Wendy was still crying, and Peter joined her again. "Just a moment! Just one moment! Just another moment of nursery!" they wailed.

"Oh, George," said the wife, "it can't hurt."

"All right, all right, if they'll only just shut up. One minute, mind you, and then off forever."

"Daddy, Daddy, Daddy!" sang the children, smiling with wet faces.

"And then we're going on a vacation. David McClean is coming back in half an hour to help us move out and get to the airport. I'm going to dress. . . . You turn the nursery on for a minute, Lydia—just a minute, mind you."

And the three of them went babbling off while he let himself be vacuumed upstairs through the air flue and set about dressing himself. A minute later Lydia appeared.

"I'll be glad when we get away," she sighed.

"Did you leave them in the nursery?"

"I wanted to dress too. Oh, that horrid Africa. What can they see in it?"

"Well, in five minutes we'll be on our way to Iowa. Lord, how did we ever get in this house? What prompted us to buy a nightmare?"

"Pride, money, foolishness."

"I think we'd better get downstairs before those kids get engrossed with those beasts again."

Just then they heard the children calling, "Daddy, Mommy, come quick, quick!"

They went downstairs on the air flue and ran down the hall. The children were nowhere in sight. "Wendy? Peter!"

They ran into the nursery. The veldland was empty, save for the lions waiting, looking at them. "Peter, Wendy?"

The door slammed.

"Wendy, Peter!"

George Hadley and his wife whirled and ran back to the door.

"Open the door!" cried George Hadley, trying the knob. "Why, they've locked it from the outside! . . . Peter!" He beat at the door. "Open up!"

He heard Peter's voice outside, against the door.

"Don't let them switch off the nursery and the house," he was saying.

Mr. and Mrs. George Hadley beat at the door. "Now, don't be ridiculous, children. It's time to go. Mr. McClean'll be here in a minute and—"

And then they heard the sounds.

The lions on three sides of them, in the yellow veld grass, padding through the dry straw, rumbling and roaring in their throats. The lions.

Mr. Hadley looked at his wife, and they turned and looked back at the beasts, which rustled slowly forward, crouching, tails stiff. Mr. and Mrs. Hadley screamed. And suddenly they realized why those other screams had sounded familiar.

"Well, here I am," said David McClean in the nursery doorway. "Oh, hello." He stared at the two children seated in the center of the open glade, eating a little picnic lunch. Beyond them was the water hole and the yellow veldland; above was the hot sun. He began to perspire. "Where are your father and mother?"

The children looked up and smiled. "Oh, they'll be here directly."

"Good, we must get going." At a distance, Mr. McClean saw the lions fighting and clawing, and then quieting down to feed in silence under the shady trees. He squinted at the lions with his hand up to his eyes. Now the lions were done feeding. They came down to the water hole to drink.

A shadow flickered over Mr. McClean's hot face. Many shadows flickered. The vultures were dropping down the blazing sky.

"A cup of tea?" asked Wendy in the silence.

Dip in the Pool

By ROALD DAHL

ON THE morning of the third day, the sea calmed. Even the most delicate passengers—those who had not been seen around the ship since sailing time—emerged from their cabins and crept up onto the sun deck where the deck steward gave them chairs and tucked rugs around their legs and left them lying in rows, their faces upturned to the pale, almost heatless January sun.

It had been moderately rough the first two days, and this sudden calm and the sense of comfort that it brought created a more genial atmosphere over the whole ship. By the time evening came, the passengers, with twelve hours of good weather behind them, were beginning to feel confident, and at eight o'clock that night the main dining room was filled with people eating and drinking with the assured, complacent air of seasoned sailors.

The meal was not half over when the passengers became aware, by a slight friction between their bodies and the seats of their chairs, that the big ship had actually started rolling again. It was very gentle at first, just a slow, lazy leaning to one side, then to the other, but it was enough to cause a subtle, immediate change of mood over the whole room. A few of the passengers glanced up from their food, hesitating, waiting, almost listening for the next roll, smiling nervously, little secret glimmers of apprehension in their eyes. Some were completely unruffled, some were openly smug, a number of the smug ones making jokes about food and weather in order to torture the few who were beginning to suffer. The movement of the ship then became rapidly more and more violent, and only five or six minutes after the first roll had been noticed, she was swinging heavily from side to side, the passengers bracing themselves in their chairs, leaning against the pull as in a car cornering.

At last the really bad roll came, and Mr. William Botibol, sitting at the purser's table, saw his plate of poached turbot with hollandaise sauce sliding suddenly away from under his fork. There was a flutter of excitement, everybody reaching for plates and wineglasses. Mrs. Renshaw, seated at the purser's right, gave a little scream and clutched that gentleman's arm.

"Going to be a dirty night," the purser said, looking at Mrs. Renshaw. "I think it's blowing up for a very dirty night." There was just the faintest suggestion of relish in the way he said it.

A steward came hurrying up and sprinkled water on the tablecloth between the plates. The excitement subsided. Most of the passengers continued with their meal. A small number, including Mrs. Renshaw, got carefully to their feet and threaded their ways with a kind of concealed haste between the tables and through the doorway.

"Well," the purser said, "there she goes." He glanced around with approval at the remainder of his flock who were sitting quiet, looking complacent, their faces reflecting openly that extraordinary pride that travelers seem to take in being recognized as "good sailors."

When the eating was finished and the coffee had been served, Mr. Botibol, who had been unusually grave and thoughtful since the rolling started, suddenly stood up and carried his cup of coffee around to Mrs. Renshaw's vacant place, next to the purser. He seated himself in her chair, then immediately leaned over and began to whisper urgently in the purser's ear. "Excuse me," he said, "but could you tell me something please?"

The purser, small and fat and red, bent forward to listen. "What's the trouble, Mr. Botibol?"

"What I want to know is this." The man's face was anxious and the purser was watching it. "What I want to know is will the captain already have made his estimate on the day's run—you know, for the auction pool? I mean before it began to get rough like this?"

The purser, who had prepared himself to receive a personal confidence, smiled and leaned back in his seat to relax his full belly. "I should say so—yes," he answered. He didn't bother to whisper his reply, although automatically he lowered his voice, as one does when answering a whisperer.

"About how long ago do you think he did it?"

"Some time this afternoon. He usually does it in the afternoon."

"About what time?"

"Oh, I don't know. Around four o'clock I should guess."

"Now tell me another thing. How does the captain decide which number it shall be? Does he take a lot of trouble over that?"

The purser looked at the anxious frowning face of Mr. Botibol and he smiled, knowing quite well what the man was driving at. "Well, you see, the captain has a little conference with the navigating officer, and they study the weather and a lot of other things, and then they make their estimate."

Mr. Botibol nodded, pondering this answer for a moment. Then he said, "Do you think the captain knew there was bad weather coming today?"

"I couldn't tell you," the purser replied. He was looking into the small black eyes of the other man, seeing the two single little sparks of excitement dancing in their centers. "I really couldn't tell you, Mr. Botibol. I wouldn't know."

"If this gets any worse it might be worth buying some of the low numbers. What do you think?" The whispering was more urgent, more anxious now.

"Perhaps it will," the purser said. "I doubt the old man allowed for a really rough night. It was pretty calm this afternoon when he made his estimate."

The others at the table had become silent and were trying to hear, watching the purser with that intent, half-cocked, listening look that you can see also at the race track when they are trying to overhear a trainer talking about his chance: the slightly open lips, the upstretched eyebrows, the head forward and cocked a little to one side—that desperately straining, half-hypnotized, listening look that comes to all of them when they are hearing something straight from the horse's mouth.

"Now suppose *you* were allowed to buy a number, which one would *you* choose today?" Mr. Botibol whispered.

"I don't know what the range is yet," the purser patiently answered. "They don't announce the range till the auction starts after dinner. And I'm really not very good at it anyway. I'm only the purser, you know."

At that point Mr. Botibol stood up. "Excuse me, all," he said, and he walked carefully away over the swaying floor between the other tables, and twice he had to catch hold of the back of a chair to steady himself against the ship's roll.

"The sun deck, please," he said to the elevator man.

The wind caught him full in the face as he stepped out onto the open deck. He staggered and grabbed hold of the rail and held on tight with both hands, and he stood there looking out over the darkening sea where the great waves were welling up high and white horses were riding against the wind with plumes of spray behind them as they went.

"Pretty bad out there, wasn't it, sir?" the elevator man said on the way down.

Mr. Botibol was combing his hair back into place with a small red comb. "Do you think we've slackened speed at all on account of the weather?" he asked.

"Oh my word yes, sir. We slacked off considerable since this started. You got to slacken off speed in weather like this or you'll be throwing the passengers all over the ship."

Down in the smoking room people were already gathering for the auction. They were grouping themselves politely around the various tables, the men a little stiff in their dinner jackets, a little pink and overshaved and stiff beside their cool, white-armed women. Mr. Botibol took a chair close to the auctioneer's table. He crossed his legs, folded his arms, and settled himself in his seat with the rather desperate air of a man who has made a tremendous decision and refuses to be frightened.

The pool, he was telling himself, would probably be around seven thousand dollars. That was almost exactly what it had been the last two days with the numbers selling for between three and four hundred apiece. Being a British ship they did it in pounds, but he liked to do his thinking in his own currency. Seven thousand dollars was plenty of money. My goodness yes! And what he would do he would get them to pay him in hundred-dollar bills and he would take it ashore in the inside pocket of his jacket. No problem there. And right away, yes right away, he would buy a Lincoln convertible. He would pick it up on the way from the ship and drive it home just for the pleasure of seeing Ethel's face when she came out the front door and looked at it. Wouldn't that be something, to see Ethel's face when he glided up to the door in a brand-new pale-green Lincoln convertible! Hello Ethel honey, he would say, speaking very casual. I just thought I'd get you a little present. I saw it in the window as I went by, so I thought of you and how you were always wanting one. You like it, honey? he would say. You like the color? And then he would watch her face.

The auctioneer was standing up behind his table now. "Ladies and gentlemen!" he shouted. "The captain has estimated the day's run, ending midday tomorrow, at five hundred and fifteen miles. As usual we will take the ten numbers on either side of it to make up the range. That makes it five hundred and five to five hundred and twenty-five. And of course for those who think the true figure will be still farther away, there'll be 'low field' and 'high field' sold separately as well. Now, we'll draw the first number out of the hat . . . here we are . . . five hundred and twelve?"

The room became quiet. The people sat still in their chairs, all eyes watching the auctioneer. There was a certain tension in the air, and as the bids got higher, the tension grew. This wasn't a game or a joke; you could be sure of that by the way one man would look across at another who had raised his bid—smiling perhaps, but only the lips smiling, the eyes bright and absolutely cold.

Number five hundred and twelve was knocked down for one hundred and ten pounds. The next three or four numbers fetched roughly the same amount.

The ship was rolling heavily, and each time she went over, the wooden paneling on the walls creaked as if it were going to split. The passengers held on to the arms of their chairs, concentrating upon the auction.

"Low field!" the auctioneer called out. "The next number is low field."

Mr. Botibol sat up very straight and tense. He would wait, he had decided, until the others had finished bidding, then he would jump in and make the last bid. He had figured that there must be at least five hundred dollars in his account at the bank at home, probably nearer six. That was about two hundred pounds—over two hundred. This ticket wouldn't fetch more than that.

"As you all know," the auctioneer was saying, "low field covers every number *below* the smallest number in the range, in this case every number below five hundred and five. So, if you think this ship is going to cover less than five hundred and five miles in the twenty-four hours ending at noon tomorrow, you better get in and buy this number. So what am I bid?"

It went clear up to one hundred and thirty pounds. Others besides Mr. Botibol seemed to have noticed that the weather was rough. One hundred and forty . . . fifty. . . . There it stopped. The auctioneer raised his hammer.

"Going at one hundred and fifty. . . ."

"Sixty!" Mr. Botibol called, and every face in the room turned and looked at him.

"Seventy!"

"Eighty!" Mr. Botibol called.

"Ninety!"

"Two hundred!" Mr. Botibol called. He wasn't stopping now—not for anyone.

There was a pause.

"Any advance on two hundred pounds?"

Sit still, he told himself. Sit absolutely still and don't look up. It's unlucky to look up. Hold your breath. No one's going to bid you up so long as you hold your breath.

"Going for two hundred pounds. . . ." The auctioneer had a pink bald head and there were little beads of sweat sparkling on top of it. "Going . . ." Mr. Botibol held his breath. "Going . . . Gone!" The man banged the hammer on the table. Mr. Botibol wrote out a check and handed it to the auctioneer's assistant, then he settled back in his chair to wait for the finish. He did not want to go to bed before he knew how much there was in the pool.

They added it up after the last number had been sold and it came to twenty-one hundred-odd pounds. That was around six thousand dollars. Ninety per cent to go to the winner, ten per cent to seamen's charities. Ninety per cent of six thousand was five thousand four hundred. Well— that was enough. He could buy the Lincoln convertible and there would be something left over, too. With this gratifying thought he went off, happy and excited, to his cabin.

When Mr. Botibol awoke the next morning he lay quite still for several minutes with his eyes shut, listening for the sound of the gale, waiting for the roll of the ship. There was no sound of any gale and the ship was not rolling. He jumped up and peered out of the porthole. The sea—

Oh Jesus God—was smooth as glass, the great ship was moving through it fast, obviously making up for time lost during the night. Mr. Botibol turned away and sat slowly down on the edge of his bunk. A fine electricity of fear was beginning to prickle under the skin of his stomach. He hadn't a hope now. One of the higher numbers was certain to win it after this.

"Oh my God," he said aloud. "What shall I do?"

What, for example, would Ethel say? It was simply not possible to tell her that he had spent almost all of their two years' savings on a ticket in the ship's pool. Nor was it possible to keep the matter secret. To do that he would have to tell her to stop drawing checks. And what about the monthly installments on the television set and the Encyclopaedia Britannica? Already he could see the anger and contempt in the woman's eyes, the blue becoming gray and the eyes themselves narrowing as they always did when there was anger in them.

"Oh my God. What *shall* I do?"

There was no point in pretending that he had the slightest chance now —not unless the goddam ship started to go backward. They'd have to put her in reverse and go full speed astern and keep right on going if he was to have any chance of winning it now. Well, maybe he should ask the captain to do just that. Offer him ten per cent of the profits. Offer him more if he wanted it. Mr. Botibol started to giggle. Then very suddenly he stopped, his eyes and mouth both opening wide in a kind of shocked surprise. For it was at this moment that the idea came. It hit him hard and quick, and he jumped up from his bed, terribly excited, ran over to the porthole and looked out again. Well, he thought, why not? Why ever not? The sea was calm and he wouldn't have any trouble keeping afloat until they picked him up. He had a vague feeling that someone had done this thing before, but that didn't prevent him from doing it again. The ship would have to stop and lower a boat, and the boat would have to go back maybe half a mile to get him, and then it would have to return to the ship and be hoisted back on board. It would take at least an hour, the whole thing. An hour was about thirty miles. It would knock thirty miles off the day's run. That would do it. "Low field" would be sure to win it then. Just so long as he made certain someone saw him falling over; but that would be simple to arrange. And he'd better wear light clothes, something easy to swim in. Sports clothes, that was it. He would dress as though he were going up to play some deck tennis—just a shirt and a pair of shorts and tennis shoes. And leave his watch behind. What was the time? Nine-fifteen. The sooner the better, then. Do it now and get it over with. Have to do it soon, because the time limit was midday.

Mr. Botibol was both frightened and excited when he stepped out onto the sundeck in his sports clothes. His small body was wide at the hips, tapering upward to extremely narrow sloping shoulders, so that it resembled, in shape at any rate, a bollard. His white skinny legs were covered with black hairs, and he came cautiously out on deck, treading softly in his tennis shoes. Nervously he looked around him. There was only one other person in sight, an elderly woman with very thick ankles and immense buttocks who was leaning over the rail staring at the sea. She was wearing a coat of Persian lamb and the collar was turned up so Mr. Botibol couldn't see her face.

He stood still, examining her carefully from a distance. Yes, he told himself, she would probably do. She would probably give the alarm just as quickly as anyone else. But wait one minute, take your time, William Botibol, take your time. Remember what you told yourself a few minutes ago in the cabin when you were changing? You remember that?

The thought of leaping off a ship into the ocean a thousand miles from the nearest land had made Mr. Botibol—a cautious man at the best of times—unusually advertent. He was by no means satisfied yet that this woman he saw before him was *absolutely certain* to give the alarm when he made his jump. In his opinion there were two possible reasons why she might fail him. Firstly, she might be deaf and blind. It was not very probable, but on the other hand it *might* be so, and why take a chance? All he had to do was check it by talking to her for a moment beforehand. Secondly—and this will demonstrate how suspicious the mind of a man can become when it is working through self-preservation and fear—secondly, it had occurred to him that the woman might herself be the owner of one of the high numbers in the pool and as such would have a sound financial reason for not wishing to stop the ship. Mr. Botibol recalled that people had killed their fellows for far less than six thousand dollars. It was happening every day in the newspapers. So why take a chance on that either? Check on it first. Be sure of your facts. Find out about it by a little polite conversation. Then, provided that the woman appeared also to be a pleasant, kindly human being, the thing was a cinch and he could leap overboard with a light heart.

Mr. Botibol advanced casually toward the woman and took up a position beside her, leaning on the rail. "Hullo," he said pleasantly.

She turned and smiled at him, a surprisingly lovely, almost a beautiful smile, although the face itself was very plain. "Hullo," she answered him.

Check, Mr. Botibol told himself, on the first question. She is neither blind nor deaf. "Tell me," he said, coming straight to the point, "what did you think of the auction last night?"

"Auction?" she asked, frowning. "Auction? What auction?"

"You know, that silly old thing they have in the lounge after dinner, selling numbers on the ship's daily run. I just wondered what you thought about it."

She shook her head, and again she smiled, a sweet and pleasant smile that had in it perhaps the trace of an apology. "I'm very lazy," she said.

"I always go to bed early. I have my dinner in bed. It's so restful to have dinner in bed."

Mr. Botibol smiled back at her and began to edge away. "Got to go and get my exercise now," he said. "Never miss my exercise in the morning. It was nice seeing you. Very nice seeing you. . . ." He retreated about ten paces, and the woman let him go without looking around.

Everything was now in order. The sea was calm, he was lightly dressed for swimming, there were almost certainly no man-eating sharks in this part of the Atlantic, and there was this pleasant kindly old woman to give the alarm. It was a question now only of whether the ship would be delayed long enough to swing the balance in his favor. Almost certainly it would. In any event, he could do a little to help in that direction himself. He could make a few difficulties about getting hauled up into the lifeboat. Swim around a bit, back away from them surreptitiously as they tried to come up close to fish him out. Every minute, every second gained would help him win. He began to move forward again to the rail, but now a new fear assailed him. Would he get caught in the propeller? He had heard about that happening to persons falling off the sides of big ships. But then, he wasn't going to fall, he was going to jump, and that was a very different thing. Provided he jumped out far enough he would be sure to clear the propeller.

Mr. Botibol advanced slowly to a position at the rail about twenty yards away from the woman. She wasn't looking at him now. So much the better. He didn't want her watching him as he jumped off. So long as no one was watching he would be able to say afterward that he had slipped and fallen by accident. He peered over the side of the ship. It was a long, long drop. Come to think of it now, he might easily hurt himself badly if he hit the water flat. Wasn't there someone who once split his stomach open that way, doing a belly flop from the high dive? He must jump straight and land feet first. Go in like a knife. Yes sir. The water seemed cold and deep and gray and it made him shiver to look at it. But it was now or never. Be a man, William Botibol, be a man. All right then . . . now . . . here goes . . .

He climbed up onto the wide wooden toprail, stood there poised, balancing for three terrifying seconds, then he leaped—he leaped up and out as far as he could go and at the same time he shouted *"Help!"*

"Help! Help!" he shouted as he fell. Then he hit the water and went under.

When the first shout for help sounded, the woman who was leaning on the rail started up and gave a little jump of surprise. She looked around quickly and saw sailing past her through the air this small man dressed in white shorts and tennis shoes, spread-eagled and shouting as he went. For a moment she looked as though she weren't quite sure what she ought to do: throw a life belt, run away and give the alarm, or simply turn and yell. She drew back a pace from the rail and swung half around facing up to the bridge, and for this brief moment she remained motionless, tense, undecided. Then almost at once she seemed to relax, and she leaned forward far over the rail, staring at the water where it was turbulent in the ship's wake. Soon a tiny round black head appeared in the foam, an arm was raised about it, once, twice, vigorously waving, and a small faraway voice was heard calling something that was difficult to understand. The woman leaned still farther over the rail, trying to keep the little bobbing black speck in sight, but soon, so very soon, it was such a long way away that she couldn't even be sure it was there at all.

After a while another woman came out on deck. This one was bony and angular, and she wore horn-rimmed spectacles. She spotted the first woman and walked over to her, treading the deck in the deliberate, military fashion of all spinsters.

"So *there* you are," she said.

The woman with the fat ankles turned and looked at her, but said nothing.

"I've been searching for you," the bony one continued. "Searching all over."

"It's very odd," the woman with the fat ankles said. "A man dived overboard just now, with his clothes on."

"Nonsense!"

"Oh yes. He said he wanted to get some exercise and he dived in and didn't even bother to take his clothes off."

"You better come down now," the bony woman said. Her mouth had suddenly become firm, her whole face sharp and alert, and she spoke less kindly than before. "And don't you ever go wandering about on deck alone like this again. You know quite well you're meant to wait for me."

"Yes, Maggie," the woman with the fat ankles answered, and again she smiled, a tender, trusting smile, and she took the hand of the other one and allowed herself to be led away across the deck.

"Such a nice man," she said. "He waved to me."

VIII

Accent on Laughter

The Cream of the Joust

By T. H. WHITE

TILTING was a great art and needed an enormous amount of practice. When two knights jousted they held their lances in their right hands, but they directed their horses at one another so that each man had his opponent on his near side. The base of the lance, in fact, was held on the opposite side of the body to the side at which the enemy was charging. This seems rather inside out to anybody who is in the habit, say, of opening gates with a hunting crop, but it had its reasons. For one thing, it meant that the shield was on the left arm, so that the opponents charged shield to shield, fully covered. It also meant that a man could be unhorsed with the side or edge of the lance, in a kind of horizontal swipe, if you did not feel sure of hitting him with your point. This was the humblest or least skillful blow in jousting.

A good jouster, like Launcelot or Tristram, always used the blow of the point, because, although it was liable to miss in unskillful hands, it made contact sooner. If one knight charged with his lance held rigidly sideways, with a view to sweeping his opponent out of the saddle, the other knight with his lance held directly forward would knock him down a lance length before the sweep came into effect.

It would take too long to go into all the interesting details of proper tilting which you had to learn, for in those days one had to be a master of one's craft from the bottom upwards. You had to know what wood was best for spears, and why, and even how to turn them so that they would not splinter or warp. There were a thousand disputed questions about arms and armor, all of which had to be understood.

Just outside Sir Ector's castle there was a jousting field for tournaments. It was a green meadow, kept short, with a broad grassy bank raised round it on which pavilions could be erected. There was an old wooden grandstand at one side, lifted on stilts for the ladies. At present it was only used as a practice ground for tilting.

Wart lay beside Merlyn in the shade of the grandstand. Merlyn, sitting with his back to all this athleticism, was practicing a spell which he had forgotten.

A humblebee came zooming between them, under the grandstand and out into the sunlight.

"Would you like to see some real knights errant?" asked Merlyn slowly. "Now, for the sake of your education?"

"Oh, I would," cried the Wart. "We've never even had a tournament since I was here."

"I suppose it could be managed. Do you prefer any particular knights?"

"King Pellinore," said the Wart immediately.

Merlyn said, "That will do very well. Put your hands to your sides and relax your muscles. Cabricias arci thuram, catalamus, singulariter, nominativo, haec musa. Shut your eyes and keep them shut. Bonus, Bona, Bonum. Here we go. Deus Sanctus, est-ne oratio Latinas? Etiam, oui, quare? Pourquoi? Quia substantivo et adjectivum concordat in generi, numerum et casus. Here we are."

While this incantation was going on, Wart experienced some queer sensations. First the words got smaller and smaller, as if he were looking at his feet through the wrong end of a telescope, and began to swirl round into a cone, as if they were at the pointed bottom end of a whirlpool which was sucking him into the air. Then there was nothing but a loud rotating roaring and hissing noise which rose to such a tornado that he felt that he could not stand it any more. Finally there was utter silence and Merlyn saying, "Here we are." All this happened in about the time that it would take a sixpenny rocket to start off with its fiery swish, bend down from its climax and disperse itself in thunder and colored stars. He opened his eyes just at the moment when you would have heard the invisible stick hitting the ground.

They were lying under a beech tree in the Forest Sauvage.

"Here we are," said Merlyn. "Get up and dust your clothes."

"And there, I think," continued the magician, in a tone of great satisfaction because his spells had worked for once without a hitch, "is your friend, King Pellinore, pricking towards us o'er the plain."

"Hallo, hallo," cried King Pellinore, popping his visor up and down.

"Hail," said Merlyn, in his most mysterious manner.

"Hail," replied the King, anxious to make a good impression.

They shook hands.

"Did you say Hail?" inquired the King, looking about him nervously. "I thought it was going to be fine, meself."

"He meant How-do-you-do," explained the Wart.

"Ah, yes, How-de-do?"

They shook hands again.

"Good afternoon," said King Pellinore. "What do you think the weather looks like now?"

"I think it looks like an anti-cyclone," said Merlyn.

"Ah, yes," said the King. "An anti-cyclone. Well, I suppose I ought to be getting along."

At this the King trembled very much, opened and shut his visor several times, coughed, wove his reins into a knot, exclaimed, "I beg your pardon?" and showed signs of cantering away.

"He is a white magician," said the Wart. "You needn't be afraid of him. He is my best friend, your majesty, and in any case he generally gets his spells muddled up."

"Ah, yes," said King Pellinore. "A white magician, what? How small the world is, is it not? How-de-do?"

"Hail," said Merlyn.

"Hail," said King Pellinore.

They shook hands for the third time.

"I shouldn't go away," said Merlyn, "if I were you. Sir Grummore Grummursum is on the way here to challenge you to a joust."

"No, you don't say? Sir What-you-may-call-it coming here to challenge me to a joust?"

"Assuredly."

"Good handicap man?"

"I should think it would be a pretty even match."

"Well, I must say," exclaimed the King, "it never hails but it pours."

"Hail," said Merlyn.

"Hail," said King Pellinore.

"Hail," said the Wart involuntarily.

"Now I really won't shake hands with anybody else," announced the monarch. "We shall simply assume that we have all met before."

"Is Sir Grummore really coming," inquired the Wart, hastily changing the subject, "to challenge King Pellinore to a battle?"

"Look yonder," said Merlyn, and both of them looked in the direction of his outstretched finger.

Sir Grummore Grummursum was cantering up the clearing in full panoply of war. Instead of his ordinary helmet with a visor he was wearing the proper tilting helm, which looked like a large coal scuttle, and as he cantered he clanged.

He was singing his old school song:

> We'll tilt together
> Steady from crupper to poll,
> And nothin' in life shall sever
> Our love for the dear old coll.
> Follow-up, follow-up, follow-up,
>   follow-up, follow-up,
> Till the shield ring again and again
> With the clanks of the clanky true men.

"Goodness," exclaimed King Pellinore. "It's about two months since I had a proper tilt, and last winter they put me up to eighteen. That was when they had the new handicaps, you know."

Sir Grummore had arrived while he was speaking, and had recognized the Wart.

"Mornin'," said Sir Grummore. "You're Sir Ector's boy, ain't you? And who's that chap in the comic hat?"

"That is my tutor," said the Wart hurriedly, "Merlyn, the magician."

Sir Grummore looked at Merlyn—magicians were considered rather middle-class by the true jousting set in those days—and said distantly, "Ah, a magician. How-de-do?"

"And this is King Pellinore," said the Wart. "Sir Grummore Grummursum—King Pellinore."

"How-de-do?" said Sir Grummore.

"Hail," said King Pellinore. "No, I mean it won't hail, will it?"

"Nice day," said Sir Grummore.

"Yes, it is nice, what, isn't it?"

"Been questin' today?"

"Oh, yes, thank you. Always am questing, you know. After the Questing Beast."

"Interestin' job that, very."

"Yes, it is interesting. Only you get tired of it," added King Pellinore.

"Well, well. It's a fine day, isn't it?"

"Yes, it is rather fine."

"Suppose we'd better have a joust, eh, what?"

"Yes, I suppose we had better," said King Pellinore, "really."

"What shall we have it for?"

"Oh, the usual thing, I suppose. Would one of you kindly help me on with my helm?"

They all three had to help him on eventually, for, what with the unscrewing of screws and the easing of nuts and bolts which the King had clumsily set on the wrong thread when getting up in a hurry that morning, it was quite a feat of engineering to get him out of his helmet and into his helm. The helm was an enormous thing like an oil drum, padded inside with two thicknesses of leather and three inches of straw.

As soon as they were ready, the two knights stationed themselves at each end of the clearing and then advanced to meet in the middle.

"Fair knight," said King Pellinore, "I pray thee tell me thy name."

"That me regards," replied Sir Grummore, using the proper formula.

"That is uncourteously said," said King Pellinore, "what? For no knight ne dreadeth for to speak his name openly, but for some reason of shame."

"Be that as it may, I choose that thou shalt not know my name as at this time, for no askin'."

"Then you must stay and joust with me, false knight."

"Haven't you got that wrong, Pellinore?" inquired Sir Grummore. "I believe it ought to be 'thou shalt.'"

"Oh, I'm sorry, Sir Grummore. Yes, so it should be, of course. Then thou shalt stay and joust with me, false knight."

Without further words, the two gentlemen retreated to the opposite ends of the clearing, fewtered their spears, and prepared to hurtle together in the preliminary charge.

"I think we had better climb up this tree," said Merlyn. "You never know what will happen in a joust like this."

They climbed up the big beech, which had low easy branches sticking out in all directions, and the Wart stationed himself towards the end of a smooth bough about fifteen feet up, where he could get a good view. Nothing is so comfortable to sit in as a big beech.

In order to be able to picture the terrible battle which now took place, there is one thing which ought to be known: a knight in his full armor of those days was generally carrying as much or more than his own weight in metal. He weighed no less than twenty-two stone, and sometimes as much as twenty-five. This meant that his horse had to be a slow and enormous weight carrier, like the farm horse of today, and that his own movements were so hampered by his burden of iron and padding that they were toned down into slow motion as in motion pictures.

"They're off!" cried the Wart, holding his breath with excitement.

Slowly and majestically, the ponderous horses lumbered into a walk. The spears, which had been pointing in the air, bowed down to a horizontal line and pointed at each other. King Pellinore and Sir Grummore could be seen to be thumping their horses' sides with their heels for all they were worth, and in a few minutes the splendid animals had shambled into an earth-shaking imitation of a trot. Clank, rumble-thumpity-thump, and now the two knights were flapping their elbows and legs in unison, showing a good deal of daylight at their seats. There was a change in tempo, and Sir Grummore's horse could be definitely seen to be cantering. In another minute King Pellinore's was doing so too. It was a terrible spectacle.

"Oh, dear!" exclaimed the Wart, feeling slightly ashamed that his own bloodthirstiness had been responsible for making these two knights joust before him. "Do you think they will kill each other?"

"Dangerous sport," said Merlyn, shaking his head.

"Now!" cried the Wart.

With a bloodcurdling thumping of iron hoofs the mighty equestrians came together. Their spears wavered for a moment within a few inches of each other's helms—each had chosen the difficult point stroke—and then they were galloping off in opposite directions. Sir Grummore drove his spear deep into the beech tree where they were sitting and stopped, dead. King Pellinore, who had been run away with, vanished altogether behind his back.

"Is it safe to look?" inquired the Wart, who had shut his eyes tight at the critical moment.

"Quite safe," said Merlyn, "it will take them some time to get back."

"Whoa, whoa, I say!" cried King Pellinore in muffled and distant tones, far away among some gorse bushes.

"Hi, Pellinore, hi!" shouted Sir Grummore. "Come back, my dear fellah, I'm over here."

There was a long pause, while the complicated stations of the two knights readjusted themselves, and then King Pellinore was at the opposite end from that at which he had started, while Sir Grummore faced him from his original position.

"Traitor knight!" cried Sir Grummore.

"Yield, recreant, what?" cried King Pellinore.

They fewtered their spears again, and thundered into the charge.

"Oh," said the Wart, "I hope they don't hurt themselves."

But the two mounts were patiently blundering together, and the two knights had simultaneously decided upon the sweeping stroke. Each held his spear straight out at right angles towards the left, and before the Wart could say anything further there was a terrific yet melodious thump. Clang! said the armor, like a motor omnibus in collision with a smithy, and the jousters were sitting side by side on the green sward, while their horses cantered off in opposite directions.

"A splendid fall," said Merlyn.

The two horses pulled themselves up, their duty done, and began resignedly to eat the sward. King Pellinore and Sir Grummore sat looking straight before them, each with the other's spear clasped hopefully under his arm.

"Well!" said the Wart. "What a bump! They both seem to be all right, so far."

Sir Grummore and King Pellinore laboriously got up.

"Defend thee," cried King Pellinore.

"God save thee," cried Sir Grummore.

With this they drew their swords and rushed together with such ferocity that each, after dealing the other a dint on the helm, sat down suddenly backwards.

"Bah!" cried King Pellinore.

"Booh!" cried Sir Grummore, also sitting down.

"Mercy," exclaimed the Wart. "What a combat!"

The knights had now lost their tempers and the battle was joined in earnest. It did not matter much, however, for they were so encased in metal that they could do each other little damage. It took them so long to get up, and the dealing of a blow when you weighed the eighth part of a ton was such a cumbrous business, that every stage of the contest could be marked and pondered.

In the first stage King Pellinore and Sir Grummore stood opposite each other for about half an hour, and walloped each other on the helm. There was only opportunity for one blow at a time, and so they more or less took it in turns, King Pellinore striking while Sir Grummore was recovering, and vice versa. At first, if either of them dropped his sword or got it stuck in the ground, the other put in two or three extra blows while he was patiently fumbling for it or trying to tug it out. Later, they fell into the rhythm of the thing more perfectly, like the toy mechanical people who saw wood on Christmas trees. Eventually the exercise and the monotony restored their good humor and they began to get bored.

The second stage was introduced as a change, by common consent. Sir Grummore stumped off to one end of the clearing, while King Pellinore plodded off to the other. Then they turned round and swayed backwards and forwards once or twice, in order to get their weight on their toes. When they leaned forward they had to run forward, in order to keep up with their weight, and if they leaned too far backwards they fell down. So even walking was a bit complicated. When they had got their weight properly distributed in front of them, so that they were just off their balance, each broke into a trot to keep up with himself. They hurtled together as it had been two boars.

They met in the middle, breast to breast, with a noise of shipwreck and great bells tolling, and both, bouncing off, fell breathless on their backs. They lay thus for a few minutes, panting. Then they slowly began to heave themselves to their feet, and it was obvious that they had lost their tempers once again.

King Pellinore had not only lost his temper but seemed to have been a bit astonied by the impact. He got up facing the wrong way, and could not find Sir Grummore. There was some excuse for this, since he had only a tiny slit to peep through, and that was three inches away from his eye owing to the padding of straw, but he looked a bit muddled as well. Perhaps he had broken his spectacles. Sir Grummore was quick to seize his advantage.

"Take that!" cried Sir Grummore, giving the unfortunate monarch a two-handed swipe on the nob as he was slowly turning his head from side to side, peering in the opposite direction.

King Pellinore turned round morosely, but his opponent had been too quick for him. He had ambled round so that he was still behind the King, and now gave him another terrific blow in the same place.

"Where are you?" asked King Pellinore.

"Here," cried Sir Grummore, giving him another.

The poor King turned himself round as nimbly as possible, but Sir Grummore had given him the slip again.

"Tally-ho back!" shouted Sir Grummore, with another wallop.

"I think you're a cad," said the King.

"Wallop!" replied Sir Grummore, doing it.

What with the preliminary crash, the repeated blows on the back of his head, and the puzzling invisible nature of his opponent, King Pellinore could now be seen to be visibly troubled in his brains. He swayed backwards and forwards under the hail of blows which were administered, and feebly wagged his arms.

"Poor King," said the Wart. "I wish he wouldn't hit him so."

As if in answer to his wish, Sir Grummore paused in his labors.

"Do you want Pax?" asked Sir Grummore.

King Pellinore made no answer.

Sir Grummore favored him with another whack and said, "If you don't say Pax, I shall cut your head off."

"I won't," said the King.

Whang! went the sword on the top of his head.

Whang! it went again.

Whang! for the third time.

"Pax," said King Pellinore, mumbling rather.

Then, just as Sir Grummore was relaxing with the fruits of victory, he swung round upon him, shouted "Non!" at the top of his voice, and gave him a good push in the middle of the chest.

Sir Grummore fell over backwards.

"Well!" exclaimed the Wart. "What a cheat! I wouldn't have thought it of him."

King Pellinore hurriedly sat down on his victim's chest, thus increasing the weight upon him to a quarter of a ton and making it quite impossible for him to move, and began to undo Sir Grummore's helm.

"You said Pax!"

"I said Pax Non under my breath."

"It's a swindle."

"It isn't, so nuts to you."

"You cad."

"No, I'm not."

"Yes, you are."

"No, I'm not."

"Yes, you are."

"I said Pax Non."

"You said Pax."

"No, I didn't."

"Yes, you did."

"No, I didn't."

"Yes, you did."

By this time Sir Grummore's helm was unlaced and they could see his bare head glaring at King Pellinore, quite purple in the face.

"Yield thee, recreant," said the King.

"Shan't," said Sir Grummore.

"You've got to yield, or I shall cut off your head."

"Cut it off then."

"Oh, come on," said the King. "You know you have to yield when your helm is off."

"Feign I," said Sir Grummore.

"Well, I shall just cut your head off."

"I don't care."

The King waved his sword menacingly in the air.

"Go on," said Sir Grummore. "I dare you to."

The King lowered his sword and said, "Oh, I say, do yield, please."

"You yield," said Sir Grummore.

"But I can't yield, you know. I am on top of you after all, am not I, what?"

"Well, I've feigned yieldin'."

"Oh, come on, Grummore. I do think you are a cad not to yield. You know very well I can't cut your head off."

"I wouldn't yield to a cheat who started fightin' after he said Pax."

"I'm not a cheat."

"You are a cheat."

"No, I'm not."

"Yes, you are."

"No, I'm not."

"Yes, you are."

"Very well," said King Pellinore. "You can bally well get up and put on your helm and we'll have a fight. I won't be called a cheat for anybody."

"Cheat," said Sir Grummore.

They stood up and fumbled together with the helm, hissing, "No, I'm not," "Yes, you are," until it was safely on. Then they retreated to opposite ends of the clearing, got their weight upon their toes, and came rumbling and thundering together like two runaway trains.

Unfortunately they were now so cross that they had both ceased to be vigilant, and in the fury of the moment they missed each other altogether. The momentum of their armor was too great for them to stop till they had passed each other handsomely, and then they maneuvered about in such a manner that neither happened to come within the other's range of vision. It was a bit funny watching them, because King Pellinore, having already been caught from behind once, was continually spinning round to look behind him, and Sir Grummore, having used the stratagem himself, was doing the same thing. Thus they wandered for some five minutes, standing still, listening, clanking, crouching, creeping, peering, walking on tiptoe, and occasionally making a chance swipe behind their backs. Once they were standing within a few feet of each other, back to back, only to stalk off in opposite directions with infinite precaution, and once King Pellinore did hit Sir Grummore with one of his back strokes, but they both immediately spun round so often that they became giddy and mislaid each other afresh.

After five minutes Sir Grummore said, "All right, Pellinore. It's no use hidin'. I can see where you are."

"I'm not hiding," exclaimed King Pellinore indignantly. "Where am I?" They discovered each other and went up close together, face to face.

"Cad," said Sir Grummore.

"Yah," said King Pellinore.

They turned round and marched off to their corners, seething with indignation.

"Swindler," shouted Sir Grummore.

"Beastly bully," shouted King Pellinore.

With this they summoned all their energies together for one decisive encounter, leaned forwards, lowered their heads like two billy goats, and positively sprinted together for the final blow. Alas, their aim was poor. They missed each other by about five yards, passed at full steam doing at least eight knots, like ships that pass in the night but speak not to each other in passing, and hurtled onwards to their doom. Both knights began waving their arms like windmills, anti-clockwise, in the vain effort to slow up. Both continued with undiminished speed. Then Sir Grummore rammed his head against the beech in which the Wart was sitting, and King Pellinore collided with a chestnut at the other side of the clearing. The trees shook, the forest rang. Blackbirds and squirrels cursed and wood pigeons flew out of their leafy perches half a mile away. The two knights stood to attention while you could count three. Then, with a last unanimous melodious clang, they both fell prostrate on the fatal sward.

"Stunned," said Merlyn, "I should think."

"Oh, dear," said the Wart. "Oughtn't we to get down and help them?"

"We could pour water on their heads," said Merlyn reflectively, "if there were any water. But I don't suppose they'd thank us for making their armor rusty. They'll be all right. Besides, it's time that we were home."

"But they might be dead!"

"They're not dead, I know. In a minute or two they'll come round and go off home to dinner."

"Poor King Pellinore hasn't got a home."

"Then Sir Grummore will invite him to stay the night. They'll be the best of friends when they come to. They always are."

"Do you think so?"

"My dear boy, I know so. Shut your eyes and we'll be off."

A Corner in Horses

By STEWART EDWARD WHITE

IT WAS dark night. The stray herd bellowed frantically from one of the big corrals; the cow-and-calf herd from a second. Already the remuda, driven in from the open plains, scattered about the thousand acres of pasture. Away from the conveniences of fence and corral, men would have had to patrol all night. Now, however, everyone was gathered about the campfire.

Probably forty cowboys were in the group, representing all types, from old John, who had been in the business forty years, and had punched from the Rio Grande to the Pacific, to the Kid, who would have given his chance of salvation if he could have been taken for ten years older than he was. At the moment Jed Parker was holding forth to his friend Johnny Stone in reference to another old crony who had that evening joined the round up.

"Johnny," inquired Jed with elaborate gravity, and entirely ignoring the presence of the subject of conversation, "what is that thing just beyond the fire, and where did it come from?"

Johnny Stone squinted to make sure.

"That?" he replied. "Oh, this evenin' the dogs see something run down a hole, and they dug it out, and that's what they got."

The newcomer grinned.

"The trouble with you fellows," he proffered, "is that you're so plumb alkalied you don't know the real thing when you see it."

"That's right," supplemented Windy Bill dryly. *"He* come from New York."

"No!" cried Jed. "You don't say so? Did he come in one box or in two?"

Under cover of the laugh, the newcomer made a raid on the Dutch ovens and pails. Having filled his plate, he squatted on his heels and fell to his belated meal. He was a tall, slab-sided individual, with a lean, leathery face, a sweeping white mustache, and a grave and sardonic eye. His leather chaps were plain and worn, and his hat had been fashioned by time and wear into much individuality. I was not surprised to hear him nicknamed Sacatone Bill.

"Just ask him how he got that game foot," suggested Johnny Stone to me in an undertone, so, of course, I did not.

Later someone told me that the lameness resulted from his refusal of an urgent invitation to return across a river. Mr. Sacatone Bill happened not to be riding his own horse at the time.

The Cattleman dropped down beside me a moment later.

"I wish," said he in a low voice, "we could get that fellow talking. He is a queer one. Pretty well educated apparently. Claims to be writing a book of memoirs. Sometimes he will open up in good shape, and sometimes he will not. It does no good to ask him direct, and he is as shy as an old crow when you try to lead him up to a subject. We must just lie low and trust to Providence."

A man was playing on the mouth organ. He played excellently well, with all sorts of variations and frills. We smoked in silence. The deep rumble of the cattle filled the air with its diapason. Always the shrill coyotes raved out in the mesquite. Sacatone Bill had finished his meal, and had gone to sit by Jed Parker, his old friend. They talked together low-voiced. The evening grew, and the eastern sky silvered over the mountains in anticipation of the moon.

Sacatone Bill suddenly threw back his head and laughed.

"Reminds me of the time I went to Colorado!" he cried.

"He's off!" whispered the Cattleman.

A dead silence fell on the circle. Everybody shifted position the better to listen to the story of Sacatone Bill.

About ten years ago I got plumb sick of punchin' cows around my part of the country. She hadn't rained since Noah, and I'd forgot what water outside a pail or a trough looked like. So I scouted around inside of me to see what part of the world I'd jump to, and, as I seemed to know as little of Colorado and minin' as anything else, I made up the pint of bean soup I call my brains to go there. So I catches me a buyer at Benson and turns over my pore little bunch of cattle and prepared to fly. The last day I hauled up about twenty good buckets of water and threw her up against the cabin. My buyer was settin' his hoss waitin' for me to get ready. He didn't say nothin' until we'd got down about ten mile or so.

"Mr. Hicks," says he, hesitatin' like, "I find it a good rule in this country not to overlook other folks' plays, but I'd take it mighty kind if you'd explain those actions of yours with the pails of water."

"Mr. Jones," says I, "it's very simple. I built that shack five year ago, and it's never rained since. I just wanted to settle in my mind whether or not that damn roof leaked."

So I quit Arizona, and in about a week I see my reflection in the winders of a little place called Cyanide in the Colorado mountains.

Fellows, she was a bird. They wasn't a pony in sight, nor a squar' foot of land that wasn't either street or straight up. It made me plumb lonesome for a country where you could see a long ways even if you didn't see much. And this early in the evenin' they wasn't hardly anybody in the streets at all.

I took a look at them dark, gloomy old mountains, and a sniff at a breeze that would have frozen the whiskers of hope, and I made a dive for the nearest lit winder. They was a sign over it that just said:

THIS IS A SALOON

I was glad they labeled her. I'd never have known it. They had a fifteen-year-old kid tendin' bar, no games goin', and not a soul in the place.

"Sorry to disturb your repose, bub," says I, "but see if you can sort out any rye among them collections of sassapariller of yours."

I took a drink, and then another to keep it company—I was beginnin' to sympathize with anythin' lonesome. Then I kind of sauntered out to the back room where the hurdy-gurdy ought to be. Sure enough, there was a girl settin' on the pianner stool, another in a chair, and a nice shiny drummer danglin' his feet from a table. They looked up when they see me come in, and went right on talkin'.

"Hello, girls!" says I.

At that they stopped talkin' complete.

"How's tricks?" says I.

"Who's your woolly friend?" the drummer asks of the girls.

I looked at him a minute, but I see he'd been raised a pet, and then, too, I was so hungry for sassiety I was willin' to pass a bet or two.

"Don't you *admire* these cow gents?" snickers one of the girls.

"Play somethin', sister," says I to the one at the pianner.

She just grinned at me.

"Interdooce me," says the drummer in a kind of a way that made them all laugh a heap.

"Give us a tune," I begs, tryin' to be jolly, too.

"She don't know any pieces," says the salesman.

"Don't you?" I asks pretty sharp.

"No," says she.

"Well, I do," says I.

I walked up to her, jerked out my guns, and reached around both sides of her to the pianner. I ran the muzzles up and down the keyboard two or three times, and then shot out half a dozen keys.

"That's the piece I know," says I.

But the other girl and the drummer had punched the breeze.

The girl at the pianner just grinned, and pointed to the winder where they was some ragged glass hangin'. She was dead game.

"Say, Susie," says I, "you're all right, but your friends is tur'ble. I may be rough, and I ain't never been curried below the knees, but I'm better to tie to than them sons of guns."

"I believe it," says she.

So we had a drink at the bar, and started out to investigate the wonders of Cyanide.

Say, that night *was* a wonder. Susie faded after about three drinks, but I didn't seem to mind that. I hooked up to another saloon kept by a thin Dutchman. A fat Dutchman is stupid, but a thin one is all right.

In ten minutes I had more friends in Cyanide than they is fiddlers in hell. I begun to conclude Cyanide wasn't so lonesome. About four o'clock in comes a little Irishman about four foot high, with more upper lip than a muley cow, and enough red hair to make an artificial aurorer borealis. He had big red hands with freckles pasted onto them, and stiff red hairs standin' up separate and lonesome like signal stations. Also his legs was bowed.

He gets a drink at the bar, and stands back and yells:

"God bless the Irish and let the Dutch rustle!"

Now, this was none of my town, so I just stepped back of the end of the bar quick where I wouldn't stop no lead. The shootin' didn't begin.

"Probably Dutchy didn't take no note of what the locoed little dogie *did* say," thinks I to myself.

The Irishman bellied up to the bar again, and pounded on it with his fist.

"Look here!" he yells. "Listen to what I'm tellin' ye! God bless the Irish and let the Dutch rustle! Do ye hear me?"

"Sure, I hear ye," says Dutchy, and goes on swabbin' his bar with a towel.

At that my soul just grew sick. I asked the man next to me why Dutchy didn't kill the little fellow.

"Kill him!" says this man. "What for?"

"For insultin' of him, of course."

"Oh, he's drunk," says the man, as if that explained anythin'.

That settled it with me. I left that place, and went home, and it wasn't more than four o'clock, neither. No, I don't call four o'clock late. It may be a little late for night before last, but it's just the shank of the evenin' for tonight.

Well, it took me six weeks and two days to go broke. I didn't know sic 'em about minin'; and before long I *knew* that I didn't know sic 'em. Most all day I poked around them mountains—not like our'n—too much timber to be comfortable. At night I got to droppin' in at Dutchy's. He had a couple of quiet games goin', and they was one fellow among that lot of grubbin' prairie dogs that had heerd tell that cows had horns. He was the wisest of the bunch on the cattle business. So I stowed away my consolation, and made out to forget comparing Colorado with God's country.

About three times a week this Irishman I told you of—name O'Toole— comes bulgin' in. When he was sober he talked minin' high, wide, and handsome. When he was drunk he pounded both fists on the bar and yelled for action, tryin' to get Dutchy on the peck.

"God bless the Irish and let the Dutch rustle!" he yells about six times. "Say, do you hear?"

"Sure," says Dutchy, calm as a milk cow, "sure, I hear ye!"

I was plumb sorry for O'Toole. I'd like to have given him a run; but, of course, I couldn't take it up without makin' myself out a friend of this Dutchy party, and I couldn't stand for that. But I did tackle Dutchy about it one night when they wasn't nobody else there.

"Dutchy," says I, "what makes you let that bowlegged cross between a bulldog and a flamin' red sunset tromp on you so? It looks to me like you're plumb spiritless."

Dutchy stopped wipin' glasses for a minute.

"Just you hold on," says he. "I ain't ready yet. Bimeby I make him sick; also those others who laugh with him."

He had a little gray flicker in his eye, and I thinks to myself that maybe they'd get Dutchy on the peck yet.

As I said, I went broke in just six weeks and two days. And I was broke a plenty. No holdouts anywhere. It was a heap long ways to cows; and I'd be teetotally chawed up and spit out if I was goin' to join these minin' terrapins defacin' the bosom of nature. It sure looked to me like hard work.

While I was figurin' what next, Dutchy came in. Which I was tur'ble surprised at that, but I said good mornin' and would he rest his poor feet.

"You like to make some money?" he asks.

"That depends," says I, "on how easy it is."

"It is easy," says he. "I want you to buy hosses for me."

"Hosses! Sure!" I yells, jumpin' up. "You bet you! Why, hosses is where I live! What hosses do you want?"

"All hosses," says he, calm as a faro dealer.

"What?" says I. "Elucidate, my bucko. I don't take no such blanket order. Spread your cards."

"I mean just that," says he. "I want you to buy all the hosses in this camp, and in the mountains. Every one."

"Whew!" I whistles. "That's a large order. But I'm your meat."

"Come with me, then," says he. I hadn't but just got up, but I went with him to his little old poison factory. Of course, I hadn't had no break- fast; but he staked me to a Kentucky breakfast. What's a Kentucky break- fast? Why, a Kentucky breakfast is a three-pound steak, a bottle of whiskey, and a setter dog. What's the dog for? Why, to eat the steak, of course.

We come to an agreement. I was to get two-fifty a head commission. So I started out. There wasn't many hosses in that country, and what there was the owners hadn't much use for unless it was to work a whim. I picked up about a hundred head quick enough, and reported to Dutchy.

"How about burros and mules?" I asks Dutchy.

"They goes," says he. "Mules same as hosses; burros four bits a head to you."

At the end of a week I had a remuda of probably two hundred animals. We kept them over the hills in some "parks," as these sots call meadows in that country. I rode into town and told Dutchy.

"Get them all?" he asks.

"All but a cross-eyed buckskin that's mean, and the bay mare that Noah bred to."

"Get them," says he.

"The bandits want too much," I explains.

"Get them anyway," says he.

I went away and got them. It was scand'lous; such prices.

When I hit Cyanide again I ran into scenes of wild excitement. The whole passel of them was on that one street of their'n, talkin' sixteen ounces to the pound. In the middle was Dutchy, drunk as a soldier—just plain foolish drunk.

"Good Lord!" thinks I to myself, "he ain't celebratin' gettin' that bunch of buzzards, is he?"

But I found he wasn't that bad. When he caught sight of me, he fell on me drivelin'.

"Look there!" he weeps, showin' me a letter.

I was the last to come in; so I kept that letter—here she is. I'll read her.

Dear Dutchy: I suppose you thought I'd flew the coop, but I haven't and this is to prove it. Pack up your outfit and hit the trail. I've made the biggest free gold strike you ever see. I'm sending you specimens. There's tons just like it, tons and tons. I got all the claims I can hold myself; but there's heaps more. I've writ to Johnny and Ed at Denver to come on. Don't give this away. Make tracks. Come in to Buck Cañon in the Whetstones and oblige.

Yours truly,
Henry Smith

Somebody showed me a handful of white rock with yeller streaks in it. His eyes was bulgin' until you could have hung your hat on them. That O'Toole party was walkin' around, wettin' his lips with his tongue and swearin' soft.

"God bless the Irish and let the Dutch rustle!" says he. "And the fool had to get drunk and give it away!"

The excitement was just started, but it didn't last long. The crowd got the same notion at the same time, and it just melted. Me and Dutchy was left alone.

I went home. Pretty soon a fellow named Jimmy Tack come around a little out of breath.

"Say, you know that buckskin you bought off'n me?" says he, "I want to buy him back."

"Oh, you do," says I.

"Yes," says he. "I've got to leave town for a couple of days, and I got to have somethin' to pack."

"Wait and I'll see," says I.

Outside the door I met another fellow.

"Look here," he stops me with. "How about that bay mare I sold you? Can you call that sale off? I got to leave town for a day or two and—"

"Wait," says I. "I'll see."

By the gate was another hurryin' up.

"Oh, yes," says I when he opens his mouth. "I know all your troubles. You have to leave town for a couple of days, and you want back that lizard you sold me. Well, wait."

After that I had to quit the main street and dodge back of the hog ranch. They was all headed my way. I was as popular as a snake in a prohibition town.

I hit Dutchy's by the back door.

"Do you want to sell hosses?" I asks. "Everyone in town wants to buy."

Dutchy looked hurt.

"I wanted to keep them for the valley market," says he, "but . . . How much did you give Jimmy Tack for his buckskin?"

"Twenty," says I.

"Well, let him have it for eighty," says Dutchy; "and the others in proportion."

I lay back and breathed hard.

"Sell them all, but the one best hoss," says he—"no, the *two* best."

"Holy smoke!" says I, gettin' my breath. "If you mean that, Dutchy, you lend me another gun and give me a drink."

He done so, and I went back home to where the whole camp of Cyanide was waitin'.

I got up and made them a speech and told them I'd sell them hosses all right, and to come back. Then I got an Injin boy to help, and we rustled over the remuda and held them in a blind cañon. Then I called up these miners one at a time, and made bargains with them. Roar! Well, you could hear them at Denver, they tell me, and the weather reports said, "Thunder in the mountains." But it was cash on delivery, and they all paid up. They had seen that white quartz with the gold stickin' into it, and that's the same as a dose of loco to miner gents.

Why didn't I take a hoss and start first? I did think of it—for about one second. I wouldn't stay in that country then for a million dollars a minute. I was plumb sick and loathin' it, and just waitin' to make high jumps back to Arizona. So I wasn't aimin' to join this stampede, and didn't have no vivid emotions.

They got to fightin' on which should get the first hoss; so I bent my gun on them and made them draw lots. They roared some more, but done so; and as fast as each one handed over his dust or dinero he made a rush for his cabin, piled on his saddle and pack, and pulled his freight in a cloud of dust. It was sure a grand stampede, and I enjoyed it no limit.

So by sundown I was alone with the Injin. Those two hundred head brought in about twenty thousand dollars. It was heavy, but I could carry it. I was about alone in the landscape; and there were the two best hosses I had saved out for Dutchy. I was sure some tempted. But I had enough to get home on anyway; and I never yet drank behind the bar, even if I might hold up the saloon from the floor. So I grieved some inside that I was so tur'ble conscientious, shouldered the sacks, and went down to find Dutchy.

I met him headed his way, and carryin' of a sheet of paper.

"Here's your dinero," says I, dumpin' the four big sacks on the ground.

He stooped over and hefted them. Then he passed one over to me.

"What's that for?" I asks.

"For you," says he.

"My commission ain't that much," I objects.

"You've earned it," says he, "and you might have skipped with the whole wad."

"How did you know I wouldn't?" I asks.

"Well," says he, and I noted that jag of his had flew. "You see, I was behind that rock up there, and I had you covered."

I saw; and I began to feel better about bein' so tur'ble conscientious.

We walked a little ways without sayin' nothin'.

"But ain't you goin' to join the game?" I asks.

"Guess not," says he, jinglin' of his gold. "I'm satisfied."

"But if you don't get a wiggle on you, you are sure goin' to get left on those gold claims," says I

"There ain't no gold claims," says he.

"But Henry Smith—" I cries.

"There ain't no Henry Smith," says he.

I let that soak in about six inches.

"But there's a Buck Cañon," I pleads. "Please say there's a Buck Cañon."

"Oh, yes, there's a Buck Cañon," he allows. "Nice limestone formation —makes good hard water."

"Well, you're a marvel," says I.

We walked on together down to Dutchy's saloon. We stopped outside.

"Now," says he, "I'm goin' to take one of those hosses and go somewheres else. Maybe you'd better do likewise on the other."

"You bet I will," says I.

He turned around and tacked up the paper he was carryin'. It was a sign. It read:

THE DUTCH HAS RUSTLED

"Nice sentiment," says I. "It will be appreciated when the crowd comes back from that little *pasear* into Buck Cañon. But why not tack her up where the trail hits the camp? Why on this particular door?"

"Well," said Dutchy, squintin' at the sign sideways, "you see I sold this place day before yesterday—to Mike O'Toole."

Gertrude the Governess: or Simple Seventeen

By STEPHEN LEACOCK

It was a wild and stormy night on the West Coast of Scotland. This, however, is immaterial to the present story, as the scene is not laid in the West of Scotland. For the matter of that the weather was just as bad on the East Coast of Ireland.

But the scene of this narrative is laid in the South of England and takes place in and around Knotacentinum Towers (pronounced as if written Nosham Taws), the seat of Lord Knotacent (pronounced as if written Nosh).

But it is not necessary to pronounce either of these names in reading them.

Nosham Taws was a typical English home. The main part of the house was an Elizabethan structure of warm red brick, while the elder portion, of which the Earl was inordinately proud, still showed the outlines of a Norman Keep, to which had been added a Lancastrian Jail and a Plantagenet Orphan Asylum. From the house in all directions stretched magnificent woodland and park with oaks and elms of immemorial antiquity, while nearer the house stood raspberry bushes and geranium plants which had been set out by the Crusaders.

About the grand old mansion the air was loud with the chirping of thrushes, the cawing of partridges and the clear sweet note of the rook, while deer, antelope and other quadrupeds strutted about the lawn so tame as to eat off the sundial. In fact, the place was a regular menagerie.

From the house downwards through the park stretched a beautiful broad avenue laid out by Henry VII.

Lord Nosh stood upon the hearthrug of the library. Trained diplomat and statesman as he was, his stern aristocratic face was upside down with fury.

"Boy," he said, "you shall marry this girl or I disinherit you. You are no son of mine."

By permission of Dodd, Mead & Company from *Nonsense Novels* and of McClelland & Stewart Ltd., Toronto, from *Laugh with Leacock*.

Young Lord Ronald, erect before him, flung back a glance as defiant as his own.

"I defy you," he said. "Henceforth you are no father of mine. I will get another. I will marry none but a woman I can love. This girl that we have never seen—"

"Fool," said the Earl, "would you throw aside our estate and name of a thousand years? The girl, I am told, is beautiful; her aunt is willing; they are French; pah! they understand such things in France."

"But your reason—"

"I give no reason," said the Earl. "Listen, Ronald, I give you one month. For that time you remain here. If at the end of it you refuse me, I cut you off with a shilling."

Lord Ronald said nothing; he flung himself from the room, flung himself upon his horse and rode madly off in all directions.

As the door of the library closed upon Ronald the Earl sank into a chair. His face changed. It was no longer that of the haughty nobleman, but of the hunted criminal. "He must marry the girl," he muttered. "Soon she will know all. Tutchemoff has escaped from Siberia. He knows and will tell. The whole of the mines pass to her, this property with it, and I —but enough." He rose, walked to the sideboard, drained a dipper full of gin and bitters, and became again a highbred English gentleman.

It was at this moment that a high dogcart, driven by a groom in the livery of Earl Nosh, might have been seen entering the avenue of Nosham Taws. Beside him sat a young girl, scarce more than a child, in fact not nearly so big as the groom.

The apple-pie hat which she wore, surmounted with black willow plumes, concealed from view a face so facelike in its appearance as to be positively facial.

It was—need we say it—Gertrude the Governess, who was this day to enter upon her duties at Nosham Taws.

At the same time that the dogcart entered the avenue at one end there might have been seen riding down it from the other a tall young man, whose long, aristocratic face proclaimed his birth and who was mounted upon a horse with a face even longer than his own.

And who is this tall young man who draws nearer to Gertrude with every revolution of the horse? Ah, who, indeed? Ah, who, who? I wonder if any of my readers could guess that this was none other than Lord Ronald.

The two were destined to meet. Nearer and nearer they came. And then still nearer. Then for one brief moment they met. As they passed Gertrude raised her head and directed towards the young nobleman two eyes so eyelike in their expression as to be absolutely circular, while Lord Ronald directed towards the occupant of the dogcart a gaze so gazelike that nothing but a gazelle, or a gaspipe, could have emulated its intensity.

Was this the dawn of love? Wait and see. Do not spoil the story.

Let us speak of Gertrude. Gertrude De-Mongmorenci McFiggin had known neither father nor mother. They had both died years before she was born. Of her mother she knew nothing, save that she was French, was extremely beautiful, and that all her ancestors and even her business acquaintances had perished in the Revolution.

Yet Gertrude cherished the memory of her parents. On her breast the girl wore a locket in which was enshrined a miniature of her mother, while down her neck inside at the back hung a daguerreotype of her father. She carried a portrait of her grandmother up her sleeve and had pictures of her cousins tucked inside her boot, while beneath her—but enough, quite enough.

Of her father Gertrude knew even less. That he was a highborn English gentleman who had lived as a wanderer in many lands, this was all she knew. His only legacy to Gertrude had been a Russian grammar, a Roumanian phrase book, a theodolite, and a work on mining engineering.

From her earliest infancy, Gertrude had been brought up by her aunt. Her aunt had carefully instructed her in Christian principles. She had also taught her Mohammedanism to make sure.

When Gertrude was seventeen her aunt had died of hydrophobia.

The circumstances were mysterious. There had called upon her that day a strange-bearded man in the costume of the Russians. After he had left, Gertrude had found her aunt in a syncope from which she passed into an apostrophe and never recovered.

To avoid scandal it was called hydrophobia. Gertrude was thus thrown upon the world. What to do? That was the problem that confronted her.

It was while musing one day upon her fate that Gertrude's eye was struck with an advertisement.

"Wanted a governess; must possess a knowledge of French, Italian, Russian, and Roumanian, Music, and Mining Engineering. Salary £ 1, 4 shillings and 4 pence halfpenny per annum. Apply between half-past eleven and twenty-five minutes to twelve at No. 41 A Decimal Six, Belgravia Terrace. The Countess of Nosh."

Gertrude was a girl of great natural quickness of apprehension, and she had not pondered over this announcement more than half an hour before she was struck with the extraordinary coincidence between the list of items desired and the things that she herself knew.

She duly presented herself at Belgravia Terrace before the Countess, who advanced to meet her with a charm which at once placed the girl at her ease.

"You are proficient in French," she asked.

"*Oh, oui,*" said Gertrude modestly.

"And Italian," continued the Countess.

"*Oh, si,*" said Gertrude.

"And German," said the Countess in delight.

"*Ah, ja,*" said Gertrude.

"And Russian?"

"*Yaw.*"

"And Roumanian?"

"*Jep.*"

Amazed at the girl's extraordinary proficiency in modern languages, the Countess looked at her narrowly. Where had she seen those lineaments before? She passed her hand over her brow in thought, and spit upon the floor, but no, the face baffled her.

"Enough," she said, "I engage you on the spot; tomorrow you go down to Nosham Taws and begin teaching the children. I must add that in addition you will be expected to aid the Earl with his Russian correspondence. He has large mining interests at Tschminsk."

Tschminsk! why did the simple word reverberate upon Gertrude's ears? Why? Because it was the name written in her father's hand on the title-page of his book on mining. What mystery was here?

It was on the following day that Gertrude had driven up the avenue.

She descended from the dogcart, passed through a phalanx of liveried servants drawn up seven-deep, to each of whom she gave a sovereign as she passed and entered Nosham Taws.

"Welcome," said the Countess, as she aided Gertrude to carry her trunk upstairs.

The girl presently descended and was ushered into the library, where she was presented to the Earl. As soon as the Earl's eye fell upon the face of the new governess he started visibly. Where had he seen those lineaments? Where was it? At the races, or the theater—on a bus—no. Some subtler thread of memory was stirring in his mind. He strode hastily to the sideboard, drained a dipper and a half of brandy, and became again the perfect English gentleman.

While Gertrude has gone to the nursery to make the acquaintance of the two tiny golden-haired children who are to be her charges, let us say something here of the Earl and his son.

Lord Nosh was the perfect type of the English nobleman and statesman. The years that he had spent in the diplomatic service at Constantinople, St. Petersburg, and Salt Lake City had given to him a peculiar finesse and noblesse, while his long residence at St. Helena, Pitcairn Island, and Hamilton, Ontario, had rendered him impervious to external impressions. As deputy paymaster of the militia of the county he had seen something of the sterner side of military life, while his hereditary office of Groom of the Sunday Breeches had brought him into direct contact with Royalty itself.

His passion for outdoor sports endeared him to his tenants. A keen sportsman, he excelled in fox hunting, dog hunting, pig killing, bat catching and the pastimes of his class.

In this latter respect Lord Ronald took after his father. From the start the lad had shown the greatest promise. At Eton he had made a splendid showing at battledore and shuttlecock, and at Cambridge had been first in his class at needlework. Already his name was whispered in connection with the All England ping-pong championship, a triumph which would undoubtedly carry with it a seat in Parliament.

Thus was Gertrude the Governess installed at Nosham Taws.

The days and the weeks sped past.

The simple charm of the beautiful orphan girl attracted all hearts. Her two little pupils became her slaves. "Me loves oo," little Rasehellfrida would say, leaning her golden head in Gertrude's lap. Even the servants loved her. The head gardener would bring a bouquet of beautiful roses to her room before she was up, the second gardener a bunch of early cauliflowers, the third a spray of late asparagus, and even the tenth and eleventh a sprig of mangel-wurzel or an armful of hay. Her room was full of gardeners all the time, while at evening the aged butler, touched at the friendless girl's loneliness, would tap softly at her door to bring her a rye whiskey and seltzer or a box of Pittsburgh Stogies. Even the dumb creatures seemed to admire her in their own dumb way. The dumb rooks settled on her shoulder and every dumb dog around the place followed her.

And Ronald! ah, Ronald! Yes, indeed! They had met. They had spoken.

"What a dull morning," Gertrude had said. *"Quel triste matin! Was für ein allerverdammter Tag!"*

"Beastly," Ronald had answered.

"Beastly!!" The word rang in Gertrude's ears all day.

After that they were constantly together. They played tennis and ping-pong in the day, and in the evening, in accordance with the stiff routine of the place, they sat down with the Earl and Countess to twenty-five-cent poker, and later still they sat together on the veranda and watched the moon sweeping in great circles around the horizon.

It was not long before Gertrude realized that Lord Ronald felt towards her a warmer feeling than that of mere ping-pong. At times in her presence he would fall, especially after dinner, into a fit of profound subtraction.

Once at night, when Gertrude withdrew to her chamber and before seeking her pillow, prepared to retire as a preliminary to disrobing—in other words, before going to bed, she flung wide the casement (opened the window) and perceived (saw) the face of Lord Ronald. He was sitting on a thorn bush beneath her, and his upturned face wore an expression of agonized pallor.

Meantime the days passed. Life at the Taws moved in the ordinary routine of a great English household. At 7 a gong sounded for rising, at 8 a horn blew for breakfast, at 8:30 a whistle sounded for prayers, at 1 a flag was run up at half-mast for lunch, at 4 a gun was fired for afternoon tea, at 9 a first bell sounded for dressing, at 9:11 a second bell for going on dressing, while at 9:30 a rocket was sent up to indicate that dinner was ready. At midnight dinner was over, and at 1 A.M. the tolling of a bell summoned the domestics to evening prayers.

Meanwhile the month allotted by the Earl to Lord Ronald was passing away. It was already July 15, then within a day or two it was July 17, and, almost immediately afterwards, July 18.

At times the Earl, in passing Ronald in the hall, would say sternly, "Remember, boy, your consent, or I disinherit you."

And what were the Earl's thoughts of Gertrude? Here was the one drop of bitterness in the girl's cup of happiness. For some reason that she could not divine the Earl showed signs of marked antipathy.

Once as she passed the door of the library he threw a bootjack at her. On another occasion at lunch alone with her he struck her savagely across the face with a sausage.

It was her duty to translate to the Earl his Russian correspondence. She sought in it in vain for the mystery. One day a Russian telegram was handed to the Earl. Gertrude translated it to him aloud.

"Tutchemoff went to the woman. She is dead."

On hearing this the Earl became livid with fury, in fact this was the day that he struck her with the sausage.

Then one day while the Earl was absent on a bat hunt, Gertrude, who was turning over his correspondence, with that sweet feminine instinct of interest that rose superior to ill-treatment, suddenly found the key to the mystery.

Lord Nosh was not the rightful owner of the Taws. His distant cousin of the older line, the true heir, had died in a Russian prison to which the machinations of the Earl, while Ambassador at Tschminsk, had consigned him. The daughter of this cousin was the true owner of Nosham Taws.

The family story, save only that the documents before her withheld the name of the rightful heir, lay bare to Gertrude's eye.

Strange is the heart of woman. Did Gertrude turn from the Earl with spurning? No. Her own sad fate had taught her sympathy.

Yet still the mystery remained! Why did the Earl start perceptibly each time that he looked into her face? Sometimes he started as much as four centimeters, so that one could distinctly see him do it. On such occasions he would hastily drain a dipper of rum and vichy water and become again the correct English gentleman.

The denouement came swiftly. Gertrude never forgot it.

It was the night of the great ball at Nosham Taws. The whole neighborhood was invited. How Gertrude's heart had beat with anticipation, and with what trepidation she had overhauled her scant wardrobe in order to appear not unworthy in Lord Ronald's eyes. Her resources were poor indeed, yet the inborn genius for dress that she inherited from her French mother stood her in good stead. She twined a single rose in her hair and contrived herself a dress out of a few old newspapers and the inside of an umbrella that would have graced a court. Round her waist she bound a single braid of bagstring, while a piece of old lace that had been her mother's was suspended to her ear by a thread.

Gertrude was the cynosure of all eyes. Floating to the strains of the music she presented a picture of bright girlish innocence that no one could see undisenraptured.

The ball was at its height. It was away up!

Ronald stood with Gertrude in the shrubbery. They looked into one another's eyes.

"Gertrude," he said, "I love you."

Simple words, and yet they thrilled every fiber in the girl's costume.

"Ronald!" she said, and cast herself about his neck.

At this moment the Earl appeared standing beside them in the moonlight. His stern face was distorted with indignation.

"So!" he said, turning to Ronald, "it appears that you have chosen!"

"I have," said Ronald with hauteur.

"You prefer to marry this penniless girl rather than the heiress I have selected for you."

Gertrude looked from father to son in amazement.

"Yes," said Ronald.

"Be it so," said the Earl, draining a dipper of gin which he carried, and resuming his calm. "Then I disinherit you. Leave this place, and never return to it."

"Come, Gertrude," said Ronald tenderly, "let us flee together."

Gertrude stood before them. The rose had fallen from her head. The lace had fallen from her ear and the bagstring had come undone from her waist. Her newspapers were crumpled beyond recognition. But disheveled and illegible as she was, she was still mistress of herself.

"Never," she said firmly. "Ronald, you shall never make this sacrifice for me." Then to the Earl, in tones of ice, "There is a pride, sir, as great even as yours. The daughter of Metschnikoff McFiggin need crave a boon from no one."

With that she hauled from her bosom the daguerreotype of her father and pressed it to her lips.

The Earl started as if shot. "That name!" he cried, "that face! that photograph! stop!"

There! There is no need to finish; my readers have long since divined it. Gertrude was the heiress.

The lovers fell into one another's arms. The Earl's proud face relaxed. "God bless you," he said. The Countess and the guests came pouring out upon the lawn. The breaking day illuminated a scene of gay congratulations.

Gertrude and Ronald were wed. Their happiness was complete. Need we say more? Yes, only this. The Earl was killed in the hunting field a few days later. The Countess was struck by lightning. The two children fell down a well. Thus the happiness of Gertrude and Ronald was complete.

The Venturers

By O. HENRY

"DID YOU ever hear that story about the man from the West?" asked Billinger, in the little dark-oak room to your left as you penetrate the interior of the Powhatan Club.

"Doubtless," said John Reginald Forster, rising and leaving the room.

Forster got his straw hat (straws will be in and maybe out again long before this is printed) from the check-room boy, and walked out of the air (as Hamlet says). Billinger was used to having his stories insulted and would not mind. Forster was in his favorite mood and wanted to go away from anywhere. A man, in order to get on good terms with himself, must have his opinions corroborated and his moods matched by someone else. (I had written that "somebody"; but an A.D.T. boy who once took a telegram from me pointed out that I could save money by using the compound word. This is a vice versa case.)

Forster's favorite mood was that of greatly desiring to be a follower of Chance. He was a Venturer by nature, but convention, birth, tradition, and the narrowing influences of the tribe of Manhattan had denied him full privilege. He had trodden all the main-traveled thoroughfares and many of the side roads that are supposed to relieve the tedium of life. But none had sufficed. The reason was that he knew what was to be found at the end of every street. He knew from experience and logic almost precisely to what end each digression from routine must lead. He found a depressing monotony in all the variations that the music of his sphere had grafted upon the tune of life. He had not learned that, although the world was made round, the circle has been squared, and that its true interest is to be found in "What's Around the Corner."

Forster walked abroad aimlessly from the Powhatan, trying not to tax either his judgment or his desire as to what streets he traveled. He would have been glad to lose his way if it were possible; but he had no hope of that. Adventure and Fortune move at your beck and call in the Greater City; but Chance is oriental. She is a veiled lady in a sedan chair, pro-

From *Strictly Business* by O. Henry. Copyright 1910, 1938 by Doubleday & Company, Inc.

tected by a special traffic squad of dragomans. Crosstown, uptown, and downtown you may move without seeing her.

At the end of an hour's stroll, Forster stood on a corner of a broad, smooth avenue, looking disconsolately across it at a picturesque old hotel softly but brilliantly lit. Disconsolately, because he knew that he must dine; and dining in that hotel was no venture. It was one of his favorite caravansaries, and so silent and swift would be the service and so delicately choice the food, that he regretted the hunger that must be appeased by the "dead perfection" of the place's cuisine. Even the music there seemed to be always playing *da capo*.

Fancy came to him that he would dine at some cheap, even dubious, restaurant lower down in the city, where the erratic chefs from all countries of the world spread their national cookery for the omnivorous American. Something might happen there out of the routine—he might come upon a subject without a predicate, a road without an end, a question without an answer, a cause without an effect, a gulf stream in life's salt ocean. He had not dressed for evening; he wore a dark business suit that would not be questioned even where the waiters served the spaghetti in their shirt sleeves.

So John Reginald Forster began to search his clothes for money; because the more cheaply you dine, the more surely must you pay. All of the thirteen pockets, large and small, of his business suit he explored carefully and found not a penny. His bankbook showed a balance of five figures to his credit in the Old Ironsides Trust Company, but—

Forster became aware of a man near by at his left hand who was really regarding him with some amusement. He looked like any businessman of thirty or so, neatly dressed and standing in the attitude of one waiting for a streetcar. But there was no car line on that avenue. So his proximity and unconcealed curiosity seemed to Forster to partake of the nature of a personal intrusion. But, as he was a consistent seeker after "What's Around the Corner," instead of manifesting resentment he only turned a half-embarrassed smile upon the other's grin of amusement.

"All in?" asked the intruder, drawing nearer.

"Seems so," said Forster. "Now, I thought there was a dollar in—"

"Oh, I know," said the other man, with a laugh. "But there wasn't. I've just been through the same process myself, as I was around the corner. I found in an upper vest pocket—I don't know how they got there—exactly two pennies. You know what kind of a dinner exactly two pennies will buy!"

"You haven't dined, then?" asked Forster.

"I have not. But I would like to. Now, I'll make you a proposition. You look like a man who would take up one. Your clothes look neat and respectable. Excuse personalities. I think mine will pass the scrutiny of a headwaiter, also. Suppose we go over to that hotel and dine together. We

will choose from the menu like millionaires—or, if you prefer, like gentlemen in moderate circumstances dining extravagantly for once. When we
have finished we will match with my two pennies to see which of us will
stand the brunt of the house's displeasure and vengeance. My name is Ives.
I think we have lived in the same station of life—before our money took
wings."

"You're on," said Forster, joyfully.

Here was a venture at least within the borders of the mysterious country of Chance—anyhow, it promised something better than the stale in-
festivity of a table d'hôte.

The two were soon seated at a corner table in the hotel dining room.
Ives chucked one of his pennies across the table to Forster.

"Match for which of us gives the order," he said.

Forster lost.

Ives laughed and began to name liquids and viands to the waiter with
the absorbed but calm deliberation of one who was to the menu born.
Forster, listening, gave his admiring approval of the order.

"I am a man," said Ives, during the oysters, "who has made a lifetime
search after the to-be-continued-in-our-next. I am not like the ordinary
adventurer who strikes for a coveted prize. Nor yet am I like a gambler
who knows he is either to win or lose a certain set stake. What I want is
to encounter an adventure to which I can predict no conclusions. It is the
breath of existence to me to dare Fate in its blindest manifestations. The
world has come to run so much by rote and gravitation that you can enter
upon hardly any footpath of chance in which you do not find signboards
informing you of what you may expect at its end. I am like the clerk in
the Circumlocution Office who always complained bitterly when anyone
came in to ask information. 'He wanted to *know!*' was the kick he made
to his fellow-clerks. Well, I don't want to know, I don't want to reason,
I don't want to guess—I want to bet my hand without seeing it."

"I understand," said Forster, delightedly. "I've often wanted the way
I feel put into words. You've done it. I want to take chances on what's
coming. Suppose we have a bottle of Moselle with the next course."

"Agreed," said Ives. "I'm glad you catch my idea. It will increase the
animosity of the house toward the loser. If it does not weary you, we will
pursue the theme. Only a few times have I met a true venturer—one who
does not ask a schedule and map from Fate when he begins a journey.
But, as the world becomes more civilized and wiser, the more difficult it
is to come upon an adventure the end of which you cannot foresee. In
the Elizabethan days you could assault the watch, wring knockers from
doors, and have a jolly set-to with the blades in any convenient angle of
a wall and 'get away with it.' Nowadays, if you speak disrespectfully to a
policeman, all that is left to the most romantic fancy is to conjecture in
what peculiar police station he will land you."

"I know—I know," said Forster, nodding approval.

"I returned to New York today," continued Ives, "from a three years' ramble around the globe. Things are not much better abroad than they are at home. The whole world seems to be overrun by conclusions. The only thing that interests me greatly is a premise. I've tried shooting big game in Africa. I know what an express rifle will do at so many yards; and when an elephant or a rhinoceros falls to the bullet, I enjoy it about as much as I did when I was kept in after school to do a sum in long division on the blackboard."

"I know—I know," said Forster.

"There might be something in airplanes," went on Ives, reflectively. "I've tried ballooning; but it seems to be merely a cut-and-dried affair of wind and ballast."

"Women," suggested Forster, with a smile.

"Three months ago," said Ives, "I was pottering around in one of the bazaars in Constantinople. I noticed a lady, veiled, of course, but with a pair of especially fine eyes visible, who was examining some amber and pearl ornaments at one of the booths. With her was an attendant—a big Nubian, as black as coal. After a while the attendant drew nearer to me by degrees and slipped a scrap of paper into my hand. I looked at it when I got a chance. On it was scrawled hastily in pencil: 'The arched gate of the Nightingale Garden at nine tonight.' Does that appear to you to be an interesting premise, Mr. Forster?"

"Go on," said Forster eagerly.

"I made inquiries and learned that the Nightingale Garden was the property of an old Turk—a grand vizier, or something of the sort. Of course I prospected for the arched gate and was there at nine. The same Nubian attendant opened the gate promptly on time, and I went inside and sat on a bench by a perfumed fountain with the veiled lady. We had quite an extended chat. She was Myrtle Thompson, a lady journalist, who was writing up the Turkish harems for a Chicago newspaper. She said she noticed the New York cut of my clothes in the bazaar and wondered if I couldn't work something into the metropolitan papers about it."

"I see," said Forster. "I see."

"I've canoed through Canada," said Ives, "down many rapids and over many falls. But I didn't seem to get what I wanted out of it because I knew there were only two possible outcomes—I would either go to the bottom or arrive at the sea level. I've played all games at cards; but the mathematicians have spoiled that sport by computing the percentages. I've made acquaintances on trains, I've answered advertisements, I've rung strange doorbells, I've taken every chance that presented itself; but there has always been the conventional ending—the logical conclusion to the premise."

"I know," repeated Forster. "I've felt it all. But I've had few chances to take my chance at chances. Is there any life so devoid of impossibilities as life in this city? There seems to be a myriad of opportunities for testing the undeterminable; but not one in a thousand fails to land you where you expected it to stop. I wish the subways and streetcars disappointed one as seldom."

"The sun has risen," said Ives, "on the Arabian nights. There are no more caliphs. The fisherman's vase is turned to a vacuum bottle, warranted to keep any genie boiling or frozen for forty-eight hours. Life moves by rote. Science has killed adventure. There are no more opportunities such as Columbus and the man who ate the first oyster had. The only certain thing is that there is nothing uncertain."

"Well," said Forster, "my experience has been the limited one of a city man. I haven't seen the world as you have; but it seems that we view it with the same opinion. But I tell you I am grateful for even this little venture of ours into the borders of the haphazard. There may be at least one breathless moment when the bill for the dinner is presented. Perhaps, after all, the pilgrims who traveled without scrip or purse found a keener taste to life than did the knights of the Round Table who rode abroad with a retinue and King Arthur's certified checks in the lining of their helmets. And now, if you've finished your coffee, suppose we match one of your insufficient coins for the impending blow of Fate. What have I up?"

"Heads," called Ives.

"Heads it is," said Forster, lifting his hand. "I lose. We forgot to agree upon a plan for the winner to escape. I suggest that when the waiter comes you make a remark about telephoning to a friend. I will hold the fort and the dinner check long enough for you to get your hat and be off. I thank you for an evening out of the ordinary, Mr. Ives, and wish we might have others."

"If my memory is not at fault," said Ives, laughing, "the nearest police station is in MacDougal Street. I have enjoyed the dinner, too, let me assure you."

Forster crooked his finger for the waiter. Victor, with a locomotive effort that seemed to owe more to pneumatics than to pedestrianism, glided to the table and laid the card, face downward, by the loser's cup. Forster took it up and added the figures with deliberate care. Ives leaned back comfortably in his chair.

"Excuse me," said Forster, "but I thought you were going to ring up Grimes about that theater party for Thursday night. Had you forgotten about it?"

"Oh," said Ives, settling himself more comfortably, "I can do that later on. Get me a glass of water, waiter."

"Want to be in at the death, do you?" asked Forster.

"I hope you don't object," said Ives, pleadingly. "Never in my life have

I seen a gentleman arrested in a public restaurant for swindling it out of a dinner."

"All right," said Forster calmly. "You are entitled to see a Christian die in the arena as your *pousse-café.*"

Victor came with the glass of water and remained, with the disengaged air of an inexorable collector.

Forster hesitated for fifteen seconds, and then took a pencil from his pocket and scribbled his name on the dinner check. The waiter bowed and took it away.

"The fact is," said Forster, with a little embarrassed laugh, "I doubt whether I'm what they call a 'game sport,' which means the same as a 'soldier of Fortune.' I'll have to make confession. I've been dining at this hotel two or three times a week for more than a year. I always sign my checks." And then, with a note of appreciation in his voice: "It was first-rate of you to stay to see me through with it when you knew I had no money, and that you might be scooped in, too."

"I guess I'll confess, too," said Ives with a grin. "I own the hotel."

The Pipe

By S. J. PERELMAN

AT APPROXIMATELY four o'clock yesterday afternoon the present troubadour, a one-story taxpayer in a wrinkled twenty-two-ounce basket weave and a repossessed Panama, was gaping into the window of Alfred Buntwell, Inc., the celebrated tobacconist in Radio City. Above his balding, gargoyle head floated a feathery cloud containing a Mazda bulb labeled "Idea!" Buntwell is a name revered by pipe smokers everywhere; his briars have probably penetrated farther into the earth's far places than the Union Jack. From the steaming jungles of the Gran Chaco to the snows of Kanchanjanga, from the Hook of Holland to the Great Barrier Reef, the white dot on the Buntwell pipestem is the sign of the sahib.

Deep in equatorial Africa, surrounded by head-hunters, Mungo Park clenched a Buntwell pipe between his teeth to maintain his fortitude; it was a battered Buntwell mouthpiece that yielded up the fate of the Franklin polar expedition.

Peering into the shop, jostled by crisp, well-fed executives hurrying toward million-dollar deals, it suddenly struck me that a Buntwell pipe was the key to my future. Here at last was a magic talisman that would transform me from a wormy, chopfallen cipher into a forceful, grim-lipped tycoon. A wave of exultation swept over me; I saw myself in the club car of the Twentieth Century Limited puffing a silver-mounted Buntwell and merging directorates with a careless nod. I, too, could become one of those enviable types who lounged against knotty-pine interiors in four-color advertisements, smoking their Buntwells and fiercely demanding Old Peg-leg Whisky.

"Give me Old Peg-leg's satin smoothness every time," I would growl. "I like a blended rye."

I squared my tiny shoulders and, baring my teeth in the half snarl befitting a major industrialist, entered the shrine. To my chagrin, no obsequious lackey sprang forward to measure my features for the correct model. A cathedral hush enveloped the shop, which had the restrained elegance of a Park Avenue jeweler's. At a chaste showcase displaying a box of panatelas marked down to a thousand dollars, a glacial salesman was attending a fierce old party with white cavalry mustaches redolent of Napoleon brandy. In the background another was languidly demonstrating a cigarette lighter to a dowager weighed down under several pounds of diamonds. I coughed apologetically and gave the salesman a winning smile to indicate that I knew my place. The old grenadier scowled at me from under beetling brows. "Confound it, sir," he roared, "you're not at a cockfight! Blasted place is gettin' noisier than the durbar!" I cleared my throat, in which a fishbone had mysteriously lodged, and made myself as inconspicuous as possible. The salesman hastily explained that the war had brought an influx of foreigners, but his client refused to be mollified.

"Should have caned the bounder," he sputtered. "Country's goin' to the demnition bowwows, dash it all! Now then, Harkrider, what's this infernal nonsense about my Burma cheroots?" He waved aside the salesman's excuse that a convoy had been sunk, commanded that Buntwell himself be summoned.

"But Mr. Buntwell has been dead sixty years, Major," Harkrider protested.

"None of your poppycock!" barked the major. "You tell Buntwell to bring 'em around personally by noon tomorrow or I close my account!" He stamped out, his wattles scarlet with rage, and I sidled forward timidly. In a few badly chosen words I indicated that I required a pipe.

"H'm-m-m," murmured Harkrider grudgingly, surveying my clothes. "Just a moment." He disappeared through a curtain and engaged in a whispered consultation with the manager. I dimly overheard a phrase that sounded like "buttersnipe"; the two were obviously discussing their lunch. At length the salesman re-entered and conducted me sullenly to a showcase. After some deliberation he extracted what appeared to be an old sycamore root fitted with a steel flange that covered the bowl.

"Know anything about pipes?" he inquired patronizingly.

"Well, not exactly," I hesitated. "I had a corncob when I was a little boy—"

"I'm not interested in reminiscences of your youth," he snapped. "Hold still." With a quick gesture he jammed the root into my mouth and backed off, studying my face critically.

"Wh-what is it for?" I stammered.

"Big-game hunting," he returned loftily. I was screwing up my courage to inquire out of which end the bullet came when he suddenly plucked it from my teeth. "No, I don't care for you in that. Let's see now—what's your club?"

"Why—er—uh—the Williams After-Shave Club," I replied politely. "You know, for men whose skins welcome that zestful, bracing tang—"

"No, no," he broke in irritably. "Where do you keep your yacht?" His face darkened and he took a threatening step forward. "You have a yacht, haven't you?"

"Oh—why—er—bub—certainly," I lied skillfully. "He's—I mean, she's laid up right now, the man's scraping her chimney. It got full of sea-weeds."

Harkrider glared at me suspiciously, clearly unconvinced.

"Yo heave ho, blow the man down," I hummed nonchalantly, executing a few steps of the sailor's hornpipe. "Thar she blows and sparm at that! A double ration of plum duff for all hands, matey!" The stratagem was successful; with a baffled grunt, Harkrider produced a green velvet jewel case and exhibited a small, charred stub encrusted with salt.

"That's been used before, hasn't it?" I faltered.

"Of course it's been used," he grated. "You don't think you're going to get a new pipe for sixty-seven dollars, do you?"

"Oh no, naturally," I agreed. "Tell you the truth, I had in mind something a bit smaller."

"Smaller?" snorted Harkrider. "You ought to have a calabash to go with that jaw of yours!"

"That's what I was telling the wife only this morning," I chuckled. "Gee, did you ever see anything like it? It's worse than an English bulldog's."

"Well, do you want a calabash or not?" he interrupted. "They're twenty dollars—though I guess you don't see that much money in a year, do you?"

Blushing like a lovely long-stemmed American Beauty rose, I explained that I merely wanted something to knock around in, a homely old jimmy pipe I could suck on while dispensing salty aphorisms like Velvet Joe. After a heart-rending plea, he finally consented to part with a factory second for thirteen dollars, equipped with an ingenious aluminum coil which conveyed the nicotine juice directly into the throat before it lost its potency. To prove my gratitude, I immediately bought a tobacco jar in the shape of a human skull, two pounds of Buntwell's Special Blend of chopped rubies and attar of roses, and a cunning all-purpose reamer equally useful for removing carbon from a pipe or barnacles from a boat. Peeling eighty-three rugs from my skinny little roll, I caught up my purchases and coursed homeward, whistling gems from *The Bartered Bride*.

Right after dinner I disposed myself in my favorite easy chair, lit a cheery blaze in the pipe, and picked up the evening paper.

When I regained consciousness there was a smell in the apartment like a Hindu suttee, and a stranger in a Vandyke was taking my pulse and what remained of my roll. If I go on improving at this rate he's promised I can get up tomorrow. That means I can go out Wednesday and go to jail on Thursday, because in the meantime I've got a date to heave a brick through a plate-glass window in Radio City.

The Young Immigrunts

By "RING W. LARDNER, JR."

WITH A PREFACE BY THE FATHER

"The Young Visiters" by "Daisy Ashford," with preface by Sir James Barrie, was the talk of literary circles (was it a hoax or was it genuine?) when this parody appeared. The influence of the style and spelling of "Miss Ashford" on "Mr. Lardner, Jr.," will be marked by readers with good memories.

Preface

THE person whose name is signed to this novel was born on the nineteenth day of August, 1915, and was therefore four years and three months old when the manuscript was found, late in November, 1919. The narrative is substantially true, with the following exceptions:

1. "My Father," the leading character in the work, is depicted as a man of short temper, whereas the person from whom the character was drawn is in reality as pleasant a fellow as one would care to meet and seldom has a cross word for any one, let alone women and children.

2. The witty speeches accredited to "My Father" have, possibly owing to the limitations of a child's memory, been so garbled and twisted that they do not look half so good in print as they sounded in the open air.

3. More stops for gas were made than are mentioned in the story.

As the original manuscript was written on a typewriter with a rather frayed ribbon, and as certain words were marked out and others handwritten in, I have taken the liberty of copying the entire work with a fresh ribbon and the inclusion of the changes which the author indicated in pencil in the first draft. Otherwise the story is presented to the reader exactly as it was first set down.

THE FATHER

CHAPTER I

MY PARENTS

My parents are both married and ½ of them are very good looking. The balance is tall and skiny and has a swarty complexion with moles but you hardly ever notice them on account of your gaze being rapped up in his feet which would be funny if brevvity wasnt the soul of wit. Everybody says I have his eyes and I am glad it didnt half to be something else tho Rollie Zeider the ball player calls him owl eyes for a nick name but if I was Rollie Zeider and his nose I wouldnt pick on somebodys else features.

He wears pretty shirts which he bought off of another old ball player Artie Hofman to attrack tension off his feet and must of payed a big price for them I heard my ant tell my uncle when they thorght I was a sleep down to the lake tho I guess he pays even more for his shoes if they sell them by the frunt foot.

I was born in a hospital in Chicago 4 years ago and liked it very much and had no idear we were going to move till 1 day last summer I heard my mother arsk our nurse did she think she could get along O.K. with myself and 3 brothers John Jimmie and David for 10 days wilst she and my old man went east to look for a costly home.

Well yes said our nurse barshfully.

I may as well exclaim to the reader that John is 7 and Jimmie is 5 and I am 4 and David is almost nothing as yet you might say and tho I was named for my father they call me Bill thank God.

The conversation amungst my mother and our nurse took place right after my father came back from Toledo where Jack Dempsey knocked Jessie Willard for a gool tho my father liked the big fellow and bet on him.

David was in his bath at the time and my mother and our nurse and myself and 2 elder brothers was standing around admireing him tho I notice that when the rest of the family takes their bath they dont make open house of the occassion.

Well my parents went east and dureing their absents myself and brothers razed hell with David on the night shift but when they come back my mother said to the nurse were they good boys.

Fine replid our nurse lamely and where are you going to live.

Connecticut said my mother.

Our nurse forced a tired smile.

Here we will leave my parents to unpack and end this chapter.

CHAPTER II

STARTING GAILY

We spent the rest of the summer on my granmother in Indiana and my father finley went to the worst series to write it up as he has followed sports of all sorts for years and is a expert so he bet on the wite sox and when he come home he acted rarther cross.

Well said my mother simperingly I suppose we can start east now.

We will start east when we get good and ready said my father with a lordly sneeze.

The next thing was how was we going to make the trip as my father had boughten a new car that the cheepest way to get it there was drive it besides carrying a grate deal of our costly bagage but if all of us went in it they would be no room left for our costly bagage and besides 2 of my brothers always acts like devils incarnite when they get in a car so my mother said to our nurse.

If you think you can manage the 2 older boys and David on the train myself and husband will take Bill in the car said my mother to our nurse.

Fine replid our nurse with a gastly look witch my mother did not see.

Myself and parents left Goshen Indiana on a fine Monday morning leaveing our nurse and brothers to come latter in the weak on the railway. Our plans was to reach Detroit that night and stop with my uncle and ant and the next evening take the boat to Buffalo and thence to Connecticut by motor so the first town we past through was Middlebury.

Elmer Flick the old ball player use to live here said my father modestly.

My mother forced a smile and soon we were acrost the Michigan line and my mother made the remark that she was thirsty.

We will stop at Coldwater for lunch said my father with a str   e as he pulls most of his lines without changeing expressions.

Sure enough we puled up to 1 side of the road just after leav   old-water and had our costly viands of frid chicken and doughnuts   nilk fernished by my grate ant and of witch I partook freely.

We will stop at Ypsilanti for supper said my father in calm to   t is where they have the state normal school.

I was glad to hear this and hopes we would get there before   s I had always wanted to come in contack with normal peaple an   nat they are like and just at dusk we entered a large size town and   ast a large size football field.

Heavens said my mother this must be a abnormal school to   ch a large football field.

My father wore a qeer look.

This is not Ypsilanti this is Ann Arbor he crid.

But I thorght you said we would go south of Ann Arbor and direct to Ypsilanti said my mother with a smirk.

I did say that but I thorght I would surprise you by comeing into Ann Arbor replid my father with a corse jesture.

Personly I think the surprise was unanimous.

Well now we are here said my mother we might as well look up Bill.

Bill is my uncle Bill so we stoped at the Alfa Delt house and got him and took him down to the hotel for supper and my old man called up Mr. Yost the football coach of the Michigan football team and he come down and visited with us.

What kind of a team have you got coach said my father lamely.

I have got a determined team replid Mr. Yost they are determined to not play football.

At this junction my unlucky mother changed the subjeck to the league of nations and it was 10 o'clock before Mr. Yost come to a semi colon so we could resume our journey and by the time we past through Ypsilanti the peaple was not only subnormal but unconsius. It was nerly midnight when we puled up in frunt of my ants and uncles house in Detroit that had been seting up since 7 expecting us.

Were sorry to be so late said my mother bruskly.

Were awfully glad you could come at all replid my ant with a ill consealed yawn.

We will now leave my relitives to get some sleep and end this chapter.

CHAPTER III

ERIE LAKE

The boat leaves Detroit every afternoon at 5 o'clock and reaches Buffalo the next morning at 9 tho I would better exclaim to my readers that when it is 9 o'clock in Buffalo it is only 8 o'clock in Goshen for instants as Buffalo peaple are qeer.

Well said my father the next morning at brekfus I wander what time we half to get the car on the board of the boat.

I will find out down town and call up and let you know replid my uncle who is an engineer and digs soors or something.

Sure enough he called up dureing the fornoon and said the car must be on the board of the boat at 3 o'clock so my father left the house at 2 oclock and drove down to the worf tho he had never drove a car in Detroit before but has nerves of steal. Latter my uncle come out to his home and took myself and mother and ant down to the worf where my old man was waiting for us haveing put the car on the board.

What have you been doing ever since 3 o'clock arsked my mother as it was now nerly 5.

Haveing a high ball my father replid.

I thorght Detroit was dry said my mother shyly.

Did you said my father with a rye smile and as it was now nerly time for the boat to leave we said good by to my uncle and ant and went on the boat. A messenger took our costly bagage and put it away wilst myself and parents went out on the porch and set looking at the peaple on the worf. Suddenly they was a grate hub bub on the worf and a young man and lady started up the gangs plank wilst a big crowd throwed rice and old shoes at them and made a up roar.

Bride and glum going to Niagara Falls said my father who is well traveled and seams to know everything.

Instantly the boat give a blarst on the wistle and I started with surprise.

Did that scare you Bill said my father and seamed to enjoy it and I suppose he would of laughed out right had I fell oberboard and been drowned in the narsty river water.

Soon we were steeming up the river on the city of Detroit 3.

That is Canada over there is it not said my mother.

What did you think it was the Austrian Tyrol replid my father explodeing a cough. Dureing our progress up the river I noticed sevral funny things flotting in the water with lanterns hanging on them and was wandering what they could be when my mother said they seam to have plenty of boys.

They have got nothing on us replid my father quick as a flarsh.

A little latter who should come out on the porch and set themselfs ner us but the bride and glum.

Oh I said to myself I hope they will talk so as I can hear them as I have always wandered what newlyweds talk about on their way to Niagara Falls and soon my wishs was realized.

Some night said the young glum are you warm enough.

I am perfectly comfertible replid the fare bride tho her looks belid her words what time do we arive in Buffalo.

9 o'clock said the lordly glum are you warm enough.

I am perfectly comfertible replid the fare bride what time do we arive in Buffalo.

9 o'clock said the lordly glum I am afrade it is too cold for you out here.

Well maybe it is replid the fare bride and without farther adieu they went in the spacius parlers.

I wander will he be arsking her 8 years from now is she warm enough said my mother with a faint grimace.

The weather may change before then replid my father.

Are you warm enough said my father after a slite pause.

No was my mothers catchy reply.

Well said my father we arive in Buffalo at 9 o'clock and with that we all went inside as it was now pitch dark and had our supper and retired and when we rose the next morning and drest and had brekfus we puled up to the worf in Buffalo and it was 9 o'clock so I will leave the city of Detroit 3 tide to the worf and end this chapter.

CHAPTER IV

BUFFALO TO ROCHESTER 76.4

As we was leaveing the boat who should I see right along side of us but the fare bride and the lordly glum.

We are right on the dot said the glum looking at his costly watch it is just 9 o'clock and so they past out of my life.

We had to wait qite a wile wilst the old man dug up his bill of loading and got the costly moter.

We will half to get some gas he said I wonder where they is a garage.

No sooner had the words fell from his lips when a man with a flagrant Adams apple handed him a card with the name of a garage on it.

Go up Genesee st 5 blks and turn to the left or something said the man with the apple.

Soon we reached the garage and had the gas tank filled with gas it was 27 cents in Buffalo and soon we was on our way to Rochester. Well these are certainly grate roads said my father barshfully.

They have lots better roads in the east than out west replid my mother with a knowing wink.

The roads all through the east are better than out west remarked my father at lenth.

These are wonderful replid my mother smuggleing me vs her arm.

The time past quickly with my parents in so jocular a mood and all most before I knew it we was on the outer skirts of Batavia.

What town is this quired my mother in a tolerant voice.

Batavia husked my father sloughing down to 15 miles per hour.

Well maybe we would better stop and have lunch here said my mother coyly.

We will have lunch in Rochester replid my father with a loud cough.

My mother forced a smile and it was about ½ past 12 when we arived in Rochester and soon we was on Genesee st and finley stoped in front of a elegant hotel and shared a costly lunch.

CHAPTER V

MY FATHER'S IDEAR

Wilst participateing in the lordly viands my father halled out his map and give it the up and down.

Look at here he said at lenth they seams to be a choice of 2 main roads between here and Syracuse but 1 of them gos way up north to Oswego wilst the other gos way south to Geneva where as Syracuse is strate east from here you might say so it looks to me like we would save both millage and time if we was to drive strate east through Lyons the way the railway gos.

Well I dont want to ride on the ties said my mother with a loud cough.

Well you dont half to because they seams to be a little road that gos strate through replid my father removeing a flys cadaver from the costly farina.

Well you would better stick to the main roads said my mother tacklessly.

Well you would better stick to your own business replid my father with a pungent glance.

Soon my father had payed the check and gave the waiter a lordly bribe and once more we sprang into the machine and was on our way. The lease said about the results of my fathers grate idear the soonest mended in a word it turned out to be a holycost of the first water as after we had covered miles and miles of ribald roads we suddenly come to a abrupt conclusion vs the side of a stagnant freight train that was stone deef to honks. My father set there for nerly ½ a hour reciteing the 4 Horses of the Apoplex in a under tone but finely my mother mustard up her curage and said affectedly why dont we turn around and go back somewheres. I cant spell what my father replid.

At length my old man decided that Lyons wouldnt never come to Mahomet if we set it out on the same lines all winter so we backed up and turned around and retraced 4 miles of shell holes and finely reached our objective by way of Detour.

Puling up in front of a garage my father beckoned to a dirty mechanic.

How do we get to Syracuse from her arsked my father blushing furiously.

Go strate south to Geneva and then east to Syracuse replid the dirty mechanic with a loud cough.

Isnt there no short cut arsked my father.

Go strate south to Geneva and then east to Syracuse replid the dirty mechanic.

You see daddy we go to Geneva after all I said brokenly but luckly for my piece of mind my father dont beleive in corporeal punishment a specially in front of Lyons peaple.

Soon we was on a fine road and nothing more happened till we puled into Syracuse at 7 that evening and as for the conversation that changed hands in the car between Lyons and Syracuse you could stick it in a day message and send it for 30 cents.

CHAPTER VI

SYRACUSE TO HUDSON 183.2

Soon we was on Genesee st in Syracuse but soon turned off a blk or 2 and puled up in front of a hotel that I cant ether spell or pronounce besides witch they must of been a convention of cheese sculpters or something stoping there and any way it took the old man a hour to weedle a parler bed room and bath out of the clerk and put up a cot for me.

Wilst we was enjoying a late and futile supper in the hotel dinning room a man named Duffy reckonized my father and came to our table and arsked him to go to some boxing matchs in Syracuse that night.

Thanks very much said my father with a slite sneeze but you see what

I have got on my hands besides witch I have been driveing all day and half to start out again erly in the morning so I guess not.

Between you and I dear reader my old man has been oposed to pugilisms since the 4 of July holycost.

Who is that man arsked my mother when that man had gone away.

Mr. Duffy replid my father shove the ketchup over this way.

Yes I know he is Mr. Duffy but where did you meet him insisted my mother quaintly.

In Boston my father replid where would a person meet a man named Duffy.

When we got up the next morning it was 6 o'clock and purring rain but we eat a costly brekfus and my father said we would save time if we would all walk down to the garage where he had horded the car witch he stated was only 2 short blks away from the hotel. Well if it was only 2 short blks why peaple that lives next door to each other in Syracuse are by no means neighbors and when we got there the entire party was soping wet and rarther rabid.

We will all catch our death of cold chuckled my mother.

What of it explained my old man with a dirty look at the sky.

Maybe we would better put up the curtains sugested my mother smirking.

Maybe we wouldnt too said my father cordialy.

Well maybe it will clear up said my mother convulsively.

Maybe it wont too replid my father as he capered into the drivers seat.

My father is charming company wilst driveing on strange roads through a purring rain and even when we past through Oneida and he pronounced it like it was a biscuit neither myself or my mother ventured to correct him but finely we reached Utica when we got to witch we puled up along side the kerb and got out and rang ourselfs out to a small extent when suddenly a closed car sored past us on the left.

Why that was Mrs. Heywood in that car explained my mother with a fierce jesture. By this time it was not raining and we got back into the car and presently over took the closed car witch stoped when they reckonized us.

And witch boy is this quired Mrs. Heywood when the usual compliments had been changed.

This is the third he is named for his father replid my mother forceing a smile.

He has his eyes was the comment.

Bill dont you remember Mrs. Heywood said my mother turning on me she use to live in Riverside and Dr. Heywood tended to you that time you had that slite attack of obesity.

Well yes I replid with a slite accent but did not add how rotten the medicine tasted that time and soon we was on Genesee st on our way out of Utica.

I wander why they dont name some of their sts Genesee in these eastren towns said my father for the sun was now shining but no sooner had we reached Herkimer when the clouds bersed with renude vigger and I think my old man was bout to say we will stop here and have lunch when my mother sugested it herself.

No replid my father with a corse jesture we will go on to Little Falls.

It was raining cats and dogs when we arived at Little Falls and my father droped a quaint remark.

If Falls is a verb he said the man that baptized this town was a practicle joker.

We will half to change our close replid my mother steping into a mud peddle in front of the hotel with a informal look.

When we had done so we partook of a meger lunch and as it was now only drooling resumed our jurney.

They soked me 5 for that room said my father but what is a extra sokeing or 2 on a day like this.

I didnt mean for you to get a room said my mother violently.

Where did you want us to change our close on the register said my old man turning pail.

Wasnt it funny that we should happen to see Mrs. Heywood in Utica said my mother at lenth.

They live there dont they my father replid.

Why yes my mother replid.

Well then my father replid the real joke would of been if we had of happened to see her in Auburn.

A little wile latter we past a grate many signs reading dine at the Big Nose Mountain Inn.

Rollie Zeider never told me they had named a mountain after him crid my father and soon we past through Fonda.

Soon we past through Amsterdam and I guess I must of dosed off at lease I cant remember anything between there and Schenectady and I must apologize to my readers for my laps as I am unable to ether describe the scenery or report anything that may of been said between these 2 points but I recall that as we entered Albany a remark was adrest to me for the first time since lunch.

Bill said my mother with a ½ smirk this is Albany the capital of New York state.

So this is Albany I thorght to myself.

Who is governor of New York now arsked my mother to my father.

Smith replid my father who seams to know everything.

Queer name said my mother sulkily.

Chapter VII

Hudson

We were turing gaily down the main st of Hudson when a man of 12 years capered out from the side walk and hoped on the runing board.

Do you want a good garage he arsked with a dirty look.

Why yes my good man replid my father tenderly but first where is the best hotel.

I will take you there said the man.

I must be a grate favorite in Hudson my father wispered at my mother.

Soon folling the mans directions we puled up in front of a hotel but when my father went at the register the clerk said I am full tonight.

Where do you get it around here arsked my father tenderly.

We have no rooms replid the senile clerk paying no tension to my old mans remark but there is a woman acrost the st that takes loggers.

Not to excess I hope replid my father but soon we went acrost the st and the woman agrede to hord us for the night so myself and mother went to our apartmunts wilst my father and the 12 year old besought the garage. When we finley got reunited and went back to the hotel for supper it was past 8 o'clock as a person could of told from the viands. Latter in front of our loggings we again met the young man who had welcomed us to Hudson and called my father to 1 side.

There is a sailer going to spend the night here he said in a horse wisper witch has walked all the way from his home Schenectady and he has got to report on his ship in New York tomorrow afternoon and has got no money so if he dont get a free ride he will be up vs it.

He can ride with us replid my father with a hiccup if tomorrow is anything like today a sailer will not feel out of place in my costly moter.

I will tell him replid the man with a corse jesture.

Will you call us at ½ past 5 my mother reqested to our lanlady as we entered our Hudson barracks.

I will if I am awake she replid useing her handkerchief to some extent.

Latter we wandered how anybody could help from being awake in that hot bed of mones and grones and cat calls and caterwauls and gulish screaks of all kinds and tho we had rose erly at Syracuse and had a day of retchedness we was all more than ready to get up when she wraped on our door long ere day brake.

Where is that sailer that stoped here last night quired my father as we was about to make a lordly outburst.

He wouldnt pay his bill and razed hell so I kicked him out replid the lanlady in her bear feet.

Without farther adieu my father payed his bill and we walked into the dismul st so I will end this chapter by leaveing the fare lanlady flaping in the door way in her sredded night gown.

Chapter VIII

Hudson to Yonkers 106.5

It was raining a little so my father bad my mother and I stand in the st wilst he went to the garage and retained the costly moter. He returned ½ a hour latter with the story that the garage had been locked and he had to go to the props house and roust him out.

How did you know where he lived quired my mother barshfully.

I used the brains god gave me was my fathers posthumous reply.

Soon we rumpled into Rhinebeck and as it was now day light and the rain had siezed we puled up in front of the Beekman arms for brekfus.

It says this is the oldest hotel in America said my mother reading the programme.

The eggs tastes all right replid my father with a corse jesture.

What is the next town quired my mother when we again set sale.

Pokippsie was my father's reply.

Thats where Vassar is said my mother as my old man stiffled a yawn I wonder if there is a store there that would have a koop for David.

I doubt if they ever heard of him said my father dryly how much do they cost.

Well I dont know.

We entered Pokippsie at lenth and turned to the left up the main st and puled up in front of a big store where myself and mother went in and purchased a koop for my little brother and a kap for me witch only took a ½ hour dureing witch my father lost his temper and when we finley immerged he was barking like a dog and giveing the Vassar yell. 2 men come out of the store with us and tost the koop with the rest of the junk in the back seat and away we went.

Doesnt this look cute on him said my mother in regards to my new kap.

What of it replid my father with a grimace and with that we puled into Garrison.

Isnt this right acrost the river from West Point said my mother with a gastly look.

What of it replid my father tenderly and soon we found ourselfs in Peekskill.

This is where that young girl cousin of mine gos to school said my father from Philadelphia.

What of it said my mother with a loud cough and presently we stoped and bought 15 gals of gas.

I have got a fund of usefull information about every town we come to said my father admireingly for instants this is Harmon where they take off the steem engines and put on the electric bullgines.

My mother looked at him with ill consealed admiration.

And what do you know about this town she arsked as we frisked into Ossining.

Why this is Ossining where they take off the hair and put on the stripes replid my father qick as a flarsh and the next place is Tarrytown where John D. Rockefeller has a estate.

What is the name of the estate quired my mother breathlessly.

Socony I supose was the sires reply.

With that we honked into Yonkers and up the funny looking main st.

What a funny looking st said my mother and I always thorght it was the home of well to do peaple.

Well yes replid my father it is the home of the ruling class at lease Bill Klem the umpire and Bill Langford the referee lives here.

I will end my chapter on that one.

CHAPTER IX

THE BUREAU OF MANHATTAN

Isn't it about time said my mother as we past Spuyten Duyvil and entered the Bureau of Manhattan that we made our plans.

What plans said my father all my plans is all ready made.

Well then you might make me your confident sugested my mother with a quaint smirk.

Well then heres the dope uttered my father in a vage tone I am going to drop you at the 125 st station where you will only half to wait 2 hours and a ½ for the rest of the family as the train from the west is do at 350 at 125 st in the meen wile I will drive out to Grenitch with Bill and see if the house is ready and etc and if the other peaples train is on time you can catch the 4 4 and I an Bill will meet you at the Grenitch station.

If you have time get a qt of milk for David said my mother with a pail look.

What kind of milk arsked my dad.

Oh sour milk my mother screemed.

As she was now in a pretty bad temper we will leave her to cool off for 2 hours and a ½ in the 125 st station and end this chapter.

CHAPTER X

N. Y. TO GRENITCH 500.0

The lease said about my and my fathers trip from the Bureau of Manhattan to our new home the soonest mended. In some way ether I or he got balled up on the grand concorpse and next thing you know we was thretning to swoop down on Pittsfield.

Are you lost daddy I arsked tenderly.

Shut up he explained.

At lenth we doubled on our tracks and done much better as we finely hit New Rochelle and puled up along side a policeman with falling archs.

What road do I take for Grenitch Conn quired my father with poping eyes.

Take the Boston post replid the policeman.

I have all ready subscribed to one out of town paper said my father and steped on the gas so we will leave the flat foot gaping after us like a prune fed calf and end this chapter.

CHAPTER XI

How It Ended

True to our promise we were at the station in Grenitch when the costly train puled in from 125 st. Myself and father hoped out of the lordly moter and helped the bulk of the family off of the train and I aloud our nurse and my 3 brothers to kiss me tho Davids left me rather moist.

Did you have a hard trip my father arsked to our nurse shyly.

Why no she replid with a slite stager.

She did too said my mother they all acted like little devils.

Did you get Davids milk she said turning on my father.

Why no does he like milk my father replid with a gastly smirk.

We got lost mudder I said brokenly.

We did not screened my father and accidently cracked me in the shins with a stray foot.

To change the subjeck I turned my tensions on my brother Jimmie who is nerest my age.

I've seen our house Jimmie I said brokenly I got here first.

Yes but I slept all night on a train and you didnt replied Jimmie with a dirty look.

Nether did you said my brother John to Jimmie you was awake all night.

Were awake said my mother.

Me and David was awake all night and crid said my brother John.

But I only crid once the whole time said my brother Jimmie.

But I didn't cry at all did I I arsked to my mother.

So she replid with a loud cough Bill was a very very good boy.

So now we will say fare well to the characters in this book.

Pvt. Stockdale vs. Classification

By MAC HYMAN

So ANYHOW, that next day I got started with classification and there really warnt too much to it ifn Sergeant King hadnt of been so anxious the way he was. But he kept trying to tell me all the time just how to do and how I should act and all; he would get me off to the side and tell me how I must try hard because if I didnt, I might just have to stay there in his barracks all the rest of my life, and how he knowed I wouldnt like that and all, and he kept on that way until he made me feel kind of anxious too after a while. But I found out soon enough there really warnt that much to it. It warnt nothing really but fitting a bunch of pegs in squares and things like that, and sitting in chairs that spin you around and all that kind of thing, so it was easy as pie, and wouldnt have been nothing ifn Sergeant King hadnt kept worrying at me all the time.

But I still done good on it all. I had one little argument with a fellow down at the radio place, and that didnt amount to nothing really—it didnt bother nobody but Sergeant King. What happened was, they set us at a table and give us a headset and a piece of paper and this fellow was standing up there talking about how we were supposed to mark down the dots and dits on a paper, but after they got started I couldnt hear no dots and dits at all over mine and told the fellow so. But then he got right unreasonable; he come bounding over saying, "Dont you know how to put a headset on? You got the thing on backward. How do you ever expect to hear anything with it that way?" And he said, real rough, "Look, put it on right. Dont you have good sense?" and some more stuff like that which I didnt appreciate too much. Then he got back up front and said this next one would be a trial run and in a minute everybody got to writing on their papers, but I didnt because they didnt sound like nothing but dots and dits to me, so I didnt do nothing but just set there, but then he come bounding back over saying, "You're supposed to mark them down! Cant you write?" which made me kind of ornery so I said, "I can write as good as the next man."

"Well, write them down then."

But he had made me kind of mad talking about writing, so I said,

"How can I write down things like that? Those little dots and dits dont mean nothing to me."

"Look," he said. "It dont matter what they mean. All you're supposed to do is mark them in this column if they sound alike, and in that one if they dont. It dont matter a bit what they mean . . ."

And I said, "Well, as far as that goes, it dont make no difference to me neither, but they still dont sound like nothing but dots and dits. . . ."

And he fumed and fussed some more with it, and said, "It don't make any difference what they sound like to you. *I* know what they mean and they dont sound that way to me; and they dont sound that way to the fellows that made them up, and they dont sound that way to the generals —so who are you to say they dont sound like anything but a lot of dots and dits."

And he kept on that way until I got right tired of it. I got up and told him he was probably right and that if him and all the generals said it didnt sound like that to them, then I just wouldnt bother with it and let them listen to it all day long if they wanted to, but then he looked at me and yelled, "Sit down!" which I didnt like too much.

"How's that?" I asked him.

"You sit down there and put those headsets back on. What do you want to cause trouble for anyhow?"

"I dont want no trouble."

And he said, "Well, sit down and take the test then. You do just what I said and that's all there is to it."

"Well, I can write just as good as the next man," I said.

And he said, "Well, go on and do it then," and didnt say it so rough this time, but more like he was asking, so I set back down and listened to the dots and dits and marked them down like he said. But it was like I told him in the first place, they just sounded like a bunch of dots and dits to me, so I just marked them all down in the same column and left, because I really didnt care too much about it nohow.

So I didnt have no trouble with it really, only Sergeant King got all upset about it and took it mighty hard. But he agreed the fellow had acted pretty unreasonable; he said, "As a matter of fact, the most *un*reasonable thing he did was ever putting the headset on you so you could hear the things." But then he took on some more how I must try hard and all like that; he said, "The rest of them wont all be that hard, Will; and if you do like they tell you, I really think we can swing this thing. You hear what I say now? Are you listening to me now? Look, I've got copies of most of the tests and we can go over them here in the barracks before you ever take them, and that way, you ought to manage all right. But you've got to try, Will. You got to do just like they tell you."

So I did that and got along better on the rest of them, just to please Sergeant King more or less. We took some more and I done right good on them and Sergeant King was right proud of it too. And one of them I done good on, he said he bet nobody had ever done anything like that as long as the field had been there. That one made him the happiest of all, I think. What it was, was this puzzle made out of steel about as thin as your little finger, and the trick was to put it back together once the Corporal had took it apart, and they was going to time us to see how quick we got it done. The Corporal explained all about it before we started; he took it apart and put it back together and showed us, and said, "There aint but one way of doing it, so you have to use your heads," and all like that, and then they passed them out to us, one each, and one fellow got a stopwatch and the other one said, "All right now: Go," and the other one mashed the watch, and everybody took to fitting them this way and that.

So I got to fitting mine too, but it didn't work out at first, so then I just reached down and got a right good grip on one of the pieces and straightened it out and slipped back inside the other one and tied them back up together, which was a right good way of doing it because I was the first one finished. So then I got up and give it to the fellow, ready to leave, but he looked kind of funny and turned it over in his hand, and looked at it some more, and said, "What did you do with this thing?"

"I put it back together like you told me," I said.

So he looked it over again and twisted it in his hand, and then he tried to pull it loose, only he couldn't make it as I had tied it up real good, and then he said, "You just wait over here for a minute until I get the Sergeant and see what to do about it." So he went over to the Sergeant and showed it to him and the Sergeant looked at it and tried to bend it and shook his head and said, "Which one done it?"

And the fellow pointed at me and the Sergeant come over and said, "What did you do to this thing?" and I told him the same as the other, and then he went at it some more but couldnt get it loose neither.

And then they started arguing about it, and the Corporal said, "Well, how would you mark him on that?"

Then the Sergeant looked at him and said, "You're supposed to be grading this. Cant you do a simple job like that?" and kept twisting it and pulling at it and getting red in the face.

And the other fellow said, "I'm supposed to mark it down if they put it back together or not and there aint supposed to be but one way of doing it, and he sho didnt do it that way. How are you going to mark a thing like that?"

So then they called the Lieutenant over and by that time I was beginning to think I hadnt passed it. They all went off in the corner and talked about it some more, and then they got together on a work bench in the corner and got a pair of pliers and a hammer and the Lieutenant held on to it while the Sergeant started whamming away at it, and they mighty near got it loose that way, only he hit the Lieutenant's hand and the Lieutenant jumped up in the air and started cussing and slinging his hand around; and they took on that way for a while so I finally got tired of waiting and left. And it warnt until I got back and talked to Sergeant King that I found out I had passed it. And I was right glad I had when I seen how he felt about it. It made him the happiest I had ever seen him; he patted me on the back and said, "Yessir, Will, I think we are going to get you classified yet. It just goes to show what the Air Force has come down to."

So then we went back to his room and went over some of the other tests I had to take.

So I done right good on all of them and didnt have no trouble at all to speak of, only I run into this Major at one of the tests and nearly had some trouble with him, but I seen there was something the matter with him and stopped myself. But he was a real peculiar fellow and had a way of saying rough things at you; he wore these big thick glasses that made his eyes look about the size of a cow's, and when we come into this room, he was standing there with his hands folded behind his back, rocking back and forth on his feet, staring right at me, like he might have knowed me from somewhere. So I looked back at him, and he kept standing there looking at me, and I thought maybe I had met him from somewhere, so I nodded and said, "Howdy," but all he done was just keep staring at me, and never opened his mouth.

So I couldnt figger him at first, and we stood around a minute and then he turned and went over to the Corporal at the desk and started talking to him, looking up at me every once in a while, and the Corporal nodded his head, and then the Major turned back around and looked at me again, and then went in this other room.

And in a little bit, they led us all in there where we set down at desks that had chairs on both sides of them, the desks lined up and down the wall, and then a bunch of officers come in and set on the other side of the desks, and then I looked up and seen this same Major just taking his chair right across from me. So I nodded and said, "Howdy," again, but he still didnt say nothing. He shuffled some papers around on his desk, not saying a word, and I waited until he had finished, and then he looked up at me, and started staring again like he did out in the hall. Then he asked me my name and I told him, and he wrote that down without even looking at the paper, staring at me all the time. And I guess he had the most peculiar eyes I ever seen. I said they was like a cow's but they warnt; they was gray and had black specks in them, and he kept them pointed right at me so I looked back at him, and it seemed we done that for a minute or so until he finally said, "Where you from, Stockdale?"

I told him Georgia, and he come back with: "That's not much of a state, is it?" which didnt sound very polite to me.

But I said, "Well, I dont live all over the state. I just live in one little place in it."

Then he kept staring and said, "That's where they have the tobacco roads and things, isnt it?"

"Maybe so, but not around my section," I said. "I never seen no tobacco planted in a road. Maybe you from some other part than me."

"No, I never been there," he said. Then he looked harder and said, "And I dont think I ever would go there. What do you think about that?"

He let it bust out and kind of leaned over the table at me, and I really didnt know what to make of him for a second. The way he kept making conversation I figgered he was trying to be friendly, but the things he said didnt make much sense, and I never had seen anybody stare like that before. So I didnt know what to make out of him. I said, "Well, I dont think nothing about it. Fact is, I aint ever thought about it before."

He said, "I dont think I would ever want to live in your rotten state. How about that?"

"Well, I guess you know where you want to live," I told him. "Besides that, things is getting right crowded around home anyhow. Some folks moved in not long ago about two miles down the road from us and land aint as cheap as it once was. So it really dont make no difference to me whether you live there or not, not that we wouldnt be mighty glad to have you . . ." I finally quit talking because he didnt seem to be listening nohow. He kept staring and by this time I was staring too.

"You mean you dont mind it when somebody says something bad about Georgia?"

"I aint heered nobody say nothing bad about Georgia."

"What do you think I been talking about?"

"Well, I aint thought too much about it," I told him. "Dont you know?"

So he went on that way for a while and then all of a sudden he just quit talking and kept looking at me, and kept looking back, and we done that for a few seconds, just setting there staring, until I could tell it was getting right hard on him. He started to say something and then stopped and looked harder and I looked hard right back, and in a little bit, he got his eyes all squenched up and mine begun to burn a little bit, and we done that a while, but I knowed he had to bat them sooner or later, and after a while his whole face was getting squenched up and then all of a sudden, he just stopped and cleared his throat and looked away altogether. He picked up the papers on the desk and wrote some more on them and then rubbed his hands over his face once or twice. Then he leaned back in his chair and I got ready to start staring again, but he didnt look at me this time. Instead, he started asking me about the most foolish bunch of questions I ever listened to. He asked about all kinds of things I had done when I was a child, and what kind of life I led, and all kinds of stuff like that, and then all of a sudden, he leaned over and said, "Why did you hate your mother?" which didnt have a thing to do with what he was talking about before.

"Sir?" I said.

"Long ago your mother beat you, didnt she?"

"Well, I dont remember. . . ."

"Did you ever try to remember?"

"I dont know that I have."

"Dont you ever try to think of it at all?"

"No, I aint, but I will ifn you want me to. I dont think it'll do much good, though, because she died when I was borned."

And that seemed to make him kind of mad; he looked at me and frowned real hard and said, "Well, why didnt you say so in the first place?" and snatched the paper around and wrote something down on it.

So I said, "I guess I should have all right," and said I just didnt think of it and so on, and then I figgered that maybe he was just leading up to it because he wanted to talk about his own mother, so I tried to give him a prod by saying, "Why? Did you hate your mother?"

"Certainly not," he said.

"Well, I wouldnt think so. Did she beat you or something?"

"Look here, now," he said. "You better watch yourself."

So I dropped it right quick. I said I just thought he might want to talk about her for a while, and tried to explain I didnt mean no harm, but he was still right upset about it and leaned over the table saying to me, "Well, I didnt say nothing about my mother, did I? I was talking about your mother. I didnt say one word about my mother."

"Well, I dont guess you did, and I'll sho talk about mine ifn you want me to, but it wont do much good like I said, because she died when I was borned . . . but now I heered Pa say one time . . ."

"Well, let's just skip it," he said.

"I can tell you what Pa said. He used to . . ."

"No. No," he said. "We'll talk about something else. What about your pa? Did he ever beat you?"

"Sho."

"Did he beat you hard?"

"Sho. Lord, I remember one time he took me out behind the pig pen and got one of them fence rails and leaned me over that fence, and Lord, I never got such a licking. Couldnt nobody beat like my pa could. I remember one time . . ."

But then he give a bounce and leaned over and stared in my face again and said, "You hated your *pa*, didnt you?" and kept his face poked right into mine.

And I couldn't think of a thing to say for a little bit. It looked like we was going to have to go through with all that staring again, and it seemed right silly to me, and I didnt want to hurt his feelings or nothing, but I told him then just as plain as I could how I felt. I said, "Sir, I dont hate my pa and I dont guess I hated my ma either, and if that's all you want to know, you can write down there on that air paper that I didnt hate neither one of them, and not my grandpa or my grandma either, because I like all my folks ceptn this one uncle I got that I aint too partial to because every time he comes out to the house, he's always wanting to rassle with our mule, and I just think he aint got very good sense because every time he comes out there he heads back for the barn and keeps the mule all wore out and tired, but there aint much harm in him neither that I can see cept him wanting to rassle with that mule, so I dont really hate . . ."

"All right," he said. "All right."

"So if you want to write that air down I'll be on my way and maybe you can find somebody else that hates their folks. . . ."

"You just sit down," he said. "We arent half through yet."

"Well, now, I'm through with that much of it. . . ."

"You what!" he said leaning over the table at me; but then he kind of stopped and set back again and rested a little bit and rubbed his face, and when he looked back at me again, he looked altogether different. He was smiling as nice as he could like he had just seen me and we was old friends. And then he leaned over and said, kind of whispering it, "Will, what do you think about the girls?"

"How's that?"

"Girls," he said. "Girls. How do you like 'em?"

"What girls is that, sir?"

"Just girls. Just any girls."

"Well, I dont like just any girls. I know there is one old girl back home that aint got hair no longer than a hound dogs, and she's the meanest girl I ever did see. One time . . ."

"I dont mean that, quite. I mean girls in a different sense. When I say girls, I mean . . ." and he hedged around some more, and twisted and turned, and finally got way off the subject, and I never heered such talking as he did then. He got all wound up and wanted to know about girls in Georgia and I'd start to tell him and he'd say, "No, I dont mean that. . . ." and then he'd be off again telling me about girls and what he meant when he said girls, and he got wound up so much it was just like I warnt there. He leaned back and put his head back and squenched up his face and talked and talked, and I listened for a while and glanced around and seen that most of the others had gone already, only he hadnt even noticed it. So I settled back and just let him go on and he kept talking about girls, only not about no particular girl but just about girls in general. So we chatted a good while about girls that way, and then I told him a joke I heered Pa tell one time, about Ike and Mike at the circus, and he was getting a right big kick out of it, leaned way across the table with his mouth open and his eyes all lit up, until he finally noticed that the others had gone, and then he set back right quick and the grin come off his face and he broke in on me and said, "Yes. Yes. Well, I guess I better let you go now."

"Well, I aint told you the end of it yet. . . ."

"No, that's all. That's not what I mean anyhow. . . ."

So I got up and told him how much I enjoyed talking with him, and he said, "Yes. Yes," and I told him if he wanted to talk about girls some more that he ought to come over to the barracks because the boys over there was always talking about the girls and knowed a lot of good jokes theirselves, and he said, "Yes. Yes. Well, that's all. Yes. Thank you," and I told him that maybe if he went out and seen some girls every once in a while he wouldnt worry so much about them, but by that time he was picking up his papers and he got them all together and pushed his chair back and kept saying, "Yes. Yes," and finally said, "Well, I better go," and took off down the hall and out the door without even saying good-by to me.

So I got through that part too all right, and Sergeant King was right proud of it. When I told him about how the Major had done and how peculiar he was and all like that, he patted me on the back and said, "Well, he was the main one I was worried about all right. And I think you done right good on it too, Will. The fact that you're still walking about in the open is proof enough of that for me. I think we might make it after all." And he seemed right happy about it. There warnt too much else to do, he said, and in a few more days I would be classified sure enough.

The Lacy Battle Flag

By WILLIAM BRINKLEY

THERE were some Navy people who bitterly resented women correspondents, claiming the war would be over years earlier if they stayed at home. It was true that they added a number of man-hours' labor in the Navy's push to the Japanese home islands. Once a detachment of five men from the Seabees, the famous Navy "Can Do!" outfit, had to put in a full day building a special head for a correspondent who decided her coverage of the war required her to visit Gug-Gug, and there was considerable complaining over this. It was difficult to have any sympathy with such complaints. After all, a war is no excuse to add to the discriminations women already endure. Besides, some of the women correspondents went above and beyond the call of duty to make themselves useful. On Tulura there was one correspondent, a fifty-five-year-old woman who represented a chain of Texas papers, who put in every Saturday afternoon in the main Public Relations building sewing on buttons and darning socks for all comers. She was a kindly if somewhat concupiscent lady who probably had more suitors than any fifty-five-year-old woman in the world. It was necessary to date her up three weeks in advance. Being a woman correspondent in the Pacific put you in a really distinctive class. The ratio of woman correspondent to military men was about 1:250,000. The Pacific needed more, not fewer women, and it was worth building an extra head here and there for them.

A few of the women correspondents flaunted the ratio. But they could hardly be blamed for obeying the oldest law (supply and demand). Some also paraded that envied mobility which derived from profession rather than sex. One war correspondent for a true-confession type of magazine used to pop into the Media Section and plant herself, legs apart, in front of a map of the world which obliterated the entire wall. Her eyes would ravage the great map as if it were a tray of French pastry and she couldn't make up her mind which piece to select, all of it being so mouth-watering.

"I wonder where I should hit next," she would think out loud. "Guadalcanal—but things must be terribly dull down there by now. Bombay—there *would* be Gandhi to interview. Sydney—we could use a little down-under stuff. Tahiti—I wonder if anyone's ever thought of asking those gentle Tahitians what *they* think about the war. . . ."

The island-stuck officers would sit at their desks and look at her menacingly out of the corners of their eyes. Ensign Christopher Tyson III would be seething. The Princeton odd-job ensign was a very handsome young man who was not accustomed to going without sex. Back in Rye, Ty had had succulent debutantes standing in line ready to give him their most precious possession. But he was a long way from Rye. When the true-confession woman would flutter out of the room after a few minutes of map-gazing, Tyson would storm to his feet.

"The b-b-b-bitch. The fanny-shaking b-b-bitch." And he would mimic her, mincing around the room, hips shaking and hand to the back of his head. "Now I wonder if I should go to Tahiti . . . or Sydney . . . or Bombay and get the true confessions of Mahatma Gandhi. I'd like to catch the b-b-bitch some dark night down in the boondocks and r-r-rape her from here to Sydney. Women correspondents! I don't see why we can't fight a war without women correspondents."

Tyson was always talking about fighting the war, always itching for sea duty.

Any woman correspondent in the Pacific became a very special person, if for no other reason than the oldest law. But the most upsetting woman correspondent ever to reach the Pacific was Debbi Aldrich. For one thing she represented a publication of a type which up until then had not been sending correspondents to the Pacific. Most of the women correspondents were with newspapers or wire services. Debbi Aldrich represented *Madame*.

When the dispatch that a *Madame* war correspondent was on her way to Tulura arrived, there was a lot of speculation as to what angle of the war she was going to cover, *Madame* being a magazine of great tone, best described by its subtitle: "The World of Women—Decor and Cuisine, Beauty and Fashion." There was certainly not a great deal of subject material for these matters in the western Pacific. "I hear she's going to do a takeout on what kind of drawers ComFleets wears," Lieutenant Morey Griffin said. There were many guesses along this line.

Debbi Aldrich turned out to be quite a dish. The critical faculties of Pacific Navy men about women were almost pathologically warped, of course, but Miss Aldrich could have held her own in Radio City. She made a spectacular entrance into the Pacific. Lieutenant Morey Griffin said later he was too embarrassed to get up from his desk for an hour. As a Correspondent's Aide, Tyson had gone out to meet her and he followed her into the Public Relations building like a cocker spaniel with its tongue hanging out. All his resentment against women correspondents had evaporated sometime between his departure for the airfield and the trip back. He was staggering under a load of three brand-new, bright red lizard-skin bags, including a hatbox wedged under his arm. In the sur-roundings the hatbox looked sensational.

"May I present Miss Debbi Aldrich!" Ty exclaimed to Lieutenant Commander Junius Randolph, the Media chief, in his excitement making a faux pas in introduction etiquette unusual for a Rye boy.

She was very beautiful. She had a sculptured face which must have had a kind of wistfulness to it before she got into the magazine business. Now there was no wistfulness but an air of being in complete command of any situation. She was very clean-looking and as smart and tailored as an illustrated ad from her famous magazine, even in her khaki slacks and shirt, and with her face faultlessly made up, her lipstick precisely modeling her small mouth. She had a junior-model body, boyish hips, and her hair, just peeking out from under a baseball cap, was cut almost as short as a man's. In fact, if one had looked at her just from the neck down, one might have had trouble, except for one feature, deciding for sure whether she was a boy or a woman. This feature left no doubt, and if the ancients were right, that it is really woman's crowning glory and a woman desirable in direct ratio to its shape and prominence, then Debbi Aldrich was certainly a queen. They were magnificent and incontestably all her own. One other tiny but startling feminine detail appeared below the neck—a half-inch of black brassiere just visible in the V of her khaki shirt.

She crossed the room briskly, held out a hand to Lieutenant Com-mander Randolph, and came right to the point.

"I'm sure it's going to be a pleasure working with you, Commander," she said in a husky, just slightly bored voice which, like her whole ap-pearance, stepped right out of the pages of her magazine. "I'm out here to do a job. I'm not on a junket. *Madame* is anxious to bring off some really different material from the Pacific. We have a feeling it hasn't really been covered—I mean, of course, as *Madame* wants it covered—" and she made a graceful gesture with her free hand. "I'm after the offbeat, if you know what I mean."

It was quite an inaugural speech, and the officers could feel the uncov-ered Pacific all around them, right here in this room, waiting to be covered by Debbi Aldrich. Griffin gave a gulp from across the room. "Well, any-thing we can do," he said with a forced laugh, "—that's what we're here for, Miss Aldrich."

"Yes, I'm sure you are, sweetie," the *Madame* correspondent said, giving Griffin a polar one-second smile before turning back to Randolph. "Right now, before I get to work, Commander—may I call you Junius?—I really could use a shower."

"Tyson!" snapped Lieutenant Commander Randolph, who before the war had run a paper in Georgia. "Give—I mean get—Miss Ahl-drich a showuh right away!"

"Yes, sir!" Tyson said, coming to attention.

It was the nearest to a military exchange the Public Relations Headquarters had ever seen.

Debbi Aldrich created a major upheaval in the Public Relations Section.
So many officers were forever sniffing around her, volunteering assistance,
to the neglect of correspondents of the opposite sex, that some of these
began to grumble that after all the Associated Press, United Press, International News Service, *New York Times,* Chicago *Daily News,* CBS, and
Time, Inc., as well as *Madame,* were covering the war and had been for
years before that goddamn fashion sheet decided it wasn't really being
covered.

Before long, Debbi Aldrich was both the most hated and most sought-
after person in the western Pacific. She was hated and sought after for
the same reason: for being an aloof, tantalizing and beautiful woman in
the midst of many men. She would come into the Media Section to use a
desk and sit there tapping out her copy on her new Hermes, her body
lithely erect in the chair, that half-inch of black bra showing in the V of
her khaki shirt. No brave bull was ever more violently disturbed by a red
muleta than the officers of the Public Relations Section by this minute
strip of cloth. No work ever got accomplished while she was present, except by herself. As she typed, absorbed in what was going on on her
Hermes, the officers would sneak glances at her and writhe in hellish
frustration, at night go back to their BOQ's and over poker hands bicker
endlessly as to her accessibility.

Ensign Tyson came very near to going crazy. "She knows that little
piece of black b-b-bra shows," he would rage. "You know what she is?
She's a sadist! That's what she is! I know these b-b-black-underwear kind
of women!"

Tyson was probably entirely wrong, for Debbi Aldrich seemed oblivious
of the effect she created and interested solely in her work, which she was
at almost constantly. She was all over the place, interviewing Seabees, sub-
mariners, admirals, amphibious crews, fly-boys, everybody. She filed reams
of copy to her magazine. Tyson knocked himself out getting jeeps, arranging interviews, even changing typewriter ribbons for her. It was obvious to everyone but Tyson himself that he would never get to first base
with Debbi Aldrich. She accepted all he offered politely but with the condescension that said it was all her right both as Debbi Aldrich and as
correspondent for *Madame,* and that anyhow he was just a boy and an
ensign boy at that.

For her escort, Debbi Aldrich looked around and tapped Admiral Boat-
wright's assistant. Captain Thornberry was fiftyish and gray-haired. It
was Thornberry who took her to the beach for swims—she carried her
two-piece black bathing suit (anything closest to her skin was always
black, it seemed) in the red lizard hatbox—Thornberry who took her to
the dances at the Island Base officers' club. Tyson was enraged at the idea

of her going around with an aging, homely captain when there was a pretty ensign like himself so available. "I can't figure her out," he fumed, "I don't see what she g-g-gets out of it. It's downright p-p-perversion. I've got it figured out! She's a lesbian!" Really, for all his looks, Tyson didn't know the first thing about women.

Debbi Aldrich had not been long on Tulura when she announced her plans to do what no woman correspondent had ever done: make a combat operation. The Media officers were sitting at their desk shuffling papers one day when she walked in and gave the word to Randolph. Ship assignments for the invasion of Nanto Shima had been relayed to the correspondents a half-hour earlier. Debbi Aldrich sauntered up to Randolph's desk and cocked her hands on her hips. Randolph looked up and saw her standing there and got quickly to his feet. Lieutenant Commander Randolph was a Georgia gentleman who had been reared to stand up in the presence of women, even those who wore pants.

"Junius. I haven't heard yet what ship I'm going on," she said, as if it were mere oversight on his part.

"But . . . theh's no arrangement on ships," Randolph mumbled in Georgian. "Theh's no arrangement for carryin' women, Miss Ahl-drich. You see, that is . . . that is, it isn't customary for women correspondents to go along on combat operations. Women stay back heah, and, ah, well, one subject the women correspondents covuh frequently is the wounded when they come back to the fleet hospitals . . . ah, that is, how the nurses and the wounded are doin'. . . . Ah, the women's angle, the nurses as related to the wounded."

"But, Junius. *Madame* isn't in the slightest interested in doing the customary," Debbi Aldrich said crisply. "I've come five thousand miles, Junius, to do something that's not customary. The fact a woman correspondent has never made an operation is precisely why *Madame* wants me to do it. Isn't that logical?"

"But, Miss Ahl-drich, ah just don't see. . . . Much as we'd like to, we can hardly refit an entah ship, knock out bulkheads and that sort of thing, to, ah, accommodate a woman. It's relatively easy on an ahland, putting up a separate, ah, cottage and that sort of thing—we've got plenty of Seabees to do that sort of thing—but on a destroyuh. . . . Ah, you see, theh are not separate facilities and the officers use, ah, things in common. Besides, the Bureau of Ships has to approve any structural changes in a naval vessel. Next destroyuh we build, we'll try to blueprint in a compahtment for women. . . ."

Randolph gave a forced laugh, in which Miss Aldrich did not join.

"Junius," she said crisply, "please don't talk to me as if I'm a retarded child. I don't know what kind of women you're used to in Georgia, but I assure you, I can take care of myself—even on a destroyer."

Lieutenant Commander Randolph looked forlornly into Debbi Aldrich's flawlessly made-up face. "Ah'm suah of that, Miss Ahl-drich. But on a Navy ship theh's . . ."

"Now, Junius, be a good boy and write me up those orders. If nothing else, my conscience wouldn't let me stay on Tulura during the operation. This isn't the nineteenth century, you know, sweetie. Women are emancipated, or haven't you heard, and we've got to do all the things the men do, and all that. That's what I'm out here for. Really, Junius, I wish you wouldn't try to give me special consideration." She reached out and touched Lieutenant Commander Randolph's hand resting on the desk, and Randolph's hand blushed violently. "I want to be treated just like anyone else."

"Puhsonally, Miss Ahl-drich," Lieutenant Commander Randolph said soothingly, "ah'd be happy to write those ohduhs up right this minute, but, you see, it's not in mah powuh . . ."

Randolph turned to his desk. The Media chief had foreseen, in the short time he had known the *Madame* correspondent, that such a demand might arise, and he had done his homework well. He had been relieved to discover that the all-encompassing *Navy Regulations,* which provides for almost every conceivable contingency, had also provided for this one. With complete assurance Randolph picked up the volume and, opening it to a marked place, turned to his last and sure resort.

"Y'see, Miss Ahl-drich, Article 116 of *Navy Regulations,* entitled 'Women on Board Ship,' reads in full as follows: 'Officers commanding fleets, squadrons, divisions, or ships shall not permit women to reside on board of, or take passage in, any ship of the Navy in commission except by special permission of the Secretary of the Navy.' "

There was a moment of silence while Randolph, closing the book, stood ready to soothe Miss Aldrich's disappointment.

"Why, you mean," Debbi Aldrich said slowly with an air of incredulousness at the simplicity of it, "that all I have to do is ask Jim Forrestal? Why, Junius, why didn't you say so in the first place?"

And Debbi Aldrich was gone, her narrow hips swiveling her across the room and through the swinging doors.

"Commander," Lieutenant Griffin broke the awed silence when she had gone, "I'll be happy to have Miss Debbi-all share my stateroom on the U.S.S. *Campfollower.*"

"Oh, be quiet, won't you? Women in trousuhs, anyhow! Damn it all!" Lieutenant Commander Randolph said. That was rather astonishing, too, for the Georgian had never before been known to lose his temper.

What exactly happened no one ever knew, but Captain Thornberry was credited with the leading role in the outcome. The outcome was that Debbi Aldrich was assigned to a ship for the Nanto Shima operation. She didn't get a destroyer but she did get a cruiser. The roster of vessels for the operation was searched and a heavy cruiser, the *Seattle,* turned up which was used ordinarily as a flagship but had no admiral aboard for the operation. The *Seattle* was to take part in the bombardment of Nanto Shima. Debbi Aldrich was to pick up the ship at Muranu, stay with her during the operation and return with her. She was dispatched to the *Seattle* and put up in the admiral's cabin.

At the same time Ensign Tyson, who had never got anything but the odd jobs nobody else wanted at Public Relations Headquarters, got the sea duty he had so long sought. It was still an odd job, but this one happened to be in great demand, for the sea duty was with Debbi Aldrich. Tyson was assigned as Public Relations officer-in-charge of Miss Aldrich for the Nanto Shima operation. There was scuttlebutt that Debbi Aldrich had arranged this, too, through Thornberry. Tyson just smiled when asked about it. "Men, I'm the obvious choice for the assignment with Miss Aldrich," he said. "You guys should have got on the ball and changed a few typewriter ribbons instead of sitting around torturing yourselves." Of course Tyson never gave anyone else a chance to change her typewriter ribbons.

The captain of the *Seattle,* Ty later related, almost had apoplexy when he and Debbi arrived aboard. The captain was a non-public-relations type. He was outraged at the idea of a woman occupying flag quarters on his ship during an assault operation.

"He couldn't say anything to Debbi," which was what Tyson called her after the operation, though he had always called her Miss Aldrich before, "though you should have seen the look on his face when she and her three suitcases including that damn red hatbox were piped aboard. But soon as she was settled in the admiral's quarters and I in the non-admiral quarters—well, I'd no sooner unzipped my duffle bag than a Marine orderly came down and said the captain wanted to see me on the double."

The captain banged on the table and shouted at Tyson, "What are you trying to do to my ship? What kind of war do they think we're fighting out here?"

"Sir, it wasn't I who assigned her. I'm just in charge of her."

"Don't tell me who assigned her out here, you impudent pup. So you're 'in charge of Miss Aldrich,'" the captain sneered. "What duty for a commissioned officer of the United States Navy!"

The captain fixed his eye on Tyson. "Do you know how many men there are on a heavy cruiser?"

"Sir, the *Seattle* carries a complement of 1,712 officers and men," said Tyson, who had boned up on the ship on Tulura before putting out to sea with the *Madame* correspondent.

The captain was irritated that Tyson should know the answer so exactly. "And do you realize how long this ship has been in the Pacific?" he snapped.

"Thirty-one months and thirteen days, sir."

"All right," the captain said furiously, "do you realize something these secret documents they let you read but shouldn't on Tulura don't tell you: Do you have any notion what just the sight of a woman, any woman, but especially this woman, has on these men who haven't even seen a white woman in thirty-one months and thirteen days?" The captain banged the table. "Do you?"

"Yes, sir, I minored in psychology at Princeton. Besides, I have something of a notion myself," Tyson said truthfully.

"The hell you do!" shouted the captain, whose concept of Tulura was of officers boozing all day and wallowing in orgies in the boondocks with nurses all night.

"I'm placing a twenty-four-hour Marine watch on the admiral's cabin!" the captain said. "No one is to be allowed up there. That goes for you, too," the captain said suspiciously.

Tyson was dismayed. "But, sir! There are certain coverage problems on which it is essential for me to confer from time to time with Miss Aldrich."

"Coverage problems!" the captain bellowed. "What does that mean in English?"

"Well, sir, I mean, what stories she would like to do, transmission problems, deadlines, censorship problems, that sort of thing," Tyson said mysteriously. "You'd be surprised, sir, how many problems these correspondents can come up with. ComFleets is most anxious that they come away with a favorable impression of the Navy, and that means we've got to take care of their problems."

Tyson's discreet dropping of "ComFleets" did the trick. Really it infuriated the captain even more, this ensign pulling ComFleets' rank on him. But there was nothing he could do about that, for the woman correspondent did come from ComFleets. However, his eye gleamed as he thought of something to do.

"All right, then," he said, pushing his lips together, "you can 'confer' with her in her cabin. Incidentally, have you ever been aboard a ship before?"

"No, sir," Tyson said shyly.

"I thought not. Well, we've no room for deadheads on the *Seattle*. Starting with the first watch you'll stand regular watches in communications in addition to conferring with that woman."

ComFleets Headquarters Public Relations officers were not supposed to be given additional duty during their visitations aboard ship, but far from being displeased, as the captain had expected, Tyson was overjoyed. He had always wanted aboard ship, and here he was standing watches, just like a naval officer! Of course, the work in the communications shack, consisting of sitting at a desk and coding and decoding messages, wasn't particularly nautical but still he was standing regular watches. They couldn't very well have made him a junior officer of the deck. The captain of the cruiser was not so angry at Tyson that he wanted his ship run aground.

The crew took a different attitude from their skipper's toward Debbi Aldrich. They were happy to have her aboard. They talked of little else. Fresh scuttlebutt was piped down almost hourly from the admiral's quarters by the Marine guard. Once Miss Aldrich asked a big Marine corporal from Oklahoma named Donahue if he would get her some Ivory soap flakes to wash out some "things." The *Seattle* had a fine laundry but the clothing it handled required somewhat more powerful soap flakes. But Donahue got a case of Ivory bar soap and got one of the carpenter's mates to shave it into fine pieces on his lathe and there were Ivory soap flakes for Miss Aldrich.

"She had them 'things' soaking in the admiral's basin when I took the soap flakes in," Donahue reported, "and Jesus Christ what 'things'! Yow-ee!"

For days the crew would talk about how Debbi Aldrich was washing out her "things" in the admiral's basin. God damn!

The moment one of the Marines came off watch he was pumped for new Aldrich poop, Donahue especially because he always acted mysterious. A swarm of sailors would surround him in Marine quarters and Donahue would hold court.

"What about that damned officer who goes up there?" a sailor with a ravenous look in his eye would ask Donahue. "You hear anything when he's inside?"

"Hell, you can't hear through them bulkheads," Donahue said. "You swabbies ought to know that."

"You sure you don't hear no noises?" the sailor said suspiciously.

Donahue would look as if his sense of delicacy had been offended.

"God damn, you swab jockeys can't never think of nothing else, I'll swear to God."

"Listen, you Gyrene bastard, we said noises. You hear any *noises?*"

Donahue shrugged. "To tell you the truth, men, I heared one or two noises. But it's been so goddamn long since I even *heared,* I just can't tell for sure if it's *them* noises."

As the ship cruised toward Nanto Shima, Debbi Aldrich's very presence aboard began to give a certain spirit, a lift, to the ship. This spirit was typified by an incident just before the bombardments.

D minus eight, as the ship was preparing to maneuver into position for the first bombardment, the captain came on the bridge, and glancing skyward, noticed a flimsy piece of cloth fluttering from the mast.

"What the hell," he muttered and flicked his binoculars to his eyes.

Studiously the captain examined the delicate and magnified fretwork. Still looking through the binoculars, he addressed the officer of the deck.

"Hepburn, am I getting old or are we flying from the mast a pair of something no one on this ship has seen for thirty-one months?"

"Yes, sir," Hepburn said nervously. "I mean no, sir, you're not getting old and yes, sir, you have correctly identified the object."

The captain snapped the binoculars down, looked quietly at Hepburn, who was standing twelve inches away, then suddenly let out a roar: "Well!!?"

"You see, sir," the officer of the deck said, his voice trembling a little, "I believe we're the first ship in naval history to carry a woman into combat and the crew had the idea of, well—flying her pennant!"

"Anyhow, sir," piped up the boatswain of the watch, boldly flinging a hand toward the transparent strip of cloth, "that's what we're fighting for!"

The crew had noted Debbi Aldrich's half-inch of black in the V-neck of her shirt. They had correctly gauged that anyone representing a magazine like *Madame* would be wearing a matching color below. They had requested and Debbi Aldrich had supplied the pennant. She was delighted that her colors—the panties were a lacy black—should lead the U.S.S. *Seattle* into battle.

The captain looked mastward again, his face reddened and swelled. Then suddenly he burst into laughter, a phenomenon many of the crew had not witnessed during three years under his command.

"Okay, Hepburn. Let's go in and give 'em hell."

The pennant stayed up. The cruiser *Seattle,* incidentally, was credited with the deadliest bombardment of any of the ships in the Nanto Shima operation.

Then one day—D plus two, it was—Debbi Aldrich disappeared from the ship. Vanished. Flick! Like that.

There was unprecedented consternation on Tulura when that first message, marked "Urgent," came in and was decoded:

"031955. Originator: U.S.S. *Seattle.* Action: ComFleets. Miss Debbi Aldrich, correspondent for *Madame* magazine, disappeared at 031910 from *Seattle.* Miss Aldrich was last seen by a Marine orderly who left his post at her quarters in flag cabin to go to ship's service and purchase her a package of cigarettes. When orderly returned, Miss Aldrich was no longer in the cabin. The officer of the deck, ship then being anchored in Nanto Bay five miles offshore, immediately instituted search. Exhaustive search of all ship spaces fails to turn up Miss Aldrich. Search of flag cabin reveals two of three pieces of luggage she brought present and accounted for but one—a red hatbox believed to be made from lizard skin—missing. All ships in area and all ground forces on Nanto Shima being notified to be on lookout for woman with red hatbox. Disciplinary action being instituted against Marine orderly and Ensign Christopher Tyson III, OinC Miss Aldrich."

ComFleets' answer was prompt and hot:

"ComFleets stupefied by your 031955. Dispatching immediately Airtrans Rear Admiral B. G. Pumphrey, chief of intelligence, to supervise search for Miss Debbi Aldrich, correspondent for *Madame* magazine, and conduct exhaustive investigation into startling laxity of *Seattle* whereby VIP passengers can quote disappear unquote from ship five miles from shore. You are hereby directed meantime to conduct relentless and unceasing search of ship ballast to bridge. Signed (Personal) ComFleets.

Viewed from the *Seattle* the whole operation on Nanto Shima, where the Marines and Army had landed and were pushing respectively north and south, ground to a halt. It was not true that the Army's search for Miss Aldrich was responsible for its temporary failure to progress southward. The Japs were to be blamed for that holdup. But all Marine and Army units were repeatedly reminded to be on the lookout for the *Madame* correspondent and supplied with detailed descriptions of the missing woman—including her red lizard hatbox, as if there might be several similar creatures, but perhaps not equipped with red lizard hatbox, wandering around the battle area—and all ships in the area were searched. For a while the Navy communications system carried almost as many Debbi Aldrich as operational dispatches. The Navy Department in Washington was putting the heat on ComFleets, which was burning up the air waves to the *Seattle* off Nanto Shima. War or no war, you just don't lose a correspondent, at least a *Madame* woman correspondent, by "disappearance." Admiral Pumphrey directed all search operations from the *Seattle's* newly vacated admiral's quarters, which at least were again rightfully occupied by flag rank.

Seven days after Debbi Aldrich vanished, Tyson, who was a prisoner-at-large awaiting his disciplinary action for losing her, was standing forlornly on deck leaning over the rail and thinking seriously about jumping in. It was a beautiful, clear day with a sea smooth as a summer pond where the *Seattle* remained at anchor in the spot from which she had not budged since Miss Aldrich disappeared. She had been ordered to remain there, like a homing pigeon's loft. Squinting shoreward, Tyson saw an LCVP bobbing its way toward the cruiser. As the boat came closer, he could see what appeared to be a rather grimy Marine sitting, legs crossed, on the engine cover. His eyes moved casually over the boat, then fetched up. The Marine's hand was resting on an object which, though grimy itself, looked familiar. It looked like a red hatbox.

By the time Tyson had rushed down to the gangway, the boat was alongside. Peering over the side—he almost fell overboard—he was just in time to see the Marine wave good-by to four other Marines and the LCVP crew and hear a familiar husky voice.

"Thanks awfully, you darling Leathernecks," the voice said. "It couldn't have been lovelier."

Tyson tore down the gangway past the startled officer of the deck.

"Debbi!" he yelled. "My God, Debbi. You've had the whole U.S. fleet looking for you! The war's almost stopped since you left! Where in the name of God have you been?"

Debbi Aldrich, correspondent for *Madame,* brushed a wisp of hair back under a Marine fatigue cap which came down over her ears. She hitched up her Marine combat trousers and pulled down her Marine jacket. They were so big for her that the sleeves came over her hands and half the pants legs had been rolled up. Her face was caked with dirt—her lips, however, were properly lipsticked. She looked up at Tyson and said, easily, "Where have I been? Why, to the wars, sweetie. Be a good boy and help me with this hatbox, will you?"

Stunned, Ty preceded her aboard with the hatbox. By this time the captain and Admiral Pumphrey were striding rapidly down to the quarterdeck. The captain was practically a stuttering maniac. But Pumphrey retained the coolness that had made him an admiral. His voice rammed like a torpedo across the quarterdeck.

"Miss Aldrich, you will be confined to your quarters until the first available air transportation to Tulura. I hope you know what this means. You're headed back to the States, Miss Aldrich."

Grimy-faced, Debbi Aldrich stood there on the quarterdeck, her body almost swallowed up in the Marine fatigues, hands on hips and cocky as a sparrow. She pushed back her hat, gave her pants another hitch and suddenly reached forward and chucked Admiral Pumphrey under the chin. The admiral drew back, startled.

"Sweetie," Debbi Aldrich said, "it was worth it."

Then she looked up slowly at the mast. The black pennant was still there. It just looked a little limp, it being a windless day.

"Happy to see my panties are still flying."

And with an insolent swagger Debbi Aldrich started to her cabin, the hoarse echo of a violent command from the admiral—who had looked mastward with a startled air—following her.

"Take those goddamn things down! What is this, a United States Navy vessel or the Pacific office of *Madame!*"

"Haul down those panties!" the captain boomed.

Down came the panties and up went the two-star flag of Rear Admiral Pumphrey, which in the confusion of the search had not previously been hoisted.

Debbi Aldrich wrote her story under confinement in the admiral's cabin. Rear Admiral Pumphrey furiously sent two Marines to empty the cabin of his gear after Debbi Aldrich had scribbled him a note: "Sweetie, are we *both* going to stay here? I do need a bath more than anything in the world. If you don't mind I don't." Her story was a good story, of its kind, beginning: "I have just become the first woman in American history to accompany an infantry patrol into battle." She wrote how simple it was.

One evening around dusk she had looked out the port of her cabin and seen an LCVP alongside the ship. It had come out for some supplies from the cruiser. She quickly threw some "things" in her hatbox. Then she sent the Marine orderly for some cigarettes, pushed her hair up under her cap and stepped out of her cabin. While the deck watch was seeing to the supplies, and in the confusion of men passing back and forth between cruiser and LCVP, she simply went down the gangway and got aboard. LCVP crews are used to carrying everything. They didn't bother to ask questions. Ashore she hitched a ride with a Marine jeep headed for the front. She stayed with a front-line Marine outfit for four days. The Marines never ask questions, particularly of women.

Then she came back. It was as simple as that.

Of course they had to send her back to the States, even though she was a correspondent for *Madame*. It was probably worth it to her, for she had a real exclusive. Tyson said he thought it was a pretty shabby thing to do, sending her back, in view of the fact she probably had a lot to do with the *Seattle*'s brilliant bombardment record. Really, he said, Debbi Aldrich was a great inspiration to the whole crew, and maybe the Navy Department in Washington knew what it was doing after all and should send a couple hundred women correspondents out here. Ty said he thought those black panties should be preserved in one of those glass cases at Annapolis where they keep famous naval battle flags.

An odd thing was that when he returned from Nanto Shima, Tyson had completely lost his stammer. Though there were cases of combat operations giving stammers to men, this may have been the first time such an operation actually cured a stammer.

Auntie Mame and the Southern Belle

By PATRICK DENNIS

A FEW uncharitable people have said that Auntie Mame married Mr. Burnside for his money. I will concede that Mr. Burnside's being the richest man under forty south of Washington, D.C., may have influenced her. But she really loved him. He was father, brother, son, Santa Claus, and lover.

Her new husband, Beau, was one of those big, genial, easygoing, lovable Southerners. He sprang from a fine, impoverished old Georgia family, but he was unique among generals' descendants in that he didn't mope around Dixie talking about the carefree days before those damnyankees ravished its land and its women. Instead, Beau had gone out and raised soybeans and peanuts while the neighboring gentry were still bemoaning the paucity of their cotton crops. By the time he was nineteen, the Burnside land was free from debt and erosion and was showing a profit. During his last year at Georgia Tech he went off to Texas to settle an estate of barren wasteland left by some migratory cousin, discovered oil on the property, and was a millionaire before he was twenty-one. Everything Uncle Beau touched seemed to turn to gold, and he was constantly amazed and delighted by his good fortune. "Just luck, sugar," he'd say to Auntie Mame. Money meant very little to him except for the pleasure it could give to others. He was high on the list of every charity in the country, he was the sole support of an ancient mother and a pack of indolent kinfolk, and he was an easy touch for anybody with a fairly plausible hard-luck story.

Uncle Beau paid up all of Auntie Mame's debts, sold her carriage house —he said that nice women didn't live on Murray Hill—returned Norah's life savings, and sent her back to County Meath with a handsome pension. He moved Auntie Mame into about ten rooms in the St. Regis Hotel and encouraged her to go right back to her old scale of spending. She was happy to oblige.

Although she was pretty much her old self, I noticed certain subtle changes. It was fashionable to be romantic in 1932, but Auntie Mame went a step farther. Her hair was fluffier, softer; there were always a lot of camellias around the rooms; her dresses seemed to run to organdy and ruffles, and there was almost a roar of crinoline beneath her skirts. When Uncle Beau insisted that she have her portrait painted, Auntie Mame commissioned a society portraitist rather than one of the stark moderns who frequented her drawing room. The finished picture gave the impression of having been executed not with a brush, but with a pastry tube, and Auntie Mame kept saying it was a pity that Winterhalter wasn't still alive.

Her speech grew slightly blurred, softer and less staccato. She called me Honey a great deal and used You-all both in singular and plural.

For my thirteenth birthday she sent a whole bale of gifts, but prominent among them were a beautiful and intricate set of antique Confederate soldiers, which I still have, a three-volume set of books on General Lee, and, of all things, a yellowed first edition of *The Little Colonel*. I knew what was coming.

That June I graduated from the Lower School to the Upper School. I could have managed to do it myself, but Auntie Mame wrote an exuberant letter to announce that she and Uncle Beau were motoring up to St. Boniface to take part in the great celebration. "Then, honey," she wrote, "I've got a big surprise. You and your Uncle Beauregard and I are all going to drive down to Georgia to spend the summer on our big old plantation and see my sweet little old mother-in-law. Excuse the haste of this letter, but the Daughters of the Confederacy are meeting here today. Can't wait to see you-all!"

She was a triumph of Southern Womanhood at the commencement exercises. She wore a fluttering white garden party dress—it looked as though it were made of spun sugar—lace gloves, lace hat, lace parasol which she twirled coquettishly, and a lace fichu which she kept dropping to be retrieved by the pimpled gallants of St. Boniface. I won the composition prize for the Lower School and she said to the English master, "Ah vow, Ah'm so proud of that child Ah could *jes bust!* But then, his daddeh was one of the most literareh boys down home."

We drove down to Georgia in Uncle Beau's big Dusenberg phaeton, stopping here to see this grand ole monument or that noble ole battlefield where our Southun boys fought and died valiantly defendin' theah beliefs. Most of the countryside looked pretty bleak to me, but Auntie Mame, who'd been through it before on the Palm Beach sleeper, spoke at some length of its gracious ole heritage and its rich memories.

When the car swept up to the pillared portico of Peckerwood, the Burnside plantation, a genial old major-domo capered out to take the bags and a mountainous colored woman who looked like the ads for pancake flour heaved and shook and said Lan'sakes about thirty times. Auntie Mame was in her element.

Beau's Texas oil money, his Cuban sugar money, his New York stock market money, his Canadian mining money had all helped to restore the gracious rooms of Peckerwood to their ante-bellum magnificence. There were damask draperies, rosewood chairs, Sheraton tables, and crystal chandeliers with hurricane chimneys. Auntie Mame said it was just dawlin'. I was shown to my room, a big chamber with a canopied bed, a Chippendale chest-on-chest, and French windows giving on the second floor piazza. There was a Yankee bathroom next to it with real post-bellum Crane plumbing.

Auntie Mame seemed a little miffed that she wasn't going to be quartered in the main house, too, but tradition had it that the son and his wife always lived in the Bride's Cottage beyond the boxwood maze in the garden. Later I think she was thankful.

"But, Beau, honeh," she kept saying as she unpacked her dimities, "when am Ah gonna meet yo sweet little ole mothah?"

Mrs. Burnside could by no stretch of the imagination be called either sweet or little. But she *was* old, and I suppose that God in His infinite wisdom had seen fit to make her mother, although I've often risked blasphemy to wonder why. She was built along the lines of a General Electric refrigerator and looked like a cross between Caligula and a cockatoo. Mother Burnside had beady little eyes, an imperious beak of a nose, sallow skin, and bad breath. She wore a stiff black wig and a stiff black dress and she sat all day long in a darkened drawing room, her pudgy hands—encrusted with dirty diamond rings—folded over her pudgy belly. She was a grim, taciturn woman, but when she put her mind to it, she could converse on several subjects: a) her exalted ancestors, b) how uppity the nigrahs were gettin', c) the Yankees, d) how unworthy everyone but Mrs. Burnside was, and e) the lamentable condition of her bowels. But usually she just sat in thin-lipped disapproval, her evil black eyes darting like a malign old parrot's.

There was one other occupant in the manor house at Peckerwood. That was Cousin Fan, the poorest relation. She was a faded, vague, timid spinster, whose penance for her poverty was to be at the constant beck and call of Mother Burnside. Miss Fan was rather sweet and pathetic in a masochistic fashion. She had an I. Q. of about thirty-five and all of her time that wasn't passed catering to the stolid whims of Mrs. Burnside was spent in doing Good Works for the Negroes and praying to a genteel and stone-deaf Episcopal God.

Miss Fan scratched at the door of my bedroom after I'd gone to the bathroom and unpacked my clothes. "Hello," she whispered, "I'm Miss Fanny Burnside, Beau's cousin. I'm sorry I wasn't at the door to greet you-all when you drove in, but I was upstairs giving Cousin Euphemia—Miz Burnside, I mean—her purge. You're Miz Beau's nephew, aren't you?"

I said I was and how did she do.

"Maybe you'd care to come down to the veranda and sit a spell. Miz Burnside don't finish her nap 'til four."

Miss Fan and I sat and rocked and eventually Auntie Mame and Uncle Beau strolled over from the Bride's Cottage. Auntie Mame was fearfully animated, kissed Miss Fan several times, and called her Cousin Fanny. The old colored man brought out a big decanter of bourbon and some Coca-Cola and Auntie Mame grew awfully cozy and familiar there on the veranda. "Ah sweah, Cousin Fanny," she shrilled, "yoah jes about as cute as a bug!"

Miss Fan tittered nervously.

It was easy to see that Uncle Beau was terribly proud of Auntie Mame. She called him her big, ole lamb-cat and kept twining his reddish-gold hair into little ringlets. Miss Fan giggled uneasily and said she was so glad that dear Cousin Beau had found such a nice little wife.

About that time there was fearful thumping from somewhere inside the house and Miss Fan's plain face went gray. "Mercy," she said, "I hope all our talking hasn't disturbed Cousin Euphemia. She almost never wakes up so early." Again the thumping, and Miss Fan flew into the house.

Auntie Mame's meeting with her mother-in-law was epic. Miss Fan came scuttling out of the veranda as Uncle Beau was pouring another round of bourbon. "She's ready to see you-all."

"Oh, isn't that dandeh, Beau, honey!" Auntie Mame gushed. "Ah jes cain't *wait!*" I could have waited an eternity.

Miss Fan timorously led the way into the back drawing room, and there sat Mother Burnside.

"Mothah, honeh," Auntie Mame squealed, and rushed up to kiss her. If Mother Burnside's pungent breath wasn't enough to stop further intimacies, her opening remark was.

"You look *oldah* than Ah expectid," she said.

Auntie Mame reeled. She never revealed her exact age and on a legal document she'd say "Over twenty-one," which no one ever seemed inclined to question. I suspected she was between thirty-five and forty, and she seemed a lot younger.

Mrs. Burnside favored Uncle Beau with her baleful black stare. "Yes, Beauregahd, you gave me to unduhstand that yoah wife was *much* youngah. You look tired, son; *mighty* tired." Beau kissed her forehead reverently and then introduced me. I took her puffed old hand and bowed in my best dancing school manner.

"You seem nice enough," she said, "for a *Yankee* boy."

Auntie Mame had by now recovered from the initial barrage and gamely tried once more. "What a lovely, lovely old Greek Revival house this is, Mother—uh, Mrs. Burnside." I noticed that all trace of her Southern accent had disappeared.

"We like it," Mrs. Burnside said tersely, and then turned to Beau and launched on a long anecdote about her bowels.

Dinner that night was a funereal affair. There was a thick soup, a great roast of pork, roast potatoes, candied yams, hominy grits, corn bread, and a pineapple upsidedown cake. I had terrible nightmares, and even Auntie Mame admitted to a slight twinge of acid indigestion. The conversation was spotty. Auntie Mame held forth valiantly on the charm of Greek Revival houses and the influence of Vitruvius brought down through Palladio, Castle, Jones, Adam, and finally Thomas Jefferson. Beau said about six times how good it was to be home, but without much conviction. Miss Fan twittered a great deal until Mrs. Burnside jabbed her viciously with a fork and said to be still. That, plus a few portentous belches, was her only contribution to the merrymaking. Directly after dinner she went to bed and Miss Fan scurried along to help her undress and to read a chapter of the Bible aloud to her. Auntie Mame's visit hadn't started out well.

It was Beau, finally, who planned the big family reunion. Left to her own devices, Mrs. Burnside wouldn't have given so much as a wake for her new daughter-in-law, but since it was owing only to Beau that she and the rest of her patrician relations weren't residing at the County Home, she gave in reluctantly when he wanted to spend some of his own money in his own home for his own wife, and the gathering of the clan was scheduled.

The bride was presented officially to her new relatives when they appeared en masse at a giant barbecue the following Sunday. At noon we were all on the veranda. Auntie Mame was looking lovely and fragile in yellow dotted swiss with a big leghorn hat, and Uncle Beau stood next to her in his ice cream suit, proud as a peacock. Mrs. Burnside was dressed for the next ice age. She sat in a rocker wearing a voluminous black silk dress, black boots, a black shawl, black glasses, a black sunshade, black gloves, and a black hat. She greeted me with a mournful belch and sent Miss Fan in for her potion.

Then the relatives started coming. Car after car creaked into the drive and parked on the spacious lawn. "Ruin the grass," Mrs. Burnside growled, and her stomach rumbled alarmingly.

I've never seen so many Southerners before or since. It seemed impossible that they were all part of the same family—or even the same county —but they were. Beau's sisters, Willie Mae, Sally Randolph, and Georgia Lee arrived first with their husbands. The sisters had each managed to have six children under the age of five and there was a lot of introducing and kissing and you-alling. Although they weren't very attractive people, Auntie Mame began to exude charm, but Mrs. Burnside didn't. Her digestive tract voiced an eloquent protest with each new face.

The relatives kept coming. They all had two first names and some of them even had two last names. There were about six men named Moultrie, four named Calhoun, eight called Randolph, and almost everybody had a Lee tucked somewhere into his or her name. To make things even more confusing, about half the women had men's names. There were ladies called Sarah John, Liza William, Susie Carter, Lizzie Beaufort— pronounced Byew-fert—Mary Arnold, Annie Bryan, Lois Dwight.

By one o'clock there were more than a hundred and twenty relatives milling around Peckerwood, all talking, and all talking *loud*. Mrs. Burnside indicated her disapproval of all this with a fanfaronade of flatulence.

Still the relatives came. Beau was the kind of man who'd be popular anywhere, and since almost all of the guests were directly or indirectly supported by him, it was safe to predict a full turnout. Auntie Mame was in her element, and above Mrs. Burnside's steady barrage of gas attacks I could hear her talking vivaciously.

At quarter-past one the Clay-Picketts, or horsy branch of the family, started piling in. They were all in riding clothes, and they were accompanied by a spotted hound who immediately jumped into Mrs. Burnside's lap, thus causing an explosion of wind which I felt sure she'd been saving for the climax of the party. I sniggered helplessly.

"Down, sir! Down, I say," Van Buren Clay-Pickett roared, and smacked the hound across the hocks, thereby eliciting a soft, moist hiccough from Mrs. Burnside. "Sorry we'ah all so late, Aunt Euphemia, but Sally Cato McDougall got unseated goin' ovah the five-bah an' we *think* she broke her collah bone. Heel, sir!" he bellowed at the dog, who'd managed to knock over three children and was now lifting his leg at the base of one of Peckerwood's six Ionic columns. "Had to shoot her mare. Cousin Clytie and Alice-Richard thought they bettah take Sally Cato to the doctah's, but they'll be along directly. When Sally Cato come to she said to tell you she was awful sorry she couldn't make the shin-dig. Down, sir, goddam it—pardon me, Aunt Euphemia—down, I say." The dog had leaped again into Mrs. Burnside's lap and burrowed his snout diligently into the folds of her black silk skirt. Again the big horseman's hand smacked the hound and a piteous eructation of outraged virtue was clearly heard from Mrs. Burnside. I had to go indoors for a minute to regain control of myself. "Down, sir. Heel, Ah tell ya!"

When I came back outdoors the rest of the Clay-Picketts had arrived— nine of them, all in riding clothes; athletic to the end. The bourbon and branch water was flowing faster and faster and Auntie Mame had gathered a rapt circle of admiring new relatives around her. Mrs. Burnside shook her head dyspeptically and popped another soda mint into her mouth.

All at once the air was split by the blare of a horn and a dark green Packard roadster slithered up the drive. The top was down and a colored boy in dark green stable livery was driving. Sitting on the folded-back roof was the most beautiful woman I've ever seen in my life. She was wearing riding clothes and her left arm was in a sling hastily improvised from a silk scarf.

"Hello, everybody, hello, you-all," she called in a throaty voice. "Sorry I'm late, but my horse had a run-in with a five-bar gate."

There was a silence and then a lot of whispering among the relatives. "Land a goshen," an old uncle with an ear trumpet cackled, "ain't that Sally Cato McDougall, the gal used to be engaged to young Beau?"

"You hush, Uncle Moultrie," Willie Mae screamed. "Yes, it sure enough is, but what *Ah'd* like to know is who in the *wuld* evah invited her."

She wasn't long in finding out. Broken wing and all, the beautiful lady jumped gracefully down from the car and ran up to Mrs. Burnside. "Mrs. Burnside," she said in her lovely voice, "I'm so sorry to be late when you went to all that trouble to invite me especially. Doctor wanted me to go straight to bed, but I told him I wouldn't miss your party for a million dollars."

The old lady burst into a big smile. "Welcome to Peckahwood, Sally Cato, it jus wouldn't be a pahty without you."

Uncle Beau looked kind of mystified.

"Beau Burnside, congratulations!" the beautiful lady said. "Now, let me see this New York bride you've gone out and got yourself." She gave Auntie Mame a lovely smile and stretched out her elegant right hand. "How do you do, Mrs. Beau. I'm Sally Cato McDougall. You got yourself a mighty wild stallion, but I reckon any woman as good looking as you can train him just fine."

Auntie Mame's face glowed with delight. "Why, Beau, why didn't you tell me about Miss McDougall? She's perfectly gorgeous!" They smiled beatifically, and then the rest of the party began gabbling with the noisy release and relief that comes over a crowd when a serious accident has been narrowly averted.

Lunch was announced, followed by an ominous belch from Mrs. Burnside, and then the barbecue began in earnest.

Auntie Mame had scored a social victory among the relatives. They all thought she was the most chowmin' Yankee lady they'd ever met and were so ardent in their praise that Mrs. Burnside was confined to her bed for the next three days. Auntie Mame was pleased to be such a success and was kept pretty busy accepting all the invitations she'd received from various cousins. But of all the people in Richmond County, she found Sally Cato McDougall the most attractive. And, of course, she was. The fact that Sally Cato had been Uncle Beau's former fiancée and was left holding the bag and a five-carat square-cut diamond when Mame and Beau eloped didn't bother her very much. Auntie Mame had been engaged a lot of times herself, and she understood that such things Just Happened. She'd never even known of Sally Cato's existence until the day of the big barbecue, so she hardly felt that she'd connived to steal the prize.

Sally Cato had been awfully friendly with Auntie Mame, too, and in a week's time the pair of them were inseparable. Sally Cato had gone North to school and learned how to speak English, she'd been to Europe a couple of times, and she was really the most cultivated girl of twenty-five Auntie Mame had ever met. She also had a straight-from-the-shoulder, honest quality that captivated everybody. She was expert at everything she did, swimming, dancing, driving, golf, tennis, and bridge—but riding and hunting were her greatest loves.

The morning after the barbecue, the green Packard roadster screeched to a stop in front of the Bride's Cottage and Sally Cato, looking crisp and lovely, skipped up to the terrace where Auntie Mame and I were having our Little Morning Chat. "Good morning, you-all," she called. "Sorry to barge in this way, but with this old sprained arm, I can't ride, can't swim, can't do anything but sit and mope. I'm so bored I could scream!"

Auntie Mame, who was also a little bored at Peckerwood when Uncle Beau wasn't around, greeted her warmly. The two ladies had quite a friendly chat and it soon appeared that they had a lot more in common than Uncle Beau. "Well, honey, the best woman won," Sally Cato said generously. Then she said, "Look, you and this youngster here must find it pretty tiresome with Beau out all day long, and I'm so lonesome at home I'd like to die. So why don't you-all come over to Foxglove for lunch. I have a younger brother just about your age, Patrick. He's a mean little devil, but at least he'll be something gayer for you than Mrs. Burnside and silly old Fanny." Auntie Mame jumped at the opportunity for a little intellectual companionship, and twenty minutes later the two women were intimately swigging bourbon on the veranda at Foxglove.

The McDougall plantation was every bit as grand as Peckerwood and the food was a lot more digestible. At lunchtime one of the strangest-looking kids I've ever seen came slinking around the boxwood hedge and eyed me coldly.

"Oh!" Sally Cato jumped, "it's *you*. I *wish* you'd stop sneaking around. It always gives me such a start. Patrick, this is my brother, Emory Oglethorpe. I hope you two can keep each other out of mischief this summer."

If you didn't know that the blood in his veins ran as blue as the Confederate flag, you'd have sworn that Emory Oglethorpe McDougall was the changeling child of some ill-starred Georgia cracker girl. He was small and wiry, with an incredible head of russet-colored hair and the biggest, greenest eyes I've ever seen. Although he was only six months my elder, Emory Oglethorpe was a century ahead of me when it came to a first-hand knowledge of evil.

Sally Cato refused to let Emory Oglethorpe have any brandy after lunch and told us to run along and play.

"I think your sister is very nice," I told him in a conversational way.

"Well, yo'ah plumb crazy, if ya do. She's an A numbah one *bitch!*" Then he said, "Wanta come down to mah shack? If ya pay me a little somethin' maybe Ah'll show ya mah pictchas." Emory Oglethorpe had constructed a one-room snuggery concealed by vines along the banks of the Savannah River. The place contained some tallow candles, a couple of orange-crate chairs, and a sagging army cot—Confederate Army, I believe—on which he had allegedly seduced quite a number of young colored girls.

"Get you a nice, tawny pickaninny girl," he croaked malevolently, "if ya give me fifty cents. Best kinda poontang there is. Ah like a good piece of dahk meat."

Upon payment of a dime he showed me an exhaustive collection of pornographic photographs, vintage of about 1900. The ladies and gentlemen in the pictures looked kind of old-fashioned, but they were indulging in very modern things. Since biology limits sex—and its variations—to about a dozen pastimes, I got a little bored with the pictures until suddenly I came upon one of Uncle Beau and Sally Cato McDougall in a most intimate position. I jumped in astonishment.

"Fooled ya, didn't Ah?" Emory Oglethorpe croaked wickedly. "Ah jest pasted pictchas of theah heads onto that photo. But Ah bet they did it, jest the same. Gawdlmighty, you shoulda seen ole Sally Cato when she hud that Beau'd got married up No'th. She liked to busted. Went goddin' and damnin' all ovah the house and swo' she'd have the hide of the duhty damn-yankee who got Beau. Ah nevah see such cay'ins-on in all mah bone days. Ah was glad. Ah hate huh! Heah, have a *cig*-arette."

I was horrified, but it was a bit of gratuitous information I was interested to get and I tucked it away among an odd collection of Little-Known Facts About Well-Known People.

When Emory Oglethorpe and I went back to the house, Auntie Mame, under the influence of both alcoholic and intellectual stimulation, had grown animated and expansive with Sally Cato. ". . . Oh, but my dear," she was saying, "I simply *adore* riding. I was practically *born* on horseback. Why, back in New York hardly a day goes by that I don't get a little workout. Up with the birds every morning for a brisk canter through Central Park!" My mouth dropped open. I suppose that Auntie Mame *had* taken a few riding lessons at some dim finishing school in her Northern past, but she'd never so much as looked at a horse in all the years I'd known her.

"Why, that's splendid, Mame," Sally Cato said. *"Most* interesting. I'll have to get hold of your cousin, Van Buren Clay-Pickett—he's Master of the Hounds down here—and organize a big hunt in your honor."

"Oh, *what* a pity," Auntie Mame said quickly. "I've left *all* my riding togs up North."

"Oh, don't you worry about that. I have dozens of things you could wear. What size shoe do you take?"

"Uh, five-B," Auntie Mame said, tucking her feet under her.

"Marvelous," Sally Cato said. "Same as I do. I can even fit you out with boots."

Auntie Mame went pale beneath her tan.

"You *do* ride astride, Mame dear?"

A hopeful gleam came into Auntie Mame's eyes. "Oh, never! Sidesaddle —*always*. Daddy, the colonel, *insisted* that I learn it. He said it was the *only* way for a lady to ride—so graceful. It was silly of him, of course, because now *nobody* rides sidesaddle, but it's the only way I know how." She finished with a sigh of relief, but her joy was short-lived.

"Now, isn't that grand!" Sally Cato said. "I just happen to have an old Champion and Wilton saddle that'll do you fine, and a lovely broadcloth habit. You *are* in luck. I used to ride sidesaddle myself, but now I always sit astride; it's a deal *safer*. Now, I'm going right in and call Van Buren Clay-Pickett over at the Stud. We never hunt in this hot weather, but I'm sure we'll all be happy to make an exception for *you*."

Having made her bed, Auntie Mame was eventually forced to lie in it. News of her equestrian prowess spread far and fast over the countryside, and at almost every family get-together the conversation was switched to quarters and withers, heaves and spavins as a concession to Auntie Mame.

The whole county buzzed with talk of Auntie Mame's forthcoming debut on the field and Uncle Beau went around with his chest puffed up like a pouter pigeon's. Van Buren Clay-Pickett quickly rounded up a flea-bitten old fox and the big hunt was scheduled for the next Sunday. I didn't know what Auntie Mame was going to do, but I hadn't reckoned with her inventive powers. Two days before the big hunt, she powdered herself dead white, put on an unbecoming shade of green, and whispered modestly to Sally Cato McDougall of a delicate and mythical female complaint. The hunt was postponed for a week.

Given a reprieve, Auntie Mame tried desperately for a new and interesting malady, but she remained in the most robust health. Fortunately she sustained a very genuine accident under the gaze of the whole family and Sally Cato on the Friday preceding the fateful hunt. Aunt Mame slipped on the highly waxed parquetry in the dining room at Peckerwood and sprained her ankle. Uncle Beau and Sally Cato rushed her to the local doctor, who taped her up and told her to keep off it for a day or two. "Then that means I *won't* be able to ride Sunday?" she asked.

"Absolutely out of the question, Mrs. Beau," the doctor said. "But of co'se you could follow the hunt in a cah."

Auntie Mame sighed blissfully and closed her eyes.

The next day Sally Cato joined Auntie Mame and Beau and me for lunch in the Bride's Cottage. Sally Cato was very solicitous of Auntie Mame's sprained ankle. Having caught Auntie Mame practicing an intricate tango step, I knew that she was feeling a lot better, but she put on a very convincing show of gallantry over pain. After dessert, Sally Cato unrolled a large and elaborate hand-drawn map of the surrounding countryside. "Mame, honey, I'm just *sick* that you can't ride Sunday. Everybody's just dying to see you on a horse, dear, *me especially.*" I didn't like her tone. "But, anyhow, Mame, I knew you'd want to follow the hunt, and Doc says it's all right for you to drive, so I stayed up 'til all hours working on this map. Now, *here's* where the chase starts, and then the fox usually runs down this way . . ." Sally Cato had done a masterful and detailed scale drawing of the Richmond County hunting territory, and she explained everything beautifully.

Uncle Beau's eyes were moist with admiration. "Gosh, Sally Cato, is there anything you *can't* do? That's one of the finest pieces of cartography I've ever seen. Of course," he said to Auntie Mame, "Sally Cato knows the field so well she could ride it blindfold. Sally Cato, you're a real brick. I never woulda thought that anyone would dream of taking all that trouble just to make a little new bride feel at home down here."

The next morning there was a lot of clomping and yelling and Hi, you-alling out in the driveway of Peckerwood. Uncle Beau was very handsome in his pink coat astride a big horse, and six different members of the hunt said, "Haa's it feel to git back on a hawse aftah gallyvantin' aroun' Noo Yoke, Boragod?" The genial horsemen sounded exactly like a minstrel show, but they all looked fine in their hunting jackets.

There was a general murmur of disappointment when Auntie Mame appeared in a natty plaid suit hobbling delicately on a ebony cane, but Sally Cato stood up on the mounting block and said, "Members of the hunt, I'm afraid I have a piece of bad news for you-all. Mrs. Beau sprained her ankle here at Peckerwood the other night and Doc won't let her ride. But she's such a devoted rider and such an ardent huntswoman that she's going to follow the hunt in her car, so she'll be in on the kill." There was a ripple of applause.

Emory Oglethorpe McDougall, who looked like a crooked jockey in his riding clothes, sidled up to me. "Ah'd rathah follow a map o' hades than that one ole Sally Cato drew up. If yo'ah smaht, you'll tell yoah Auntie Mame to jes git *lost.*"

"You're crazy," I said.

"Okay," he said, "drive on, fool, hell's only half full."

Auntie Mame hopped into Beau's open Dusenberg with surprising agility. I went along with her to open and close the thousands of gates that blocked off the hundreds of dirt and clay roads snaking over the countryside. Auntie Mame had never fully mastered the automobile, but after startling several horses, we lurched off in a cloud of blue monoxide gas. Rolling out to the field behind the pack, Auntie Mame squeezed my knee affectionately and said, "Oh, darling, I'm so thankful for this sprain. Maybe now they'll get over this horse craze. It was sweet, though, of Sally Cato to make this wonderful map. I just hope I won't be sick when they kill that poor little fox."

With a great deal of trouble, Auntie Mame got the car headed in the right direction and the hunt was on. We jogged over red clay roads for nearly an hour, turning into this lane and then that one. Occasionally we'd lose sight of the pack and then they'd appear again. I hopped out about a million times to open slack, splintery old gates and then shut them after the car had jogged through. It was a remarkable map, because we were always just a little ahead of the hunt. Sally Cato had been almost clairvoyant in her knowledge of where and when the fox would be. The roads were terrible, powdery with red dust and deeply rutted. Auntie Mame drove like a startled hare and my liver got a thorough shaking up. She looked a little scared, but once or twice she shouted, "Yoicks, there they go." Another time she called, "Tallyho!" Just why, I wasn't sure.

After an eternity of bouncing and lurching, we came to the worst road of all. It ran in deep clay ruts straight across a sloping meadow. Neither horse nor hound was in sight. Auntie Mame stopped the car and busied herself with her compact. "Mercy," she said, "now we've lost them."

Then there was a thunder of hoofs and yelping of hounds. A small black fox dashed down the hill with the pack in hot pursuit. "Here they come, Auntie Mame," I yelled. They were headed straight for us. Auntie Mame dropped her lipstick. Now the horses appeared over the rise. Frantically Auntie Mame tried to start the car; it spluttered and gagged, but nothing happened. She tried again. The pack was drawing nearer and nearer, the horses pummeling down the hill.

"The key, Auntie Mame!" I shouted.

"Oh, yes," she said wildly. The fox was desperately close. Auntie Mame switched on the ignition and the car bounded forward just as a small cannon ball of black fur darted into the road. There was a terrible screech of brakes and I was thrown forward against the windshield. Then all hell broke loose. Hounds, horses, and riders descended on us like an avalanche. Nearly three dozen riders were thrown, and two big bay mares rammed into the Dusenberg so hard the front fender and hood had to be replaced. A third mount was half in and half out of the back seat, whinnying horribly. All in all, there were more horses shot that day than at the Battle of Gettysburg, and when the final casualty list was posted there were six broken ankles, four broken arms, a fractured leg—compound— three cases of concussion, a dislocated pelvis, and countless bruises and abrasions. The riders who were able to walk and speak raced down to the car in a fury and Aunt Mame fainted dead away. I was almost hysterical, but still able to hear Emory Oglethorpe McDougall growl, "What'd

Ah tell yuh?", and to note the bitter smile of triumph on Sally Cato's face. Auntie Mame had been in for the kill, all right. The fox lay dead under the car.

If Auntie Mame had been the subject of a good deal of county conversation before the fateful fox hunt, she was now the absolute mania of the riding set. Emory Oglethorpe made it perfectly clear to me that she was now referred to as "that crazy, damnyankee woman who killed all ouah hawses." People for miles around talked of nothing else, and every day the telephone buzzed with hesitant voices saying how sorry they were that they'd be unable to come to Bride's Cottage for lunch or that they had to postpone indefinitely the little dinner they'd planned in Auntie Mame's honor. Auntie Mame, after two weeks of being the uncontested belle of the county, now seemed about as popular as General Sheridan.

Mother Burnside seemed to feel a lot better after the news of her daughter-in-law's downfall, and managed to come downstairs for dinner every night. Between soda mints and waves of wind, she favored us all with such reminiscences as, "When *Ah* was a young bride theah was nothin' Ah loved and adohed moah than huntin'. Ah was a regulah Diana." Beau sat tight-lipped and looked grim and embarrassed. And one evening when Mother Burnside's memoirs of field and flatulence were particularly trying, Miss Fan lent Auntie Mame a handkerchief and whispered, "Don't you pay any heed to her, Miz Beau, she *hated* hunting and she rode worse than I did!" But Miss Fan's mousy solicitude did little to comfort Auntie Mame. She was *persona non grata* in the entire community, and she knew it. The only one who still offered her friendship was Sally Cato McDougall.

"But, Mame, honey," she'd say, "don't cry like that. It wasn't your fault—everybody knows accidents will happen. If the others are too narrow-minded to forgive and forget, well, to hell with them. *I'm* still your friend. You know that."

Auntie Mame was intensely grateful to Sally Cato. They saw each other daily, and Sally Cato *was* the only person who was nice to her. Even Uncle Beau seemed stiff around Auntie Mame.

I saw a lot of Emory Oglethorpe while Auntie Mame was in purdah. He taught me how to smoke and chew and drink a vile kind of dandelion wine he concocted. "Didn' believe me, didja, when Ah tole yuh Sally Cato was out to have yoah Auntie's hide. Lawd, man, she knew you-all'd be drivin' acrosst that field jes when the pack was. She knows the huntin' country like the back of huh ha-yand. You shoulda huhd huh laughin' and screamin' an' ca'yin' on aftah all them hawses spilled to hell an' gone ovah yoah Auntie's cah. Ah thought it was a pretty funny-lookin' sight, mahself. Don' worry, Sally Cato's gonna get Beau back if she has to kill yoah Auntie doin' it." He chuckled maliciously. "Ole Sally Cato's nevah lost a bet, o' a race, o' a man in huh life, and she sho don't inten' ta staht now. Heah, take the resta this packa Luckies."

I was beginning to be half convinced that Emory Oglethorpe was right, although it didn't seem possible that Sally Cato would stoop to anything so low.

But that evening I began to appreciate Emory Oglethorpe's appraisal of his sister. Sally Cato, who was the great favorite of Mrs. Burnside's, dined with us at Peckerwood. She looked very Southern, very romantic, very beautiful in white lace, and she was charm itself. Auntie Mame, who had been openly snubbed in the millinery department of J. B. White's that afternoon, looked tired, and what's more, she looked old.

Mother Burnside was unusually talkative that night, and in her oblique fashion she let poor Auntie Mame have it right between the eyes. She spoke of nothing but Sally Cato. Sally Cato's beauty, her youth, her wealth, her ancient lineage, her seat on a horse, how lovely she'd looked at the last Hunt Ball, how vital and healthy she always seemed, how typically, charmingly, radiantly Southern she was. "A real, genu-wine daughtah of ouah own fay-ah county. A blue-blooded young flowah of the Old South and of ouah glorious community wheah every family has a rich background of great traditions and wheah no strangeh has trespassed since the Wah of the *See*-cession."

Auntie Mame claimed a sick headache and left right after dinner. She'd been having a lot of sick headaches lately, and Beau said, "What, again?"

I went up to my room early. It was hot and humid and I couldn't sleep, so I stuck one of Emory Oglethorpe's cigarettes in my mouth and went out onto the upstairs piazza. But the cigarette hung dead on my lips, for below me I could see the red ends of two other cigarettes and I heard Sally Cato's voice, low and urgent. "Oh, Beau," she said, "I *know* Mame's nice. Believe me, I love her just as much as you do, but is she *right* for *you*? Beau, honestly, all I want is your happiness. I took it pretty hard when I heard you'd married her instead of me, but truly, that's all water over the dam. Mame's a grand woman, but Beau, does she *belong* down here?"

"Mame's a Yankee," Beau said stiffly, "and they have different ways from ours."

"Oh, Beau, I realize all that. After all, I'm her only *friend*. But Beau, I keep asking myself, can she give you the family, the home, the children that are a part of our Southern heritage? *Can* she, Beau?"

"I don't know why not," Beau said with a note of doubt.

"Well, Beau, just remember, your happiness is all I want. I've got to get up early tomorrow for the hunter trials, so I'll run along now. Want to give me a little kiss for old times' sake?" The cigarettes dropped to the grass and there was no more talking. They just stood there in the shadows, kind of wrapped around each other, and didn't move for a long, long time.

Wretchedly I turned away, and as I did, something woolly brushed across my face. I was too frightened to utter a sound. Then a bony hand clutched my arm and a voice whispered, "Come in here, child." It was Miss Fan.

She led me into her hot little room. "Give me a cigarette," she breathed. "I know you have some, I saw them in your wardrobe."

We smoked in silence. She was a lot better at it than I.

"I suppose you heard—Beau and that, that dreadful Sally Cato?"

I nodded.

"Now do you understand? Now do you see why you've got to get your aunt out of here—and Beau, too?"

I bobbed my head dumbly.

"Lord knows I'm only a poor old spinster—no better than a servant in this house and at the beck and call of that terrible old shrew twenty-four hours a day. I have no business saying all this, but Miz Beau is the only person in this whole godforsaken county who's ever treated me like a human being. Beau's a nice boy, too. That's why you've got to get them out of here, before it's too late. Before that dirty old woman and that slut of a girl wreck the whole thing. Every day I hear the two of them up in her bedroom, plotting, plotting, plotting. Do you understand, child? Do you *see? Get your aunt out of here.* Quick, before those two ruin her. Now go to bed, child. Oh, yes, and leave those cigarettes here."

The next day I tried in a bumbling, callow way to warn Auntie Mame about Sally Cato, but I did it so badly that she flew at me in a rage. "What!" she cried, sitting bolt upright.

"I *said,* Auntie Mame, did you ever stop and think that maybe Sally Cato *isn't* your friend? After all, she used to be engaged to Uncle Beau, and *she* was the one who drew that map and made you kill all those horses, and Emory Oglethorpe says . . ."

"Emory Oglethorpe says," she mimicked shrilly, "Emory Oglethorpe says . . . Who *cares* what that little goat-eyed hellion says! As for *you,* I'm ashamed—yes, *good and ashamed*—that any nephew of mine could be so small-minded, so petty and rotten as to entertain for one moment such a filthy, vile notion. The idea!" At that moment Sally Cato's big Packard roadster was gliding up the drive. "Here comes Sally Cato now. I will spare you the embarrassment of seeing her. Get out of here and don't come back until you can think and speak like a gentleman. Sally Cato's the only real friend I've got down here, and I won't hear another word about her. Now scat!"

Crestfallen, I loped away. I hadn't mentioned what had happened the night before, because I didn't want to hurt Auntie Mame's feelings. She loved Uncle Beau an awful lot—she must have, or she wouldn't have put up with life at Peckerwood.

But when Sally Cato drove away, Auntie Mame seemed terribly nervous and upset and called me into the Bride's Cottage. "Oh, Patrick, Patrick," she moaned, "whatever am I to do now?"

"Do about what?"

"Sally Cato was just here and she's planning another of those ghastly rodeo things. She says the only way I can redeem myself with the people in the county is to show them what a wonderful horsewoman I am. Now I have to ride and, oh, Patrick, it wasn't true, all that business about my loving horses. I *loathe* them."

"Why don't you just admit that you were only kidding, Auntie Mame?" I said with certain childlike innocence. "Then they won't expect you to ride."

"What! Be made even a worse laughingstock than I am now? I'd rather die!"

"But that's exactly what may happen to you if you go out on this hunt."

"Better to die in the saddle," she said nobly, and shuddered.

"Well, cheer up, Auntie Mame, you can always come down with a cold or sprain your ankle again before the hunt."

"But it's *tomorrow, at six o'clock in the morning!*"

Uncle Beau was out at a landowners' meeting that night, and Auntie Mame and I dined silently in the Bride's Cottage. Auntie Mame was trying to read *Fleurs du Mal* when the station wagon from Foxglove drove up to the door. Emory Oglethorpe hopped out carrying a big box, a pair of boots, a silk hat, and a leather sidesaddle. "Evenin'," he grunted in his nutmeg-grater voice, "ole Sally Cato tol' me to hustle these hawse duds ovah to yoah Auntie Mame. Man o' man, you oughta see Sally Cato, she's whoopin' an' hollerin' all ovah the stables. Sez she vows yoah Auntie Mame ain't nevah been on so much as a merry-go-round. She's takin' all kinds o' bets on the hunt an' givin' odds of a hundred to one. The hawse she's picked fo' yoah Auntie Mame'll be ovah in the van tomorrah mawnin'. You betta tell yoah Auntie to break huh laig o' somethin' befo' she breaks huh neck. Well, so long, Ah gotta fine piece o' high yallah waitin' fo' me back to the shack."

I felt as though the black broadcloth riding habit I carried in to Auntie Mame were a shroud. She looked aghast and began to tremble. "Oh, God, Sally Cato's sent over the whole outfit." Then she eyed the sidesaddle. "Am I supposed to *sit* on that jock strap?" She began to cry, and she was still weeping softly on her pillow when I went back to the big house.

By the time I was dressed next morning I heard hoofs clomping up the drive. The whole county—all except those who were still convalescing from Auntie Mame's last performance on the hunt field—was congregated in front of Peckerwood. There were even a few people from across the Carolina border. They seemed less hearty than they had the last time, and there was a malicious, conspiratorial feeling in the air.

Somehow Auntie Mame and I didn't give the impression of *haute cou-*

ture. I was wearing a castoff outfit of Emory Oglethorpe McDougall's and he was nearly a head shorter than I was. From certain angles Auntie Mame looked very dashing in Sally Cato's broadcloth riding costume and her brow was misleadingly serene under the tall silk hat. But the jacket was a trifle tight here, a trifle loose there, and the skirt dragged a little. Then, too, the size five boots must have been misery. Auntie Mame chain-smoked a lot and took several nips from a silver flask. She tried to seem lighthearted and cheery, but she looked ill at ease, and all the riders eyed her suspiciously.

Sally Cato cantered up on a fine big mare, followed by Emory Ogle-thorpe and a van from Foxglove. There was a terrible amount of stomp-ing and kicking coming from inside the van, and with a good deal of trouble two grooms finally led the biggest, meanest-looking horse I've ever seen down the runway.

Sally Cato kissed Auntie Mame warmly. "How *unusual* you look this morning, Mame honey," she said. "Excuse me just a moment, dear, I want to run in and say a word to Mrs. Burnside."

In a minute she was back. I looked up to the second-story piazza and saw old Mother Burnside standing there with a funny, unpleasant expres-sion on her face. Sally Cato skipped over to Auntie Mame. "This is the horse I picked especially for you, Mame dear," she said with a sly smile. "His name is Lightning Rod, and he's as gentle as a lamb."

Lightning Rod was an Irish hunter, seventeen and a half hands high; a gelding who'd never quite reconciled himself to a life of celibacy. He looked at Auntie Mame with blood in his eye and pawed the ground savagely. Sally Cato stroked his muzzle. "He's a booful ole darlin', dat's wot he is."

Emory Oglethorpe slithered up to me. "He's the goddamndest, most vicious piece o' hawse flesh in Richmond County, *that's* what he is. O'nery son-of-a-bitch shoulda been shot two yeahs ago when he trompled Uncle Grady half to death. Least, that's what the *vet* said. That cussed ole plug's been cockeyed crazy an' runnin' roun' the pastcha evah since. Took six niggahs all yestiddy aftahnoon to ketch him."

Sally Cato clapped her elegantly gloved hands and said, "Your atten-tion, everyone, we are now going to have the unique privilege of hunting with one of New York City's most famous equestriennes, Mrs. Beau Burn-side." She winked maliciously, but not quickly enough for Auntie Mame to miss. Auntie Mame's eyes opened wide. There was a ripple of repressed mirth among the riders. Only Beau had an air of innocence.

I was already astride a spastic old nag when three grooms led Lightning Rod to the mounting block and Auntie Mame climbed gingerly aboard. I breathed a silent prayer and I noticed that Auntie Mame's lips were moving, too.

All the way out to the field I tried to keep as close as possible to Auntie

Mame, but Lightning Rod had a pernicious habit of kicking out behind so that she had the road pretty much to herself. I hoped she wouldn't be hurt too much when she fell. We ambled along placidly enough, even though I received the distinct impression that all dogs, most people, and some horses made Lightning Rod nervous and irritable. Finally we got to the starting place. Lightning Rod whinnied eerily and reared. But surprisingly enough, Auntie Mame stayed on. A couple of the people seemed impressed. Sally Cato just sneered.

As we were about to start, the Peckerwood station wagon raced up to the field with a scared-looking Negro at the wheel. Miss Fan jumped out and screamed, "Stop! That horse is mad!" But she was too late. The fox had been released and was dashing wildly across the meadow, the hounds hot on his trail; simultaneously, Cousin Van Buren Clay-Pickett and Auntie Mame led off and the hunt was under way. There was no stopping her now.

I'd thought surely that Auntie Mame would have the good sense to select a nice soft-looking hummock and throw herself off, but she didn't. Instead, she and Lightning Rod galloped hell-for-leather after Cousin Van Buren. "Gawdlmighty, what a seat Miz Beau has!" someone shouted. I turned around to see who could be so deranged and my eye caught an expression on Sally Cato's face that was awful to behold.

We raced off, leaving poor old Miss Fan screaming incomprehensible things. The old nag I was riding wasn't good for much more than glue, but at least it kept up with the pack long enough for me to see Auntie Mame and Lightning Rod sail over a jagged stone wall that threw two others. Auntie Mame lost her silk hat and her hair floated out wildly, but still she kept on going.

"Ja see huh cleah that woll?" someone called. "That damn-yankee gal's got *style*. Soo*pub* hawsewoman. Pufeckly soo*pub!*"

We rode for better than an hour, thundering over the springy turf, scraping beneath low-hanging branches, and splashing through muddy creeks. Auntie Mame was out of sight most of the time, and even Uncle Beau and Sally Cato found it impossible to keep up with her. At one point she and Lightning Rod took a sort of detour through a whole field of feeding corn, but still they had no trouble in catching up with the Master of the Hounds. Another time the horse charged into an old lean-to and right out the other side with Auntie Mame still aboard. There was a lot of clucking and squawking and chickens flew out from every direction. In a flash I saw that one old hen, gamer than most, was even perched on Auntie Mame's shoulder, but the sheer velocity of the wind soon sent it flapping helplessly into the air.

Once again I lost sight of her when Lightning Rod plunged into a patch of woods, but Auntie Mame soon appeared again wearing something that looked like a laurel wreath and not even holding the reins.

"Ah vow," one of the more cultivated cousins screamed, "don't she look like a verytibble Greek goddess!"

"Landagoshen," another one roared, "she ain't even hangin' on. If that don't beat all!"

Then she raced ahead again and disappeared from view.

At last we bounded up to a big, flat plateau overlooking a wide expanse of low green meadow ending abruptly with a high floodwall that ran along the banks of the Savannah River. This was where the hunt must end, unless the poor fox could manage to scale the six-foot wall.

By then the fox, the hounds, Van Buren Clay-Pickett, and Auntie Mame were so far ahead that there was no hope of ever catching up, although Beau and Sally Cato McDougall were in hot pursuit about a quarter of a mile behind. Suddenly Lightning Rod spurted ahead still faster and gave every appearance of trying to overtake Cousin Van Buren.

"Ah cain't unduhstand that Yankee-style huntin'," one of the men shouted. "Mighty bad fo'm to pass the Mastuh."

"It ain't huh fault," another rider yelled. "That crazy McDougall hawse is runnin' away with huh, that's what!"

"Gawdlmighty, yo' *right*."

I wanted to shut my eyes tight, but the terrible fascination of the scene before me was too strong. When I opened them again Lightning Rod had not only passed the Master, but the hounds as well, and finally the fox. He was a matter of yards from the six-foot floodwall and still he tore onward.

"Lawd, he's goin' to dash the damn-yankee gal to death!"

"Moultrie, Ah cain't look!" the woman next to me screamed, and swooned in her saddle.

With Auntie Mame still hanging on, Lightning Rod charged the floodwall. Suddenly his hoofs left the ground and he leaped for the wall, but it was too much for him. His mammoth chest struck the top and he fell back with a thump that could be heard all over Richmond County. Auntie Mame, however, kept right on going. She cleared the wall by a good four feet and disappeared behind it. There was a terrible splash, and then silence. Another woman swooned but nobody paid any attention. The rest of us raced pell-mell down to the meadow just in time to see Auntie Mame emerge from the Savannah River.

Just then a rickety old Chevrolet bounced across the meadow and jolted to a stop. An apoplectic little man jumped out and jogged up to the cluster of panting horses. It was the county veterinarian. "Great day in the mornin'," he shouted, "I bin followin' this pore little lady fo' the last half houah. Most amazin' feat of hawsemanship I evah *did* see. Why she wasn't killed I nevah *will* know. Well, I *thought* I reckinized that hawse, an' now Ah'm *positive*. It's that crazy Lightning Rod belongs to Sally Cato McDougall." His angry blue eyes sought out Sally Cato. "Sally

Cato," the vet screamed, "Ah *tole* you two yeahs ago that hawse was mad. Ah *commanded* you to have him shot!" He looked at Lightning Rod, sprawled in agony on the ground. "Now Ah guess Ah git to do the job mahself." He pulled a .45 automatic out of his holster. "Sally Cato, it's *you* Ah oughta be shootin'. To let *anybody*—even a soopub hawsewoman like this little lady heah—ride on that hawse is tantymount to muhduh. Yes, Ah said plain, premeditated *muhduh*. You oughta have yo name read outta every huntin' pack in the who' county." With one shot he put the pathological Lightning Rod out of his misery and Auntie Mame burst into tears.

Uncle Beau swept Auntie Mame up to his saddle and, dirty and wet and scratched as she was, he kept hugging her and kissing her and calling her his Little Yankee Valkyrie.

The rest of the members were agog at the glory of Auntie Mame, and I noticed that they all seemed to find it desirable not to ride anywhere near Sally Cato as we all ambled back to the field where the pavilion was set up for the Hunt Breakfast. Once Sally Cato reined her horse over toward Uncle Beau's. "Beau," she said urgently, "if you'll only let me explain . . ." But he gave her a terrible look and cantered ahead with his arms tenderly around Auntie Mame.

The Hunt Breakfast was sensational. No one could talk of anything but Auntie Mame's magnificent seat. She was christened "Mame, the Huntress," and everyone toasted her time after time as the greatest horsewoman ever to grace Richmond County. Auntie Mame got awfully high on bourbon, but when I finally had a chance to get near her, she held me tight and whispered: "Patrick, darling, tell me, am I still alive? I got my thigh stuck so tight in that sidesaddle thing I thought I never *would* fall off."

Cousin Van Buren Clay-Pickett had leaped to the top of the buffet to propose another hunt on the following Sunday when a Western Union boy shambled in with a telegram for Auntie Mame. It read: IMPERATIVE YOU RETURN NEW YORK IMMEDIATELY TO JUDGE INTERNATIONAL HORSE SHOW STOP A DEVOTED FAN INSISTS

THE COMMITTEE

"Oh, dear," Auntie Mame cried petulantly, hastily gulping down a full tumbler of bourbon. "What a bore. But I suppose we must go back North. Onward and upward, always, you know, to new triumphs on the turf."

Going Places with Art Buchwald

I

CRASHING THE *SAUNA* BARRIER

IT NEVER occurred to me to go to Finland. Not that I had anything against Finland personally; it was just that, with Paavo Nurmi retired, there didn't seem much reason for going there. But a nice man from Finnair, the nationalized Finnish airlines, told me that they were opening a new route from Paris to Helsinki and offered me a free ride to celebrate the occasion. They even said they'd treat me to a Finnish bath and throw in a reindeer-steak dinner. With these choice morsels dangled in front of my eyes, I had no reason to refuse, and I can't say I'm sorry.

The one word that constantly crops up in everybody's conversation in Finland is *sauna*—the native Finnish bath. But in Finland a sauna is not just a bath—it is a way of life. A sauna is to a Finn what a pub is to a Britisher, what a café is to a Frenchman, what a television set is to an American. The whole social life of the family revolves around the sauna. People build their saunas before they build their houses. Business deals, marriages, divorces and even births are transacted in a sauna. The world trembles, governments topple, fortunes fall, but the Finnish bath has remained the same ever since the prehistoric day when an anonymous Slav (or was it a Teuton?) poured some cold water on some hot rocks and started to perspire.

"What a wonderful idea," he was quoted as telling a *Time* correspondent. "This is better than taking a bath. I predict a great future for saunas."

Little did he know how right he would be.

The typical Finnish sauna is a single-room log building with stones on top of an uncovered furnace. When the sauna is heated the smoke is not let out but allowed to circulate around the room, heating the ceiling, the walls and the benches. Hence, if a man sits in such a room for any length of time he must produce either blood, sweat or tears.

Every hotel in Finland has a sauna, and there is nothing more pleasing for a foreigner than to tell the room clerk to prepare one for him at the end of a hard sightseeing day. Usually, if you time it right, a sauna can

From *The Brave Coward* by Art Buchwald published by Harper & Brothers. Copyright 1953 by New York Herald Tribune, Inc.

take the place of the cocktail hour, and the price, I'm happy to add, is no higher than the price of a dry martini.

I had extraordinary luck the day I decided to take one at the Hotel Vakunna in Helsinki. I was given for an attendant the very same woman who had given a sauna to movie actor Gregory Peck when he paid a visit to Helsinki last year. Her name was Leena, and when it was revealed in the newspapers that she had given Peck a Finnish bath, she became the most sought-after sauna attendant in all of Finland. Next to meeting Jan Sibelius there is no greater honor in Finland than to be given a bath by Leena of the Vakunna.

Leena, a strapping, husky woman in her fifties, is a modest rubber, and to look at her you would never think she had met Gregory Peck, much less given him a sauna. But next to her heart of gold is nothing but tough muscle, and when you're put in Leena's hands, bones crack, legs go limp and heads go spinning on the floor.

Leena made me strip completely and then, with a gentle shove, threw me into the torture chamber. She grabbed a pail of cold water and threw it on red-hot rocks. Steam started to rise in the room. The second pail of cold water she threw on the corpse writhing on the floor.

Then she threw more water on the rocks. The temperature of the room had reached the melting point of steel, but Leena did not seem satisfied. Suddenly I realized what she was trying to do. She was trying to crash the sauna barrier. I yelled through the mist, "Please don't make it any hotter than you made it for Gregory Peck."

She didn't seem to hear me.

Finally she stuck a long cake tester in me and realized I was done.

Then Leena took a bundle of birch branches and started whipping the body. The Finns will tell you they do this to give your corpse a nice fragrance, but actually it's so the victim can't smell his own burning flesh. Leena whisked me from the top down, and in no time at all she was whisking the soles of my feet.

"It's very important that the soles of the feet should be well whisked," she explained. "Only a well-whisked man knows the true glories of a sauna. Even Gregory Peck looked better after he was whisked."

After the whisking I was given a bath and then rinsed off with water. The Finns prefer to jump in a lake or roll in the snow after their sauna but since the Vakunna sauna is located on the seventh floor of a building and there was no snow in Helsinki at that time of year, Leena let me off lightly with a 31-degree-Fahrenheit shower. She then wrapped me in one of the hotel's towels and let me thaw out in a quiet hospital bed in a little room off the bath.

I've had other saunas while I've been in Finland, even one above the Arctic Circle in Lapland, but as far as I'm concerned the one Leena gave me at the Vakunna was the highlight of my trip. I can't help believing in some small way that a little of Gregory Peck has rubbed off on me.

II

VENICE A LA HEMINGWAY

Every person who comes to Venice is influenced in some way by one of the great writers who have written about the city. Hemingway has probably influenced me more than anyone, and without *Across the River and into the Trees,* I doubt if I'd even have enjoyed being there.

Take, for example, the night when I went to dinner at the Gritti Palace Hotel with my wife. It was a good dinner, an imposing dinner, a lobster dinner, and the lobster he was good. When he arrived he was dark and green and unfriendly and cost a day's wages, but when they grilled him he was red and I wouldn't have traded five suits for him.

I looked across the table at my wife. She looked good. Almost as good as the lobster. "She looks as lovely as a gondola," I thought to myself, "or Stan Musial or Joe DiMaggio. She could drive a home run into the canal if I let her." I held her hand tightly. "I love you and I'm glad you're you," I told her. "Daughter, let's go for a ride in a gondola after dinner."

"What is this daughter business?" my wife said. "And stop holding my hand so tight. I can't eat my lobster."

"My poor daughter, my little daughter, my only daughter," I said. "Who do you love?"

"If you call me daughter once more," my wife said, "I'm going to hit you with this bottle of wine. And while you're in this mood, would you mind telling me what you were doing all afternoon on the beach with Gina Lollobrigida?"

"Moon is my mother and father," I told her. "A lobster fills with the moon. When he is dark he is not worth eating, little daughter."

"I wasn't talking about the lobster," she said. "I was talking about Lollobrigida."

"Please, daughter. You must try to understand my attitude. When you have killed so many you can afford to be a little wild."

"How many have you killed?"

"One hundred and eighty sures, not counting possibles."

"And you have no remorse?"

"None."

"Well, I do, and you'd better watch your step."

"Come, daughter, come, let's not think of Lollobrigida. We will find a gondola and you will be you and I will be me and the gondolier will be him."

"I'm warning you about this daughter business."

We walked outside. Now she looked more like Mickey Mantle or a young Bobby Feller. What a pitcher she'd make, I thought.

We found a gondola which was long and good and brave and true and it was our gondola for as long as we wanted it, for that's how it is in Venice. A man can either take a gondola or leave it alone. Only tourists and lovers take gondolas in Venice, I thought. Tourists and lovers and people who can afford them. Where does that leave me?

"Why can't we take a motorboat?" my wife asked. "A gondola is awfully slow."

"Because you're my wife and we're alone and it is Venice and I want to hold you close and I want you to hold me close and anyway it's cheaper than taking a motorboat."

"The canal smells," she said.

"So does war. So do the Russians. So do lobsters and garlic and perfume. Everything smells, daughter. We've just got to get used to it. Have you ever skied in the dark?"

"Listen, I'm getting sick of this nonsense. Let's go back to the Lido and see one of the movies. You came down for the film festival."

"The pictures smell almost as much as the canal. Except for Marlon Brando and Cary Grant and Frank Sinatra and some selected short subjects, I'd rather be in a gondola with you."

"The Italian starlets seem to have attracted your attention."

"They're nothing compared to the 'Star-Spangled Banner' or baby shrimps at the Taverna or sole at the Colombo or you at first base for the New York Yankees. I looked at them as I would look at any live animals in the jungle. Let's go to Harry's for one last drink before I kiss you once and for all forever and for a day."

"I want to go back to the hotel," my wife said. "The gondola or the lobster have made me sick."

"Which one, daughter?"

"How the hell do I know?"

"All right, I'll take you home and read you Dante and tell you about war and the Krauts and the very brave boys and guys like Pete Quesada and Red Smith and the Montana National Guard. Now before you get sick, daughter, kiss me and love me straight and true."

It must have been the last "daughter," because before I knew it I was in the canal with all my clothes on. But it was good to be alive and wet and in love and in Venice. Hemingway couldn't have had a better time.

Gamesmanship

(OR THE ART OF WINNING GAMES WITHOUT ACTUALLY CHEATING)

(A SELECTION)

By STEPHEN POTTER

ORIGINS.

What is gamesmanship? Most difficult of questions to answer briefly. "The Art of Winning Games Without Actually Cheating"—that is my personal "working definition." What is its object? There have been five hundred books written on the subject of games. Five hundred books on play and the tactics of play. Not one on the art of winning.

I well remember the gritty floor and the damp roller towels of the changing room where the idea of writing this book came to me. Yet my approach to the thing had been gradual.

In those days I used to play lawn tennis for a small but progressive London college—Birkbeck, where I lectured. It happened that my partner at that time was C. Joad, the celebrated gamesman, who in his own sphere is known as metaphysician and educationist. Our opponents were usually young men from the larger colleges, competing against us not only with the advantage of age but also with a decisive advantage in style. They would throw the service ball very high in the modern manner: the backhands, instead of being played from the navel, were played, in fact, on the backhand, weight on right foot, in the exaggerated copybook style of the time—a method of play which tends to reduce all games, as I believe, to a barrack-square drill by numbers; but, nevertheless, of acknowledged effectiveness.

In one match we found ourselves opposite a couple of particularly tall and athletic young men of this type from University College. We will call them Smith and Brown. The knock-up showed that, so far as play was concerned, Joad and I, playing for Birkbeck, had no chance. U. C. won the toss. It was Smith's service, and he cracked down a cannon ball to Joad which moved so fast that Joad, while making some effort to suggest by his attitude that he had thought the ball was going to be a fault, never-

From *The Theory and Practice of Gamesmanship* by Stephen Potter. Reprinted by permission of Henry Holt & Company and Rupert Hart-Davis, Ltd.

theless was unable to get near with his racket, which he did not even attempt to move. Score: fifteen-love. Service to me. I had had time to gauge the speed of this serve, and the next one did, in fact, graze the edge of my racket frame. Thirty-love. Now Smith was serving again to Joad—who this time, as the ball came straight towards him, was able, by grasping the racket firmly with both hands, to receive the ball on the strings, whereupon the ball shot back to the other side and volleyed into the stop netting near the ground behind Brown's feet.

Now here comes the moment on which not only this match, but so much of the future of British sport was to turn. Score: forty-love. Joad called across the net, in an even tone:

"Kindly say clearly, please, whether this ball was in or out."

Crude to our ears, perhaps. A Stone Age implement. But beautifully accurate gamesmanship for 1931. For the student must realize that these two young men were both in the highest degree charming, well-mannered young men, perfect in their sportsmanship and behavior. Smith stopped dead.

SMITH: I'm so sorry—I *thought* it was out. (*The ball had hit the back netting twelve feet behind him before touching the ground.*) But what did you think, Brown?

BROWN: I *thought* it was out—but do let's have it again.

JOAD: No, I don't want to have it again. I only want you to say clearly, if you will, whether the ball is in or out.

There is nothing more putting off to young university players than a slight suggestion that their etiquette or sportsmanship is in question. How well we know this fact, yet how often we forget to make use of it. Smith sent a double fault to me, and another double fault to Joad. He did not get in another ace service till halfway through the third set of a match which incidentally we won.

That night I thought hard and long. Could not this simple gambit of Joad's be extended to include other aspects of the game—to include all games? For me, it was the birth of gamesmanship.

WINMANSHIP.

The assiduous student of gamesmanship has little time for the minutiae of the game itself—little opportunity for learning how to play the shots, for instance. His skill in stroke-making may indeed be almost non-existent. So that the gamesman who finds himself winning in the early stages of the match is sometimes at a loss. Therefore, this seems to me the place to set down a few words of help and friendly advice to the winning gamesman, to help him keep his lead; to assist him to maintain his advantage, and rub his opponent's face in the dirt.

Very often the opponent will show signs, just as he is beginning to lose, of being irritated by distractions. At golf, "somebody has moved." At billiards, "somebody talked." Take this opportunity of making him feel that he is not really a player at all by talking on these lines:

> "Somebody yelling, did you say? Do you know, I didn't notice it. I'm a fool at games. Don't seem to be able to be aware of anything outside them, when I'm playing the shot. I remember, once, Joyce Wethered was putting. Eighteenth green—semifinal. An express train went by within fifteen feet of her nose.
> "'How did you manage to sink that putt—with that train . . .?'
> "'What train?' she said."

Always tell the same story to the same man, for your example. (See under "Story, constant repetition of, to the same person.")

In my own view there is only one correct time when the gamesman can give advice: and that is when the gamesman has achieved a *useful* though not necessarily a *winning* lead. Say three up and nine to play at golf, or, in billiards, sixty-five to his opponent's thirty. Most of the accepted methods are effective. E.g., in billiards, the old phrase serves. It runs like this:

GAMESMAN: Look . . . may I say something?

LAYMAN: What?

GAMESMAN: *Take it easy*.

LAYMAN: What do you mean?

GAMESMAN: I mean—you know how to make the strokes, but you're stretching yourself on the rack all the time. Look. Walk up to the ball. Look at the line. And make your stroke. Comfortable. Easy. It's as simple as that.

In other words, the advice *must be vague,* to make certain it is not helpful. But, in general, if properly managed, the mere giving of advice is sufficient to place the gamesman in a practically invincible position.

(Note. According to some authorities, the advice should be quite genuine and perfectly practical.)

The uses of the last of the three basic plays for winmanship are, I think, no less obvious, though I believe this gambit is less used than the other, no doubt because a certain real skill in play is involved, making it a little out of place in the gamesman world. I have worded the rule as follows: LET THE GAMESMAN'S ADVANTAGE OVER AN OPPONENT APPEAR TO BE THE RESULT OF LUCK, NEVER OF PLAY. Always sporting, the good gamesman will say:

> "I'm afraid I was a bit lucky there . . . the balls are running my way. It's extraordinary, isn't it, how once they start running one way, they go on running one way, all through an entire game. I know it's impossible according to the law of averages . . ."

and so on, till your opponent is forced to break in with a reply. Unless he sees through the gambit and counter-games, he is likely to feel an ebbing of confidence if he can be made to believe that it is not your play (which he knows is liable to collapse) but Fate, which is against him.

GUESTMANSHIP.

The object of guestmanship is difficult to achieve. The host is at an advantage. He is playing on his home ground. He knows the ropes. He has armies of friends. There are plenty of opportunities for making his guest feel out of it. But by the time Gamesman G. L. Court had finished with him, an average host would wonder whether he was a host in any valid sense except the unpleasant one of having to pay: indeed, he would begin to wonder whether he was really a member of his own club.

G. L. used to start, very quietly, (A) by some such question as this: (1) "Have you got a card room here?" (knowing that, as a matter of fact, they hadn't). Or (2) (In the wash place): "Do you find you manage all right with two showers, in the summer?" He would then (B) find some member whom he knew, but his host didn't, and carry on an animated conversation with this man. Discover "at the last moment" that his host had never met him. Introduce them, with surprised apologies, and tell the host later that he really must get to know this fellow—his interest and influence, etc. At luncheon, Court would always know some special ale, or even only a special mustard, the existence of which in the club, after fifteen years' use of it, the host had rather lamely to explain he knew nothing about. Court then would ask why X was on the Committee, and why Y wasn't, and make use of a host of facts which he had been able to pick up from a lightning study of lists, menus, pictures of former captains, etc., which he had studied during his host's temporary absence paying some bill.

BRIDGEMANSHIP.

Bridge, up to 1935, was virgin ground for the gamesman, but every month new areas of the game are being brought within his field.

We are working now on methods by which the gamesman can best suggest that he usually moves in bridge circles far more advanced than the one in which he is playing at the moment. This is sometimes difficult for the mediocre player, but a primary gamescover of his more obvious mistakes is the frank statement, with apologies, that the rough and ready methods of this ordinary kind of bridge, played as it is for amusingly low stakes, are constantly putting him off. "Idiotic. I was thinking I was playing duplicate." Refer to the "damnably complicated techniques" with which matchplay is hedged around. During the post-mortem period after each hand, give advice *to your opponents* immediately, before anyone else has spoken about the general run of the play. Tell the opponent on your left that "you saw her signaling with her third discard." At first she will not realize that you are speaking to her, then she will not know what you are talking about, and will almost certainly agree. Invent "infringements" committed by your opponents in bidding, tell them that "it's quite all right —doesn't matter—but in a *match* it would be up to me to ask you to be silent for three rounds. Then if your partner redoubles, my original bid resumes its validity." Refer frequently to authorities. Refer to some formula in the *Silver Book of End-Play Squeezes.*

It is usual, as part of intimidation play, to *invent a convention* (if playing with a fellow gamesman as partner). Explain the convention to your opponents, of course, e.g.:

GAMESMAN: Forcing two and Blackwood's, partner? Right? And Gardiner's as well? O.K.

LAYMAN: What's Gardiner's?

GAMESMAN: Gardiner's—oh, simply this. Sometimes comes in useful. If *you* call seven diamonds *or* seven clubs and then one of us doubles without having previously called no trumps, then the doubler is telling his partner, really, that in his hand are the seven to Queen, *inclusive,* of the next highest suit.

LAYMAN: I think I see. . . .

GAMESMAN: The situation doesn't arise very often, as a matter of fact.

The fact that the situation does not arise more often than once in fifty years prevents any possible misunderstanding with your partner.

This phase of Intimidation Play is often called "Conventionist" or "Conventionistical."

HOME GAMES.

There is an excellent alternative to the development of a private game in your own home. That is to do the same thing in a house belonging to someone else. This is not only inconvenient to the real owner of the house; it places you in the fine gamesposition of "playing on a strange court."

J. Strachey has invented a form of indoor hockey which is played with the pointed end of an ordinary walking stick as the club. As a game it is feebleness itself; but Strachey uses an interesting gamesplay in its execution.

The game is played in an old shed, five to fourteen a side. Early in the game Strachey says:

"Hi—whoa! Look, everybody. Wait a minute, wait a minute. Wait a minute, everybody. We mustn't lift our sticks above the knee, must we. Or else one of us will get the most awful cut. Right."

He then proceeds, quite deliberately, to lay about him to right and left so that nobody can come near him. Through this method he has amassed an amazing sequence of wins to his credit.

CHESS.

Potter's Opening.

This is supposed, now, to be the name of an effective opening, simple to play and easy to remember, which I have invented for use against a more experienced player who is absolutely certain to win. It consists of making three moves at random and then resigning. The dialogue runs as follows:

SELF: Good. Excellent. (Opponent has just made his third move.) I must resign, of course.

OPPONENT: Resign?

SELF: Well . . . you're bound to take my Bishop after sixteen moves, unless . . . unless . . . And even then I lose my castle three moves later.

OPPONENT: Oh, yes.

SELF: Unless you sacrifice there, which, of course, you wouldn't.

OPPONENT: No.

SELF: Nice game.

OPPONENT: Yes.

SELF: Pretty situation . . . very pretty. Do you mind if I take a note of it? The *Chess News* usually publishes any stuff I send them.

It is no exaggeration to say that this gambit, boldly carried out against the expert, heightens the reputation of the gamesman more effectively than the most courageous attempt to fight a losing battle.

Biographical Notes

RACHEL L. CARSON

(1907–)

IT SEEMED that Rachel Carson had told lay readers all they possibly could want to know of ocean lore in her resoundingly successful *The Sea Around Us* in 1951, but a few years later she defied all the rules of publishing probabilities by hitting the jackpot again with *The Edge of the Sea*. Never has there been so famous a specialist in the fields of oceanography and marine biology!

Miss Carson grew up in Springdale (near Pittsburgh) and never so much as had a glimpse of the sea until she graduated from Pennsylvania College for Women. Much of her subsequent research was done in the laboratories at Woods Hole, Massachusetts, and Beaufort, North Carolina, but it is when she is sailing the sea itself, or roaming along its shores, that she is happiest.

GILBERT C. KLINGEL

(1908–)

By profession Gilbert Klingel is a metallurgist for a large steel corporation—Armco. Most of his work has been technical, but his chief outside interest has been natural history, particularly marine biology. After a rather unorthodox education devoted to whatever attracted him most, he pioneered in undersea exploration and photography. His two books— *Inagua* and *The Bay*—are the results of his submarine activities. In 1953 he was awarded the Burroughs Medal for writing in the field of natural science.

"In Defense of Octopuses" is a chapter from *Inagua*. The rest of the book is equally off-beat and informative.

THOR HEYERDAHL

(1914–)

As ethnologist, explorer and author, Thor Heyerdahl has expounded the theory that inhabitants of the Pacific Islands originated partly in prehistoric South America. To prove it, he and five scientists drifted on a balsa-wood raft, such as the Incas used, until they reached a Polynesian atoll. The story of their expedition is told dramatically in his Odyssey to the South Seas, *Kon-Tiki*. Born in Larvik, Norway, Thor Heyerdahl follows the tradition of his adventurous Viking ancestors.

BIOGRAPHICAL NOTES

MAX BEERBOHM
(1872–1956)

The irrepressible Max Beerbohm, critic, caricaturist, essayist, novelist and wit, was one of the dominant figures of late-Victorian and early-twentieth-century English letters. In retirement in Italy for many years before his death at the age of eighty-four, he became a living legend and the symbol of a vanished age. He was the author of *And Even Now, A Christmas Garland, The Happy Hypocrite* and *Zuleika Dobson,* not to mention many biting caricatures of the illustrious and obscure.

I recall dancing once with the late Constance Collier at a night club a few years before her death. She was not so light on her feet as she undoubtedly had been in her youth, but her spirit remained indomitable. "You are sweet to dance with an old lady like me," she told me. "Are you in the theater?" "No, Miss Collier," I replied. "I'm a book publisher." "Ah, yes," she nodded. "Have you ever published anything by Max Beerbohm?" "Indeed I have," I assured her. "His *Zuleika Dobson* is one of the consistently popular titles in our Modern Library series."

Miss Collier stopped dancing abruptly. "But my dear young man," she exclaimed. "Don't you *know? I* am Zuleika Dobson! Max wrote that book for *me.* We were engaged for twelve years."

"Twelve years?" I echoed. "Why didn't you marry him?" "Poor, dear Max," sighed Miss Collier. "He had carpet slippers in his soul. . . ."

ANNE MORROW LINDBERGH
(1906–   )

Best known for her thoughtfully serene book *Gift from the Sea,* Anne Morrow Lindbergh had previously won for herself a large and enthusiastic following with her other writings, *North to the Orient, Listen! the Wind, The Steep Ascent,* and, since, with a recently published volume of poetry called *The Unicorn.* Before the Second World War she lost many of her adherents with her badly timed *The Wave of the Future,* in which she undertook to defend the philosophy of Fascism. Since then her books have regained an impressive number of devotees. She is married to the world-famous aviator and is the mother of five children.

STEPHEN VINCENT BENÉT
(1898–1943)

The winner of the Pulitzer Prize for poetry in 1929 for his *John Brown's Body* was born in Bethlehem, Pennsylvania, the grandson and son of professional military men and the younger brother of William Rose Benét. After graduation from Yale University in 1919, Stephen Vincent Benét devoted himself to writing novels, verse and short stories, the best known of which are *Heavens and Earth, Ballads and Poems, The Devil and Daniel Webster* and *Tales Before Midnight*. His eerie "The King of the Cats" and, admittedly, "By the Waters of Babylon," too, bob up with regularity in anthologies of quality.

GEORGE MEREDITH
(1828–1909)

In the fifty years of his prolific literary career, George Meredith wrote books which reflect the wide range of his interests: satire, adventure, realistic novels and poetry. Among the works of fiction that have retained their vitality almost a century after they were written are *The Egoist, Diana of the Crossways, The Tragic Comedians, The Ordeal of Richard Feverel, The Shaving of Shagpat* and many others. Born in Portsmouth, England, he was educated at the Moravian School in Germany. He died at the age of eighty-one.

IRWIN SHAW
(1913–   )

Author of three novels—*The Young Lions, The Troubled Air* and *Lucy Crown*—many distinguished short stories and several plays, Irwin Shaw worked his way to literary prominence from a humble beginning as an undergraduate dramatist, columnist and ghost writer. He continued his training as a postgraduate by fashioning suspenseful radio serials. Born in Brooklyn, he became a star football player and is now an accomplished Alpine skier. His home is in Switzerland, but he is frequently summoned to Hollywood, where he is in constant demand as a brilliant and fabulously paid screen writer.

Irwin Shaw's vitality and *joie de vivre* are boundless. A friend recently said of him, "Irwin's the kind of man who makes all other persons at a party seem a little bit nicer and gayer than they really are." Who could ask for a finer compliment than that?

THOMAS WOLFE
(1900–1938)

The brief and tormented life of Thomas Wolfe is fully recorded in his four thinly disguised autobiographical novels: *Look Homeward, Angel, Of Time and the River, The Web and the Rock* and *You Can't Go Home Again*. Endowed with extraordinary natural gifts, he poured out torrents of prose as if he knew that his time was short and the compulsions to write too overwhelming to restrain. He was born in Asheville, North

Carolina, and attended the University of North Carolina at Chapel Hill. A man of huge and commanding presence, his physical appearance matched the monumental character of his work. He died of a brain tumor at the age of thirty-seven.

Nothing came easily to Tom Wolfe. His long-time editor and confidant, Max Perkins, told of a day Wolfe was asked to autograph a copy of *Look Homeward, Angel* for an old friend. For a full twenty minutes he paced up and down Perkins' office, worrying about a proper inscription. Finally, he snatched up a pen and scribbled, "Sincerely, Thomas Wolfe."

ALINE BERNSTEIN
(1880–1955)

Most widely known as a stage and costume designer, in a career which she began in 1924 and carried on to her death, Aline Bernstein was responsible for the *décor* of scores of plays in the New York theater. She was one of the founders of the Museum of Costume Art in New York City and was the author of four books: *An Actor's Daughter, Three Blue Suits, The Journey Down* and *Miss Condon*.

Mrs. Bernstein's daughter, Edla, is a successful writer of detective novels; her sister, Ethel, is a VIP at Fifth Avenue's exclusive Bergdorf Goodman.

JOHN GALSWORTHY
(1867–1933)

Born in Kingston, Surrey, John Galsworthy was educated at Harrow and New College, Oxford. Called to the Bar in 1890, he continued to read law for four years, but made no attempt to practice. While traveling from Australia to South Africa, he met and encouraged a ship's officer who had a half-written novel. The budding author's name was Teodor Korzeniowski and the novel was titled *Almayer's Folly*. Thus began a friendship with Joseph Conrad that lasted until his death. Galsworthy is best known for *The Forsyte Saga,* begun in 1903 and completed in 1920, the chronicle of the Edwardian middle class in all its insular complacency. Galsworthy's bibliography of novels and plays is formidable. They assure him a highly honored place in the history of English letters.

John Galsworthy shared with Rudyard Kipling and Conrad the distinction of being the most avidly collected English authors when the ownership of "first editions" became a "must" for every self-respecting Wall Street speculator in the fabulous twenties. In 1928, a first edition of *The Forsyte Saga* fetched as high as two hundred dollars a copy. Then came the crash of 1929, and prices of first and "limited" editions tumbled almost as drastically as Electric Bond and Share.

Galsworthy's *Forsyte Saga* remains one of my own all-time favorites and so does his *The Apple Tree*. What wonderful movies could be based on both of them!

RICHARD HARDING DAVIS
(1864–1916)

The prototype of the dashing adventurous war correspondent of our recent fiction, Richard Harding Davis brought to journalism the flair for being on the spot where and when big news events broke. His was that highly personalized kind of reporting which was always enveloped in a romantic aura. Born in Philadelphia and educated at Swarthmore, Lehigh and Johns Hopkins, he became a newspaperman at twenty-two and a popular short-story writer shortly thereafter. His Van Bibber-stories, with their easy air of intimacy in New York high society, brought him a fortune, and his dispatches during the Spanish-American War made him an idealized hero of his time. *The Bar Sinister* is considered his finest story.

CHARLES BATTELL LOOMIS
(1861–1911)

In constant demand as an entertainer and reader of his whimsical sketches of everyday American life, Charles Battell Loomis was a popular figure on the lecture circuit at the turn of the century. He was born in Brooklyn, became a chicken farmer in Torringford, Connecticut, and then a contributor of light verse and jokes to *Puck* and other humor magazines of his period. His books in fifteen volumes include *Just Rhymes* (1899), *Cheerful Americans* (1903), *A Holiday Touch* (1908) and *Just Irish* (1909).

FRED ALLEN
(1894–1956)

Fred Allen was one of the wittiest, most generous, altogether lovable "personalities" I ever have known, and because all those qualities predominate in his autobiography, *Much Ado About Me*, it will continue to find an audience as long as the theater flourishes in America.

Fred won fame and fortune in radio and television, but his real love was reserved for the big-time vaudeville that met its Waterloo when silent movies came into their own. He was born in Boston (real name: John Florence Sullivan) and began his theatrical career while employed in the children's reading room of the Boston Public Library, essaying a juggling act for a librarians' party. One girl told him, "You're crazy to keep working here at the Library. You ought to go on the stage." Reflects Allen in his book, "If that girl only had kept her mouth shut, I might have wound up as head man at the Boston Public Library."

Fred Allen died suddenly on March 17, 1956, a few hours before he was to have performed his weekly stint on TV's *What's My Line?* It was a sad day we other panelists never will forget.

MAURICE HERZOG

(1919–   )

Prior to the ascent of Annapurna, no mountain peak of 8,000 meters ever had been reached by man. Maurice Herzog, a guide trained in climbing in the Alps, and the leader of the French Himalayan Expedition, accomplished, with his companions, the summit of the 26,493-foot mountain in June of 1950. In the exaltation of his achievement, Herzog lost his fur gloves—a terrible disaster in that freezing cold. After the descent, Herzog's condition went from bad to worse, and little by little all of his toes and most of his fingers had to be amputated.

No greater tale of outdoor adventure exists than Herzog's account of the conquest of Annapurna.

J. A. HUNTER

(1887–   )

The man whose name perfectly fits his profession was born in Shearing, Scotland, but has spent most of his adult life in Africa. He lives in Nairobi, Kenya, where he acts as Game Controller. His books, *Tales of the African Frontier* and *Hunter,* provide authentic information and guidance for the big-game sportsman and pulse-quickening excitement for those who have to take their hunting vicariously.

ROLAND PERTWEE

(1886–   )

The obvious implication in the title of Roland Pertwee's autobiography, *Master of None,* is that he is a jack of all trades. This tacit admission is borne out by the formidable number of plays, novels, short stories, film and television scripts he has written during a career that has spanned more than half a century. He studied painting, furthermore, under John Sargent, and histrionics under H. B. Irving!

Like many other Englishmen, Pertwee is a dedicated fisherman. His *Fish Are Such Liars*—and what a honey of a story it is!—will give the reader ample evidence of his knowledge of the subject.

JOHN P. MARQUAND
(1893-   )

From the time of his graduation from Harvard in 1915 until 1921, John P. Marquand was a working newspaperman. Then he began an independent career as a writer of fiction and for almost four decades has maintained his position as one of America's foremost novelists.

Best known and loved among his score of books are *The Late George Apley, Wickford Point* and *H. M. Pulham, Esq.* (all now available in one compact volume entitled *North of Grand Central*), *Point of No Return, Sincerely, Willis Wayde* and *Life at Happy Knoll*—not to mention a series of fascinating "whodunits" featuring that inscrutable detector of dirty work, Mr. Moto. Mr. Moto recently made a welcome return to the scene with his crimes.

Although Mr. Marquand was born in Wilmington, Delaware, he rates today as a Very Proper Bostonian. He is also a judge of the Book-of-the-Month Club, and one of the finest gentlemen in the United States of America.

JAMES A. MICHENER
(1907-   )

James Michener grew up in Doylestown, Pennsylvania, and was graduated from Swarthmore College. After several years of university teaching, he became an editor in the textbook department of Macmillan's, where he remained until the outbreak of World War II.

His experiences in the Navy provided the material for *Tales of the South Pacific*, which won the Pulitzer Prize in 1947 and was adopted into the fabulously successful musical *South Pacific*. Since then everything James Michener has written has turned to gold: *Fires of Spring, Return to Paradise, The Voice of Asia, The Bridges at Toko-ri, Sayonara, The Bridge at Andau*, and, in collaboration with A. Grove Day, *Rascals in Paradise*. He is also the author of the authoritative work on Japanese prints, *The Floating World*.

Asked by the author of a first novel for his formula of success, Michener gravely advised, "Work hard, make your book as good as you possibly can, and, above all, make sure that Rodgers and Hammerstein get a copy!"

W. SOMERSET MAUGHAM
(1874-   )

At the age of eighty-four W. Somerset Maugham, lately given to referring to himself as "The Old Party," writes with the *élan* of youth and an undiminished zest for a good story. His sumptuous estate on the French Riviera is an author's dream come true.

A list of his books would fill pages of this volume, but mention of only a few of the familiar titles will suggest the range of his inexhaustible interests: *Of Human Bondage, The Moon and Sixpence, Cakes and Ale, Ashenden, The Razor's Edge,* etc. Among the hit plays to his credit are *The Letter, The Circle, The Constant Wife* and *Our Betters.*

Mr. Maugham recalls his elation when Sir Edmund Goss, dean of English critics, wrote an enthusiastic review of Maugham's first novel, *Liza of Lambeth,* in 1897. Until he died in 1928, however, Sir Edmund never met Maugham without patting him on the shoulder and murmuring, "Capital piece of work, that *Liza of Lambeth.* How smart you were never to write anything else!"

And because there is supposed to be at least one atrocious pun in every Cerf compilation, I give you the story of the trapper who came to town to purchase a case of soft drinks and a copy of *Of Human Bondage.* He left both on a table in a lunch room and wandered about for a while. When he came back the book had disappeared. "You having some trouble?" asked the proprietor. "I sure am," answered the trapper. "I've found my pop but I've lost my Maugham!"

FRANK O'CONNOR
(1903–   )

A native of Cork, Ireland, and exuding Irish charm from every pore, Frank O'Connor came to the United States in 1952 as a visiting lecturer at Northwestern, Harvard and Chicago universities, where he promptly transformed virtually the entire student bodies into O'Connorseurs.

In his own land, O'Connor had been a librarian for thirteen years and a Director of the Abbey Theater in Dublin for three. Now he lives part of every year in America and frequently contributes short stories—all distinguished—to our leading national magazines.

KATHERINE MANSFIELD
(1888–1923)

Born in Wellington, New Zealand, Katherine Mansfield was sent to England at an early age for her education. After attending Queen's College in London, she began to contribute short stories to *The New Age.* Illness plagued her and made her seek relief in different climates. Before her death in Fontainebleau, France, she met and married the English critic John Middleton Murry. She is the author of seven volumes of uniformly distinguished short stories and several collections of poems and miscellany.

HARRY STILLWELL EDWARDS
(1855-1938)

In 1896 Harry Stillwell Edwards, journalist and author, was awarded the then unprecedented prize of $10,000 by the Chicago *Record* for his novel *Sons and Fathers*. His subsequent books were *Fifth Dimension* (1912), *Eneas Africanus* (1919) and a volume of verse, *Little Legends of the Land* (1930). Born in Georgia, he had the opportunity to study the folkways of the Negro on his home grounds. He also had the advantageous position for observation accorded the postmaster in the city of Macon.

Eneas Africanus is a unique story in *Reading for Pleasure*—an authentic example of rich American folklore that sells year after year in editions ranging from paperbacked pamphlets to handsomely printed, leatherbound keepsakes.

BEN AMES WILLIAMS
(1889-1953)

Born in Macon, Mississippi, Ben Ames Williams came north to attend Dartmouth College. He was graduated in 1910 and went to work as a reporter on the Boston *American,* where he remained for six years. Encouraged by the sale of a few short stories, he abandoned journalism for the career of a free-lance writer. Beginning in 1916 he had some four hundred stories published in a great variety of magazines, but principally in the *Saturday Evening Post*. Most of his tales have their locale in Maine, but occasionaly he writes of his Southern childhood and Midwest boyhood. In addition to his enormous output of stories, he is the author of some thirty books.

JAMES THURBER
(1894-   )

America's two greatest living humorists are James Thurber and E. B. White, and it was no accident that the late Harold Ross corralled both of them when he was bulling his *New Yorker* magazine into being. The best was barely good enough for Ross!

Thurber was born in Columbus and educated after his fashion at Ohio State. His satires, fantasies, short stories, fables, complaints and highly individualized drawings have since brought him a full measure of fame. A boyhood accident cost him one eye, and he has had increasing trouble with the other—but it is his inner vision that has sustained him and delighted his readers.

"I regard Thurber," declares Frank Sullivan, "as Ohio's gift to the oppressed of all nations and I am glad that he is around. The moral of that is: always look a gift horse in the face, especially if Thurber drew it."

JOHN O'HARA

(1905-   )

When John Henry O'Hara (he hates the "Henry") begins to write he knows exactly what he wants to say. This enables him to leave off in the middle of a sentence one evening and take up again without hesitation the next morning—or week, if necessary. It also enables him to name the exact day he will finish an important novel before he has written a word of it—and unfailingly live up to the schedule he has drawn for himself.

John O'Hara was born in Pottsville, Pennsylvania, the thinly disguised locale of many of his books. He has served hitches as ship steward, railroad freight clerk, press agent, ace reporter and Hollywood script expert, and is the author of *Appointment in Samarra, Butterfield 8, A Rage to Live, Ten North Frederick,* other novels, some plays and five full volumes of top-drawer short stories. His libretto for *Pal Joey* revolutionized the Broadway musical-comedy world in 1940.

Ten North Frederick won the National Book Award for fiction in 1956. It also provoked numerous set-tos with self-appointed snoophounds and censors. The winner and obvious champion for a long time to come: John O'Hara.

BUDD SCHULBERG

(1914-   )

Budd Schulberg has never written a novel that wasn't an immediate best seller, and never—well, hardly ever—arrived on time for a dinner engagement. The blare of a jazz band or the sound of a padded glove against a punching bag will distract him from a scheduled conference with a $100,000 movie contract at stake!

He was born in New York City, but, at the age of four, was taken to Hollywood by his father, who was destined to become head of Paramount Pictures. Schulberg was one young man, however, who defied Horace Greeley and came back East—to Deerfield Academy and Dartmouth College. Barely graduated from the latter, he wrote *What Makes Sammy Run?* and added "Sammy Glick" to our language as a synonym for the all-American heel.

There followed *The Harder They Fall, The Disenchanted* (a thinly disguised fictional biography of F. Scott Fitzgerald) and *Waterfront* (an exposé of conditions on the docks that became one of the great motion pictures of our time). His best short stories are available in a volume called *Some Faces in the Crowd.*

WILLIAM FAULKNER

(1897–   )

Nobel laureate in literature in 1950, twice winner of the National Book Award and the Pulitzer Prize, William Faulkner has published twenty-three volumes within three decades. He is acknowledgedly one of the first among the world's living writers. Born in Mississippi, his lifelong home has been in Oxford, but his mythical Yoknapatawpha County is a land of his own creation, and all its people have sprung from his imagination. "Race at Morning" appears in the volume of his hunting stories entitled *Big Woods*.

William Faulkner rarely bothers to read reviews of his books. He didn't even glance at the two-part profile of him that was featured some time ago in *Life* magazine. His mother read it, however, and registered her disapproval by wiring a cancellation of her subscription. "First telegram my mammy sent in years," commented Mr. Faulkner.

No one for small talk either, Faulkner has been known to hold forth indefinitely when the subject turns to the distillation of good whiskey. He was nursing a tall glass of bourbon one afternoon when his hostess asked, "May I add some water to that whiskey?" "Ma'am," answered Faulkner coldly, "if the good Lord had intended water to be in this bourbon, He'd have put it there!"

EDITH WHARTON

(1862–1937)

Edith Newbold Jones, chronicler of upper-crust American society in the days of its "innocence," was brought up in New York City. Her ancestors included aristocratic Rhinelanders and Schermerhorns, and, on her maternal side, General Ebenezer Stevens of the Revolutionary Army. Miss Jones married banker Edward Wharton of Boston, and then startled her own set by becoming a professional writer. To make matters worse, she wrote about the moneyed folk with whom she always had associated—and the public loved her books. In the Newport of those days, that wasn't considered much better than joining a burlesque troupe!

Two of Edith Wharton's books are widely read to this day: *Ethan Frome* and *The Age of Innocence*. Notable also among her more than two score published works were *The Valley of Decision, The House of Mirth* and *Hudson River Bracketed*.

ISAK DINESEN

(1885–   )

The bilingual Isak Dinesen, the nom de plume of Baroness Karen

Blixen of Rungstedlund, writes with equal felicity in Danish and English. Born in Denmark, she went in 1914 to British East Africa, where she and her husband operated a large coffee plantation. *Out of Africa* records her experiences in the colony with consummate artistry. Her *Seven Gothic Tales, Winter's Tales* and *Last Tales* are books of short stories cherished by discerning readers everywhere for their sensibility, plot ingenuity and insight into the nuances of character.

"Isak Dinesen" is not the only nom de plume under which Baroness Blixen has plied her art. During the war she wrote a cloak-and-dagger adventure tale called *The Angelic Avengers,* but, uncertain at the last moment, insisted that it be ascribed to a mythical "Pierre Andrézel." The judges of the Book-of-the-Month Club were not fooled. They had earmarked every other of Baroness Blixen's books, and they chose this one with equal alacrity.

JAMES STEPHENS
(1882–1950)

The self-educated poet and storyteller James Stephens was born in Dublin, where he grew up to be the very image of the pixielike, slyly humorous, half-pint Irishmen he describes so graphically in his tales.

The year 1912 marked the publication of Stephens' outstanding book, *The Crock of Gold,* and the spread of his reputation throughout Europe and America. An authority on the folklore of the Emerald Isle, he wrote with the rich Irish blend of knowledge and fantasy such beloved books as *Deirdre, In the Land of Youth, The Demi-Gods, The Charwoman's Daughter, Irish Fairy Tales* and two volumes of short stories, *Etched in Moonlight* and *Here Are Ladies.*

ERNEST HEMINGWAY
(1898–   )

Nobel Prize winner in 1954, Ernest Hemingway, the son of an Illinois country doctor, began his writing career as a reporter on the Kansas City *Star.* During the First World War he served on the Italian front and was seriously wounded. After the armistice he became foreign correspondent for the Toronto *Star* and for the Hearst Syndicate in Paris. There he wrote *The Sun Also Rises* and *A Farewell to Arms* and immediately became world famous. His terse, unadorned style of writing, especially in his short stories, became a model for hosts of imitators, but no one has yet succeeded in rivaling him.

Hemingway lives today in Cuba, where he wrote *The Old Man and the Sea,* but he remains a wanderer at heart and there is equal likelihood that a note addressed to him will reach him in the African jungle, Mexico, a fishing colony off Key West, or Toots Shor's bistro in midtown New York.

At Shor's, he told Columnist Earl Wilson, "I've got three unpublished novels in the bank already and a fourth one on the way." "In the bank?" echoed the puzzled Wilson. "That's right," nodded Hemingway. "I put 'em away and let 'em ripen. When I need cash I take one out."

V. S. PRITCHETT
(1900–   )

Victor Sawdon Pritchett, author and critic, now a VIP on the *New Statesman & Nation,* disposes of his early career in two succinct sentences: "I first earned my living in the leather and photography business. I then went to France where I sold feathers and theater tickets."

Mr. Pritchett has contributed many witty and not always approving articles about writing and writers in America to our leading literary journals. One of his own best-known books (written in collaboration with Elizabeth Bowen and Graham Greene) is *Why Do I Write?* The answer to that question is apparent in his cynical story "Sense of Humor."

RICHARD SHERMAN
(1906–   )

From Bancroft, Iowa, Richard Sherman went to Harvard, where he was chairman of the editorial board of the *Crimson* and a member of the staff of the *Advocate.* He was graduated in 1928 and went to work for *The Forum* and then *Vanity Fair.* After seven years of magazine training, he became a free-lance writer in 1935 and has remained one ever since. His stories have appeared in the leading national magazines and several have been honored by inclusion in prize anthologies. In addition, he is the author of three novels: *To Mary, with Love, The Unready Heart* and *The Bright Promise.* Herbert Mayes, editor of *Good Housekeeping,* rates "Barrow Street" among the most effective stories he ever has purchased for his magazine.

E. B. WHITE
(1899–   )

If there is one book from the current American crop that still will be popular fifty years from now, I'd like to place my bet on *Charlotte's Web.* I rate it superior to *Alice in Wonderland.*

Elwyn Brooks White, the author of *Charlotte's Web,* was born in Mount Vernon, New York, and educated at Cornell. At *The New Yorker* magazine, he writes a good part of the sparkling "Talk of the Town" department. When the habitual chaos of the *New Yorker* office overpowers him, he seeks rest and seclusion, with his wife, Katharine, near the village of Brooklin, Maine. It was here that he developed the characters of Charlotte the Spider, Wilbur the Pig and Templeton the Rat. Charlotte's ingenuity makes Wilbur one of the best-publicized pigs of his era, spared permanently from the humiliating fate of being served at the Christmas dinner table with a candied apple jammed into his mouth. Nor will they ever carve him up for bacon and ham. Wilbur is one pig who never will have to give his seat to a lady!

"Animals are a weakness to me," admits Mr. White. "Maybe this doesn't explain why I wrote *Charlotte's Web,* but I can't tell why I sneeze, either. A book"—and who is there to say him nay?—"is a sneeze."

Other sneezes—or books—by Mr. White include *One Man's Meat, Stuart Little, Here Is New York* and *The Second Tree from the Corner.*

A. E. COPPARD
(1878–1957)

Alfred Edgar Coppard's lot was not an easy one. His formal schooling ended at the age of nine, when he was apprenticed to a trousers maker in London, but he studied doggedly by himself, and read poetry in his few spare hours.

Coppard began writing at the age of forty. His first book—*Adam and Eve and Pinch Me*—was published on April Fool's Day, 1921. It also was the first book put out by the famous Golden Cockerel Press, and became a collector's item overnight. From then on, until his death at seventy-nine, Coppard had ready for his publishers a book of stories or verse almost every year. None of them, alas, achieved a large sale, and fame and riches eluded Coppard to the end, but among discerning readers and critics his reputation is secure.

HEYWOOD BROUN
(1888–1939)

Heywood Broun was a dedicated newspaperman. On the New York *Tribune* he turned in some of the best sports stories that have ever been written. In 1921, he joined the staff of the *World,* where he became scared to death of the editor, Herbert Bayard Swope. His dawning preoccupation with the class struggle manifested itself clearly in the Sacco-Vanzetti case in 1927. He regarded the execution of these two men as a flagrant miscarriage of justice and wrote two devastating columns about the case that belong with the great pieces of invective of all time.

Ralph Pulitzer, of the *World,* asked Broun to write no more on this controversial subject and Broun staged a one-man strike. The quarrel was patched up, but Broun never forgot it, and two years later accepted a fabulous offer from Roy Howard of the *Telegram*. The last years of his life were devoted principally to the organization and promotion of the American Newspaper Guild.

Broun loved the theater, and the majority of his reviews were gentle and encouraging. One evening, however, an actor named Geoffrey Steyne gave a performance that displeased him. Broun allowed that Mr. Steyne was the worst actor on the American stage. Mr. Steyne sued. The whole principle of dramatic criticism was at stake in this suit; if the actor won it, obviously, a dangerous precedent would have been established.

The case was dismissed, fortunately, and it remained only to see what Broun would say about Mr. Steyne on the occasion of his next Broadway appearance. The big night finally arrived, and the next morning initiates turned eagerly to Broun's review. He did not so much as mention Geoffrey Steyne until the last sentence of his last paragraph. This read simply, "Mr. Steyne's performance was not up to his usual standard."

TRUMAN CAPOTE
(1924-   )

Truman Capote, of the New Orleans Capotes, was twenty-four when his first novel, *Other Voices, Other Rooms,* was published. The critics embraced the book, and Truman promptly was hailed as a prodigy—an appellation bestowed in equal measure for his undeniable talent and for a photograph of himself draped languidly over a couch, "his eyes fixed in a stare of childlike wonder beneath a set of straggling bangs." Capote enjoyed the furor, complained only when another young writer, Gore Vidal, began to get equal billing. "Vidal calling himself a boy wonder!" Capote was heard to scoff one day. "Why, he's twenty if he's a day."

Capote's subsequent books proved that he was no flash in the pan. *The Tree of Night, The Grass Harp* and *The Muses Are Heard* all have been solid successes. Magazine editors and Hollywood producers, furthermore, avidly seek his services—when they can find him. Truman likes to travel—as luxuriously as circumstances will permit. So far, he has no cause for complaint. Last seen, he was boarding a private airplane for a fortnight of contemplation in the fashionable Bahamas.

ALAN BECK
(1910-   )

At seventeen, Alan Beck played chaperon to twelve hundred mules from east St. Louis to Algeria and Spain at the magnificent honorarium of one dollar a day. At eighteen, he was an ordinary seaman for the Dollar Line for a trip around the world. Now he is the editor of *The Pilot's Log,* the journal of the New England Life Insurance Company of

Boston. He was born in St. Louis and received degrees from Westminster College and the University of Missouri. He insists that he is the only resident of Hingham, Massachusetts, who can ride a bicycle backwards.

MOSS HART
(1904-   )

Moss Hart, one of the most successful playwrights and directors of our era, and the life of all the countless parties he gives and attends, gained his experience the hard way, and if you find that hard to believe, wait until you read his forthcoming autobiography, *Act One*.

Moss was born on Fifth Avenue—but at the wrong end. It was 107th Street, as a matter of fact, and the whole family was desperately poor. An engagement as "social director" in the Catskills did not improve his fortunes to any noticeable extent, but did provide invaluable experience. He even had a chance to act himself. Ever since, he's been ready—aye, panting—to dash on stage at the drop of an understudy.

Co-authorship with George S. Kaufman of *Once in a Lifetime* made Moss Hart rich overnight and, despite a positive genius for throwing money away, his fortune grows and grows, via such smash hits as *Lady in the Dark, Winged Victory* and *Light Up the Sky,* lucrative stopovers in Hollywood, and, most recently, his superb directorial chore for *My Fair Lady*.

Moss Hart has one beautiful wife (Kitty Carlisle) and two beautiful children (Christopher and Cathy). It was the latter two, of course, who inspired the Klobber System.

HARLAN MILLER
(1897-   )

Harlan Miller studied first to be an engineer and then a lawyer, but when his first columns appeared in the undergraduate newspaper at Iowa State College, he knew he was destined to be a journalist. Since then he has traveled the world over in search of material and won this rare accolade from Mike Cowles, publisher of *Look*: "The best-known, loved, cussed, and discussed writer in the State of Iowa."

DOROTHY CANFIELD FISHER
(1879-   )

Born in Lawrence, Kansas, the daughter of an educator and an artist, Dorothy Canfield Fisher studied at Ohio State, the Sorbonne and Columbia University. Her interest in education led her to write books on the subject, with particular emphasis on the methods of Dr. Maria Montessori, the Italian school reformer. Since 1912, when her first well-known novel, *The Squirrel-Cage,* appeared, there has been a succession of books about colleges, French peasants, New England villages and whatever else interested Mrs. Fisher's searching mind. Best known of her works in fiction is *The Deepening Stream.* Mrs. Fisher lives in Arlington, Vermont, where she is regarded as the living symbol of the Green Mountain State.

OWEN JOHNSON
(1878–1952)

Lawrenceville, the prep school five miles west of Princeton, New Jersey, boasts of Owen Johnson as the man who did most to make it famous. *The Prodigious Hickey, The Tennessee Shad, The Humming Bird* and *The Varmint,* detailing the adventures of ingenious adolescents on or near the school campus, were devoured by a generation that now looks back on these books with nostalgic joy. Johnson's final book of the series, *Stover at Yale,* was most successful of all.

Johnson was a New Yorker, socially prominent, and five times wed. His mature novels have been forgotten, but his Lawrenceville tales remain deservedly popular.

F. SCOTT FITZGERALD
(1896–1940)

From Saint Paul, Minnesota, where he was born, to Princeton University, where he was educated, to the AEF in the First World War, where he became an officer, and into the glittering world of the 1920's, F. Scott Fitzgerald, first alone, later with his wife Zelda, moved with gay abandon. His early books, *This Side of Paradise* and *The Beautiful and the Damned,* enjoyed enormous popularity. The direct descendant of the author of "The Star-Spangled Banner" was himself on the way to becoming a banner around which a generation rallied. In 1925 he wrote *The Great Gatsby* and followed it, nine years later, with *Tender Is the Night.* He died at forty-four, after a disastrous servitude in Hollywood, leaving an unfinished work, *The Last Tycoon,* as his final testament.

For the full story of Fitzgerald's heart-breaking career, read Arthur Mizener's biography, *The Far Side of Paradise,* or Budd Schulberg's memorable novel *The Disenchanted.*

THOMAS BURKE
(1887–1945)

Born in London, Thomas Burke spent his childhood in and near that grim, crime-ridden slum district known as Limehouse. It became the locale for his most successful novels and short stories.

The American edition of *Limehouse Nights* was given impetus by a D. W. Griffith film called *Broken Blossoms* and a haunting song number, introduced in *Charlot's Revue* by Gertrude Lawrence. This was the show, in fact, in which both Miss Lawrence and Beatrice Lillie made their American debuts—a "first night" that those fortunate enough to attend (myself, for instance) never will forget!

JOHN COLLIER

(1901–   )

At nineteen, John Collier, who was born in London, was writing poetry good enough to be published in book form. It was ten years later, how-ever, when his bent for somewhat diabolical, off-beat fiction manifested itself. The occasion was the appearance of his first novel, *His Monkey Wife,* which has just been republished, some twenty-seven years later, in America.

Collier's stories, notes Basil Davenport, "reveal the master of an irony so perfectly balanced that his horror is hardly ever quite free of humor, nor his humor of horror."

SAKI

(Hector Hugh Munro)

(1870–1916)

The Saki story in *Reading for Pleasure,* you will notice, follows one by John Collier, which is very fitting and proper, since the style and subject matter of the body of their writings bear striking resemblances.

Saki was born in Burma, the son of an inspector general of the Burma police, but brought up in Devonshire by a pair of unnaturally strict British aunts. He soon betrayed a whimsical sense of humor, an uncommon gift for writing, a love of animals and a complete indifference to money. At the outset of World War I he enlisted as a private and was killed in action some months thereafter.

The pseudonym "Saki" derives from Omar Khayyám.

MARC CONNELLY

(1890–   )

Not content with the role of dramatist, Marc Connelly is also a pro-ducer, director and manager of his own and other works for the stage. Everything he does is performed with a flair, whether it be spinning a choice anecdote, performing an intricate parlor trick or lecturing at Yale. Connelly was born in McKeesport, Pennsylvania, but acquired his cos-mopolitan manner as a member of the famous Round Table at the Algonquin and as a co-founder of *The New Yorker* magazine.

In collaboration with George Kaufman, Marc Connelly wrote *Dulcy, To the Ladies, Merton of the Movies* and *Beggar on Horseback*. Alone, he fashioned Roark Bradford's book *Ol' Man Adam an' His Chillun* into the memorable *The Green Pastures,* winner of the 1930 Pulitzer Prize.

F. TENNYSON JESSE
(No date–   )

Fryniwyd Tennyson Jesse is the grand niece of Alfred, Lord Tennyson, the daughter of a clergyman and the wife of the English playright H. M. Harwood. She began her career as a painter at the age of fifteen, exhibited pictures in Liverpool and Leeds and illustrated a book. In London she became a reporter for the *Times* and *Daily Mail,* wrote book reviews for the *Times Literary Supplement* and the *English Review*. During the First World War she was a correspondent at the front. She insists that her "chief passion is murder," but in a literary sense only, since she has become an authority on murder mysteries. In addition to her novels and her *Murder and Its Motives,* she has edited a number of cases for the *Notable British Trial Series*. As further evidence of her love of mystery, Miss Jesse refuses to divulge the date of her birth.

RICHARD CONNELL
(1893–1949)

Richard Edward Connell's first newspaper job was in Poughkeepsie, New York, when he was ten years old. He covered baseball games at ten cents a game for the paper edited by his father. At Harvard, before graduation in 1915, he was an editor of the *Daily Crimson* and the *Lampoon*. After a stint in an advertising office he became a free-lance writer of fiction in 1919 and has been one ever since. He has had some three hundred stories published in American and English magazines. His books are *The Sin of Monsieur Pettipon, Apes and Angels, Variety, Mad Lover, Murder at Sea, Ironies, Playboy* and *What Ho!*

RAY BRADBURY
(1920–   )

Ray Douglas Bradbury was born in Waukegan, Illinois, not far from the house where thirty-nine-year-old Jack Benny first saw the light of day. When Bradbury came of age, in 1941, he began writing stories and sold fifty-one of them to pulp magazines in the ensuing four years. Thereafter he began appealing to a more discriminating audience as well. Today he is regarded as one of the outstanding writers of science fiction in the world.

The Bradbury story reprinted in this volume, "The World the Children Made," was first called to my attention by my then fifteen-year-old son, Christopher. After you have read it, you will understand why my son's boundless enthusiasm made my wife and me gulp a couple of times and start wondering. . . .

ROALD DAHL
(1916–   )

Roald Dahl may be the only major short-story writer who speaks both Norwegian and Swahili. He didn't learn them in South Wales, where he was born, nor at Repton School, where the present Archbishop of Canterbury was his headmaster, but his parents taught him Norwegian, and he picked up Swahili working for the Shell Oil Company in Tanganyika. Flying during World War II for the R.A.F., he wrote the famous story about the "Gremlins" which was adopted for the screen by Walt Disney.

After the war, Dahl turned his hand to stories of a more macabre nature. The best of them—including "Dip in the Pool"—have been collected in a volume called *Someone Like You.*

T. H. WHITE
(1906–   )

Terence Hanbury White was born in Bombay, India, and educated at Cambridge. Writing ostensibly about the Age of Chivalry and the Arthurian legends, unpredictable Mr. White has crowded in so many extraneous items (modern slang, for example, and mysticism, and psychological patter, and rollicking burlesque) that literal-minded librarians have despaired of classifying his books properly.

None of his other novels has come within a mile of equaling the popularity of *The Sword in the Stone,* one of whose most hilarious chapters is reprinted herein.

STEWART EDWARD WHITE
(1873–1946)

From Grand Rapids, Michigan, where he was born, Stewart Edward White went to Ann Arbor to attend the University of Michigan and then to Columbia University. In New York, under the guidance of Brander Matthews, he was encouraged to write and sell one of his first short stories, "A Man and His Dog." Thus began a devotion to writing that was to be continuous for almost half a century, from 1900 to his death. Listed in his principal works are some fifty novels and countless short stories, the best of them robust and lighthearted tales of cowboys and the rugged West. Among the more popular of his books are *The Westerners, The*

Blazed Trail, The Adventures of Bobby Orde, Arizona Nights and *The Rules of the Game.*

STEPHEN LEACOCK
(1869–1944)

By profession a practitioner of the "dreary science," economics, but by avocation and pleasure a humorist, Stephen Butler Leacock was for many years Canada's most distinguished literary figure. He took the serious labors of the economist lightly and the tasks of the humorist seriously. Long the head of the Department of Economics and Political Science at McGill University in Montreal, he retired in 1936, but he never stopped doing what he enjoyed most—creating laughter. His works range from *Economic Prosperity in the British Empire* to *Nonsense Novels.*

Because of his long string of honorary degrees, Leacock's Canadian friends usually addressed him as "Doctor." The purser of an Atlantic liner, who had heard him thus referred to for three days, stepped up to him one evening and said, "Doctor, could I prevail upon you to examine the star of last year's Ziegfeld Follies? She slipped on the promenade deck and I fear she has sprained her hip." Leacock ruefully admitted later, "I rushed there like a startled gazelle, but alas! two doctors of divinity had beaten me to it."

O. HENRY
(William Sydney Porter)
(1862–1910)

Fifty years after O. Henry's highly flavored, trick-ending stories about New York first began to delight the reading public, they remain the standard by which all similar literature is judged. His "four million" have become the "nine million," the slang that highlights his dialogue has been superseded by other passing catch phrases, restaurants and hotels that served as his locale were razed a generation ago, but O. Henry is still hailed as the prose laureate of Manhattan Island.

O. Henry, of course, is a pseudonym. His real name was William Sydney Porter. Born and bred in Greensboro, North Carolina, he moved on to Texas in 1882. There he became involved in irregularities at the bank where he worked, and was committeed to prison for three years. That's when he began to write short stories.

In 1902, O. Henry came, saw and conquered New York. For eight years he wrote feverishly. When he died of tuberculosis at forty-eight, he had written and sold over six hundred stories. "Pull up the shades so I can see New York," were his last words. "I don't want to go home in the dark."

S. J. PERELMAN
(1904–   )

S. J. Perelman, master parodist, describes his style as an amalgam of "the elegant variation, the cast-iron idiom, the battered ornament, the sturdy indefensible, the side-slip, and the unequal yoke-fellow." What that adds up to is that since he graduated from Brown in 1925, he has been tickling the funny bones of his readers with such choice tidbits as *Dawn Ginsbergh's Revenge, Parlor, Bedlam and Bath, Crazy Like a Fox, Westward Ha!* and *The Road to Miltown.* On the side, he wrote a musical with Ogden Nash called *One Touch of Venus* (ah, there, Mary Martin!), and is at the moment riding higher than ever as co-writer of the sparkling script for Todd Almighty's *Around the World in Eighty Days.*

Mr. Perelman once baffled an innocent girl reporter by informing her, "I have Bright's disease—and he has mine."

RING LARDNER
(1885–1933)

One of the outstanding sports writers and short-story masters of our time, Ring Lardner, of Niles, Michigan, has been variously hailed as "a supreme humorist," "a wonderful friend," "a slave of the bottle," "a puritanical pessimist" and "the bitterest satirist of his day."

His hilarious stories about a baseball rookie, *You Know Me, Al,* which made him famous in 1916, reduced to the ridiculous the hero-worshiping slop that had dominated the sports pages before his emergence. So many readers asked Lardner to name the man on whom his caricature was based that he added this footnote to subsequent editions: "The original of Jack Keefer is not a ball player at all, but Jane Addams of Hull House, a former Follies girl."

Succeeding stories like "Haircut," "Champion" and "A Day with Conrad Green" showed that Lardner's humor was tinged with cynical despair and contempt for false values. He died of heart disease, resentful and disillusioned, at forty-eight.

A bit of Lardner's dialogue I recall with particular delight went: "BUSINESS MAN: Been having any luck with your hogs this year? FARMER: Oh, we don't play for money!"

MAC HYMAN
(1923–   )

Cordele, Georgia, is the birthplace of Mac Hyman, author of the hilarious novel *No Time for Sergeants.* During the Second World War he served overseas, as a lieutenant in the Air Force, and was a member of the flight crew that took pictures over Hiroshima the morning after the first atomic bomb was exploded. After the war, he re-enlisted in the Air Force and was assigned to Houston, Texas. It was there he began to write his first novel, *No Time for Sergeants*. It was published in the fall of 1954.

Ever since, the American public has been roaring over the misadventures of Mac Hyman's blundering, imperturbable hillbilly, Will Stockdale—first in book form, then, in turn, on television, Broadway, and finally on the screen. To quote an eminent critic, *No Time for Sergeants* is "a four-star, one hundred percent wowser."

WILLIAM BRINKLEY
(1917-   )

William Brinkley was born in 1917 in Custer City, Oklahoma, a minister's son and the youngest of five children. His career in journalism was successful from the start, interrupted only by four years of active duty in the Navy, and the day *Don't Go Near the Water* was published he was locked tight in an office banging out his biggest feature story for *Life* magazine.

Brinkley's experiences in the Navy provided him with material to spare for *Don't Go Near the Water*. He participated in the Anzio, Elbe, and Southern France operations, and later, in the Pacific, was in on the Okinawa invasion and the early stages of the Japanese occupation.

For the motion-picture rights to *Don't Go Near the Water*, Bill Brinkley got virtually everything but the M.G.M. commissary and a statue of Louis B. Mayer.

PATRICK DENNIS
(1921-   )

The creator of Auntie Mame enjoys five distinct personalities. By birth he is Edward Everett Tanner III. By literary choice he is sometimes (1) Patrick Tanner, or (2) Virginia Rowans (author of *The Loving Couple* and *Oh, What a Wonderful Wedding*), or (3) Sarah Brooks, or (4) Patrick Dennis, who, besides dreaming up Auntie Mame, wrote *Guestward Ho!* with Barbara Hooton. Got everything straight? Obviously, Mr. Dennis is a pseudonymphomaniac!

This quintuplet-in-one was born and educated in Chicago, never went to college—and has no regrets. Rosalind Russell is so wonderful as Auntie Mame that Mr. Dennis must have been thinking of her subconsciously when he first put pen to paper. He claims now that he has retired at the ripe old age of thirty-five, but the odds are a hundred to one his five incarnations will keep him busy for the rest of his life.

ART BUCHWALD

(1925–   )

Art Buchwald, this editor's favorite American in Paris, is a new kind of foreign correspondent, not so much interested in diplomatic double talk as in telling tourists how to get through the Louvre in six minutes, and how to pinch sultry sirens in Rome without getting pinched themselves as a result. Buchwald also possesses an uncanny knack for conning movie and TV stars into revealing their true inner selves when their writers and press agents are not on hand to protect them. He is positively the only Paris newspaper ace who participated in Happy Chandler's "victory march" in the Chicago Democratic Convention of 1956.

Buchwald was born in Mount Vernon, is an ex-marine, is happily married and writes a column that now appears in over forty newspapers. His two books are *Art Buchwald's Paris* and *The Brave Coward.*

STEPHEN POTTER

(1900–   )

A Londoner all his life, graduate of Oxford and ex-member of the Cold-stream Guards, Stephen Potter was a serious writer indeed in the early stages of his career. His was the pioneer critical work on D. H. Lawrence and he also edited the definitive Nonesuch Press edition of the writings of Coleridge.

Potter learned his satiric method in a ten-year stretch of servitude at the British Broadcasting Company. It was his books on Gamesmanship, Lifemanship, and One-Upmanship that made him internationally famous, and enabled him to make a triumphal lecture tour in the United States. His experiences on this tour are detailed with characteristic verve and good humor in *Potter on America.*

Potter's wife, Heather, is the founder and sole director of the one and only successful marriage bureau in Europe. Potter won her, he says, by "woomanship": he abandoned the Gradually Awakening Interest approach straight off, and staked all on the unmatched-sock ploy. "It aroused her mother instinct immediately," he says, "and it was then only a question of time till she melted into my arms."

These biographical notes were compiled in May, 1957. As changes become necessary, they will be incorporated in future editions.

BENNETT CERF

Index

Set in Linotype Granjon
Format by Katharine Sitterly
Manufactured by The Haddon Craftsmen, Inc.
Published by HARPER & BROTHERS, *New York*